Animal Nutrition

McGRAW-HILL PUBLICATIONS IN THE AGRICULTURAL SCIENCES

R. A. Brink, *Consulting Editor*

Adriance and Brison · Propagation of Horticultural Plants
Ahlgren · Forage Crops
Anderson · Diseases of Fruit Crops
Brown and Ware · Cotton
Carroll and Krider · Swine Production
Christopher · Introductory Horticulture
Cruess · Commercial Fruit and Vegetable Products
Dickson · Diseases of Field Crops
Eckles, Combs, and Macy · Milk and Milk Products
Elliott · Plant Breeding and Cytogenetics
Fernald and Shepard · Applied Entomology
Gardner, Bradford, and Hooker · The Fundamentals of Fruit Production
Gustafson · Conservation of the Soil
Gustafson · Soils and Soil Management
Hayes, Immer, and Smith · Methods of Plant Breeding
Herrington · Milk and Milk Processing
Jenny · Factors of Soil Formation
Jull · Poultry Husbandry
Kohnke and Bertrand · Soil Conservation
Laurie and Ries · Floriculture
Leach · Insect Transmission of Plant Diseases
Maynard and Loosli · Animal Nutrition
Metcalf, Flint, and Metcalf · Destructive and Useful Insects
Nevens · Principles of Milk Production
Paterson · Statistical Technique in Agricultural Research
Peters and Grummer · Livestock Production
Rather and Harrison · Field Crops
Rice, Andrews, Warwick, and Legates · Breeding and Improvement of Farm Animals
Roadhouse and Henderson · The Market-milk Industry
Robbins, Crafts, and Raynor · Weed Control
Steinhaus · Principles of Insect Pathology
Thompson · Soils and Soil Fertility
Thompson and Kelly · Vegetable Crops
Thorne · Principles of Nematology
Tracy, Armerding, and Hannah · Dairy Plant Management
Walker · Diseases of Vegetable Crops
Walker · Plant Pathology
Wilson · Grain Crops
Wolfe and Kipps · Production of Field Crops

The late Leon J. Cole was Consulting Editor of this series from 1937 to 1948.
There are also the related series of McGraw-Hill Publications in the Botanical Sciences, of which Edmund W. Sinnott is Consulting Editor, and in the Zoological Sciences, of which Edgar J. Boell is Consulting Editor. Titles in the Agricultural Sciences were published in these series in the period 1917 to 1937.

ANIMAL NUTRITION

Leonard A. Maynard, A.B., Ph.D., Sc.D.

PROFESSOR OF NUTRITION AND BIOCHEMISTRY, EMERITUS
CORNELL UNIVERSITY
MEMBER, NATIONAL ACADEMY OF SCIENCES

John K. Loosli, B.S., M.S., Ph.D.

PROFESSOR OF ANIMAL NUTRITION
COLLEGE OF AGRICULTURE
CORNELL UNIVERSITY

FIFTH EDITION

New York Toronto London
McGRAW-HILL BOOK COMPANY, INC. 1962

ANIMAL NUTRITION

 Library of Congress Catalog Card Number 61-13757

41047 THE MAPLE PRESS COMPANY, YORK, PA.

Preface

The field of nutrition has moved forward at an accelerated pace, year by year, since the fourth edition of this text was published. The need for a further extensive revision became increasingly clear as the new knowledge accumulated. In making this revision for a fifth edition the authors have faced two major problems. One has been the study and evaluation of the tremendous number of papers in the field which have appeared during the past five years. The other has been the selection, from this voluminous material, of the information which seemed most important for a text of this kind, having in mind the desirability of not markedly increasing the size of the new edition. The latter objective, based on the expressed preference of many teachers using the text, has in turn imposed the task of eliminating less important material from the previous edition.

In preparing this edition, the general framework and character of the book established by the senior author in the first edition, and followed in later ones, have been preserved. The text presents the principles of nutrition and their applications to feeding practice. It not only presents facts but shows how many of them have been obtained, illustrating experimental methods which will continue to develop new facts in the future. Like other rapidly advancing fields, new discoveries in the science of nutrition, which add to our knowledge, inevitably cause some modification in ideas previously held. Inevitably also, some of the reported discoveries prove only partially true. A textbook of nutrition must portray these developments, but it must avoid making final judgments in matters which are in dispute or which require further interpretation for their practical application. As in previous editions, such has been the aim in preparing the present one.

The many literature citations made, following the practice of previous editions, have been selected in the interests of both teacher and student.

They serve (1) to show the historical development of the field and acquaint the student with the classic papers, (2) to provide authority for statements made when new facts are involved or if the facts remain in dispute, (3) to furnish sources from which the student may obtain more detailed information on a specific topic, and (4) to serve the teacher by listing references from which he may select assigned readings. Apart from those listed to show the historical development and to document new findings, the literature citations have been made on the basis of their usefulness to illustrate the points under discussion and of their availability to those students who are the principal users of the text. This latter consideration has meant giving preference to papers in the English language and in journals having a wide circulation. The student should appreciate that such a selection has resulted in an unbalanced representation of nutrition research on a world-wide basis.

In preparing the revision the authors have been greatly aided by suggestions which have been received from teachers who have been using the book, including many former students. Their assistance is gratefully acknowledged. The authors are indebted to their Cornell colleagues who have aided in the revision of some of the topics, particularly Professors S. A. Asdell, Louise J. Daniel, S. L. Leonard, A. L. Neal, and R. G. Warner. They also gratefully acknowledge the secretarial assistance of Mrs. Anne Wilcox, Mrs. Reha J. Loosli, and Miss Ellen Loosli in typing the manuscript, reading proof, and preparing the indexes.

Leonard A. Maynard
John K. Loosli

Contents

Part I

General Bases of Nutrition

Chapter 1
The Expanding Field of Nutrition

The great French chemist Lavoisier[1] is frequently referred to as the founder of the science of nutrition. He established the chemical basis of nutrition in his famous respiration experiments carried out before the French Revolution. His studies led him to state, "La vie est une fonction chimique." Thereafter chemistry became an important tool in nutrition studies. Through its application in physiological studies the old idea that the nutritive value of food resided in a single "aliment" was proved wrong in the first quarter of the nineteenth century. The need for protein, fat, and carbohydrates became recognized. For the remainder of the century, nutritional science and practice were concerned primarily with these nutrients and a few mineral elements. The large expansion in the nutrition field has occurred during the last forty-five years with the discovery of the vitamins, of the role of amino acids, and of several more essential mineral elements. Today we know that the body needs over forty different nutrients, in contrast to the three recognized a century ago.

While much of our current knowledge has resulted from direct attacks on evident nutritional and health problems of animals and man, equally important discoveries have come from more basic studies of the functioning of the animal organism, of the physiological and biochemical changes involved, and of the effects of various dietary variables. In many instances, under inspired leadership, research has shown the way to better practice before the need for it was recognized. An outstanding example of such a contribution is the feeding experiment with single

[1] Antoine Lavoisier (1743–1794) introduced the balance and thermometer into nutrition studies. He discovered that combustion was an oxidation, and he showed that respiration in the body involved the combination of carbon and hydrogen with oxygen from inspired air and that the quantities of oxygen absorbed and carbon dioxide given off depended on the food intake and the work done. With Laplace, he designed a calorimeter by means of which it was demonstrated that respiration is the essential source of body heat. The science of nutrition was undoubtedly set back many years when Lavoisier's career was ended by the guillotine.

plants planned by Babcock[2] and carried out at the Wisconsin Experiment Station over fifty years ago.

Babcock, the chemist, recognized that, when cows were being fed a combination of several feeds from different plant sources, there was no way of knowing what particular contribution each was making to the animals' needs. He conceived the idea of trying out rations made up entirely from a single plant. This proposal seemed decidedly impractical to animal husbandmen, who, in those days, thought more of their cows than of the possible value of such an experiment. Eventually Babcock was given the use of two cows, but when one died after three months, the experiment was abandoned lest another valuable animal be lost also. Later, his idea was carried out in an extensive experiment by his younger colleagues Hart and Humphrey, with the later cooperation of McCollum and Steenbock. Five-month-old heifer calves were selected. Four were placed on a ration made entirely from the wheat plant, four on a similar ration from the oat plant, and four on a ration from the corn plant. Another four received a ration of feeds from all three plants. These rations were made up to be alike as regards their contents of all the organic nutrients then known to be essential, and salt was fed in addition.

In the course of the experiment, striking differences developed between the group on the corn plant and the one on wheat. At the end of a year, similar gains in weight had been made, but the corn-fed animals were much the sleeker and more vigorous. When the animals were bred, remarkable differences occurred in the outcome. Each of the corn-fed group produced a normal calf which developed into a vigorous animal, while all of the calves from the wheat group either were dead at birth or died soon after. The corn-fed group produced three times as much milk in the month following calving as did the other group. The later results continued to be strikingly in favor of the corn plant. Exhaustive chemical studies of the feeds and excreta of the cows and of the tissues of the calves which died or were killed for autopsy failed to find any explanation of the results. It was concluded that the wheat plant contained something toxic or, perhaps, that it lacked something supplied by corn. It was years before new discoveries provided the true answer.

This experiment made it clear that there were marked differences in nutritive values which could not be detected by any chemical means available at the time and that the current scientific bases for formulating rations were seriously inadequate. More important, the experiment led to the conviction that simplified diets must be used for the solution

[2] Stephen M. Babcock (1843–1931), who is most widely known for his invention, the Babcock test, made many pioneer contributions in the fields of dairy chemistry and animal nutrition. Following six years at the New York Experiment Station, he served for twenty-five years as chemist and assistant director at the Wisconsin Experiment Station.

of nutrition problems. It stimulated the use of the purified-diet method (Sec. 10.3), which resulted in the discovery of the first vitamin (Sec. 8.1) in 1913 and which has been so largely responsible for the newer knowledge of nutrition. The report of this Wisconsin experiment[3] is well worth reading by every student. He should enjoy forming his own opinion, in the light of modern knowledge, as to just what was wrong with the wheat ration. The far-reaching influence of this experiment should convince even the most practical-minded person that no one is wise enough to predict in advance what research is of practical value and what is not. Fundamental facts provide the only adequate bases for meeting current practical problems as well as for advancing nutritional science.

The modern discoveries in nutrition have resulted from studies with a wide variety of species. The contributions of the laboratory rat to our knowledge of vitamins, amino acids, and minerals have been enormous. The discovery of insulin and of the role of nicotinic acid in the prevention and cure of pellagra exemplifies the debt that we owe to the dog. Guinea pig experiments showed us the specific cause of scurvy and how to prevent it. The pioneer work that led to the discovery of thiamine was carried out with the chick, and this species has continued to help solve many puzzles in the field of vitamins. Monkeys, mice, and hamsters all have contributions to their credit. Even the lower forms, particularly bacteria, have played a large role in the discovery of growth factors, in the assay of our foods for various nutrients, and in explaining how these nutrients function in metabolism. Today the nutritional scientist realizes that basic, or pilot, experiments with one of these various species, selected in accordance with the objective of the study, provide the best approach for the solution of many of the problems in the nutrition of man and farm animals.

The expanding developments in the field of nutrition have resulted from the application of the knowledge and techniques of many different sciences. The physiologist and biochemist have long worked as a team in studying the body's need for food and how this food is metabolized. But the advancement in many areas was slow until the aid of scientists in other fields was obtained. The identification of the various vitamins lagged until the organic chemist became interested in their isolation and synthesis. Thanks to his efforts, commercial sources of many of them have become available both for further experimental work and also for use in feeding practice. The physicist has given us X rays, the spectrograph, isotopes, chromatography, and other tools and has shown us how they can be used for the advancement of nutrition. The geneticist has discovered breed differences in nutritive requirements and in the efficiency of food utilization. He has even developed new strains of certain

[3] E. B. Hart et al., Physiological effect on growth and reproduction of rations balanced from restricted sources, *Wisconsin Agr. Expt. Sta. Research Bull.* 17, 1911.

lower forms that will detect specific vitamin and amino acid deficiencies in our foods. The microbiologist has assisted greatly in the recent discoveries of the nutritional roles that bacteria play in the rumen of the cow and sheep and in the intestine of other species. Microbiological methods have greatly speeded up the development of our knowledge regarding the vitamin and amino acid content of foods.

The significance of these contributions from the various fields of science will become apparent in the discussions in the succeeding chapters. The modern student of nutrition must have an appreciation of the important relations of these basic sciences to the solution of the problems of the expanding field. He must have a real working knowledge of chemistry and physiology, particularly, if he is to understand present-day developments and apply them in feeding practice. Such a knowledge will also help him to evaluate the significance of new facts as they are discovered and enable him to modify his practice accordingly.

The essentiality of several nutrients has been a comparatively recent discovery because they are needed in traces only. Here we think first of the vitamins, but 0.1 mg. of cobalt per day makes the difference between life and death in a sheep. A lack of that minute amount was responsible for tremendous livestock losses in certain parts of the world before their specific cause was discovered. We express protein requirements in pounds or grams, but a few milligrams or micrograms of certain other nutrients are just as important for health and production.

Studies of some of these "trace" mineral elements have shown that the character of the soil on which we grow our food crops plays an important role in determining their nutritive value. We have also learned that varieties of the same crop differ in nutritional quality and that various cultural factors have an influence here also. Thus, animal and human nutrition ties back into agriculture and to the soil, stressing the importance of yields of nutrients as distinguished from the consideration of tons or bushels per acre alone.

We have learned that the soil may contribute toxic elements to our food supply as well as essential ones. Some of the vitamins, as well as the minerals, that are essential in small amounts may prove harmful at higher intakes. Poor nutrition can result from too much as well as too little. Further, a suitable balance between certain nutrients is important.

The recent developments have served to stress the interrelationships between human and animal nutrition. Superficially, the rations of man and animals have little in common, since the kinds of food eaten are so different. Yet the essential constituents of these rations, that is, the elements required for adequate nutrition, are largely the same whatever the species. The general principles of nutrition are identical. Both man and animals draw upon the same basic food supply—the products of the soil. In the emergency of war and its aftermath we became conscious of the fact that, while animals concentrate the nutrients of food crops into more nutritious and palatable forms for the human diet, they waste basic food resources in the process. Animal production had to be curtailed accordingly, particularly in European countries, to conserve human food.

The most successful human diet, however, in terms of the optimum nutrition of a people, is one that contains liberal amounts of animal products. There is a real nutritional justification for an animal industry, though its extent may be governed by economic considerations. The nutritive value and palatability of animal products consumed by man are influenced by the ration of the animal and by processing factors. These aspects cannot be neglected by an industry that exists primarily to provide human food. The producer of milk, meat, and eggs needs to know something about their nutritive values. This is another example of the interrelationships between human and animal nutrition that the student should keep in mind.

Despite the large advances that typify the expanding field of nutrition, there are many "unknowns" for further study. It is doubtful whether all the essentials of an adequate diet for any species have been discovered. Certainly, much more needs to be learned regarding the quantitative requirements of our farm animals for some of the more recently discovered nutrients. This fact is evident in the recently published reports, referred to specifically later, setting forth nutrient requirements for farm animals. Much more information is also needed about the quantitative occurrence of the recently discovered nutrients in our foodstuffs.

Most of our present knowledge of nutrition requirements has been gained from comparatively short-time studies. As higher and higher productive performance is sought in our farm animals, we recognize the limitations of our measures of adequate nutrition from the standpoint of productive life. The rearing of breeding stock, milk-producing animals, and laying hens represents an initial cost which, for greatest return, must be spread over a long period of profitable production. The desirability of rapid growth, not only to bring animals into production as soon as possible but also to develop the highest producers, has been a dominant idea in current nutrition thought. Recent discoveries in nutrition have resulted in feeding practices which have markedly accelerated the growth rate. At the same time, however, an increasing appreciation has developed that a large number of animals, which are highly promising from the standpoint of growth performance, fail to come into profitable production or have an abnormally short productive life. The large turnover of cows is a serious problem in the dairy business. Along with the factors of inheritance and of disease, the nutritional aspect deserves further study. There is need for a reconsideration of the nutrition of the animal from birth, with profitable productive life rather than rate of growth as the dominant viewpoint.

Many years ago, in a very thought-provoking article McCay and Crowell[4] challenged the current view that the most rapid growth, as measured by increase in weight and size, is the ideal for maximum health and long life, and they cited evidence obtained with various species in support of their thesis. As regards farm animals, studies with dairy cows, both in Europe and in this country, have shown that lifetime performance tends to be better when they are raised from calfhood on a low plane of nutrition instead of on a high level (Sec. 14.11). Clearly, increase in weight and size is a very inadequate measure of the complete development of the organism. It is possible that in stressing this general measure we have neglected factors vital to the correlated and optimum growth of the diverse organs and glands upon which later production and longevity depend. The enhanced growth in weight and size which has resulted from large intakes of recently discovered dietary essentials may be accentuating the limiting effect of as yet unidentified factors required for complete development and continued function. There may well be no conflict between rapid growth and length of productive life, provided the growth obtained is complete and correlated in all it aspects. But we may have no adequate knowledge at the present time of how to measure this growth and thus may be providing a nutrition which is far from optimum to achieve it.

The nutrition worker who is a true scientist recognizes the limitations of present knowledge. He realizes that findings which have later proved to be inadequate have been responsible for practical recommendations which did not prove effective. He is becoming more conservative accordingly. But overenthusiasm or error has characterized many of the popular articles in the field of nutrition, and some of those who have food products for sale seem to have no inhibitions at all. It is not surprising that the layman is puzzled by what he reads and that reasoning or actual experience may convince him that the field is overexpanded. There has been an overexploitation of present knowledge, but the need for research to fill in the many gaps in this knowledge cannot be denied, and the accomplishments of the recent decades make it evident that further intensive studies will prove highly beneficial to human and animal welfare. There should be a curtailment of premature conclusions and recommendations for practice and an expansion of critical research by competent workers who have the patience to carry through the long-time experiments demanded for the complete solution of current problems.

[4] C. M. McCay and Mary F. Crowell, Prolonging the life span, *Sci. Monthly*, **39**: 405–414, 1934.

From the discussions that follow the student will become conscious of the many gaps, and even of some contradictions, in present knowledge. Such a situation exists in every scientific field as one approaches its borders, but these borders are being constantly extended by research, and the new ground gained is being consolidated. Continued activities in these directions are particularly needed in the field of nutrition. In the words of the late Professor Hart,[5] of the University of Wisconsin, we should "chart all the factors in nutrition, organic and inorganic, and study their distribution, physiology, pathology, and interplay. Put the need for these factors on a quantitative basis with optimum allowance for the complete cycle of the animal's life." Thus will the field of nutrition continue to expand for the benefit of the livestock industry and human welfare.

ORGANIZATION OF THE SUBJECT MATTER OF NUTRITION

The foregoing discussion indicates that the field of nutrition is a broad one, involving many diverse though related areas. The orderly and effective presentation of its subject matter to the student involves difficult problems, accordingly. At the outset, therefore, it may be helpful to both the student and instructor to outline the organization of the subject matter as presented in this text. The presentation is divided into four parts:

1. General bases of nutrition, comprising Chaps. 1 to 3
2. The nutrients and their metabolism, comprising Chaps. 4 to 9
3. Methods of measuring body needs and the nutritive values of feeds, comprising Chaps. 10 to 12
4. The nutritive requirements for various body processes and productive functions, comprising Chaps. 13 to 17

SELECTED LITERATURE

Blaxter, K. L.: Efficiency of feed conversion by different classes of livestock in relation to food production, *Federation Proc.*, **20** (Part III):268–274, 1961.

Maynard, L. A.: Animal species that feed mankind: the role of nutrition, *Science*, **120**:164–166, 1954.

Mitchell, H. H.: Adaptation to undernutrition, *J. Am. Dietet. Assoc.*, **20**:511–515, 1944.

Zscheile, F. P.: Role of genetics in food quality improvement, *Nutrition Revs.*, **8**:65–69, 1950.

[5] Edwin B. Hart (1874–1953), a biochemist, was an outstanding teacher and investigator of biochemistry and nutrition for over forty years. His pioneer studies with both laboratory and farm animals are frequently referred to in this text.

Chapter 2
The Animal Body and Its Food

Nutrition involves various chemical and physiological activities which transform food elements into body elements. At the outset, therefore, a brief consideration of the chemical composition of the animal body in relation to the composition of its food is useful to give a general picture of the nutrition process, the detailed aspects of which are presented in later chapters.

COMPOSITION OF THE ANIMAL BODY

Over eighty years ago the famous English scientists Lawes and Gilbert[1] performed the pioneer and laborious task of analyzing the entire bodies of farm animals. Since that time, many similar studies have been made by other workers, with the result that we have a large body of data regarding the composition of various species at different ages and in varying states of nutrition. From these data the figures given in Table 2.1 have been assembled to provide a general picture of the gross composition of mature animals in a good state of nutrition and to show that different species are very similar in this respect.

2.1. Water and Organic Substances. The data in Table 2.1, given in round numbers, are subject to large variations according to age and nutritional state, as well as to differences among individuals. On a percentage basis, the water content shows a large decrease with age in early life. In the case of cattle, for example, the water content is approxi-

[1] Agricultural science owes a tremendous debt to John B. Lawes (1814–1900) and Joseph H. Gilbert (1817–1901) for their pioneer work in the fields of agronomy and animal nutrition, begun in 1843 and continued for over half a century. The experiment station which they founded at Rothamsted, England, rapidly gained fame throughout the world, and it remains today an outstanding center of research in the plant sciences. Their studies of the composition of the animal body are published under the title: Experimental enquiry into the composition of the animals fed and slaughtered as human food, *Trans. Roy. Soc.* (*London*), **149**:493–680, 1859.

mately 95 per cent for the embryo shortly after conception, 75 to 80 per cent at birth, 66 to 72 per cent at five months, and 50 to 60 per cent in the mature animal. The variations for a given age are due primarily to the nutritional state as reflected in the store of fat. Very fat animals have less than 50 per cent of water at maturity. The percentage of fat normally increases with age, but it is highly variable at all times, depending upon the level of food intake. Its variation affects the percentages of the other constituents, and this is particularly true for water. Missouri workers, for example, found a thin steer to contain 18 per cent of fat and 57 per cent of water, in contrast to 41 per cent of fat and 42 per cent of water for a very fat animal.

In view of the wide differences in fat content which may occur, much less variable figures for the other constituents are obtained by expressing them on a fat-free (protoplasmic) basis. On this basis the gross composition of the mature animal body, less the contents of the digestive tract, is represented by the following approximate figures: water, 75 per cent; protein, 20 per cent; and mineral matter, 5 per cent. These figures are subject to little variation after the animal is nearly full grown, though there is a slight decrease in water throughout life.

TABLE 2.1. PERCENTAGE GROSS COMPOSITION OF THE ANIMAL BODY*

Species	Water	Protein	Fat	Mineral matter
Steer...........	54	15	26	4.6
Hog...........	58	15	24	2.8
Sheep..........	60	16	20	3.4
Hen...........	56	21	19	3.2
Mare..........	60	17	17	4.5
Man...........	59	18	18	4.3

* Less contents of digestive tract.

The data of Table 2.1 do not reveal the very small amount of carbohydrate which is present in the body. Though occurring as much less than 1 per cent at any given moment, it is constantly being formed and broken down in metabolism and thus performs a multitude of vital functions. The only species differences shown in the table which may be considered significant are certain ones for mineral matter, reflecting differences in relative size of skeleton.

The chemical groups which make up the gross composition of the body are not evenly distributed throughout the various organs and tissues but are more or less localized according to their functions. Water is an essential constituent of every part of the body, but its quantitative distribution varies greatly in different parts. Blood plasma contains 90 to

92 per cent, muscle 72 to 78 per cent, bone approximately 45 per cent, and the enamel of the teeth 5 per cent.

Proteins are present in every cell and, as such, are the principal constituent, other than water, of the organs and soft structures of the body such as the muscles, tendons, and connective tissues. Most of the fat is localized in the adipose tissue, or fat depots, which occur under the skin, around the intestines, around the kidneys and other organs; but it is also present in the muscles, bones, and elsewhere. In fact every cell contains substances classed with the fats. The small amount of carbohydrate present in the body is found principally in the liver, muscles, and blood.

2.2. Mineral Composition. The mineral matter of the body comprises a large number of elements present in varying amounts in different parts, according to the functions they perform. The percentages of the principal mineral constituents of the body are indicated by the following data:

Element	*Per cent*	*Element*	*Per cent*
Calcium	1.33	Chlorine	0.11
Phosphorus	0.74	Magnesium	0.041
Sodium	0.16	Sulfur	0.15
Potassium	0.19		

SOURCE: A. G. Hogan and J. L. Nierman, Studies in animal nutrition. VI. The distribution of the mineral elements in the animal body as influenced by age and condition, *Missouri Agr. Expt. Sta. Research Bull.* 107, 1927.

These data are averages of analyses of 18 steers of varying ages. They are expressed as a percentage of the entire body less the contents of the digestive tract. It is noted that, aside from calcium, the elements occur as fractions of a per cent only. Despite their small amounts, they are absolutely essential to life. These average data for the steer are subject to variation according to age and state of fattening. The data for other species show a similar pattern, though differing quantitatively, as is to be expected.

Calcium, the mineral occurring in largest amounts in the body, is present almost entirely in the bones and teeth as phosphate and hydroxide. The phosphorus which is combined with calcium to form the skeleton accounts for approximately 80 per cent of the body supply. The remainder is widely distributed in combination with certain proteins and fats and as inorganic salts. Sulfur occurs throughout the body as a part of the protein molecule. Sodium, potassium, and chlorine are present almost entirely as inorganic salts in the various fluids. Most of the magnesium is present in the bones, but it is also found widely distributed elsewhere in the body.

In addition to the elements listed in the table, there are many others which are present in smaller amounts, some of which are known to be necessary for life. Iron is an essential constituent of the hemoglobin of the blood and occurs in lesser amounts throughout the organs and in the various tissues. Iodine, copper, zinc, manganese, cobalt, and probably fluorine are essential for either structural or metabolic purposes. Boron, silicon, bromine, aluminum, nickel, and arsenic are among the additional elements which have been reported as normally occurring in the body, though they have no known function.

2.3. The Blood. From the standpoint of nutrition, the composition of the blood is of special importance in that it is the medium by which the nutrients are carried to the various parts of the body and by which the waste products of metabolism are removed. The blood makes up from 5 to 10 per cent of the body weight, depending upon the species and nutritive state. Values for farm animals at different ages, determined by the use of isotopic phosphorus (Sec. 3.16), have been reported by Hansard and coworkers.[2] The figure for birds is higher than for mammals. The blood volume is related primarily to the active tissues of the body. Thus the larger the amount of adipose tissue, the lower is the percentage of blood for the body as a whole. For example, it has been shown in the case of the hibernating woodchuck that the figure for blood percentage increases as it uses up its fat reserve.

The corpuscles make up from 30 to 45 per cent of the blood, depending upon the species. This percentage value is the *hematocrit reading*. The solid matter of the red corpuscles consists almost entirely of the iron-containing protein hemoglobin. In certain lower forms, however, the protein of the corpuscles contains an element other than iron as its respiratory pigment. The *Pinna squamosa*, a shellfish, has a protein called pinnaglobulin which contains manganese. Lobsters, crabs, and snails have the copper-containing hemocyanin.

The plasma contains 10 per cent of solids, more than half of which are proteins. The remainder consists principally of various fatty substances, sugar, nonprotein nitrogen compounds, and inorganic salts. The principal inorganic elements are sodium and chlorine, with potassium, calcium, magnesium, phosphorus, and others occurring in much smaller amounts. Most of the sodium and chlorine are combined together, but various other combinations of these and other elements occur, such as sodium bicarbonate, disodium phosphate, and potassium chloride.

2.4. Muscle and Other Tissues. All movements of the body and of the organs and tissues which take part in life processes depend upon muscle action. Thus muscle tissue is distributed throughout the body. Skeletal muscle, which comprises about one-half the total body, contains about 75 per cent of water. Protein makes up 75 to 80 per cent of the dry

[2] Sam L. Hansard and coworkers, Blood volume of farm animals, *J. Animal Sci.*, **12**:402–413, 1953.

matter. The remainder consists principally of fat, with small amounts of carbohydrate (glycogen) and mineral matter. The *epithelial tissues*, which comprise the skin, hair, feathers, the linings of the alimentary tract, respiratory tract, and genitourinary tract and occur elsewhere in the body, consist primarily of keratin. This is a highly insoluble protein which provides the protective and resistant qualities needed. *Connective tissue* is found in cartilage, tendons, ligaments, and the matrix of bone and provides an intercellular binding substance throughout the body. It consists of insoluble protein fibers, usually collagen, imbedded in a matrix or ground substance. The brain and nerves consist of *nervous tissue*, which is comprised mainly of various lipids and of complexes of lipid, protein, and carbohydrate. In later chapters, mention will be made of certain specific compounds in these various tissues.

2.5. Estimation of Gross Body Composition. Data on the gross composition of the body provide specific information on its stage of development and state of nutrition (nutriture) not obtainable by merely weighing the animal or its products. Thus slaughter and chemical analysis are techniques frequently employed in feeding experiments (Sec. 10.8). The obvious limitation of these procedures, apart from being laborious, is that data on a given animal can be obtained only once, although what is most desired is information on its changing body composition as a result of the ration fed. Much recent study has therefore been given to the estimation of the gross body composition of the living animal, and very useful procedures have been developed accordingly.

The methods are based on the recognition that a highly predictable inverse relationship exists between the concentrations of water and of fat in the body and that in the fat-free, water-free body the proportions of protein and ash remain constant. The basic procedure is the determination of the body water. This can be done by a series of methods all based on dilution techniques. These involve the injection of compounds known to go into solution in body water and the quantitative determination of the dilution of a marker used, after equilibrium has been reached. The compounds most commonly employed are antipyrine and its analogues and the isotopes deuterium and tritium. After the water content has been measured, the contents of fat, protein, and ash can be calculated. The method is illustrated for cattle by the report of Reid and coworkers.[3] The following equation is given for calculating fat content from the measured water:

$$Y = 355.88 + 0.355X - 202.91 \log X$$

[3] J. T. Reid, G. H. Wellington, and H. O. Dunn, Some relationships among the major chemical components of the bovine body and their application to nutritional investigations, *J. Dairy Sci.*, **38**:1344–1359, 1955.

where Y = fat content (per cent) and X = water content (per cent). The protein and ash contents are calculated from the finding that the fat-free dry body contains 80.3 per cent of protein and 19.7 per cent of ash.

Similar studies for sheep and swine have been reported.

COMPOSITION OF PLANTS AND THEIR PRODUCTS

Food must supply nutrients which can be used to build and renew the components of the body and to form its products such as milk, eggs, and wool, and it must furnish energy for the processes involved. After weaning, most of our farm animals obtain all of their food supply from plants. While there are certain animal species which are entirely carnivorous, the plant kingdom is the original and essential source of all animal life, because plants are able to utilize the energy of the sun to build substances which will nourish the animal. Plants make use of carbon dioxide, water, nitrates, and other mineral salts to form carbohydrates, fats, and proteins which the animals must have to build their bodies and which are broken down in life processes. Thus plants store and animals dissipate energy.

2.6. Plants and Their Parts. Plants contain the same substances that are found in the animal body, but the relative amounts present are very

TABLE 2.2. APPROXIMATE PERCENTAGE COMPOSITION OF TYPICAL PLANTS AND THEIR PRODUCTS*

	Water	Protein	Fat	Carbohydrates	Mineral matter	Calcium	Phosphorus
Green plants:							
Corn	69	2.5	0.8	26	1.7	0.27	0.22
Alfalfa	73	5.2	0.8	19	2.4	1.72	0.31
Timothy	72	3.2	1.0	22	2.0	0.47	0.34
Dried plant products:							
Corn stover	12	5.2	1.5	76	5.1	0.29	0.05
Corn grain	14	9.0	3.9	72	1.3	0.03	0.31
Soybean	8	34.9	18.1	34	4.7	0.23	0.59
Alfalfa leaves	11	21.3	2.8	55	9.5	2.38	0.29
Alfalfa stems	10	9.6	1.2	74	5.7	0.89	0.22

* Most of these data were taken from the publication Joint United States–Canadian Tables of Feed Composition, *Natl. Acad. Sci.–Natl. Research Council Publ.* 659, 1959.

different. Plants also show much larger differences in composition among species than do animals. The composition of certain typical plants and plant products is given in Table 2.2. These data are presented for the purpose of comparing them with data previously given for the animal body (Table 2.1) and of illustrating certain useful generalizations regarding differences in composition among plants and their various products.

The analyses of three green plants are given to show the general composition of the living plants at the stage when vegetative growth is practically completed but before the seed has matured. These data reveal the fact that the principal constituent of living plants is water, even as is true of the animal body. This water content decreases as the seed is matured. The striking difference in the composition of plants and animals is the fact that the dry matter of plants consists principally of carbohydrate. This constituent serves as both structural and reserve material, while in animals protein comprises the structure of the soft tissues and fat is the reserve. Thus, although the animal body contains only a trace of carbohydrate, this nutrient is the principal constituent of the food of most species. It serves as a source of energy, either currently or as a reserve in the form of fat, into which it is readily transformed.

The data for dried plant products, representing the moisture basis to which they are reduced after curing for storage, are given to bring out certain generalizations regarding differences in composition among the various parts of the plant. The figures for corn stover and corn grain provide a comparison between the vegetative portion of the plant and its seed. The data for the soybean illustrate some characteristics of legume seeds, and those for the alfalfa products bring out certain differences between leaves and stems.

Protein is primarily a constituent of active tissues, and thus leaves are much richer in this nutrient than are stems, as the data for alfalfa show. Leafy, legume hays such as alfalfa and the clovers always contain more protein than the grass hays such as timothy. As the plant matures, there is a movement of protein from the vegetative parts to the seed to provide for the requirements of growth during germination. Thus, at maturity, the seed contains a higher percentage of protein than the rest of the plant, as is indicated by the figures for corn grain and corn stover.

Fat is also higher in the leaves than in the stems and generally is highest in the seeds, where it serves as a condensed reserve of energy for later germination. In most seeds, of which corn and other cereals are examples, the principal store of energy is in the form of carbohydrates, but oil-bearing seeds, such as the soybean, cottonseed, and flax, contain their reserve primarily as fat, as their name implies. These seeds are used as commercial sources of oil, leaving oil meals as by-products for animal feeding. Oil-bearing seeds are also much higher in protein than are the cereal seeds.

In all plant products, with the exception of the oil-bearing seeds, carbohydrate is the principal constituent, even as it is in the plant as a whole.

The nature of this carbohydrate differs markedly according to whether it is serving as a reserve of structural element. In seeds, it occurs principally as starch, which is the reserve carbohydrate, while in stems and to a much lesser extent in leaves, a considerable proportion of it is present as cellulose, the principal structural carbohydrate. The outer coats of seeds also contain cellulose as a structural and protective element. Since cellulose and related compounds, classed by the nutrition chemist as *crude fiber*, are much less digestible than starch, the various parts of plants differ markedly in nutritive value according to their digestibility. Feeds which are high in cellulose and related compounds and thus of low digestibility, such as hay, straw, and silage, are classed as *roughages*. The term *concentrates* is used to denote those low in crude fiber and highly digestible. Here are included the seeds and most of their by-products.

2.7. Mineral Matter. The amount of mineral matter in plants is highly variable in different species as well as in the different plant parts. From the standpoint of animal nutrition, we are particularly interested in the fact that the percentage distribution of the mineral elements of plants differs markedly from that in animals. To illustrate this fact, data for calcium and phosphorus in plants, the elements which make up over 70 per cent of body ash, are given in Table 2.2. With the exception of the legumes, which are always rich in calcium, these elements make up a rather small part of the ash of plants. Both are exceeded by potassium, an element in which we are much less interested in animal nutrition. Calcium is primarily associated with the vegetative portion of the plant, and the leaf is richer than the stem. Without exception, seeds are low in calcium compared with the other parts of the plant, though oil-bearing seeds are higher than others. In contrast to calcium, phosphorus is richer in the seeds than in the rest of the plant. Leaves are richer than stems. The calcium and phosphorus content of the vegetative part of the plant is influenced by soil and other cultural factors.

2.8. By-product Feeds. The feeds of animals obtained from plants consist not only of forage crops, seeds, and roots but also of by-products arising from the processing of various plant materials, notably seeds, in the manufacture of products used for human food and for industrial purposes. The bran and middlings which arise from flour milling, gluten feed which is a by-product of cornstarch manufacture, and the meals which are the residues of the pressing of oil from oil-bearing seeds are all familiar examples of the very large number of by-product feeds. Their composition is usually very different from that of the seed or other material from which they arise. This is illustrated by the figures in Table 2.3, which are taken in a condensed form from data presented by

Osborne and Mendel.[4] While these data must be considered as approximate only in view of the rather large percentage of undetermined material, they serve to show the large differences in composition among the different parts. The endosperm consists very largely of starch, the reserve material, and contains very little of the less digestible carbohydrates. In contrast, the seed coats are characterized by a high content of cellulose and related compounds which provide the needed protective qualities. They are also richer in protein, fat, and mineral matter than the endosperm or the seed as a whole. The embryo is especially rich, compared with the other parts, in protein and fat and is lowest of all in cellulose. Most of the vitamin content of the entire kernel is found in the seed coats and embryo.

TABLE 2.3. PERCENTAGE DISTRIBUTION OF NUTRIENTS IN THE PARTS OF THE WHEAT KERNEL*

Part of wheat kernel	Protein	Fat	Starch, sugar, etc.	Cellulose, pentosans, etc.	Ash	Undetermined
Whole kernel	11.3	2.2	66.4	8.0	2.0	10.1
Endosperm	11.2	1.2	81.4	2.1	0.4	3.7
Seed coats	17.6	8.3	7.0	43.9	8.6	14.6
Embryo	40.3	13.5	24.3	1.7	4.8	15.4

* Thomas B. Osborne and Lafayette B. Mendel, The nutritive value of the wheat kernal and its milling products, *J. Biol. Chem.*, **37**:557–601, 1919.

Thus the milling of wheat leaves a feed for animals which is richer in protein, fat, mineral matter, and vitamins than the entire kernel but which is somewhat less digestible because of the larger amount of the higher carbohydrates. It is the endosperm which provides the white flour for human food. A yield of approximately 70 per cent is obtained, which means that a portion of the endosperm is left behind with the seed coats and embryo which constitute the by-products of the milling process.

While wheat by-products have a high feeding value, this is by no means true for all by-product feeds. Oat mill by-product, for example, which

[4] Thomas B. Osborne (1859–1929), chemist of Connecticut Agricultural Experiment Station at New Haven, and Lafayette B. Mendel (1872–1935), professor of physiological chemistry at Yale University, collaborated in nutrition research for over twenty years. Their outstanding discoveries, particularly in the fields of proteins and vitamins, which are frequently referred to in this book, assure them lasting recognition as pioneers in developing the newer knowledge of nutrition. In addition to their joint work, Osborne became the leading authority of the world on the vegetable proteins, while Mendel made many important contributions on various aspects of nutritional physiology and was an inspiring teacher to a host of students who are now carrying on his work in many laboratories.

is the residue from oatmeal production, contains less than half as much protein and over twice as much fiber as the seed itself, because it consists mostly of the hull. It is therefore of low digestibility and nutritive value. On the other hand, the pressing or solvent extraction of soybeans, cottonseed, and flaxseed to obtain their oils for human food or industrial use provides products that are highly digestible and of special value for their protein content.

Similarly, many important feeds, used mostly in swine and poultry rations, result from the processing of animal products. Here are included tankage, meat scraps, fish meal, milk by-products, and many others.

A knowledge of the processes from which by-product feeds arise and thus of their make-up in terms of the different parts of the original material is a very helpful guide to their composition and feeding value.

THE ROLE OF WATER IN THE ANIMAL BODY

It has been mentioned that water makes up over 50 per cent of the composition of the body and that many tissues contain 70 to 90 per cent of this substance. In fact, one may consider the living elements of the body as water inhabitants even as are the true aquatic species. This water is not simply an inert material or merely a solvent but is an active and structural constituent. If a frog's egg weighing a few milligrams is placed in sterile filtered water, a tadpole weighing several grams results. The tadpole contains less dry matter than the original egg, for a part of it has been used to furnish energy for the developmental process. The increase in weight is due to the taking up of water which has become an essential part of the organism. The vital role of water in the body is indicated by Rubner's[5] observation that the body can lose practically all of its fat and over half of its protein and yet live, while a loss of one-tenth of its water results in death. Adolph[6] in an excellent review of water metabolism has pointed out that water ranks far above every other substance in the body as regards rate of turnover, whether the comparison is made absolutely in gram molecules per day or relatively in per cent of the body content. Since it is the nutrient required in largest amounts, its consideration provides an appropriate introduction to nutritional physiology.

2.9. Properties and Functions of Water. Water is the ideal dispersing medium because of its solvent and ionizing powers which facilitate cell

[5] Max Rubner (1854–1932), a pupil of Voit, served for over forty years at the University of Berlin, first as professor of hygiene and later of physiology. He made many pioneer contributions to the science of nutrition, particularly in the field of energy metabolism, as later discussions show.

[6] Edward F. Adolph, The metabolism and distribution of water in body and tissues, *Physiol. Rev.*, **13**:336–371, 1933.

reactions and because of its high specific heat which enables it to absorb the heat of these reactions with a minimum rise in temperature. Cannon[7] has pointed out that: "The heat produced in maximal muscular effort continued for 20 minutes would be so great that if it were not promptly dissipated it would cause albuminous substances of the body to become stiff like a hard boiled egg." The latent heat of vaporization of water also plays an important role in regulating body temperature. Other properties of large significance in physiology are the high surface tension, the tendency to form hydrates, and the high dielectric constant of water. The functions of water in digestion, in the transport of metabolic products, and in excretion are obvious. Its functions are far more diverse and basic, however, than represented by its roles as a solvent and as a substrate for body reactions. It actually takes part in these reactions, as illustrated by the hydrolysis of proteins, fats, and carbohydrates which takes place in digestion and inside the body and by the many anabolic or catabolic changes in intermediary metabolism which require the chemical addition or release of water. Many illustrations of these functions of water are given in following chapters which discuss the metabolism of the other nutrients.

Water plays many special roles. As synovial fluid, it lubricates the joints, and as cerebrospinal fluid, it acts as a water cushion for the nervous system. In the ear, it transports sounds, and in the eye, it is concerned with sight. Recently developed quantitative techniques, including the use of isotopes, are producing new facts with respect to the dynamic roles of water in the various fluids and tissues of the body. An excellent detailed discussion of the functions of water in the body, electrolyte-water interrelationships, water equilibrium in health and disease, and related topics is to be found in a series of articles reporting a symposium held by the Nutrition Society of Great Britain.[8] In view of the variety of its functions and the magnitude of its requirements, water can be considered the most important essential nutrient.

2.10. Metabolic Water. Most of the water which is utilized by the animal body is ingested, either as such or as a component of the food. There is a further available source which is provided by metabolic processes and which is thus called metabolic water. When the carbohydrate glucose is burned to furnish energy for body processes, carbon dioxide and water result:

$$C_6H_{12}O_6 + 6O_2 \longrightarrow 6CO_2 + 6H_2O$$

[7] Walter B. Cannon was professor of physiology at Harvard Medical School. The quotation is from his book The Wisdom of the Body, W. W. Norton & Company, Inc., New York, 1932.

[8] R. A. McCance (Symposium chairman), Man's need for water, *Proc. Nutrition Soc.*, **16**:103–134, 1957.

By calculations from this equation, it can be shown that the metabolism of glucose yields 60 per cent of its weight as water. This figure can be taken as an approximate one for all carbohydrates. Similarly, the metabolism of protein produces approximately 42 per cent of its weight as water, while in the case of fat the figure is over 100 per cent. A given intake of pure fat yields more water in its metabolism than an equal weight of water itself. Metabolic water is also produced by the dehydration synthesis of body proteins, fats, and carbohydrates. Under certain physiological conditions, metabolic water plays an important role in the animal economy. It suffices to meet the needs of hibernating animals. These animals metabolize their reserves of carbohydrate and fat to provide energy for their vital processes, and this metabolism produces enough water to balance that lost by respiration and evaporation. The various roles of metabolic water in the vital processes of plants and animals have been discussed in a very interesting way by Babcock.[9]

2.11. Factors Governing Water Excretion and Requirement. The body's need for water is governed by many factors. Approximately 75 per cent of the tissue formed during growth is water, and in the mature animal such special processes as milk and egg production require water in accordance with the amount of the product being formed. Aside from these needs for the formation of tissue and products, there are large requirements for water to balance that lost by excretion through the gut, kidneys, lungs, and skin. These losses are related to body size, and in rats, a voluntary intake of 800 ml. daily per square meter of body surface has been noted. But the losses are conditioned by body processes and are thus highly variable according to the diet, nature of the metabolic end products, and other factors. The losses through the gut vary with the nature of the diet. They increase with the level of roughage intake and with the intakes of other feeds which have laxative qualities. In general, the larger the proportion of undigested material, the greater the loss. In cattle the fecal material contains about 80 per cent of water. The feces are much drier in the case of sheep on the same ration, illustrating the fact that there are species differences in water loss through the gut. In all species and under all normal conditions, the losses are very small compared with the very large amount of water secreted into the tract in the digestive juices. Actually, the total daily volume of digestive secretions is several times greater than the plasma volume of the body. Normally, almost all the water thus secreted is reabsorbed. In diarrhea large losses occur, resulting in dehydration, and serious consequences if the trouble persists.

The amount of water excreted in the urine is highly variable, depend-

[9] S. M. Babcock, Metabolic water: its production and role in vital phenomena, *Wisconsin Agr. Expt. Sta. Research Bull.* 22, 1912.

ing upon many factors. The kidneys regulate the volume and composition of body fluids, excreting more or less water depending upon intake, outgo through other channels, and the amounts of catabolic products, viz., minerals and nitrogenous end products such as urea, for which water must serve as a solvent. Through its powers of filtration and then of concentration of the filtrate by the reabsorption of water, the kidney can reduce this loss to a minimum. The larger the amounts of minerals and protein in the diet, the greater the loss, increasing the water requirement accordingly. Another reason why a high protein diet increases the water requirement is that less metabolic water is formed in its catabolism than is the case for fat or carbohydrate. In certain pathological conditions excess water is retained in the tissues, body cavities, and elsewhere, causing *edema*.

There are marked species differences in water excretion according to the nature of the nitrogenous end products. In mammals the principal end product of protein catabolism is urea, which is soluble in water and toxic to the tissues in concentrated solution. Thus much water is required to dilute it to a harmless concentration, remove it from the tissues, and excrete it. Uric acid, the principal nitrogenous end product in birds, is excreted in nearly solid form with minimum loss of water. Further, the breakdown of protein to uric acid provides more metabolic water than does its catabolism to urea. Thus, other conditions being equal, birds have a lower water requirement than mammals and are much less sensitive to the temporary deprivation of it. Mammals will live longer without food than without water, and the consumption of food, especially protein food, without water hastens death as the result of the accumulation of toxic end products. Birds, snakes, and insects survive much longer under these conditions. Clothes moths, which contain 50 per cent of water in their bodies, live throughout their cycle on food containing 10 per cent or less of this compound. They excrete uric acid, and thus the small amount of water obtained as a component of their food, plus their metabolic water, suffices.

Expired air is saturated with water and, even for an animal at rest in a cool environment, represents a substantial loss. This loss is greatly increased by physical activity and other factors which step up pulmonary exchange. There are also substantial constant losses through the skin via the sweat glands. Perspiration losses represent an evaporation of water for the dissipation of heat in the regulation of body temperature (Sec. 11.11). They increase with muscle activity and temperature. In most animals the sweat glands are few or absent. Under these conditions, the lungs play an important role in the dissipation of heat. The constantly occurring excretion of water vapor through the lungs and skin is largely responsible for the body losses referred to as *insensible per-*

spiration, which represents the difference between the gaseous intake and outgo. These losses are of considerable magnitude and are related to the environmental temperature and humidity and to the nature of the metabolism, including water intake. When the latter is limited, they may exceed the losses in the urine.

Babcock cites the ability of the camel to accomplish long journeys with little water as illustrating the application of various factors which economize water requirement. This animal eats mostly carbohydrate food under these conditions and thus produces little urea for excretion. It depends upon fat stored in its hump for a part of its energy requirement, and the metabolism of this fat in turn provides a maximum amount of metabolic water. Evaporation from the skin is reduced by a thick coat of hair, and the feces are dry. For all species the water intake is a function of dry-matter consumption. Fasting greatly decreases the need for water. Dogs have been found to ingest only one-fourth as much water on days when no food was given compared with the amount taken on an adequate diet.

2.12. Water Requirements. It is evident that the body must receive sufficient water to balance its losses in addition to the amount required for the formation of new tissue or products, but it is also clear that the requirement will vary widely according to the magnitude of the various factors which govern the losses and that there are marked species differences as well. Thus the determination of the water requirements for a given species and set of conditions is of limited value for any general recommendations. Leitch and Thomson[10] have issued an excellent review of factors governing water intake and of the data dealing with the requirements of various classes of stock. All feeds supply some water, and highly succulent ones, such as silage and green forage, make a substantial contribution to the water requirement. Other conditions being equal, young animals have higher water needs per unit body size than do mature ones. The immediate effect of water restriction is to lessen food consumption, and thus growth and food efficiency, as shown by Crampton and Lloyd[11] with rats.

Fortunately, except under pathological conditions, there are no deleterious effects from an excessive consumption of water. Thus the requirements can best be taken care of in practice by making sure that the animals have the opportunity to consume all they desire at frequent intervals. The importance of frequent access to water for animals having a high requirement has been clearly shown in studies with milking cows.

[10] I. Leitch and J. S. Thomson, The water economy of farm animals, *Nutrition Abstr. & Revs.*, **14**:197–223, 1944.

[11] E. W. Crampton and L. E. Lloyd, The effect of water restriction on the food intake and food efficiency of growing rats, *J. Nutrition*, **54**:221–224, 1954.

These animals need 4 to 5 lb. of water for each pound of milk produced. They will consume more when watered twice a day than once a day and still more if water is before them at all times, and they will produce more milk where they have free access to water.

2.13. The Determination of Water. The water present in a biological material is commonly determined by drying it to constant weight at the temperature of boiling water, and this is a satisfactory procedure for most routine analyses. Not all the water, however, at least in certain materials, is removed by this procedure. The unremoved portion represents water existing in films which has a very low vapor pressure even at 100°C. Thus a refined method involves drying in partial vacuum. Strictly speaking, no figures for moisture content can be considered as absolute values, since their magnitude is influenced by the three variables involved in the determination—temperature, pressure, and time. When the dried material is to be used for subsequent determinations with which previous oxidation might interfere, the drying is carried out in an inert gas such as nitrogen. Certain materials must be dried below 100°C. to avoid alterations in some of their constituents. Other special procedures are required for certain products.

SELECTED LITERATURE

Callow, E. H.: Comparative studies of meat. I. The chemical composition of fatty and muscular tissue in relation to growth and fattening, *J. Agr. Sci.*, **37**:113–129, 1947.

Clark, R., and J. I. Quin: Studies on the water requirements of farm animals in South Africa. I. The effect of intermittent watering on Merino sheep, *Onderstepoort J. Vet. Sci. Animal Ind.*, **22**:335–343, 1949.

——— and ———: Studies on the water requirements of farm animals in South Africa. II. The relation between water consumption, food consumption and atmospheric temperature as studied on Merino sheep, *Onderstepoort J. Vet. Sci. Animal Ind.*, **22**:345–356, 1949.

Dukes, H. H.: The Physiology of Domestic Animals, 7th ed., Comstock Publishing Associates, Inc., Ithaca, N.Y., 1955.

Ellenberger, H. B., J. A. Newlander, and C. H. Jones: Composition of the bodies of dairy cattle, *Vermont Agr. Expt. Sta. Bull.* 558, July, 1950.

Hansard, Sam L., and W. A. Lyke: Measurement of total body water in sheep using I^{131} labeled 4-iodo-antipyrine, *Proc. Soc. Exptl. Biol. Med.*, **93**:263–266, 1956.

Mitchell, H. H., and associates: The chemical composition of the adult human body and its bearing on the biochemistry of growth, *J. Biol. Chem.*, **158**:625–637, 1945.

Schneider, Burch Hart: Feeds of the World: Their Digestibility and Composition, West Virginia University, Morgantown, W.Va., 1947.

Winchester, C. F. and M. J. Morris: Water intake rates of cattle, *J. Animal Sci.*, **15**: 722–740, 1956.

Chapter 3
Some Physiochemical Bases and Measures of Life Processes

While most biological reactions can be duplicated in the test tube, the living organism can perform quickly and easily reactions which in the test tube require prolonged intervals or special conditions, such as high temperature. For example, it takes a 30 per cent solution of hydrochloric acid 5 hr. at a temperature above 100°C. to hydrolyze protein, whereas enzymatic hydrolysis in the digestive tract will accomplish the same result in less than half the time at a temperature of 37°C. and in a nearly neutral medium. The body tissues would be destroyed by the strong reagents and the high temperatures of the test tube. Although much remains to be learned as to how biological reactions take place, it is recognized that they are assisted by various physiochemical phenomena which play special roles in life processes. An understanding of certain of these phenomena is helpful in explaining various nutrition processes.

3.1. Surface Phenomena. Each cell is separated from its medium and from other cells by a membrane, and the nucleus within the cell is surrounded by a membrane. At these surface boundaries many of the important reactions, both physical and chemical, occur, such as the formation of cartilage and bone which takes place at the boundary between the cell nucleus and its cytoplasm.

The molecules of a liquid have a pronounced attraction for each other. At the surface this cohesive attraction is unbalanced, which means that work must be done on a molecule to take it from a position within the body of the liquid to a position in the surface. Thus there is resident in every unit area of surface a certain amount of potential energy which is known as the surface energy per unit area. The *surface energy* per unit area is equal to what is known as the *surface tension.* Since the potential energy of any system always tends toward a minimum, the surface area tends to become as small as possible, as is exemplified by the spherical form of a drop. Again, since the surface energy tends to become a minimum, any substance present which will lower the surface energy will tend to become concentrated at the surface, and this phenomenon is known as *adsorption*.

3.2. Emulsions. An emulsion is a suspension of two immiscible liquids in each other, which are held in a more or less permanent suspension by some substance acting as a film or an emulsifying agent. Oil and water, which are immiscible, can be shaken into an emulsion which is fairly permanent by the use of an appropriate emulsifying agent. Fat exists in milk in the form of an emulsion. Emulsification of two liquids may result in a semisolid state, as exemplified by such products as mayonnaise; lanolin, which is wool fat with 25 per cent of water added; and the solid alcohol sold under the name of Sterno. The phenomenon is due to surface-tension relations, for the emulsifying substance is a surface-tension reducing agent. Emulsification results in an increase in surface and thus facilitates surface reactions. The bile salts act as the agents in the emulsification of fat in the intestine, whereby a greater surface is afforded for the action of the fat-digesting enzyme.

3.3. Osmotic Pressure. If a solution and the pure solvent are placed in contact, a homogeneous solution results under the action of diffusion. If, however, the solution and solvent are separated by a semipermeable membrane, i.e., one through which the solvent can pass but the solute cannot, a special phenomenon arises which is illustrated in Fig. 3.1. The vessel consists of two compartments separated by a membrane *mm* through which water can pass but dissolved sugar cannot. Water is placed in one compartment and a solution of sugar in the other, so that both are at the same level, designated as *a*. Under these conditions, water diffuses through into the sugar solution, and the level in this compartment rises while it falls in the other, the final levels being indicated by *b*. This takes place in opposition to the hydrostatic pressure, represented by the differences in level of the two columns, under the influence of a force which is called *osmotic pressure*. This pressure is determined by the number of particles in solution, whether molecules or ions. Thus, for a given solution, the higher the concentration the greater the osmotic pressure; and, at the same concentration of solute, solutions of highly ionized substances have greater osmotic pressures than solutions of weakly ionized substances.

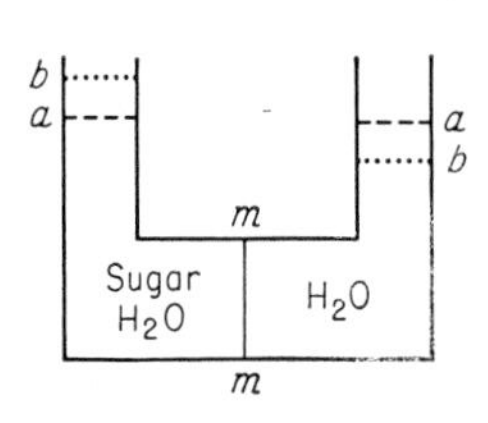

FIG. 3.1. Osmotic pressure.

Since all body fluids contain dissolved substances, they all exhibit osmotic pressure. This pressure is subject to variation according to the kind and concentration of the particles dissolved, and thus osmotic relationships play an important role in physiological processes. If the content of a cell has a lower osmotic pressure than its liquid medium, water tends to pass out of the cell and it shrinks; if the situation is reversed, the cell swells and may burst. For example, when a red corpuscle is placed in a solution of much lower osmotic pressure, it swells and bursts with the liberation of hemoglobin, the red coloring matter of the blood. The phenomenon is called *hemolysis.* Solutions which are alike as regards osmotic pressure are said to be *isotonic,* while the terms *hypertonic* and *hypotonic* denote solutions of higher and lower pressure, respectively. A *physiological salt solution* is one containing 0.85 per cent of sodium chloride, a concentration which is isotonic with blood and other tissue fluids. Substances which are injected into the blood or tissues are placed in such a solution so that osmotic relations will not be disturbed.

3.4. The Colloidal State of Matter. If common salt is dissolved in water, the dissolved particles are of ionic size and cannot be seen even through the ultramicroscope. The solution is clear, and no settling occurs. If, on the other hand, fine sand is shaken with water, a suspension is formed in which the suspended particles of sand are many, many times larger than the ions of the dissolved salt, and the particles gradually settle out. While both the dissolving of the salt and the suspension of the sand are purely physical phenomena, the condition of the distributed or dispersed particles and their subsequent behavior are very different because of the wide difference in their size. An intermediate condition can occur in which the particles dispersed are larger than molecules but smaller than those of the suspension described. This condition is referred to as the colloidal state of matter. The particles are large enough to be seen by the ultramicroscope, but not large enough to settle out. A colloidal solution has many properties which are very different from those exhibited by a true solution such as one of salt and water, and these properties are very important in biology.

The essential characteristic of a colloidal solution is particle size. There is no one size, however, which defines the colloidal state. Colloidal solutions may grade into true solutions on the one hand and into suspensions on the other, and the same substance may exist either in a true solution or in the colloidal form, depending upon how the solution is prepared. Colloidal properties are exhibited, however, only within a certain range of particle size. The colloidal state of matter has been arbitrarily defined as one in which the size of the particles dispersed lies within the range 1 to 100 mμ (millimicron).

3.5. Properties of Colloidal Solutions. In a colloidal system the distributed particles are spoken of as the *disperse,* or *internal phase,* while the solvent is called the *dispersion medium,* or *external phase.* Some substances, such as kaolin and various metals, consist of solids when in the colloidal state and are called suspensoids, or lyophobic colloidal substances, in contrast to certain others designated as lyophilic, because, in aqueous solution they have an attraction for the water such that the disperse phase may contain large quantities. Most of the colloidal substances which are important in physiology are of the lyophilic type. Many lyophilic colloidal solutions solidify without the separation of water. This is called *gelling*. The protoplasm of cells of higher animals is a gel, and its movements and other activities are due to adsorption and loss of water, actions which are influenced by the salts in the cell fluid and the reaction of the latter. Gelling helps explain permeability. Thus the nutrition of the cell and its aggregates is a function of the above phenomena.

Many substances in the colloidal state are only slightly ionized and thus are only slightly reactive chemically. While chemical combinations thus occur, physical combinations are considered by most authorities to be of much more importance. Physical combinations take place through adsorption, a property which is exhibited to a high degree because of the large surface of the colloidal particle. Owing to the large size of the particles dispersed and their lack of ionization, colloidal solutions exhibit little osmotic pressure. Substances in the colloidal state diffuse slowly and are unable to pass through a parchment membrane. This property is taken advantage of to separate them from substances of smaller particle size, such as salts, in a solution. The process is called *dialysis*. Most colloidal substances are electrically charged. Placing colloidal solutions in an electric field shows that in some the dispersed particles are electropositive while in others they are electronegative.

3.6. Reaction Velocity, Catalysis. The rate of any chemical reaction is proportional to the product of the active masses of the reacting substances at that time. This is the *law of mass action*. The reaction velocity also increases with rise in temperature. More important is the influence of catalysis. A *catalyst* is a substance which alters the speed of a chemical reaction without being used up in the process. Most catalysts accelerate, but negative catalysis is known. In general, the velocity of catalyic reactions is proportional to the amount of catalyst present provided the reacting substances are present in relatively large amounts.

3.7. Free Energy Change. The energy released from biological reactions which is available for useful work is called the free energy change (ΔF), as distinguished from heat energy (ΔH). All body reactions which proceed spontaneously under the influence of a catalyst release energy. They are *exergonic* reactions:

$$A + B = C[-\Delta F]$$

Reactions which require energy, that is, endergonic reactions, cannot take place unless the needed free energy is simultaneously released from some exergonic reaction. The two reactions involved are called coupled reactions. For example, the formation of glycogen from glucose requires energy $[+\Delta F]$. This energy is furnished by the formation of adenosine diphosphate (ADP) from adenosine triphosphate (ATP), an exergonic reaction. Free energy is provided by splitting of a "high-energy," or "energy-rich," phosphate bond (frequently designated by the symbol $\sim$) in ATP. Thus the two reactions:

$$\text{ATP} + H_2O \longrightarrow \text{ADP} + H_3PO_4[-\Delta F]$$
$$\text{Glucose} \longrightarrow \text{Glycogen } [+\Delta F]$$

The chemical formulas for ATP and ADP are discussed in Sec. 6.3. The energy-rich bond of ATP yields four or five times as much free energy when hydrolyzed as the ordinary ester-phosphate bond (hexose phosphate).

In the catabolism of carbohydrates, fats, and proteins in the body, free energy is released, which is trapped by ATP and in turn used to support endergonic reactions such as syntheses. This is the principal mechanism by which food serves as a source of energy for body processes. The reactions which take place in muscle action, the principal process requiring free energy, are discussed in Sec. 17.2.

3.8. Enzymes. All life processes are dependent on the action of enzymes. While their functions in digestion have long been recognized, the knowledge of their basic roles in such body processes as energy metabolism, secretion, nerve conduction, synthesis and degradation of body tissues, and many others is a comparatively recent development. Enzymes are responsible for the formation of all the organic compounds found in animals and plants.

Enzymes are catalysts secreted by living cells and are thus frequently referred to as biocatalysts. Like all catalysts they hasten chemical and physical reactions without being used up in the process, but they have many special characteristics. They are extraordinarily specific in their action. A given enzyme can catalyze one particular reaction only and is effective only in a narrow pH range. For example, the optimum pH range for pepsin is 1.8 to 2.0, and the outside limits of its activity are pH 1 and pH 3. Most enzymes are also very sensitive to temperature, being destroyed much below the boiling point of water. Another characteristic of biocatalysts is their activity. It has been estimated that one molecule of the enzyme catalase will decompose 5 million molecules of H_2O_2 per minute at 0°. Enzymes are responsible for reactions in the body which in the laboratory would require such strong chemical reagents and high temperatures as to be incompatible with life. For example, the degradation of the cellulose of roughage in the laboratory requires a boiling acid or other drastic treatment, whereas it occurs in the rumen at a pH close to neutrality and at body temperature, under the action of enzymes secreted by the microorganisms present.

The modern knowledge of enzymes dates from 1926, when Sumner[1] isolated the enzyme urease in crystalline form and proved these crystals to be protein. This work was followed four years later by the isolation

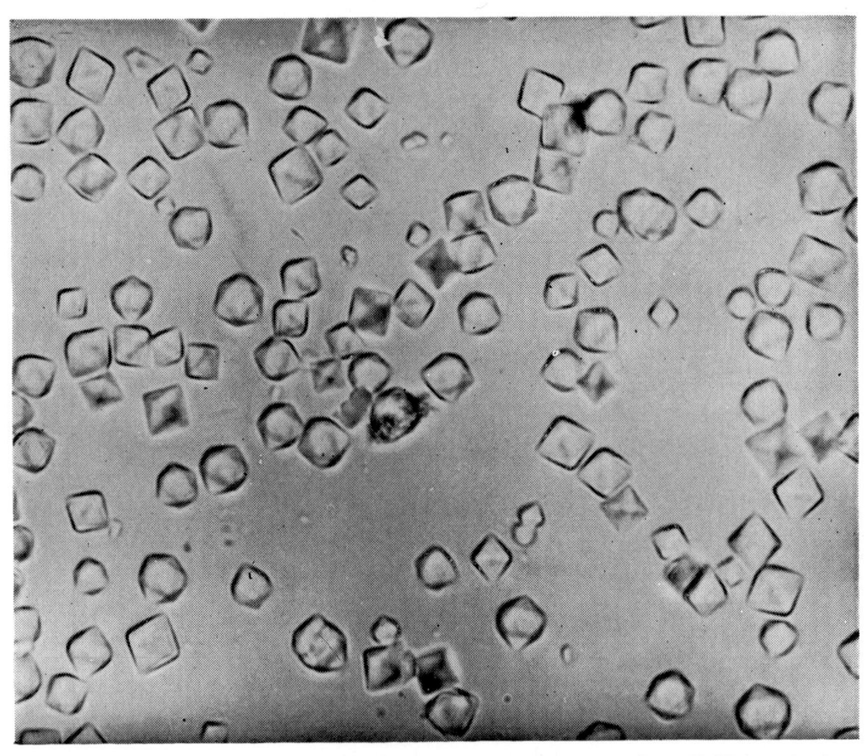

FIG. 3.2. Crystalline urease. (*Courtesy of J. B. Sumner, Cornell University.*)

of pepsin by Northrup of the Rockefeller Institute. Today more than 30 enzymes have been crystallized and shown to be proteins. Most of them are colorless, but some have a color as a result of being compounds of specific proteins with certain colored prosthetic groups. The enzymes

[1] Dr. James B. Sumner (1887–1955) was professor of biochemistry and director of the laboratory of enzyme chemistry at Cornell University, where he had served for forty-one years as a teacher and a tireless investigator in the field of enzymes. For his outstanding accomplishments, notably for his pioneer work in isolating urease and establishing its protein nature, he was awarded the Scheele Medal at Stockholm, Sweden, in 1937 and the Nobel prize in chemistry in 1946.

catalase and peroxidase are combinations of protein with iron-porphyrin compounds called hemes. The fact that each enzyme is designed by nature to control a specific reaction and the immense number of different reactions which occur in life process make it clear that the maintenance of body functions calls for the activities of a host of different enzymes. Many undoubtedly remain to be discovered, but present knowledge is indicated by the estimate that in muscle alone some 60 different ones occur.

Certain enzymes are secreted as a *zymogen,* or *proenzyme,* which requires another substance for its activation. For example, pepsinogen secreted in the stomach is activated by hydrochloric acid of the gastric juice to form pepsin. Certain enzyme systems consist of a protein part, the *apoenzyme,* and a dialyzable component, a *cofactor,* essential for the activity of the total enzyme. Many metallic ions thus serve as cofactors, and here lies an important role for several of the trace mineral elements. For example, molybdenum serves as a cofactor for xanthine oxidase, an enzyme required in protein catabolism. Certain enzymes contain trace elements as constituents, as well. Mahler and Green[2] have reviewed the literature dealing with enzymes in which metals function. *Coenzymes* are nonprotein organic compounds which serve as cofactors. Several vitamins function as components of coenzymes. For example, thiamine as pyrophosphate is the coenzyme for the enzyme carboxylase. Riboflavin phosphate is a coenzyme which forms the prosthetic group attached to the protein of Warburg's yellow enzyme. There are antienzymes which oppose the action of certain enzymes, acting specifically as antimetabolites (Sec. 8.29).

Enzymes are named in a variety of ways: on the basis of occurrence (e.g., pepsin), the substance acted upon (e.g., sucrose), the type of reaction (e.g., oxidase), and others. Enzymes are important in our food supply as well as in body processes. Some of the enzymes in plant and animal tissues continue their activity uncontrolled after death occurs, with both beneficial and harmful results. Through a process known as autolysis the enzymes in muscle meats have a tenderizing effect during storage. In the processing of vegetables, enzymes cause darkening and other undesirable effects which are prevented by blanching, a heat treatment which inactivates the enzymes. Enzymatic actions form the basis of many industrial operations. The brewer employs malted barley, containing the enzyme amylase, to convert starch to sugar. Then yeast cells containing zymase are added to ferment the sugars to alcohol.

3.9. Biological Oxidation-Reduction. The animal body derives its energy from the oxidation of the end products of food that are absorbed

[2] H. R. Mahler and D. E. Green, Metallo-flavo-proteins and electron transport, *Science,* **120**:7–12, 1950.

after undergoing digestive breakdown in the alimentary tract. The food metabolites—sugars, amino acids, and fatty acids—are combined with oxygen in the various tissue cells to yield carbon dioxide, water, and energy. This process is known as biological, or physiological, oxidation.

With every oxidation there takes place a simultaneous reduction. Oxidation-reduction processes, fundamentally, are similar whether living or nonliving systems are involved. Oxidation of a molecule involves the combination with oxygen or the removal of hydrogen, or, specifically, the loss of electrons. From the viewpoint of physical chemistry, oxidation occurs when there is a loss of electrons, and reduction takes place when there is a gain of electrons. Therefore, during oxidation electrons are transferred from the substance being oxidized to the substance that is reduced.

Substances that can be oxidized with ease at low temperature inside the body cannot be oxidized with molecular oxygen under similar conditions outside the body. It is apparent, therefore, that the body possesses catalytic systems capable of promoting such reactions under the comparatively mild conditions existing during biological oxidations.

The process of oxidation occurring in cells is exceedingly complex and involves, in many cases, a series of chain reactions that are controlled at each stage by a specific enzyme or oxidation-reduction carrier in such a way that the energy is not liberated in a single explosive reaction and dissipated immediately as heat, but is liberated gradually or parceled out in such manner as to be physiologically utilizable.

The present view, based on experimental work, postulates that the tissues contain enzymes which activate the hydrogen of the substance to be metabolized. They are called dehydrogenases and are specific for the particular substrate or metabolite on which they act. Also present in the tissues are enzymes, called oxidases, that activate molecular oxygen. In addition to the foregoing, the tissues contain other biocatalysts that act as mediators or carriers and have the unique ability to undergo reversible oxidation-reduction. They change easily from the oxidized form to the reduced form and back again and thus function to transfer the hydrogen, or electrons, from the metabolite to the oxygen. Thus, the oxidation of food substances in the tissues is not a single-stage process but a series or chain of separate but interdependent (linked) chemical reactions, involving not only molecular oxygen and activation of the metabolite but substances that act as carriers or bridges by virtue of their ability to be reversibly oxidized or reduced.

3.10. Hydrogen-ion Concentration. Since most of the reactions which occur in the body take place in water solutions, the ions of water have a special significance in physiology. It is well understood that the acidity or basicity of a solution is due to hydrogen or hydroxyl ions. According to the theory of Arrhenius[3] their presence and activity are due to the ionization of compounds containing them, and the greater the degree of ionization the greater is the activity, as shown by conductivity measurements. The purest water that can be prepared shows a slight but definite conductivity. According to the theory, this means that there is some dissociation:

$$H_2O \longrightarrow H^+ + OH^-$$

It is possible through conductivity measurements to calculate the number of ions actually dissociated. It has been found that the concentration of each ion, expressed in moles per liter, is 1 in 10,000,000, 1×10^{-7}, an expression which is more easily visualized by writing it as a fraction, $1/10^7$. It is also known that the concentration of hydrogen ions $[H^+]$* times the concentration of hydroxyl ions $[OH^-]$[1] equals a constant K, which is 10^{-14} at 25°C. At neutrality $[H^+]$ is 10^{-7} and $[OH^-]$ is 10^{-7}. According to the law of mass action, if the concentration of either ion is increased, the other must diminish correspondingly:

$[H^+]$ $[OH^-]$
10^{-7} times 10^{-7} equals 10^{-14} (neutral)
10^{-8} times 10^{-6} equals 10^{-14} (alkaline)
10^{-6} times 10^{-8} equals 10^{-14} (acid)

Thus the measurement of the concentration of one ion will tell us whether the solution is acid or alkaline and the degree. This is what is done where reaction is expressed as the $[H^+]$, and the solution is acid or alkaline according as $[H^+]$ is greater or less than 10^{-7}. Concentrations lying between those represented by integral powers of 10 are expressed by coefficients; e.g., the $[H^+]$ of saliva is approximately 2×10^8 (slightly alkaline).

3.11. pH Values. Fortunately, we have a simpler method of expressing $[H^+]$ than the one just described, thanks to the suggestion of Sorenson that the negative exponent be used directly. The value so used is called the *hydrogen-ion exponent,* or *pH value.* It bears the following relation to $[H^+]$:

$$\text{pH} = \log \frac{1}{[H^+]}$$

[3] Svante Arrhenius (1859–1927) was a Swedish scientist, one of the founders of the modern physical chemistry. Later research has caused physical chemists to modify the concept in so far as degree of dissociation is concerned and to explain differences in conductivity on other grounds. They speak of activity instead of dissociation and of hydrogen-ion activity instead of hydrogen-ion concentration. This modification does not interfere with the application of the hydrogen-ion concept in physiology.

* The brackets indicate "concentration" of the ion whose symbol is enclosed in them.

A pH of 7 represents neutrality, a value below 7 denotes an acid solution, and one above 7, an alkaline solution. Decimals take the place of the coefficients used in the expression of $[H^+]$. For example, a pH value of 5.6 denotes an acidity greater than 6 but less than 5.

It is essential to remember that the pH is logarithmic. A solution with a pH of 6 has 10 times as many hydrogen ions as one with a pH of 7, and a pH of 5 represents a concentration which is 100 times that of pH 7. The difference between pH 5.0 and 5.1 is many times greater than that between 5.9 and 6.0.

Expressing acidity and alkalinity as a pH value differentiates between strong and weak acids and bases. *N*/10 hydrochloric acid and *N*/10 acetic acid solution have the same strength in terms of *titratable acidity*. But hydrochloric acid is a strong and acetic a weak acid. Though they both show the same number of hydrogen ions on titration, hydrochloric acid has many more dissociated or active at any moment. pH measures this *actual acidity* as distinguished from the titratable acidity. An *N*/10 solution of hydrochloric acid has a pH value of 1.09, while an *N*/10 solution of acetic acid has a value of 2.85, which indicates a much weaker acid in terms of hydrogen-ion concentration. The reactions of the biological organism to acids and bases are controlled by the actual acidity, and thus a measure of the hydrogen-ion concentration is more useful than titratable acidity.

The determination of hydrogen-ion concentration can be carried out colorimetrically by the use of standard solutions and indicators which change color at different concentrations of the ion. It is also made directly by the use of a glass or hydrogen electrode. These methods are described in textbooks of physical and physiological chemistry.

3.12. Buffer Action. The pH of the blood varies between 7.35 and 7.43. The range 7.0 to 8.0 is the extreme compatible with life. Yet the blood constantly receives large amounts of acid, such as H_2SO_4 and H_3PO_4, from protein breakdown. In order to hold its pH constant under these conditions, the blood contains substances called *buffers*, the action of which may be illustrated as follows:

$$\underset{\text{(slightly alkaline)}}{NaHCO_3} + \underset{\text{(strong acid)}}{HA} \longrightarrow \underset{\text{(neutral salt)}}{NaA} + \underset{\text{(weak acid)}}{H_2CO_3}$$

The buffer $NaHCO_3$ reacts with the strong acid to produce an acid of low hydrogen-ion concentration. Buffers are substances which prevent sudden or great changes in hydrogen-ion concentration when acid or alkali is added to a system. All biological reactions take place in a buffered medium because sudden or large changes in acidity or alkalinity are incompatible with life.

3.13. Electromagnetic Radiation. When one turns on his radio, he is not likely to think of the similarity between the process of sending and receiving the program which he selects and the process of turning on an electric light whereby its filament becomes luminous. Yet both processes involve the transfer of energy through space in the form of waves, and the mechanism is the same in both cases. The physicist classes both as electromagnetic radiation. In the same class belong the light rays which are responsible for photosynthesis, the ultraviolet rays which produce vitamin D in our bodies and in our foods, the X rays which have manifold uses in physiology and medicine, and many others. Thus the student of nutrition must know something about the nature of this electromagnetic radiation and about the language which the physicist uses in describing it.

When energy is being liberated from the radio sending station, periodic electrical and magnetic disturbances are set up in space surrounding the station and travel away as waves at a velocity which is slightly less than 3×10^{10} cm. per second. It is believed that all the other rays previously mentioned are identical in nature with radio waves and that they travel with the same velocity. All differ, however, in wavelengths and in the frequency of the vibration associated with the wave motion. What is meant by wavelength can be pictured by thinking of water waves and the distance from the crest of one to the crest of the next. Velocity, wavelength, and frequency bear the following simple relation to each other:

$$c = \nu\lambda$$

in which c = the velocity, ν (nu) = the frequency, λ (lambda) = the wavelength. Since the velocity is constant for all forms of radiation, frequency and wavelength must vary inversely with each other. The relationship is like that between the steps of a boy and a man walking together. The boy takes shorter steps and thus more per unit of time to keep pace with the man.

3.14. The Spectrum. The physicist has studied electromagnetic radiation ranging in wavelength from about 10^5 down to 10^{-5} cm. This range is conveniently divided into several loosely defined divisions according to the methods of production and of studying the radiation, giving what is called the electromagnetic spectrum illustrated in Fig. 3.3. The conventional divisions are given at the top, and the wavelengths at various points are indicated at the bottom. Since the differences in wavelength are so great from one end of the spectrum to the other, it is convenient to use more than one unit in expressing the wavelength over the entire range. For the shortest, such as the gamma (γ) and X rays, the angstrom unit (Å.) is commonly employed. As the waves become longer the millimicron, or millimu ($m\mu$), comes into use; for those which are still longer, the μ, or micron; and finally, the centimeter and meter are employed. The rays which are commonly met in nutrition studies are expressed in either angstrom units or millimu. The lengths represented by these units are as follows:

$$\text{A.} = 0.1\ m\mu = 0.0001\mu = 0.000{,}000{,}01\ \text{cm.}\ (10^{-8}\ \text{cm.})$$

It is noted that visible light occupies a very small part of the electromagnetic spectrum. It comprises the wavelengths lying between approximately 4000 Å. (400 $m\mu$) and 8000 Å (800 $m\mu$), of which the shortest are the violet and the longest the red rays. In addition to visible light, the ultraviolet and X rays are the ones in which we are most interested from the standpoint of nutritional physiology. The infrared waves are also called heat waves—because they exhibit a heating effect

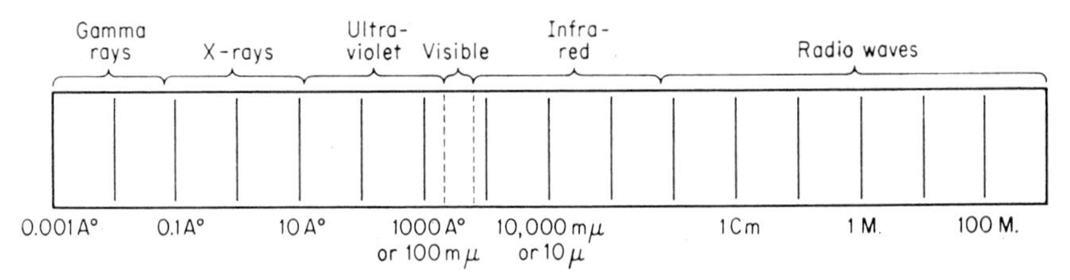

FIG. 3.3. Spectrum of electromagnetic radiation. (*Courtesy of L. L. Barnes, Cornell University.*)

which can be detected by placing a blackened thermometer in their path. This effect is taken advantage of in the treatment of certain diseases. All these various radiations represented in the spectrum are commonly included under the term light, though the human eye is sensitive to only a narrow range.

No single source of electromagnetic radiation will provide rays of all lengths. The radiation which reaches us from the sun lies principally in the visible range and in certain portions of the ultraviolet and infrared. Various artificial sources are used to produce wavelengths lying in specific ranges. Ultraviolet rays are commonly obtained from the carbon arc or a mercury-vapor lamp. X rays result when high-speed electrons (cathode rays) strike a solid metal target. Radio waves are produced by vacuum-tube oscillators, and γ rays by the spontaneous or artificial disintegration of atomic nuclei.

3.15. Absorption of Radiation. In considering the effect of radiation on biological processes, it is important to bear in mind that it is only those wavelengths absorbed by the medium which produce any change in it. For example, it is the light which is absorbed by water, not that which passes through, which raises the temperature. Since matter is made up of atoms which consist of electrical charges, it is not difficult to understand that radiation resulting from electrical and magnetic disturbances may in turn cause disturbances in the atoms of matter on which it falls. When radiant energy is absorbed by matter, various processes may occur, such as a rise in temperature, the removal of an electron from an atom, and various other changes in the structure of the molecules of the substance. These processes involve the transfer of energy from the radiation to the absorbing substance. A given change in the absorbing substance may require a definite amount of energy, and this fact determines what wavelengths are effective in bringing about a given change and thus what ones are absorbed in the process. The formation of vitamin D

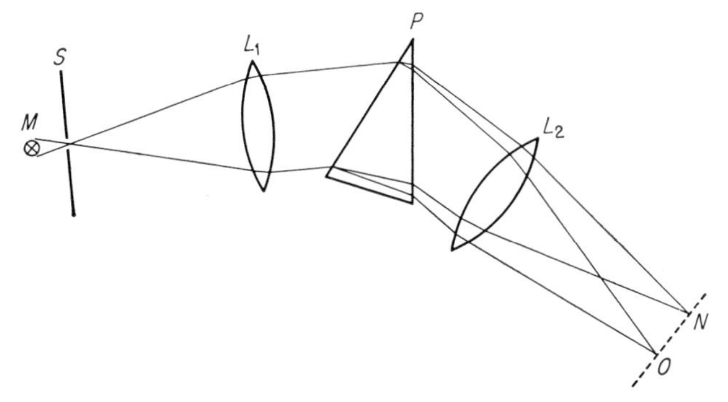

FIG. 3.4. The spectrograph. (*Courtesy of L. L. Barnes, Cornell University.*)

from ergosterol (Sec. 8.13) by ultraviolet light is an example of a molecular change resulting from the absorption of radiation.

A substance may absorb radiant energy over a wide range of wavelengths, or it may absorb only a very narrow band of radiation. The wavelengths absorbed by a given substance can be determined by a spectrograph such as is illustrated diagrammatically in Fig. 3.4. A source of light is employed which emits a continuous spectrum, i.e., a source which emits light of all possible wavelengths over a certain selected range, such as 300 to 800 mμ. When such a source M is placed in front of the slit S of a spectrograph, the lens L_1 makes its rays parallel. The prism P refracts the rays, the shorter wavelengths being changed in direction more than the longer ones. As these refracted rays pass through lens L_2, there will result a broad band of light between N and O, the wavelengths becoming shorter and shorter from N to O. If now we introduce some substance into the path of the light between M and S and if this substance absorbs light of some wavelength intermediate between that falling at N and that falling at O, then there will be a region between N and O which is not illuminated so strongly as it was before the substance was introduced. If a photographic plate is placed in the position NO, the characteristic absorption spectrum of the substance is recorded on the plate. If absorption spectra for light of wavelengths lying in the visible range are being studied, glass lenses and a glass prism may be used, but for work in the ultraviolet, too much of the radiation is absorbed by the glass itself, and thus quartz must be substituted.

Absorption spectra have proved very useful in identifying complex organic compounds and in studying their structure. As is discussed in Chap. 8, they have contributed largely to our knowledge of the chemical nature of certain vitamins and have also provided methods for their assay. The *photoelectric colorimeter* is a crude type of absorption spectrometer in which a filter is used to isolate a band of wavelengths in the spectrum, the absorption of which is a function of the number of absorbing molecules in the path of the light.

Emission spectra, including X-ray spectra, are used for analysis of atomic constituents of substances important in nutrition, notably the trace mineral elements.

3.16. Isotopes as "Tracers" in Metabolism. The use of isotopes of elements, either the less abundant naturally occurring, stable ones, such as heavy hydrogen, or radioactive isotopes obtained by nuclear reactions, represents a contribution of modern physics to biology which has become an important tool in nutrition studies. For example, heavy hydrogen, H^2, can be introduced into a fat and the course of that fat traced in metabolism by appropriate methods for detecting the isotope. Similarly, heavy nitrogen, N^{15}, can be employed to study the metabolism of specific amino acids. Wartime and postwar atomic research has been primarily responsible for the large production and consequent use of radioactive isotopes. In the production of these isotopes the nucleus of an atom is altered to obtain a new kind of atom which is unstable and which disintegrates with emission of particles and electromagnetic radiation. There are several ways in which these unstable isotopes can be produced. For example, deuterons may be accelerated in a cyclotron and used to "bombard" various stable atoms. Such a bombardment may be used to produce unstable P^{32} from stable P^{31}. The unstable atom in turn disintegrates into S^{32} and a β particle. Similarly, the bombardment of boron produces radioactive carbon, C^{11}, which in turn disintegrates into B^{11} plus a positron and a γ ray. Some radioactive isotopes disintegrate very rapidly; others very slowly. The "half-life" for a given isotope is the time required for one-half of the atoms of the sample to disintegrate. Thus, C^{11} has a half-life of only 20 min., while P^{32} has a half life of 14 days.

Radioactive isotopes can be introduced into various compounds to study their metabolism. For example, P^{32} and Ca^{45} are used to study the absorption, bone deposition and mobilization, and excretion of these minerals. The isotopes can be identified and quantitatively measured in the various compounds, structures, and fluids in which they occur by means of a Geiger counter, which detects either the particle or electromagnetic radiations that they emit upon disintegration.

Experiments carried out by the use of isotopes have revolutionized many of our ideas regarding fats, proteins, and minerals; this will be discussed later. Important contributions in the fields of protein and fat metabolism by the use of concentrated stable isotopes are interestingly set forth in the book by Schoenheimer.[4] Detailed information on the use of radioactive isotopes is to be found in the text by Comar.[5] The use of both stable and radioactive isotopes in nutritional biochemistry has been reviewed by Harris.[6]

SELECTED LITERATURE

Hawk, Philip B., Bernard L. Oser, and William H. Summerson: Practical Physiological Chemistry, 13th ed., McGraw-Hill Book Company, Inc., New York, 1954, chap. 1.

Sumner, James B., and G. Fred Somers: Chemistry and Methods of Enzymes, 2d ed., Academic Press, Inc., New York, 1953.

[4] Rudolph Schoenheimer, The Dynamic State of Body Constituents, Harvard University Press, Cambridge, Mass., 1942.

[5] C. L. Comar, Radioisotopes in Biology and Agriculture, McGraw-Hill Book Company, Inc., New York, 1955.

[6] Robert S. Harris, Isotopes in Nutritional Biochemistry, *Borden's Rev. Nutrition Research,* **20**:39–59, 1959.

Part II

The Nutrients and Their Metabolism

Chapter 4
The Carbohydrates and Their Metabolism

The group of foodstuffs called carbohydrates includes the sugars, starch, cellulose, gums, and related substances. Though none of these substances, with the exception of a small amount of sugar and glycogen, occurs as such in the animal body, several derivatives are present combined with lipids or protein. The carbohydrates form the largest part of the animal's food supply, however. This follows from the fact that carbohydrates make up three-fourths of the dry weight of the plant world upon which animal life primarily depends for its food supply.

TABLE 4.1. CLASSIFICATION OF CARBOHYDRATES

- I. Monosaccharides
  - 1. Pentoses, $C_5H_{10}O_5$
    - Arabinose
    - Xylose
    - Ribose
  - 2. Hexoses, $C_6H_{12}O_6$
    - Glucose
    - Fructose
    - Galactose
    - Mannose
- II. Disaccharides, $C_{12}H_{22}O_{11}$
  - Sucrose
  - Maltose
  - Lactose
  - Cellobiose
- III. Trisaccharides, $C_{18}H_{32}O_{16}$
  - Raffinose
- IV. Polysaccharides
  - 1. Pentosans, $(C_5H_8O_4)x$
    - Araban
    - Xylan
  - 2. Hexosans, $(C_6H_{10}O_5)x$
    - Dextrin
    - Starch
    - Cellulose
    - Glycogen
    - Inulin
  - 3. Mixed polysaccharides
    - Gums
    - Mucilages

The carbohydrates in the plants arise by means of photosynthesis, the most important chemical reaction in nature. The reaction involves the formation of intermediate products, but it may be simply represented as follows:

$$6CO_2 + 6H_2O + 673 \text{ kcal.} \longrightarrow \underset{\text{Glucose}}{C_6H_{12}O_6} + 6O_2$$

The carbohydrates of the plant are in turn used by the animal as a source of energy for its life processes, and thus, all animal life also is dependent upon the process of photosynthesis.

4.1. Classification of Carbohydrates. The carbohydrates owe their name to the fact that they contain carbon combined with hydrogen and oxygen which are usually in the same ratio as in water. Chemically they are polyhydroxy aldehydes and ketones or substances which yield them on hydrolysis. An abbreviated classification, which includes the members in which we are particularly interested in nutrition, is presented in Table 4.1.

It is noted that the various members of a given subgroup have the same empirical formula. They have, however, different structural formulas and exhibit different degrees of optical activity. This ability to rotate the plane of polarized light is an important distinguishing feature of the sugars, many of which are stereoisomers of each other. In addition to the compounds falling under the classification given in Table 4.1, certain related substances or groups, such as *uronic acids, hemicelluloses, polyuronides,* and *lignin,* require consideration in this chapter.

THE CHEMISTRY OF THE CARBOHYDRATES

Only a few of the *monosaccharides* occur free in nature. Most of them are obtained as hydrolytic or fermentation products of more complex plant constituents. They are often called the simple sugars. All are soluble in water. They are classified into subgroups on the basis of the number of carbon atoms in the chain. There are trioses, tetroses, and others, as well as the pentoses and hexoses given in the table.

4.2. Pentoses. The pentose sugars have been found as such in small amounts in certain plants, but they occur primarily in a polymerized form in the pentosans. Upon the hydrolysis of hay, oat hulls, corn cobs, and many woods, *xylose* is produced. *Arabinose* is obtained from gum arabic and other gums. *Ribose* occurs in several compounds which play essential roles in animal metabolism, such as the compounds adenosine diphosphate (ADP) and adenosine triphosphate (ATP); the vitamin riboflavin; and ribonucleic acid (RNA) and deoxyribonucleic acid (DNA), which are present in every living cell. These compounds are discussed later.

4.3. Hexoses. The hexoses comprise a large group of sugars, several of which play a significant role in nutrition either as components of foods or as products of metabolism in the body. *Glucose* and *fructose* are the only ones which occur free in nature. Of those occurring in combined form, galactose is of special importance in nutrition. The hexoses are divided into aldoses and ketoses according to whether they contain aldehyde or ketone groups. Thus glucose is an aldo sugar, while fructose is a keto sugar. The general formulas for the two classes of hexoses are as follows:

```
   H
  /
C=O           CH2OH
|             |
CHOH          C=O
|             |
CHOH          CHOH
|             |
CHOH          CHOH
|             |
CHOH          CHOH
|             |
CH2OH         CH2OH
Aldohexose    Ketohexose
```

It is noted that each has five hydroxyl groups. The number of *stereoisomers* which can occur among the sugars is evident from these formulas. The formula for aldohexose has four asymmetric carbon atoms, and thus 16 stereoisomers are theoretically possible. Of these, four optically active forms are known to occur in nature, and the others have been prepared in the laboratory. Eight stereoisomers of ketohexoses are theoretically possible, of which two have been found in nature. The physiologically important hexoses are glucose, fructose, galactose, and mannose.

The 16 stereoisomeric aldohexoses consist of 8 pairs of mirror images of each other, viz., D-glucose and L-glucose, D-galactose and L-galactose, and 6 other pairs. Similarly, the 8 ketohexoses occur as 4 pairs of mirror images. The letter prefixes denote a conventional basic structural configuration and not direction of rotation. *Specific rotation* is indicated by + or — signs in parentheses, viz., D(+)-glucose and D(—)-glucose. The properties of D-glucose indicate that it exists in solution in several forms, which are in equilibrium with each other. The normal, or ordinary, forms have a pyranose ring structure. The following formula for the α stereoisomer illustrates this structure and shows the numbering of its carbon atoms.

```
          6CH2OH
           |
           C-------------O
  H       /|5             \      H
  |      / H               \     |
  C4                         1 C
  |  \   OH          H       / |
  OH  \  |3          |2     /  OH
         C-----------C
         |           |
         H           OH
```

α-D-Glucopyranose

Sugars containing an aldehyde or ketone group have a reducing power which classes them as *reducing sugars*. For example, when they are boiled with an alkaline solution of copper sulfate, such as Fehling solution, the cupric ion is reduced to a cuprous ion present as the oxide, a brick-red precipitate. This is an important reaction which is made use of for both qualitative tests and quantitative determinations. The reaction is not specific, however, because it is given by other reducing substances.

The *glucose* which occurs in nature has the D configuration, and it has a specific rotation of +52.5° which accounts for its other name, *dextrose*. Glucose is found widely distributed, though in small amounts, in fruits and plant juices and also in honey. It is obtained commercially by the hydrolysis of cornstarch, which is a product of the same process which yields corn-gluten feed and meal for animal feeding. Glucose is of special interest in nutrition, because it is the principal end product of the digestion of higher carbohydrates, the form in which these nutrients circulate in the blood and the form in which they are utilized to furnish energy. It has a sweet taste but is not so sweet as cane sugar. It is fermented by yeast to form ethyl alcohol and carbon dioxide, and it also undergoes an acid fermentation. Glucose is a reducing sugar.

Galactose is an aldohexose which occurs in milk sugar in combination with glucose. It is a reducing sugar and has a specific rotation of +80°. Certain compounds of galactose, viz., galactosides, occur in the brain and nervous tissue.

Mannose is an aldohexose occurring in mannans, a group of polysaccharides widely distributed in plants. It has a specific rotation of +14.6°.

Fructose is the only important ketohexose. It occurs freely along with glucose in fruits and honey and in combined form in higher carbohydrates. Fructose has a specific rotation of −92°, which accounts for its other name, *levulose*. It is sweeter than sucrose and readily undergoes fermentation.

Glucosamine is an amino sugar in which one of the OH groups of glucose is replaced by NH_2. It occurs in chitin in the shell coverings of invertebrates and in the mucin present in saliva and gastric juice. *Galactosamine* occurs along with glucuronic acid in chondroitin sulfate which, combined in a glycoprotein (Sec. 6.2), is a major component of cartilage.

4.4. Disaccharides. The disaccharides derive their name from the fact that they are combinations of two molecules of monosaccharides. Their general formula, $C_{12}H_{22}O_{11}$, indicates that one molecule of water is eliminated in the combination. They are soluble in water, though in varying degrees.

Sucrose is made up of a combination of one molecule of D-glucose and one of D-fructose. It occurs in sugar cane and sugar beets and thus is the sugar used on the table and in cooking. It occurs also in ripe fruits, in tree sap (whence maple sugar), and elsewhere in nature. Sucrose has a specific rotation of +67°, but it is not a reducing sugar. On hydrolysis with the enzyme *sucrase* or with dilute acids, sucrose is split into its constituent monosaccharides. The resulting sugar mixture is levorotatory. Since the hydrolysis thus results in a change from a dextro to a

$$\underset{\text{Sucrose}}{C_{12}H_{22}O_{11}} + H_2O \longrightarrow \underbrace{\underset{\text{Glucose}}{C_6H_{12}O_6} + \underset{\text{Fructose}}{C_6H_{12}O_6}}_{\text{Invert sugar}}$$

levo rotation, the process is called *inversion* and the mixture of glucose and fructose is called *invert sugar*.

Maltose consists of two molecules of D-glucose joined together, as is evident on its hydrolysis by *maltase* or by acids. It derives its name from the fact that it is produced from starch by the action of malt, which contains the starch-hydrolyzing enzyme diastase. Maltose is a reducing sugar and is strongly dextrorotatory (136°).

Lactose is the sugar of milk and consists of one molecule of glucose and one molecule of galactose, which are produced by hydrolysis with *lactase* or acids. It is a reducing sugar with a specific rotation of +55°, and it is only one-sixth as sweet as sucrose. Lactose is of special interest in nutrition, because it makes up nearly half of the solids of milk, nature's food for the young, and because it does not occur in nature except as a product of the mammary gland. This sugar has several physiological properties distinguishing it from others. It is less likely than glucose or sucrose to undergo acid fermentation in the stomach, a process which may result in irritation. Lactose promotes acidity in the intestine, favoring the development of desirable types of bacteria, the acidophilic organisms, and opposing the growth of the undesirable putrefactive bacteria. Several studies have shown that this sugar favors calcium and phosphorus assimilation. It has been definitely established by Lengemann[1] that the site of action of lactose in improving calcium utilization is the intestine and not somewhere after absorption. The absorption of magnesium and other alkaline earth metals was also found to be enhanced. The mechanism of the action is unknown. Lactose is more slowly absorbed than other sugars, which results in certain physiological advantages, but it also means that large intakes are likely to cause diarrhea.

4.5. Trisaccharides. The trisaccharides consist of three monosaccharides, as the name indicates. Raffinose is a trisaccharide which occurs in

[1] F. W. Lengemann, The site of action of lactose in the enhancement of calcium utilization, *J. Nutrition,* **69**:23–27, 1959.

sugar beets, cottonseed, and elsewhere and which is composed of glucose, galactose, and fructose. On hydrolysis it first yields fructose and the disaccharide melibiose. The latter, which is isomeric with lactose, is next broken up into glucose and galactose.

4.6. Polysaccharides. The polysaccharides are complex carbohydrates which are polymerized anhydrides of a large but undetermined number of the simple sugars, as their empirical formulas indicate. The various subgroups are rather ill-defined, and there is a lack of agreement as regards their classification. They are of high molecular weight, and most of them are insoluble in water. Upon hydrolysis by acids and enzymes, they are broken down into various intermediate products and finally into their constituent monosaccharides. Quantitatively, they are the most important nutrients in feeds of plant origin.

4.7. Starch. The reserve material of most plants consists primarily of starch. When this polysaccharide is hydrolyzed with acids or enzymes, it is changed into dextrin, maltose, and finally into glucose. Structurally it consists of a linear chain of glucose units combined with a branched chain of these units. In the ripening of fruits, there is a change of starch into sugars. The starches of different plants differ as regards the size and shape of their grains. These properties furnish a means of microscopic identification. Strictly speaking, the various starches are not pure carbohydrates because they contain minute amounts of acid radicals, which are sometimes fatty acids and which sometimes contain phosphorus. Starch gives a characteristic blue color with iodine.

In certain plants, notably the Jerusalem artichoke, *inulin* replaces starch as the reserve material. Inulin is a polysaccharide which yields fructose on hydrolysis.

4.8. Glycogen. The small amount of carbohydrate reserve in the animal body exists in the liver and muscles in the form of glycogen, which resembles starch in certain properties as well as in function. It is therefore frequently called "animal starch." Glycogen is present in lower as well as in higher animal life. Toward the end of the larval period, it makes up 33 per cent of the dry weight of bee larvae. It is also present in yeasts and certain other fungi. Differing from starch, glycogen consists of a branched-chain molecule of glucose units only, is soluble in water, and gives a brown to red color with iodine, but both yield glucose as the sole end product on hydrolysis.

4.9. Dextrins. This is an ill-defined group of intermediate compounds resulting from the hydrolysis and digestion of starch, and they are also produced from starch by the action of heat. They occur temporarily in both plants and animals as a result of metabolic processes and are particularly abundant in germinating seeds. The dextrins are much more soluble than the starches, and their molecules are certainly much smaller.

Like lactose, dextrin furnishes a favorable medium for the development of acidophilic organisms in the digestive tract.

4.10. Cellulose. This polysaccharide consists of a linear chain of glucose units. It is more resistant to chemical reagents than is starch. Weak acids and alkalies have little effect on cellulose, but it can be hydrolyzed by strong acids to glucose. It is dissolved by an ammoniacal copper solution—Schweitzer's reagent. It is not acted upon by any enzyme secreted by mammalian tissues, but bacteria break it down. These are properties which have an important bearing on its usefulness in nutrition. There are many different celluloses in which the number of polymerized glucose molecules has been variously determined to range from 900 to 2000.

Cellulose occurs in a nearly pure form in cotton, a simple cellulose. As the framework of plants and the protective coating of their seeds, it occurs combined with various aromatic derivatives, notably lignin.

4.11. Pentosans. This group of polysaccharides differs from cellulose in yielding pentose sugars on complete hydrolysis with acids, and most of the group, at least, are much less resistant to acids and alkalies. The pentosans make up about 20 per cent of the complex carbohydrates in hays and occur in lesser proportions in various concentrates, such as the oil meals. When pentosans are boiled with hydrochloric acid, *furfural,* an aldehyde, is produced. This reaction is the basis of the quantitative determination of pentosans, and it is used in the commercial production of furfural from oat hulls and corncobs.

4.12. Hemicellulose. The term hemicellulose is used by the plant chemist to denote a group of substances, including pentosans and certain hexosans, which are much less resistant to chemical agents than is cellulose. This group is commonly defined as carbohydrate substances that are insoluble in boiling water but soluble in dilute alkali and hydrolyzed by dilute acids to simple sugars and frequently to *uronic* acids, notably glucuronic and galacturonic. In the latter case, the substances are referred to as *polyuronides.* Glucuronic, and probably galacturonic acid, also serves as a detoxicating agent in the body for such substances as phenols by forming harmless conjugation products that are excreted. Glucuronic acid is definitely known to be produced in body metabolism for this purpose. The hemicelluloses are widely distributed in forage crops and in certain other feeds. Their recognition as a group is important in considering the digestibility of the higher carbohydrates (Sec. 4.17).

4.13. Lignin. The woody parts of plants, such as cobs, hulls, and the fibrous portions of roots, stems, and leaves, contain a complex, indigestible substance called lignin. Its chemical structure remains uncertain. Products which have been isolated by different methods and from different sources and designated as lignin vary in chemical composition. For the present at least the term must be considered to designate a group of substances having a common basic structure but differing as regards attached units. The substances contain carbon, hydrogen, and oxygen, but the proportion of carbon is much higher than in carbohydrates. Nitrogen is also present, ranging from 1 to 5 per cent in different products isolated. Methoxy groups have been reported to occur in percentages ranging from 5 to 15 or more. The percentage increases as the plant matures. The nucleus is a polyhydroxy aromatic compound. Thus, lignin cannot be classed as a carbohydrate, but it is discussed along with this group of compounds because it occurs in intimate association with cellulose and is included with the carbohydrates in the conventional methods of feed analysis. Its recognition as a separate entity is important because of its dominant influence on the degree of digestibility of many feeds.

4.14. The Determination of Carbohydrates for Nutritional Purposes. The analysis of feeds for all the individual carbohydrates would obviously be a tremendous task, particularly as the procedures for some of the higher ones are long and difficult. Thus, in the routine analysis of feeding stuffs the carbohydrates are determined as two groups: *crude fiber* and *nitrogen-free extract* (NFE). The separation is obtained by a chemical method devised over eighty years ago by Henneberg and Stohmann[2] and known as the Weende method after the name of their experiment station. After the removal of the water and fatty material from a given sample of feed, it is boiled for 30 min. with weak sulfuric acid (1.25 per cent) and then for the same time with alkali of the same strength. This procedure removes the proteins, sugars, and starch, leaving as a residue most of the cellulose and other complex polysaccharides along with some mineral material. The loss on ignition of this dried residue is taken as the crude fiber. Since the crude fiber consists primarily of cellulose and other polysaccharides which serve as the structural and protective parts of plants, it is evidently higher in hay and similar roughages than in the grains, and it is higher in those seed by-products which consist largely of the outer coatings, such as wheat bran or oat hulls, than in the seed as a whole.

The nitrogen-free extract, which comprises the sugars, starch, and a large part of the material classed as hemicellulose, is determined by difference. It is represented by the figure obtained when the sum of the

[2] Wilhelm Henneberg (1825–1890) and Friedrich Stohmann (1832–1897) were pioneer German workers in the nutrition of farm animals. Their work included respiration studies, digestion trials, and chemical analyses of feeds and animal tissues. Their early studies, including their work on crude fiber, are reported in their two-volume publication Beiträge zur Begründung einer rationellen Fütterung der Wiederkäuer, vols. I, II, Schwetschke u. Sohn, Brunswick, 1860, 1865.

water, ash, protein, fat, and crude fiber of a feed is subtracted from 100. Since the figure is determined by difference instead of directly, it includes the cumulative errors of the other determinations and thus is not an exact value. The total error here involved is not a serious one from the standpoint of routine feed analysis and of the use of the value in practice, and thus the indirect procedure is employed in place of the more time-consuming direct determination of the various sugars and starch. Primarily because it contains the starch, nitrogen-free extract makes up the principal constituent of most feeds of plant origin.

Though the Weende method is an empirical one which does not provide any sharp separation into chemical groups, it is useful because it is a simple procedure which makes a distinction between the more digestible and the less digestible carbohydrates. The distinction is by no means absolute, for crude fiber undergoes a very considerable breakdown in the digestive tract of Herbivora under the action of microorganisms, particularly in ruminants, and it does not remain entirely unattacked in Omnivora (Sec. 4.17). Further, the nitrogen-free extract includes pentosans and small amounts of other complex polysaccharides which are by no means completely digestible. On the other hand, lignin, which is little digested by any species, is partially removed by the alkali of the Weende method.

4.15. Lignin and Cellulose Content as Measures of Digestibility. The knowledge that the partition of the higher carbohydrates into crude fiber and NFE provides only an approximate distinction between the more and the less digestible constituents has led several investigators to test out methods that might provide a more useful partition in this respect. Particular attention has been given to cellulose and lignin. In 1938 Crampton and Maynard[3] proposed a procedure for partitioning the carbohydrate of feeds into cellulose, lignin, and other carbohydrates in a study in which the limitations of the Weende method are clearly revealed. Since that time various investigators have given attention to this problem using improved methods, as reviewed by Ely and coworkers.[4] These workers analyzed orchard grass hay at different stages of maturity for various constituents included with the conventionally determined crude fiber and NFE and studied their digestibility with milking cows. They found that various cellulose and pentosan fractions had a similar digestibility and concluded that grouping them into a "holocellulose" fraction which could be analytically determined would provide a useful indicator of digesti-

[3] E. W. Crampton and L. A. Maynard, The relation of cellulose and lignin content to the nutritive value of animal feeds, *J. Nutrition*, **15**:383–395, 1938.

[4] R. E. Ely and coworkers, A study of the crude fiber and nitrogen-free extract of orchard grass hay and the digestibility of some of the constituents by milking cows, *J. Dairy Sci.*, **36**:334–345, 1953.

bility. On the basis of their studies with pasture herbage, Richards and Reid[5] have suggested the replacement of the crude-fiber analysis with an analysis for lignin, which is generally found to be either not digested at all or only slightly so, and the measurement by difference of the other compounds now included as crude fiber or NFE.

It may be expected that continuing studies along the above lines will result in the adoption of a new system of partitioning the carbohydrates of feeds, which will be simple from the chemical standpoint and which will have much more nutritional significance than the present system of proximate analysis.

CARBOHYDRATE METABOLISM

From the standpoint of nutrition, two processes are essential for life—the assimilation of food and the removal of waste products. The food consists of complex chemical units, such as proteins and fats; the waste products are simple compounds, such as carbon dioxide and water. The sum of the changes which food undergoes in its conversion to excretory products is called *metabolism.* Some reserve this term for the changes which occur in the absorbed food and which are involved in the breakdown of body tissues, processes which are also referred to as *intermediary metabolism.* These various metabolic changes are governed by physiological processes with which the student is assumed to be familiar in a general way from a previous study of physiology. Thus in the discussions to follow for the carbohydrates and other nutrients these changes as a whole are traced only in outline, as a background for a detailed consideration of certain features which from the standpoint of nutrition require a more extended discussion than they receive in an elementary course in physiology.

4.16. Carbohydrate Digestion in Nonruminants. In the various species of farm animals there are marked differences in the anatomy and physiology of their alimentary tracts. These differences are of greatest nutritional significance between ruminants and nonruminants, affecting both the nature of the digestion processes and the kinds of feed which can be utilized. In the animals with simple stomachs, starch and any disaccharides present in the feed are broken down to monosaccharides by enzymes secreted in the digestion tract, in accordance with the hydrolytic changes previously discussed. Since starch predominates in most rations, the principal end product is glucose. When milk is included in the ration, as is always the case for the suckling, galactose is

[5] C. R. Richards and J. T. Reid, The digestibility and interrelationships of various carbohydrate fractions of pasture herbage and a resolution of the components of crude fiber and nitrogen-free extract, *J. Dairy Sci.*, **36**:1006–1015, 1953.

also formed; and fructose is a digestion product of feeds, containing sucrose, such as sugar beets. These processes are common to all species, but in ruminants other pathways are quantitatively much more important.

There are no enzymes secreted in the alimentary tract which will digest cellulose or the other higher polysaccharides. They are subject, however, to breakdown by enzymes secreted by microorganisms inhabiting the tract, as is discussed in detail in the following paragraphs. In nonruminants the bacterial action occurs to a certain extent in the large intestine and is of large significance in the case of the horse and rabbit.

4.17. The Microbial Digestion of Carbohydrates. Of the symbiotic organisms which break down these higher carbohydrates, bacteria are the most important. This symbiotic relationship occurs widely in animals which live on food of plant origin, but it is developed to the highest degree in ruminants, since the rumen provides both the capacity and other factors which are most favorable to its activity. This is the first example in this study of the beneficial roles played by microorganisms in the digestive tract of various species. In addition to aiding digestion through the breakdown of the higher carbohydrates, these organisms are responsible for the synthesis of certain essential nutrients, specifically amino acids and vitamins. While this microbic activity is of practical importance primarily in the case of ruminants, examples of its significance for other species will be met in later discussions.

In 1884 Tappeiner in Germany showed that large quantities of volatile fatty acids, notably acetic, were produced from the in vitro fermentation of cellulose by bacteria from the rumen of the ox. While it was soon established that the process occurred in vivo, our quantitative knowledge of this rumen activity and of its role in nutrition has developed largely in the last twenty years, particularly through the use of the permanent rumen fistula technique described in 1886 by the French physiologist Colin. The modern developments, which have dealt both with the production of the acids in the rumen and with their fate in metabolism, were stimulated by the English physiologist Barcroft and grew out of a large cooperative research project inaugurated in the Unit of Animal Physiology at Cambridge University during the Second World War. The pioneer work has been reviewed by Elsden and Phillipson.[6] Active studies have continued in several countries.

The acids and gases which are formed by microbial action in the rumen are the end products of various intermediary reactions. Cellulose, pentosans, and starch are hydrolyzed to monosaccharides and then fermented. The proportion of the acids formed varies with the

[6] S. R. Elsden and A. T. Phillipson, Ruminant digestion, *Ann. Rev. Biochem.*, **17**: 705–726, 1948.

nature of the ration, the organisms present, and other factors. Acetic makes up from two-thirds to three-fourths or more of the total. Propionic stands next in order of amount, followed by butyric. Small amounts of other acids have been reported. The much more reliable quantitative data now available than formerly are largely the result of the application of partition chromatography. It cannot be concluded that all of the volatile acids found in the rumen arise directly from carbohydrate fermentation. Some may come from the action of microorganisms on protein or other nitrogenous compounds (Sec. 6.15).

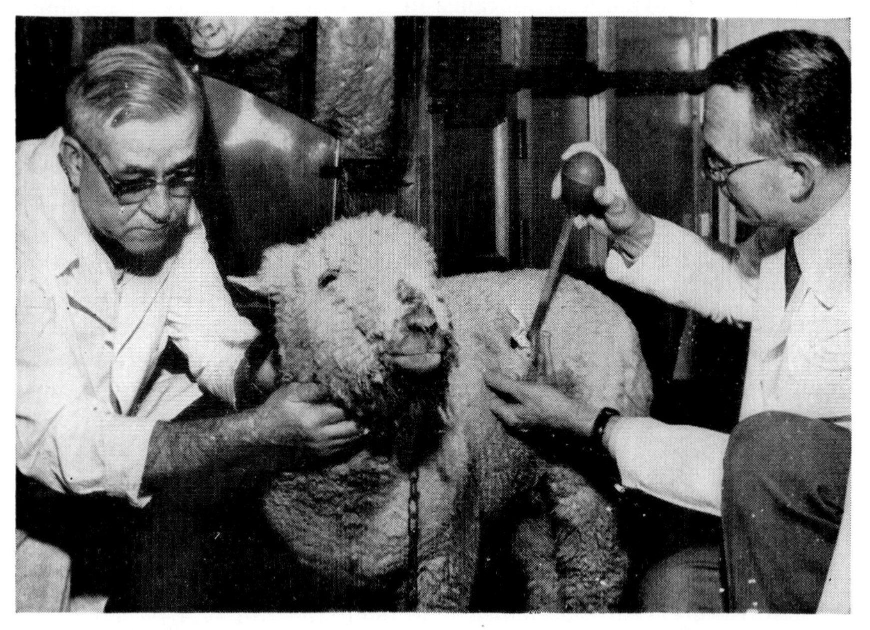

FIG. 4.1. Withdrawing rumen contents through a fistula. (*Courtesy of Harold H. Williams, Cornell University.*)

There may also be some introconversion of acids after their production. The gases formed are methane and carbon dioxide, and under some conditions hydrogen. The magnitude of microbial digestion is indicated by studies with cattle indicating that 40 to 80 per cent of the dry-matter intake disappears in the rumen and reticulum, some 80 per cent of which is carbohydrate.

Of the fibrous constituents of the feed, lignin is very resistant to microbial attack, which explains why it is so little digested. Cellulose is much more readily broken down, and the hemicelluloses, as a group, are the most digestible of the three. Starch and sugars are readily converted to acids and gases, and in the ruminant this is the chief pathway of their digestion. The growth of bacteria in the rumen results in the synthesis of certain bacterial polysaccharides which may be digested farther on in the tract.

While the rumen is the principal seat of the bacterial breakdown of carbohydrates, this breakdown occurs in significant amounts in the large intestine of herbivora. This is particularly true for the horse, and in this species there is also considerable activity in the cecum. The process has also been shown to occur to a limited extent in the pig, dog, and cat. In all species studied the same three acids have been identified as the principal products.

The student is referred to the paper by Howard[7] for a review of various studies on carbohydrate metabolism in the rumen.

4.18. Bloat. Bloat is a widespread and serious trouble in cattle and sheep which is characterized by the accumulation of gas in the rumen. It most frequently occurs when these animals are pastured on alfalfa or clover. The accumulation of gas results because excessive frothing and the formation of a stable foam during rumen fermentation interfere with the normal elimination of the gas by belching. A number of factors have been found to contribute to foam formation, notably soluble proteins in fresh forage, saponins, salivary mucoproteins, and special slime-producing bacteria.

The administration of antifoaming agents, such as oil, has a protective effect, but only for a short period for a given dose. Experiments have shown that the addition of the oil to the drinking water has a continuous beneficial effect. More satisfactory results have been obtained by spraying the antifoaming agent on the fresh forage. Pasture spraying has been used as a practical control measure in New Zealand and Australia. A review of the causes of bloat and of its treatment with antifoaming agents is to be found in the report by Reid.[8] Antibiotics also aid in controlling bloat (Sec. 9.2.).

4.19. Factors Governing Microbial Digestion of Crude Fiber. Since in Herbivora 20 per cent or more of the ration may consist of substances that can be digested only by the action of microorganisms, the factors which may govern this activity are obviously of large importance. The quantitative relations involved in the microbiotic decomposition of carbohydrates vary according to the kind and number of the microorganisms present, which in turn are under the influence of the character of the food. It has been shown, for example, that the addition of easily digestible carbohydrates such as starch, cane sugar, or molasses to the ration of cattle reduces the digestibility of the fiber, and this observation

[7] B. H. Howard, Metabolism of carbohydrates by rumen bacteria, *Proc. Nutrition Soc.*, **18**:103–108, 1959.

[8] C. S. W. Reid, The treatment and prevention of bloat with antifoaming agents, *Proc. Nutrition Soc.*, **18**:127–130, 1959.

has been explained on the ground that the bacteria attack the simpler carbohydrates by preference. It is clear that such a shift in substance attacked would lower the nutritive value of the entire carbohydrate portion of the ration, in that less crude fiber would be digested and more of the absorbable sugar would be lost as gases. There is also evidence that the character of the roughage, irrespective of its fiber content, has an influence on the nature of the bacterial flora and on their activity. The replacement of poor quality hay by alfalfa has been shown to stimulate microbic activity, suggesting that the latter hay may supply specific vitamins or other factors needed for the best growth of the bacteria in question. The higher protein content of the better hay might be the explanation, however, since it has been shown that protein-rich feeds promote the microbiological breakdown of fiber. This is a very active field of study as regards both the chemical and microbiological aspects. As an example, Williams and coworkers[9] have reported that with low protein diets increases in starch intake reduced the concentration of microorganisms in the rumen of sheep and changed their type. With higher protein levels no such effect occurred. At all starch levels protein addition increased the digestibility of dry matter.

The differences in the extent of crude-fiber digestion in the various animal species are readily explainable on the basis of the varying opportunities presented for the action of microorganisms. Ruminants are able to digest at least 50 per cent of the crude fiber of most feeds and other Herbivora can do nearly as well, in contrast to the Omnivora, which have only a limited ability to digest the complex polysaccharides. Anatomical differences in the digestive tract explain why hay and other roughages can form such a large part of the rations of cattle, sheep, and horses and yet be tolerated in only limited amounts by pigs and chickens.

For a given species and animal, there are differences in the degree of the breakdown of crude fiber from different sources which are intimately associated with its chemical and physical nature. The complex polysaccharides of mature plants are less well digested than they are in young, growing plants. The crude fiber of growing pasture grass, fresh or dried, is more digestible than that of hay. Early-cut hay is more digestible than hay cut in late bloom or in seed. The difference is due to both chemical and physical structure and particularly to the presence of certain substances, notably lignin, which are deposited in the cell wall with age. The lignin is not only indigestible itself, but it also lowers the digestibility of the cellulose and other complex carbohydrates.

Differences in crude-fiber digestibility have an influence on the digesti-

[9] V. J. Williams and coworkers, Ruminal flora studies in the sheep. IV. The influence of varying dietary levels of protein and starch upon digestibility, nitrogen retention, and free microorganisms of the rumen, *Australian J. Biol. Sci.*, **6**:142–151, 1953.

bility of all nutrients because intact fiber hinders the action of the digesting enzymes on the other nutrients. This is true not only for the various plant parts, such as the stems and seeds with their protective coatings, but it is also true for each cell with its fibrous membrane. Only the tenderest of these membranes are permeable to the enzymes without previous decomposition or rupture. Of course, cellulose-splitting organisms are not the only factors here involved in the destruction of protective coatings, for the cell membrane can be ruptured by the mechanical processes of digestion or softened and disintegrated by chemical action in the digestive tract. But microbiotic action plays a very large role in connection with the fibrous rations of Herbivora, and thus the nature and amount of the crude fiber present are important factors governing the extent of the digestibility of the various nutrients in the ration.

Much information is being gained regarding microbial digestion in the in vitro studies using artificial rumens in which the natural conditions are simulated. Increasing attention is being given to the bacteriology of the rumen, as is indicated by the review by Doetsch and Robinson[10] which discusses in vivo and in vitro techniques and various studies of the effects of dietary constituents on cellulose and dry-matter digestion. As we learn more about the conditions which promote the maximum activity of rumen organisms we shall also learn how to take fuller advantage of the rumen processes on which the digestion of the higher carbohydrates depends. It is evident that research on these microbial processes is important to enable us to make the most effective use of roughage in feeding cattle and sheep, particularly the low-grade roughage which is available on many farms. The application of the knowledge that is being gained is illustrated by the success reported by Beeson and Perry[11] in getting daily gains of a pound or more with steers fed approximately 15 pounds of ground cobs daily with a supplement supplying protein, minerals, and vitamins.

4.20. Bulk. Crude-fiber content is an important factor governing the bulk of a ration, whatever may be the significance implied in the rather variable usage of this term. As used in connection with a grain mixture the term refers to the weight of a given volume of the feed. For example, oats, which weight approximately 1 lb. to the quart, are bulky in contrast to corn meal, which weighs 1½ lb. on the same basis. The bulky concentrates are in general those which are high in crude fiber, although the air spaces between the particles also contribute to bulk. For the ration as a whole, increasing the roughage portion with its high-fiber content increases its bulk. The importance of making up a concentrate

[10] Raymond N. Doetsch and Roslyn Q. Robinson, The bacteriology of the bovine rumen: a review, *J. Dairy Sci.*, **36**:115–142, 1953.

[11] W. M. Beeson and T. W. Perry, Balancing the nutritional differences of roughages for beef steers, *J. Animal Sci.*, **11**:501–515, 1952.

mixture so that it will have a certain amount of bulk is stressed by many authorities in order to avoid the formation of a doughlike mass in the stomach which is not readily attacked by the digestive juices. The physiological evidence for this point of view, however, is not entirely conclusive.

Bulk is also considered important from the standpoint that a certain distention of the digestive tract is desirable for the tract's most effective functioning, particularly in the elimination of the feed residue. Of course, this distention can be brought about by a large intake of any kind of food, but it is particularly accomplished for the tract as a whole by indigestible material such as crude fiber. In fact, in human nutrition the term roughage is used synonymously with bulk to denote the indigestible portion of the diet. Bulk is promoted by ability to absorb water. Some fibrous materials, such as agar, absorb large quantities of water, while others, such as regenerated cellulose, do not. Linseed oil meal, which is much lower in fiber than wheat bran, absorbs three times as much water and thus, in this sense, is a more bulky feed in the digestive tract.

The influence of bulk in promoting the elimination of feed residues is essentially a laxative effect. It is recognized that feeds high in crude fiber tend to be laxative and that a fiber which readily absorbs water and swells is more laxative than one which does not, at least for certain species. A nonfibrous feed which absorbs a large amount of water is less effective, because it is largely digested and thus does not reach the portion of the tract occupied primarily by feed residues. Of course, bulk is not the sole cause of laxative effect, for many feeds are laxative because of specific chemical substances contained in them which promote peristalsis. In certain species, including man, large intakes of fiber cause intestinal irritation and other gastrointestinal troubles.

The degree of bulk which is desirable naturally depends upon the species, in view of their variability as regards size and anatomy of their digestive tracts. It is also dependent upon the level of production sought. Too much bulk lessens the consumption of digestible nutrients, and thus the intake of bulky material of low digestibility must be limited. Though alfalfa may be ideal as a sole ration from the standpoint of promoting the normal activity of the digestive tract, high-producing cows cannot consume enough of it to meet their needs for nutrients. On the other hand, a high intake of a ration too low in bulk may result in indigestion and in the animal going "off feed."

4.21. Influence of Rumen Activity on Milk-fat Percentage. Following the initial observations by Powell[12] some twenty years ago that a limited

[12] E. B. Powell, One cause of fat variation in milk, *Proc. Am. Soc. Animal Production,* 1938, pp. 40–47; Progress report on the relation of the ration to the composition of milk, *J. Dairy Sci.,* **24,** 504–505, 1941.

intake of roughage fed in a finely ground state to dairy cows resulted in a lowering of the fat content of the milk, several other workers have noted a similar effect, particularly when the roughage was cut to less than half the normal amount and the concentrate mixture increased accordingly. The later studies have emphasized the importance of the nature of the concentrate mixture. Rations containing large amounts of soluble or readily fermentable carbohydrates produce the maximum lowering (30 to 40 per cent). It has been found that any ration which results in a marked lowering produces changes in the movements of the rumen and in the physical and chemical composition of the digesta. There is a marked drop in the concentration of acetic acid and a corresponding rise in propionic. These changes are reflected in the blood into which the acids are absorbed. Based on the finding that acetate is a precursor of milk fats (Sec. 16.11), on evidence that its secretion is lowered by a low acetate level in the blood, and on related data, the explanation is made that the effect of certain rations in lowering the fat content of milk is due to changes in the concentrations of acetic and propionic acids resulting from their digestion. The experimental basis for these findings is to be found in the papers by Balch and coworkers.[13]

4.22. Absorption and Utilization of Fatty Acids. As a result of the pioneer studies of Barcroft and associates[14] and later investigations by others, it has become clearly established that the fatty acids produced by fermentation are directly absorbed into the blood from the rumen, reticulum, omasum, and large intestine. In view of the magnitude of these end products of carbohydrate metabolism in ruminants, the question of their usefulness to the body is one of special importance. Propionic acid is a glycogen-former and thus can follow the same path in metabolism as glucose. While neither acetic nor butyric is a glycogen-former, they are rapidly metabolized and serve the energy needs of the body. Both can enter the metabolic cycle of fat and thus form body fat. Acetic can be utilized by the mammary gland of ruminants in the synthesis of the short-chain fatty acids of milk. It also is burned in the citric acid cycle, the same mechanism by which the end products of carbohydrates and protein are metabolized to furnish energy (Sec. 4.26). It is clear, therefore, that, apart from the gases, the products of carbohydrate fermentation serve as sources of energy for body processes and

[13] C. C. Balch and coworkers, Studies of the secretion of milk of low fat content by cows on diets low in hay and high in concentrates. VI. The effect on the physical and biochemical processes of the reticulorumen, *J. Dairy Research,* **22**:270–289, 1955. D. A. Balch, An estimate of the weights of volatile fatty acids produced in the rumen of lactating cows on a diet of hay and concentrate, *Brit. J. Nutrition,* **12**:18–24, 1958.

[14] J. Barcroft, R. A. McAnally, and A. T. Phillipson, Absorption of volatile acids from the alimentary tract of the sheep and other animals, *J. Exptl. Biol.,* **20**:120–129, 1944.

for the formation of body fat, even as is the case for the simple sugars resulting from digestion by enzymes secreted in the alimentary tract. It should be emphasized that this is the pathway by which a large share of the energy ingested as carbohydrates by ruminants serves the body.

4.23. Absorption and Metabolism of Hexose Sugars. While there is evidence that glucose can pass into the blood stream from the rumen, the monosaccharides arising from carbohydrate digestion are produced primarily in the intestine. The glucose and other hexose sugars are here absorbed and transported to the liver, where they are converted into glycogen, which in turn is gradually reconverted into glucose, the form in which all carbohydrates serve the body. The formation of glycogen from glucose is an enzymic reaction requiring energy which is furnished by ATP.

$$\text{Glucose} + \text{ATP} \longrightarrow \text{glycogen} + \text{ADP} + PO_4[\Delta F^-]$$

Glucose-6-phosphate and glucose-1-phosphate are intermediates. For a continuous reaction there must be a coupled energy-yielding reaction to provide high-energy phosphate bonds to unite with ADP to reform ATP. In the breakdown of glycogen, glucose-1-phosphate is first formed under the action of phosphorylase and in turn changed, stepwise, to glucose-6-phosphate and to glucose. While the liver is by far the largest single storehouse of glycogen, it is found in limited amount in practically all tissues, notably in the muscles. In fact, the total found in all muscles may exceed that present in the liver. The main purpose of this glycogen is to provide an easily available source of energy-producing material for use as needed. Thus each tissue may have a small store, but the liver contains the main supply which, when thrown into the general circulation as sugar, becomes available for use by any tissue in the body.

The glycogenolytic function of the liver provides a mechanism whereby the blood-sugar level may be held within the comparatively narrow limits compatible with normal metabolism. The blood of cows and sheep contains from 40 to 60 mg. of sugar per 100 ml., a lower level than in nonruminants. Newborn ruminants have levels comparable to other species, which decrease as the rumen becomes functional. This drop is believed to be due to metabolic changes following the onset of the bacterial fermentation of carbohydrates in the rumen. Birds have higher blood-sugar values than do mammals, but cold-blooded animals show very low figures, such as 20 mg. commonly found for the frog.

The temporary storage of glycogen following carbohydrate absorption prevents *hyperglycemia*, i.e., a blood-sugar level above the normal range; and the later release of this glycogen as glucose to balance the withdrawal of sugar from the blood by the tissues prevents the opposite, *hypoglycemia*. This glycogenolytic function of the liver is influenced by certain hormones. Adrenalin and the diabetogenic hormone act to increase the sugar level. Insulin has the opposite effect. If this control fails, either hyperglycemia or hypoglycemia may result.

4.24. Transformation of Sugar into Fat. The ability of the liver and other tissues to store sugar as glycogen is limited, and thus, when the carbohydrate intake regularly exceeds the current need of the body for energy purposes, sugar is transformed into fat. This process takes place on a large scale in the fattening of animals, since their food consists principally of carbohydrates. This formation of body fat from carbohydrate food was first demonstrated by Lawes and Gilbert[15] by means of a slaughter experiment. They chose pigs from the same litter and of the same size. Some of these animals were slaughtered at the start and analyzed as controls, while the others were killed after being fed for an extended period on a low-fat ration of known composition. The data obtained from the analysis of these animals, compared with the data from the controls, showed that the pigs had stored more fat than could have resulted from all of the fat and protein fed and, therefore, that a part of their fat must have been formed from carbohydrates. The formation of milk fat from carbohydrate was demonstrated by Jordan and coworkers[16] in a somewhat similar way by feeding a ration low in fat and showing that the milk fat exceeded that which could have come from the total protein and fat in the food, while the weight and appearance of the animal indicated that the milk fat could not have been made at the expense of body fat.

The formation of fat from carbohydrate is also readily demonstrated by means of the carbon balance (Sec. 11.5) and by the measurement of gaseous exchange (Sec. 11.3). The transformation consists of many intermediary steps involving the breakdown of the glucose molecule into simple units and the synthesis of glycerol and fatty acids from these units. The exact mechanism is unknown.

The lack of evidence that fat, other than the glycerol part, can be converted into carbohydrates has long been stressed. Recent studies, however, make it increasingly evident that the metabolism of carbohydrate, fat, and protein result in the production of a number of common intermediates (Sec. 4.26). This means that the older distinctions in the

[15] See footnote, p. 10.

[16] W. H. Jordan and C. G. Jenter, The source of milk, fat, *New York Agr. Expt. Sta. Bull.* 132, 1897; W. H. Jordan, C. G. Jenter, and F. D. Fuller, The food source of milk fat, with studies on the nutrition of milch cows, *ibid.*, 197, 1901. Whitman H. Jordan (1851–1931), following service at the Connecticut, Pennsylvania, and Maine agricultural experiment stations, was director of the New York experiment station at Geneva for twenty-five years. As one of the pioneers in the development of experiment-station work, he championed the view that the maintaining of rigidly scientific investigation was the most useful function of these stations.

metabolism of the three groups are disappearing and also that body mechanisms for their interconversion are recognized to exist.

4.25. The Formation of Tissue Carbohydrates. Small amounts of carbohydrates and their derivatives occur as structural elements in certain tissues. Pentoses are constituents of cell nucleic acids, and galactose exists in combination with lipids in nervous tissue. Various carbohydrate groups occur in many conjugated proteins, and cartilage, bones, and tendons contain an amino polysaccharide. The synthesis of these carbohydrate-containing structural elements and their subsequent catabolism represent a phase of carbohydrate metabolism which is little understood.

The formation of lactose in milk secretion represents a special carbohydrate synthesis which takes place on a large scale (Sec. 16.10).

4.26. The Catabolism of Glucose. Citric Acid Cycle. The utilization of carbohydrates, either for fat formation or for energy purposes, involves a series of chain reactions carried out under the influence of specific enzymes and coenzymes. A catabolic pathway which carbohydrates share with fats and protein is the citric acid cycle (Fig. 4.2).

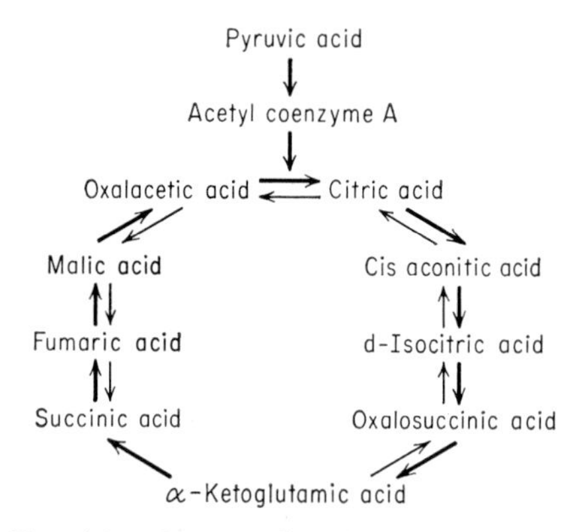

FIG. 4.2. Citric acid cycle (Krebs cycle).

Glucose is catabolized in different ways by various stepwise reactions to pyruvic acid which is, in turn, converted under the action of coenzyme A (Sec. 8.42) to acetyl-coenzyme A, the active rapidly metabolized form of acetate. This compound enters the cycle, condensing with oxalacetate to form citric acid. A sequence of reactions indicated by the heavy arrows follows, under the influence of specific enzymes. The net result is the production of two molecules of carbon dioxide and water from one molecule of acetic acid entering the cycle as acetyl-coenzyme A and the regeneration of one molecule of oxalacetic acid which can in turn combine with another entering molecule of the activated acetate. In the course of the cycle, hydrogen atoms and carbon dioxide molecules are split off at different points, releasing free energy which is captured in ATP to serve endergonic body processes. The hydrogen atoms combine with oxygen supplied the tissues by the lungs to form water, involving a series of reactions in which various enzymes take part. The above is a very abbreviated description of the cycle. For details on the various chemical reactions involved, the student is referred to a textbook of biochemistry.

The cycle is a mechanism by which all those metabolites which are convertible into acetic acid, or any component of the cycle, can be catabolized to carbon dioxide and water. Thus it is the pathway for the final catabolism of fats and the majority of the amino acids. The cycle is an important mechanism through which pyruvic acid is changed into various other intermediates. It serves as a metabolic pool in which the intermediate catabolic products of carbohydrates, fats, and proteins are merged, both for further catabolism and for synthesis.

The catabolism of glycogen and glucose in muscle action follows a different pathway and is discussed later (Sec. 17.2).

While the normal end products of carbohydrate metabolism are carbon dioxide and water, which are excreted through the lungs, skin, and urine, in diabetes there is a failure of this metabolism whereby the glucose content of the blood is greatly increased and the sugar is excreted in the urine. Normally the urine contains only traces of sugars, and the occurrence of a measurable amount is called *glycosuria*. In diabetes the body tissues waste away, the alkali reserve of the blood is decreased by the acidosis, and the body is poisoned by the accumulated, incompletely catabolized products. This disease is very common in man, and it occurs occasionally in dogs, but it is very rare in farm animals.

SELECTED LITERATURE

Annison, E. F.: Volatile fatty acids in the sheep rumen, *Biochem. J.*, **57**:400–405, 1954.

Bohman, V. R., and associates: The utilization of molasses and urea in the rations of growing dairy cattle, *J. Dairy Sci.*, **37**:284–293, 1954.

Browne, C. A.: The origin and application of the term, nitrogen-free extract, in the valuation of feedingstuffs, *J. Assoc. Offic. Agr. Chemists*, **23**:102–108, 1940.

Ellis, Gordon H.: Report on lignin and cellulose in plants, *J. Assoc. Offic. Agr. Chemists*, **32**:287–291, 1949.

Pounden, W. D., and J. W. Hibbs: The influence of pasture and rumen inoculation on the establishment of certain microorganisms in the rumen of young dairy calves, *J. Dairy Sci.*, **32**:1025–1031, 1949.

Shaw, J. C., and coworkers: Production of low-fat milk. I. Effect of quality and quantity of concentrate on the volatile fatty acids of the rumen and on the composition of the milk, *J. Nutrition*, **69**:235–244, 1959.

Teague, H. S., and L. E. Hanson: The effect of feeding different levels of a cellulosic material to swine, *J. Animal Sci.*, **13**:206–214, 1954.

Chapter 5
The Lipids and Their Metabolism

Plant and animal materials contain a group of substances, insoluble in water but soluble in ether, chloroform, and benzene, which are most commonly referred to as lipids. The group includes the fats and several closely related or associated compounds, such as the phosphatides, sterols, and others. From the standpoint of the amounts present in the animal body and its food, the fats are by far the most important members of the group, but several of the other lipids play very significant roles in nutrition and in physiology. As an example, one may cite ergosterol, which is a mother substance of vitamin D. Like the carbohydrates, the fats contain carbon, hydrogen, and oxygen, but they are relatively much richer in the first two, as is shown by the following percentage figures:

	Carbon	Hydrogen	Oxygen
Fat............	77	12	11
Starch..........	44	6	50

Certain compound lipids contain nitrogen and phosphorus also. In the body the lipids serve as a condensed reserve of energy, as structural elements, and as essentials for various reactions in intermediary metabolism.

5.1. Classification of Lipids. In using the term lipids to designate this group of physiologically important compounds, the nomenclature and classification suggested by Bloor are followed (Table 5.1). Sometimes the term fat is employed to include the group as a whole. In addition to their distinctive properties as regards solubility, the lipids are characterized by being esterlike combinations of fatty acids or by being capable of forming such combinations, and they are substances which can perform useful functions in living organisms. These charac-

TABLE 5.1. CLASSIFICATION OF THE LIPIDS*

Simple lipids—esters of the fatty acids with various alcohols
  Fats—esters of the fatty acids with glycerol†
  Waxes—esters of the fatty acids with alcohols other than glycerol
Compound lipids—esters of the fatty acids containing groups in addition to an alcohol and fatty acid
  Phospholipids—substituted fats containing phosphoric acid and nitrogen—*lecithin, cephalin, sphingomyelin*
  Glycolipids—compounds of the fatty acids with a carbohydrate and containing nitrogen but no phosphoric acid—*cerebrosides*
  Aminolipids, sulfolipids, etc.—groups which are at present not sufficiently well characterized for classification
Derived lipids—substances derived from the above groups by hydrolysis
  Fatty acids of various series
  Sterols—mostly large molecular alcohols, found in nature combined with the fatty acids and soluble in the fat solvents

* W. R. Bloor, Biochemistry of the fats, *Chem. Revs.*, **2**:243–300, 1925–1926.
† Commonly called triglycerides, or neutral fats.

terizations serve to exclude organic compounds which qualify as regards solubility but which have no biochemical or physiological relationships to the true members of the group.

5.2. The Fatty Acids. Since the fatty acids are constituents of most of the other lipids, it is helpful to take them up first. A list of those which commonly occur in plant and animal fats is given in Table 5.2. Melting points are listed for those which are solid above 15°C. The term "poly-

TABLE 5.2. FATTY ACIDS COMMONLY FOUND IN LIPIDS

Acids	Formula	Melting point, °C.
Saturated acids:		
Butyric (butanoic)	$C_4H_8O_2$	Liquid
Caproic (hexanoic)	$C_6H_{12}O_2$	Liquid
Caprylic (octanoic)	$C_8H_{16}O_2$	16
Capric (decanoic)	$C_{10}H_{20}O_2$	31
Lauric (dodecanoic)	$C_{12}H_{24}O_2$	44
Myristic (tetradecanoic)	$C_{14}H_{28}O_2$	54
Palmitic (hexadecanoic)	$C_{16}H_{32}O_2$	63
Stearic (octadecanoic)	$C_{18}H_{36}O_2$	70
Arachidic (eicosanoic)	$C_{20}H_{40}O_2$	76
Lignoceric (tetracosanoic)	$C_{24}H_{48}O_2$	86
Unsaturated acids:		
Palmitoleic (hexadecenoic)	$C_{16}H_{30}O_2$	Liquid
Oleic (octadecenoic)	$C_{18}H_{34}O_2$	Liquid
Linoleic (octadecadienoic)	$C_{18}H_{32}O_2$	Liquid
Linolenic (octadecatrienoic)	$C_{18}H_{30}O_2$	Liquid
Arachidonic (eicosatetraenoic)	$C_{20}H_{32}O_2$	Liquid
Clupanodonic (docosapentaeonic)	$C_{22}H_{34}O_2$	Liquid

unstaturated fatty acids" is frequently applied to those having more than one double bond.

The names in parentheses represent the modern chemical nomenclature. The suffixes denote state of saturation: *-anoic*, saturated; *-enoic*, one double bond; *dienoic*, two double bonds; *-trienoic*, three double bonds; *-tetraenoic*, four double bonds; *-pentaenoic*, five double bonds. These double bonds are reflected in the formulas for the acids, in the smaller number of hydrogen atoms relative to the carbon atoms present. Unsaturated acids have lower melting points and are more reactive than the saturated acids of the same number of carbon atoms. It is noted, for example, that stearic acid melts at 70°C., whereas oleic, linoleic, and linolenic are liquid at room temperature, although all have 18 carbon atoms. These characteristics are important in physiology because they influence the properties of the fats and other liquids in which the fatty acids are combined. Unsaturated acids can exist in different isomeric forms.

All of the acids listed in the table have an even number of carbon atoms, since, with a few exceptions, these are the only ones which occur in nature. The first four listed are classed as volatile, since they can be distilled with steam. The saturated acids have the general formula $C_nH_{2n}O_2$, and the melting point rises throughout the series. Butyric acid occurs in milk fat. The acids from caproic to myristic are present in only a few fats, including the fat of milk and the oil of the coconut and related plants. Palmitic, oleic, and stearic acids are widely distributed in plant and animal fats generally. Linoleic, also called linolic, makes up a large percentage of many plant fats but occurs in only limited amounts in animal fats. Arachidonic acid is found in limited amounts in the fat of various animal tissues. Clupanodonic acid is a highly unsaturated acid occurring in fish oils.

THE FATS AND WAXES

5.3. The Structure of Fats. The chemical nature of the fats was established in 1814 by the brilliant work of the French chemist Chevreul. They are esters formed by the union of the trihydroxy alcohol, glycerol, with three molecules of fatty acids. Three molecules of water must be split out, and thus a dehydrating agent is required. Using R–COOH as the general formula for a fatty acid, the formation of a fat may be illustrated as follows:

$$\begin{array}{llll} CH_2OH & HOOC{-}R & & CH_2{-}OOC{-}R \\ | & & & | \\ CHOH & + HOOC{-}R & \longrightarrow & CH{-}OOC{-}R + 3H_2O \\ | & & & | \\ CH_2OH & HOOC{-}R & & CH_2{-}OOC{-}R \\ \text{Glycerol} & \text{Fatty acids} & & \text{Fat} \end{array}$$

The fatty acids may be alike or different. For example, glycerol may combine with three molecules of palmitic acid to form tripalmitin, a simple triglyceride, or it may combine with one molecule each of oleic, palmitic, and stearic acids to form palmito-oleo-stearin, a mixed triglyceride. The reaction shown above is a reversible one in that fats may be split into glycerol and fatty acids under the action of dilute mineral acids, enzymes, or steam. The process is essentially a hydrolysis. Enzymatic hydrolysis occurs in digestion. While the term fat is employed for all triglycerides, the term oil is used in industrial classifications to denote those which are liquid below 20°C. Most vegetable fats fall into the latter class. Fats are colorless in the pure state, but naturally occurring ones may contain pigments. Thus, milk fat and egg fat contain carotene and xanthophyll.

The fats which occur in nature consist of triglycerides containing different fatty acids in varying proportions. The distribution of the principal fatty acid constituents of some animal and vegetable fats is illustrated by the data in Table 5.3. Considerable variation among

TABLE 5.3. FATTY ACIDS AS A PERCENTAGE OF TOTAL FATTY ACIDS* AND PHYSICAL CONSTANTS OF SOME COMMON FATS

	Butterfat	Lard	Coconut fat	Soybean fat	Corn fat	Cotton-seed fat
I. Saturated acids:						
Butyric	3.2					
Caproic	1.8	....	0.2			
Caprylic	0.8	....	8.2			
Capric	1.4	....	7.4			
Lauric	3.8	....	47.5			
Myristic	8.3	....	18.0	....	....	2.0
Palmitic	27.0	32.2	8.0	8.5	7.0	19.0
Stearic	12.5	7.8	2.8	3.5	2.4	2.0
Total saturated	58.8	40.0	92.8	21.1	9.4	24.4
II. Unsaturated acids:						
Oleic	35.0	48.0	5.6	17.0	45.6	20.1
Linoleic	3.0	11.0	1.6	54.4	45.0	55.5
Linolenic	0.8	0.6	....	7.1		
Melting point, °C	28 to 36	35 to 45	20 to 35	Liquid at ordinary temperature		
Iodine No.	26 to 38	40 to 70	8 to 10	130 to 137	105 to 125	100 to 115
Saponification No.	220 to 241	193 to 220	250 to 260	190 to 194	87 to 93	190 to 200
Reichert-Meissl No.	23 to 33	....	6 to 8			

* Most of these data were taken from a compilation prepared by Verz R. Goddard and Louise Goodall, issued by the Agricultural Research Service, U.S. Department of Agriculture, May, 1959.

different sources of the same type of fat is to be expected because the composition of the fat of a given species of animal is affected by its ration and because marked varietal differences occur among plant sources. It is noted in the table that, with the exception of coconut fat, which is a special case, plant fats are much higher in unsaturated acids than are the animal products, notably in linoleic, which has special nutritional importance as is discussed later (Sec. 5.28). Butter is a unique fat containing butyric acid and differs from other animal fats because of its content of all the lower fatty acids. It is a special synthetic product of the mammary gland.

The fatty acid make-up of a fat determines its specific chemical and physical properties. Certain constants used for measuring these properties are listed in the last lines of the table. They are very useful for identifying fats and for determining properties which have nutritional significance. These constants are given as a range, since they reflect the variation in fatty-acid distribution. Some samples will fall outside the ranges given.

5.4. Melting Point. Since a naturally occurring fat consists of a more or less variable mixture of glycerides, its melting point is variable and not sharp. Nevertheless the determination provides a useful measure of hardness. For the fats which are liquid at ordinary temperatures, the *solidifying point* rather than the melting point is generally used as the measure. Although variable according to the make-up of the fat, the temperature of solidification is always lower than that of melting. While the presence of acids of a low molecular weight tends to make for a low melting point, the degree of unsaturation is also an important factor influencing this constant. This is readily evident by comparing the amounts of unsaturated acids in soybean and corn fats, which are liquid at ordinary temperatures and solidify between —5 and —10°C., with the amounts in coconut fat, which melts at 20°C. or above. Though coconut fat has much smaller amounts of unsaturated acids than lard, it melts at a lower temperature because of its high content of acids of low molecular weight.

5.5. Iodine Number. An unsaturated fat easily unites with iodine, two atoms of this element being added for each double bond. Thus the iodine number is a measure of the degree of unsaturation. It is defined as the number of grams of iodine absorbed by 100 g. of fat, and it is the most useful single measure of the character of fat. The value of 130 for soybean oil, which reflects its high degree of unsaturation, may be contrasted with the figure of 8 for coconut oil.

5.6. Saponification Number. When a fat is boiled with alkali, such as sodium hydroxide, it is split into glycerol and the alkali salt of the fatty acids. These alkali salts are called *soaps*, and the process is called *saponification*. The process occurs in digestion under the action of the sodium salts in the bile. The amount of alkali required to saponify a given amount of fat is a measure of the length of the fatty-acid chains present; for, the smaller the fatty-acid molecules, the greater is the number of these molecules per gram of fat and, thus, the larger the amount of alkali required for saponification. This measure is called the saponification number. As an illustration, butterfat with its large percentage of the lower fatty acids has a much higher saponification number than corn oil, which contains mostly acids with 18 carbon atoms. Saponification splits a mixture of lipids into a *saponifiable fraction*, which consists principally of fatty acids, and an *unsaponifiable fraction*, or residue, which contains the sterols. All naturally occurring fats, such as those listed in Table 5.3, contain some unsaponifiable materials.

5.7. Reichert-Meissl Number. The determination of the amount of water soluble, steam-volatile fatty acids present is a useful measure of the character of butterfat and for detecting adulteration in it, since the large percentages of these acids in butterfat are a distinctive feature. This measure is called the Reichert-Meissl number. The fatty-acid distribution given in Table 5.3 shows why coconut fat is the only one, aside from butter, which gives a value of any size. It is also evident that butterfat and coconut fat are easily distinguishable by this constant.

Other commonly employed constants are the *refractive index*, which measures hardness, and the *acid number*, which measures the amount of free fatty acids.

5.8. Oxidation of Fats. Fats are readily oxidized at the double bond, and as this occurs, the fat becomes more viscous, or harder. This reaction takes place in the drying of paints, involving oxidation of the highly unsaturated acids in the linseed oil, which commonly is the carrier of the pigment. Vegetable oils are classified on the basis of their drying properties as nondrying, semidrying, or drying oils. The last include the oils which are highly unsaturated. The rapid oxidation of a highly unsaturated fat generates much heat. Herein lies the cause of the spontaneous combustion of oily rags.

5.9. Rancidity. Both oxidative and hydrolytic changes are responsible for the development of rancidity in different fats. Various decomposition products result. Peroxides are formed as intermediate compounds, and hence the *peroxide number* is used as a measure of rancidity. The changes occur especially in the presence of heat, light, and moisture. Certain substances called *prooxidants,* such as copper and iron salts, catalyze the process that is thus referred to as *autoxidation.* Ultraviolet light is particularly effective in hastening this process. On the other hand, many other compounds, referred to as *antioxidants,* retard the development of rancidity. Many vegetable oils have natural antioxidants present, while animal fats, particularly when refined, have little such activity. Vitamin E is a very effective antioxidant. Since rancid fats have disagreeable flavors and odors, their acceptability as foods is always impaired even though their nutritive value may not be affected. The latter can happen. Vitamin A, carotene, and vitamin E are subject to destruction by rancid fats, as has been shown for stored grains, meals, and concentrate mixtures.

5.10. Hydrogenation of Fats. Double bonds will take on hydrogen as well as oxygen, though less readily. A catalyst is required. This process of hydrogenation produces a saturated, and thus a hard fat out of an unsaturated, soft one. This saturation of the double bonds makes the fat less reactive and thus tends to prevent the oxidative changes of rancidity. Thus hydrogenation is used for improving the keeping qualities of certain fats, especially vegetable oils, used for food; this process produces solid cooking fats. The oils are not completely hydrogenated because, if this were done, the products would be too hard for convenient use. Completely hydrogenated cottonseed oil melts around 62°C. and gives no iodine number, whereas the partially hydrogenated products used in cooking melt between 35 and 43°C. and have an iodine number of 60 to 75.

5.11. Body Fats. Terroine[1] classified the body lipids into two groups: the "constant element" and the "variable element." Terroine's distinction was based upon the fact that during periods of inadequate food intake the variable element is drawn upon to furnish energy for body processes, while the constant element remains intact to preserve the essential structures of the body. While this concept has been modified by recent discoveries as to the dynamic state of fat (Sec. 5.22), it remains a useful one. The constant element represents the part which is essential as a constituent of functioning cells and consists primarily of phospholipids and sterols. The variable element is the much larger group and represents the fat which has been deposited as an energy reserve. This depot fat consists principally of triglycerides of palmitic, stearic, and oleic acids, with much smaller amounts of various others. The fatty-acid distribution varies with the species. Cold-blooded animals have softer, and thus more unsaturated, fats than warm-blooded animals. In general, Carnivora have softer fats than Herbivora. Terroine has given a detailed discussion of these species differences. For a given animal, there are also certain differences according to the location of the fat depot. Although a given species tends to deposit a fat of constant composition, the nature of the diet has a marked influence, as is discussed later.

5.12. Waxes. When a fatty acid combines with one of the higher monohydroxy or dihydroxy alcohols, a wax results. For example,

[1] Émile F. Terroine, Contribution à la connaissance de la physiologie des substances grasses et lipoïdiques, *Ann. sci. nat. Zool.*, 4(10):5–397, 1920. Terroine was director of the Institut de Physiologie Générale at the University of Strasbourg. He has made many outstanding contributions in the fields of energy and protein metabolism and in comparative physiology.

palmitic acid is combined with myricyl alcohol, $C_{30}H_{61}OH$, in beeswax and with cetyl alcohol, $C_{16}H_{33}OH$, in spermaceti. Waxes have high melting points and are difficult to saponify and thus not readily digested. They occur as secretions or excretions in many animals, particularly insects, and in many forms of plant life, especially as protective coatings.

COMPOUND LIPIDS

5.13. Phospholipids. As their name indicates, the phospholipids, also called phosphatides and phospholipins, are lipids containing phosphorus. They are present in every plant and animal cell and evidently play a fundamental role in cellular structure and activity. All of them on hydrolysis yield fatty acids and phosphoric acid, and most of them yield glycerol and a nitrogenous base. One group of phospholipids is called *lecithins,* the general formula for which is given below:

```
                O
                ||
H2C—O—C—R1
 |
 |              O
 |              ||
HC—O—C—R2                                   (CH3)3
 |                                                |
 |              O                                 N—OH
 |              ||                                |
H2C—O—P—O—(CH2)2—N(CH3)3                CH2
                |                  |              |
                OH                 OH             CH2OH
              Lecithin                            Choline
```

R_1 and R_2 represent the residues of the molecules of fatty acids. Thus the lecithins may be considered as fats in which one of the fatty acids has been replaced by phosphoric acid and the nitrogenous base choline. The various members of the group contain different combinations of fatty acids. Though some which contain two saturated acids are known, most of them contain at least one unsaturated acid and several contain two. They are essential constituents of all body cells.

The *cephalins* are phospholipids which are similar to the lecithins with the exception that they contain amino-ethyl alcohol (hydroxy-ethyl amine) in place of choline. Recently a new type of cephalin, containing the amino acid serine, has been identified. Inositol (Sec. 8.60) is a constituent of certain compounds of the cephalin group. The *sphingomyelins* yield, on hydrolysis, fatty acids, choline, phosphoric acid, and the complex nitrogenous base sphingosine. They contain no glycerol. Both cephalins and sphingomyelins are found in various body tissues, notably in the brain.

Because of their preponderance of unsaturated fatty acids, the phospholipids of animal tissues are in general much more unsaturated than is the case for the neutral fats. This has naturally led to the view that the functions of the phospholipids are associated in some way with their high degree of unsaturation, a property which would tend to make them more reactive than the triglycerides. It appears significant that fatty acids in active tissues are present principally as phospholipids, while the inactive adipose tissues consist primarily of neutral fat. According to the commonly accepted concept of fat metabolism, neutral fats undergo desaturation and are then changed to phospholipids, as preliminary steps in their oxidation. The phospholipids adsorb relatively larger amounts of water than do neutral fats, and thus they are more readily dispersed in the body fluids. This has suggested that they are a form in which fats are transported in the blood and other fluids.

Phospholipids are found in both the seeds and leaves of plants. In the seeds they probably represent reserve material, since they disappear during germination, but in the leaves they are evidently an integral part of the protoplasm.

The *glycolipids* derive their name from the fact that they contain a carbohydrate group, which is galactose. They also contain a fatty acid and sphingosine. They are found particularly in the brain and thus are frequently called *cerebrosides.*

5.14. Choline. This compound is the most important component of the lecithin molecule in the sense that a dietary source of it is normally required for the adequate body synthesis of the phospholipid. Experimentally a lack of dietary choline has been found to produce or be concerned in the production of a variety of troubles in various animals, such as growth failure, fatty livers and hemorrhagic kidneys, "slipped tendon" in chicks and poults, and other pathological changes. These comparatively recent findings have led investigators to class choline as a vitamin, although its existence in essential body constituents was recognized long before the first vitamin was discovered. The detailed discussion of this substance is therefore included under vitamins (Chap. 8). An important physiological role of choline is based upon the methyl groups in its structure (see formula, page 71). These are known as "biologically labile methyl groups" for reasons explained later (Sec. 8.49). *Acetylcholine* is a derivative of choline which is essential for nerve functioning.

THE STEROLS

The sterols are solid alcohols of high molecular weight having a ring structure. There are other substances of biological importance, such as the bile acids and sex hormones, which have a similar ring structure.

The sterols and related substances are referred to as *steroids*. The common basic structure, shown below, has a carbon atom at each point and junction. Modification of this structure and the addition of side chains result in a large variety of compounds differing widely in physiological properties. The sterols belong to the unsaponifiable fraction of lipids. While this fraction is relatively small in most animal and vegetable fats, some fish-liver oils are very rich in it, notably the liver oils of certain sharks which contain 90 per cent of unsaponifiable matter.

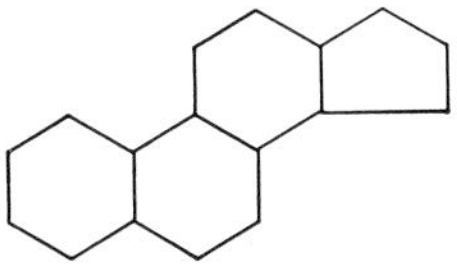

5.15. Cholesterol, $C_{27}H_{45}OH$. The most important sterol in animal tissues is cholesterol. It occurs free and in ester combination with highly unsaturated fatty acids in cells and in the blood. Cholesterol is undoubtedly an essential cell constituent. In the blood it may be concerned with fat transport. The compound is synthesized in the body from acetate, and thus it is not a dietary essential. In Omnivora, however, which consume animal fats, the diet may be an important source of the levels found in the blood. *7-Dehydrocholesterol* is a provitamin of vitamin D (Sec. 8.13).

Coprosterol, $C_{27}H_{47}OH$, is a sterol found in the feces which is a product of the reducing action of bacteria in the lower intestine.

5.16. Phytosterols. The sterols of plants are called phytosterols, of which there are several, e.g., sitosterol, present in corn. They are probably end products of plant metabolism. *Ergosterol*, $C_{28}H_{43}OH$, is a plant sterol of outstanding interest because by activation with ultraviolet light it forms vitamin D. Aside from ergosterol no sterols found in plants are appreciably absorbed into the animal body.

5.17. The Determination of Lipids. In routine feed analysis, the lipids are determined as *ether extract*. The feed is dried to a moisture-free basis and then extracted for 16 hr. with anhydrous ethyl ether. The extract is weighed after the evaporation of the ether. In addition to lipids, ether extracts plant pigments, such as chlorophyll, xanthophyll, and carotene, and traces of various other substances. Ether also removes certain *essential oils*, which are nonlipid products consisting primarily of aromatic esters, aldehydes, and ethers. Thus the use of the term ether extract as a synonym for fat, in speaking of the nutrient composition of feeds and rations, is not strictly accurate. In certain leafy materials, the amount of ether extract other than esters of fatty acids may represent 25 to 40 per cent of the total. In those foods, however, which we recognize to be the chief sources of dietary fat, viz., seeds and animal products, the ether extract consists very largely of triglycerides. Certain desert-range forage plants present a special case in that, as shown by Cook and associates,[2] they contain 10 per cent or more of ether extract consisting mostly of essential oils which provide no useful energy.

Special methods are required for the complete extraction of lipids from certain plant and animal tissues. There are also special procedures for the determination of the individual members of the lipid group, and such determinations are essential in many studies of fat metabolism.

LIPID METABOLISM

Though, following the nursing stage, the lipids make up only a small part of the diet of most animals, the metabolism of fat is of great importance in nutrition, both because of the vital roles played by specific lipids and also because of the extensive fat formation which occurs in the body in fat deposition, in the secretion of milk, and in other functions. Lipids occur as essential constituents in every cell in the body. While the depot fat serves primarily as a source of energy, that deposited under the skin serves also as a nonconducting layer which prevents the too rapid escape of body heat, and that around the viscera and certain other organs performs a supporting function.

5.18. The Digestion of Lipids. As reviewed by Garton,[3] in vitro studies have shown that triglycerides undergo hydrolysis in the rumen to a large degree. A portion of the glycerol thus produced is fermented to propionic acid. Some hydrogenation of the unsaturated acids takes place. Little specific information is available regarding the action of rumen bacteria on other lipids. The hydrolytic products of rumen action, with the exception of any glycerol fermented, and other ingested lipids pass on into the small intestine. This is the sole seat of lipid digestion in nonruminants. The triglycerides are hydrolyzed by the pancreatic lipase, which is aided by the saponifying and emulsifying action of the bile. To the extent that compound lipids are present, there arise in addition small amounts of other products such as phosphoric acid and nitrogen bases, but the free sterols are not acted upon in the digestive tract. The sterol esters may be hydrolyzed, setting free their fatty acids. From a quantitative standpoint these free and combined sterols are a negligible part of the ration. Of the plant pigments which make up a sizable fraction of

[2] C. Wayne Cook, L. A. Stoddart, and Lorin E. Harris, Determining the digestibility and metabolizable energy of winter range plants by sheep, *J. Animal Sci.*, **11**:578–590, 1952.

[3] G. A. Garton, Lipids in relation to rumen function, *Proc. Nutrition Soc.*, **18**:112–117, 1959.

the ether extract of certain feeds, notably leafy material, some, such as chlorophyll, are destroyed in the digestive tract, while others are not attacked.

Fats as such are highly digestible. Their digestibility is influenced somewhat by the length of the carbon chains and the state of saturation. In general, digestibility in omnivora is decreased as the content of saturated acids of 18 or more carbon atoms increases, according to human and rat studies. Mattson[4] has concluded, from rat studies, that the governing factor in this decrease is the content of *simple* triglycerides of these saturated acids. In the case of farm animals, where little fat is consumed as such, the over-all digestibility of the fat-containing feeds influences the extent of fat digestion, irrespective of its chemical make-up.

5.19. Fecal Lipids. The ether extract of the feces consists of digestible fats which have escaped the action of the digestive juices, lipids which are not absorbable, such as plant sterols, and nonlipid material of food origin, such as pigments. It is recognized that the feces may also contain *metabolic fat,* which is ether-soluble fecal material of body origin such as the residues of digestive juices, as distinguished from undigested or unabsorbed food lipids. The ether extract of the feces of Carnivora and Omnivora shows that the lipids of the rations commonly fed these species are nearly completely digested. It is considered that a sizable portion of this extract represents metabolic fat, though the question has been extensively studied only in the dog. In the case of Herbivora, fat digestion is much less complete, owing primarily to the protective action of undigested cellulose surrounding the fat, which serves as a barrier against digestive action in general. The ether extract of the food of Herbivora also contains relatively more nonabsorbable material, such as pigments.

5.20. The Absorption and Transport of Fat. The fatty acids resulting from lipase action are absorbed from the intestine, aided by the bile, and are recombined into neutral fat in the intestinal wall, with lecithin as a probable intermediate. There is evidence that minutely emulsified fat and the partial hydrolytic product, monoglyceride, can be absorbed as such into the lymphatics. The extent to which this process occurs remains unsettled. The absorbed fat enters the general circulation by the portal vein to the liver and via the lymphatic system and the thoracic duct. Because of its insolubility in water, this absorbed fat gives a milky appearance to the blood, which is referred to as *lipemia.* In addition to neutral fat, the blood contains fatty acids as phospholipids and cholesterol esters and also as a cholesterol-lipoprotein complex which has been ascribed a major role in fat transport.

[4] F. H. Mattson, The absorbability of stearic acid when fed as a simple or mixed triglyceride, *J. Nutrition,* **69**:338–342, 1960.

Some of the absorbed fat, particularly that entering the blood through the lymphatic system, may be directly deposited in the tissues. Much of the absorbed fat undergoes metabolism in the liver. Here the formation of lecithin is of great nutritional importance, a reaction which requires choline and which is aided by various lipotropic agents discussed later. This reaction provides a mechanism by which fat is transported from the liver to the tissues. Otherwise, "fatty livers" result from the abnormal accumulation of fat.

5.21. Fat Deposition. The depot fat is formed not only from ingested fat but also from carbohydrates (Sec. 4.24) and sometimes from protein. Approximately 50 per cent of the adipose tissue is found under the skin, i.e., subcutaneous fat. The balance is located around certain organs, notably the kidneys, in the membranes surrounding the intestines, in the muscles, and elsewhere. Adipose tissue is not entirely inert. It has a blood and nerve supply, and as a result various reactions, such as desaturations and the conversion of carbohydrate to fat, can take place.

The Missouri workers[5] reported an extensive study of the fat deposited in various parts of the steer. The data show that different fat deposits vary in water content (4.5 to 14.4 per cent), in nitrogen content (0.18 to 0.62 per cent), and in character, as shown by different physical constants. The nitrogen in fat deposits occurs principally in connective tissue.

Since adipose tissue always contains some water, it is evident that fat deposition involves a deposition of water also. With a ration rich in fat, there is some retention of water in all tissues, including the blood. Fat deposits are considered to be water-in-oil emulsions, in which albumin, lecithin, or soaps act as the emulsifying agent. When the depots are called upon to furnish energy, there may be a retention of water in place of the fat. This has been clearly shown for the human subject by Newburgh and Johnston.[6] By taking account of the water intake and outgo, as well as the energy metabolism, they found that obese individuals frequently maintained or even increased their weight temporarily on a reducing diet, because water was being stored despite the fact that depot fat was being used up. Particularly striking is the observation of Trowbridge[7] that the kidney fat of a steer on a submaintenance ration for 11 months contained 81.4 per cent of water, 9.6 per cent of protein, and only 4.6 per cent of fat, whereas for a check animal the figures were 5.5, 1.7, and 93.1 per cent, respectively. These observations illustrate the limita-

[5] P. F. Trowbridge, C. R. Moulton, and L. D. Haigh, Composition of the beef animal and energy cost of fattening, *Missouri Agr. Expt. Sta. Bull.* 30, 1919.

[6] L. H. Newburgh and M. W. Johnston, Endogenous obesity—a misconception, *J. Am. Dietet. Assoc.* **5**:275–285, 1930.

[7] P. F. Trowbridge, The resorption of fat, *Proc. Am. Soc. Animal Nutrition,* 1910, pp. 13–20.

tions of the weight measure as the sole criterion of nutritive state in maintenance or in fattening. The fat-water relationships in adipose tissue may have a bearing on the amount of "shrink" in animals rapidly fattened for market.

5.22. Dynamic State of Body Fat. The modern discoveries made by the use of isotopes (Sec. 3.16) have shown that the fats in the body are in a state of flux. Fatty acids from the depots are being constantly mobilized and transported. Absorbed fatty acids merge with these from the depots. Some of the acids of this pool are constantly being converted into others. Some are degraded, while others are combined with glycerol and transported back to the depots. All of these reactions are so balanced that mixtures of fatty acids in the depots, blood, and organs tend to remain qualitatively and quantitatively constant. The studies that established this new knowledge are interestingly reviewed by Schoenheimer,[8] the pioneer investigator in this field.

5.23. Relation of Food Fat to Depot Fat. The nature of the depot fat is markedly influenced, however, by the character of its food source. This is of large practical importance, since the degree of hardness of this fat is a considerable factor in the market value of the carcasses of meat animals. This is particularly true for hogs as indicated by the "soft pork" problem. The influence of the kind of fat fed upon the character of the body fat is strikingly shown by the following data obtained by Anderson and Mendel with rats in which the oils listed furnish 60 per cent of the energy intake.

Food fat	Iodine number of food fat	Iodine number of body fat
Soybean oil	132	123
Corn oil	124	114
Cottonseed oil	108	107
Peanut oil	102	98
Lard	63	72
Butterfat	36	56
Coconut oil	8	35

SOURCE: William E. Anderson and Lafayette B. Mendel, The relation of diet to the quality of the fat produced in the animal body, *J. Biol. Chem.*, **76**:729–747, 1928.

Anderson and Mendel found that the iodine numbers of body fat deposited from various carbohydrates and proteins fell approximately within the range 55 to 70. This range, representing fat synthesized within the body, was thus considered to typify the normal depot fat of the

[8] Rudolph Schoenheimer, The Dynamic State of Body Constituents, Harvard University Press, Cambridge, Mass., 1942.

rat. Taking this range as a base line, the data for the various oils given above show the striking influence of large intakes of fats differing widely as regards degree of saturation from that normally deposited. It is noted, however, that the extremes exhibited by the food fats are never reached by the body fats, reflecting the capacity of the organism, in depositing ingested fat, to modify the latter where it is widely different from the normal deposit. Whether this is accomplished by preferential catabolism or by saturation or by desaturation prior to deposition cannot be stated. The data given illustrate the fact that carbohydrates produce a less unsaturated and thus a harder body fat than do most fats found in feeds of vegetable origin.

Many experiments have shown that fat deposition in the hog follows the same principles illustrated above for the rat. The data in Table 5.4

TABLE 5.4. INFLUENCE ON HOG CARCASS OF ADDING VARIOUS OILS TO A BASAL RATION OF CORN AND TANKAGE*

Oil supplement	Firmness grade†	Melting point, °C.	Iodine number	Fatty acids: Oleic, per cent	Fatty acids: Linoleic, per cent	Fatty acids: Total saturated, per cent
Peanut oil, 4.1%	MS	34.3	72.4	47.9	13.8	32.5
Cottonseed oil, 4.1%	H	45.3	64.4	35.9	15.7	43.0
Soybean oil, 4.1%	MS	31.2	75.7	43.3	18.6	33.8
Corn oil, 4.1%	MS	36.3	76.3	45.0	16.8	33.0
Corn oil, 11.5%	O	24.5	97.2	41.4	31.4	23.1

* Data from N. R. Ellis and H. S. Isbell, Soft pork studies. II. The influence of the character of the ration upon the composition of the body fat of hogs. III. The effect of food fat upon body fat, as shown by the separation of the individual fatty acids of the body fat, *J. Biol. Chem.*, **69**:219–248, 1926.

† H = hard, MS = medium soft, O = oily.

from the work of Ellis and Isbell demonstrate the effect of adding various oils to a ration of corn and tankage, which by itself produces a firm fat in hogs. The percentage of fat in these rations is much smaller than that used in obtaining the data previously cited for the rat, and thus the effects are less marked. It is noted, however, that the ration containing cottonseed oil, having the lowest iodine number of the oils used, was the only one which produced a carcass graded as hard. This grade is reflected in a high melting point, a relatively low iodine number, and the highest percentage of saturated fatty acids. All the other oils, when added at the same level as the cottonseed, produced medium-soft carcasses, readily explainable by the constants and fatty-acid distribution of their fats. Increasing the level of corn oil produced an oily carcass with fat which melted at room temperature and which consisted of unsaturated acids to the extent of 73 per cent.

The data in Table 5.4 explain why soybeans and peanuts, feeds rich in highly unsaturated fats, can be used in only a limited way for fattening hogs without producing soft pork (Fig. 5.1). With both hogs and cattle fed the usual fattening rations, the deposited fat becomes harder with age, owing to an increased rate of deposition which results in relatively more of this fat being formed from carbohydrate.

Deposits of soft fat can be modified by a change in diet. When, after a period on feeds rich in unsaturated fat, a ration which will produce

FIG. 5.1. Lard from hard, soft, and oily carcasses. (*Taken from O. G. Hankins, N. R. Ellis, and J. H. Zeller, Some results of soft pork investigations. II. U.S. Dept. Agr. Bull.* 1492, 1928.)

a hard fat is given, the deposited fat gradually becomes harder. Ellis[9] described such a change in hogs, which results when a ration containing peanuts is followed by corn and nonsoftening supplements. The process is called "hardening off" and is taken advantage of in feeding practice in finishing hogs for market. Anderson and Mendel[10] showed that the process takes place more rapidly where the animal is fasted for a period before the hardening ration is given. The recent discoveries regarding the dynamic state of fat explain why this process occurs. While experiments have shown that the feeding of tocopherol, an antioxidant, to hogs makes their fat somewhat less susceptible to oxidative rancidity, the practical importance of this finding seems doubtful.

[9] N. R. Ellis, Changes in quantity and composition of fat in hogs fed a peanut ration followed by a corn ration, *U.S. Dept. Agr. Tech. Bull.* 368, 1933. (See also earlier papers cited.)

[10] William E. Anderson and Lafayette B. Mendel, The relation of diet to the quality of the fat produced in the animal body, *J. Biol. Chem.*, **76**:729–747, 1928.

5.24. Food Fat and Milk Fat. The character of the food fat has the same influence on the nature of the milk fat as it does on the depot fat. This is shown in Fig. 5.2, which presents data taken from the work of Maynard, McCay, and Madsen.[11] In this experiment, a ration containing approximately 3.5 per cent of fat on a dry-matter basis was used. In the first and third periods the grain mixture was selected to have a high iodine number, primarily by the inclusion of ground flaxseed, while in the middle period the iodine number was reduced to a low value by the omission of the flaxseed and the inclusion of coconut-oil meal. The curve shows that a change in the iodine number of the food fat from 107 to 43 resulted, in the first 24 hr., in a drop in the value for milk fat from 38 to 32, with a later drop to approximately 26 as the

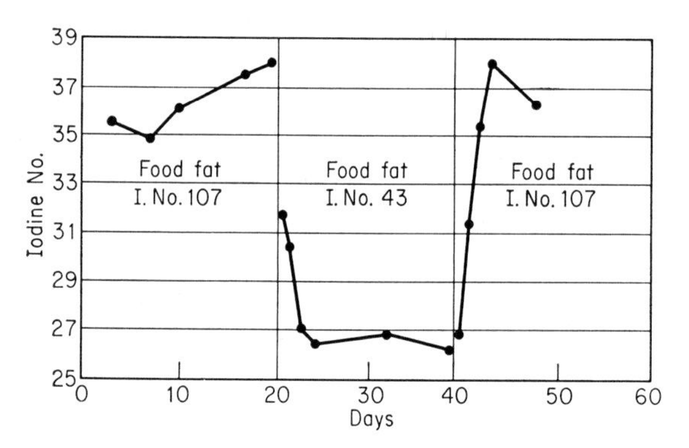

FIG. 5.2. The iodine number of milk fat as influenced by food fats of high and low degrees of unsaturation.

minimum. The restoration of the food fat of high iodine number resulted in a quick rise in the milk-fat value to its level during the first period. These rapid and large changes with a ration which contained only about 3.5 per cent of fat are striking indeed. Later studies have specifically shown that the essential fatty acids (Sec. 5.28) in milk fat can be increased by dietary fats rich in them.

5.25. The Catabolism of Fats. The ultimate catabolic products of fat are normally carbon dioxide and water, which are excreted through the kidneys, lungs, and skin. Our knowledge of the various stages of the catabolic process is very incomplete. According to the widely accepted theory of Leathes and Raper, the triglycerides, prior to their oxidation, are desaturated and then changed to the more reactive

[11] L. A. Maynard, C. M. McCay, and L. L. Madsen, The influence of food fat of varying degrees of unsaturation upon blood lipids and milk fat, *J. Dairy Sci.*, **19**: 49–53, 1936.

phospholipids, these processes taking place in the liver. Presumably hydrolysis precedes oxidation with the formation of fatty acids and glycerol, whence the metabolism of the glycerol can follow the same course as the carbohydrates. One of the mechanisms by which the fatty acids are broken down is β-oxidation through which the two carbon atoms at the carboxyl end of the chain are split off at a time, under the action of enzymes, notably coenzyme A which contains the vitamin pantothenic acid. The two carbon units are actually split off as an acetyl-coenzyme A complex and thus enter the citric acid cycle for ultimate oxidation to carbon dioxide and water.

5.26. Ketosis. The entrance of acetyl-coenzyme A into the cycle depends upon certain simultaneous oxidative steps in carbohydrate catabolism. If these steps do not occur normally, the two carbon fragments from fat catabolism accumulate and produce acetoacetic acid, dihydroxy butyric acid, and acetone. These are the *ketone bodies* responsible for the condition known as *ketosis.* As the bodies accumulate in the blood, *acetonemia* results and they spill over into the urine, producing *acetonuria,* thus providing clinical symptoms of the metabolic failure. Since two of the ketone bodies are rather strong acids, their excessive production uses up the alkali reserve of the blood, producing acidosis. The carbon dioxide transporting power of the blood is lessened, and cellular oxidation is decreased. This is a serious condition which in extreme cases results in coma and death.

Ketosis is the physiological condition responsible for two serious livestock troubles—acetonemia in dairy cattle and "pregnancy disease" in sheep. In both species high blood and urine ketone levels, a low blood sugar, and a depleted glycogen reserve, accompanied by a lack of appetite, occur. In the milking cow there is a sharp drop in yield. Glucose injection is an effective clinical treatment, acting to increase the liver glycogen and blood-sugar levels and to decrease the ketone levels. Successful treatments have also been recently reported with hormone preparations, notably cortisone, which lead to glycogen production from protein catabolism. In view of the clinical picture in ketosis, many experiments have been conducted in the hope of preventing or curing the trouble through dietary means with generally unsuccessful results. The feeding of high levels of sugar or molasses is without effect. Various vitamins have been tried with negative results. Some promising results have been obtained by feeding sodium propionate which is absorbed from the rumen as propionic acid, a glycogen former. Further studies are required to demonstrate the extent of the usefulness of this procedure.

5.27. Fat Synthesis. Isotope studies have definitely shown that body fat can be formed from acetic acid. Presumably a multiple condensation of two-carbon units, specifically acetyl-coenzyme A complex, occurs to form chains of even-numbered carbon units—the usual structure found in body fats. The fact that fat can be synthesized from two-carbon units explains why carbohydrate, and even protein catabolic products, can result in fat deposition, since this unit is the common intermediate in the citric acid cycle. In the fattening of farm animals carbohydrate is by far the principal food source.

5.28. Essential Fatty Acids. Despite the fact that certain lipids are essential constituents of animal tissues, the knowledge that carbohydrates are readily changed into fat and that such essential lipid constituents as phospholipids and cholesterol can be made in the body naturally led to the view that lipids as such are not required in the diet. This viewpoint was changed some thirty years ago by the studies of Burr and Burr.[12] These investigators found that, with a diet almost entirely devoid of fat, rats developed a scaly condition of the skin and a necrosis of the tail, accompanied by failure of growth and eventual death. Harmful effects on reproduction and lactation performance were also noted. The addition of small amounts of pure linoleic acid was strikingly effective in preventing or curing these conditions, but saturated acids were ineffective. Later, arachidonic and linolenic acids were each found partially effective in correcting the troubles. These two, along with linoleic, are commonly referred to as the essential fatty acids (EFA). Deficiency symptoms have been experimentally produced in mice, dogs, pigs, chicks, calves, and guinea pigs. Suggestive evidence that calves, lambs, and kids need these acids in their rations has also been produced. In vitro studies have failed to find evidence that they are synthesized by rumen bacteria. Fat deficiency in the pig is illustrated in Fig. 5.3. Note the loss of hair and the scaly, dandruff-like dermatitis.

While the body can synthesize saturated fatty acids and oleic acid as outlined in Sec. 5.27, it apparently does not have the enzymes necessary to synthesize those with two or more double bonds which are essential for cell structure. Although we speak of three acids as being dietary essentials, it is evident that some introconversion occurs. Here there are species differences. In the rat either linoleic or arachidonic will apparently serve as the source of the other two for growth. In the chick linolenic acid is convertible to the other two. Limitations of analytical methods have handicapped the production of quantitative data regarding the introconversions which may occur in different species. Actually, linoleic may be the sole dietary essential if vitamin B_6 is

[12] George O. Burr and Mildred M. Burr, A new deficiency disease produced by the rigid exclusion of fat from the diet, *J. Biol. Chem.*, **82**:345–367, 1929; On the nature and role of the fatty acids essential in nutrition, *ibid.*, **86**:587–621, 1930.

present, since this vitamin provides a mechanism by which arachidonic can be synthesized from linoleic. Early studies with rats showed that the minimum needs could be met when 1 per cent of the total calorie intake was supplied by linoleic acid. It has been found by Peifer and Holman,[13] however, that the EFA are concerned in the utilization of other fats, particularly saturated fats, and that with diets high in such fats the EFA requirement to prevent deficiency is increased accordingly. Thus the requirement is a variable one. These findings of Peifer and

FIG. 5.3. Fat deficiency resulting from a diet containing 0.06 per cent of ether extract. (*Courtesy of W. M. Beeson, Purdue University.*)

Holman may have important significance in human nutrition since customary diets contain 35 to 40 per cent of the total calories as fat.

Without specific studies, one cannot draw any conclusions on the extent to which the data obtained with rats may apply to farm animals. Their rations are relatively low in total fat. Further the EFA are widely distributed among feed fats. For example, corn oil, soybean oil, cottonseed oil, peanut oil, and certain others are excellent sources (Table 5.3). In view of the nature and amounts of fat that are commonly found in

[13] James J. Peifer and Ralph T. Holman, Effect of saturated fat upon essential fatty acid metabolism in the rat, *J. Nutrition,* **68**:155–168, 1959.

the rations of farm animals, it seems probable that any need they may have would thus be supplied. But this is a matter that needs further study.

Beginning in 1942, a series of papers appeared from the Netherlands reporting that summer butter contained a special growth factor for rats, identified as *vaccenic acid*, an isomer of oleic. Later studies, both in this country and by the Dutch workers themselves, indicate clearly that this acid does not have any specific nutritive effect and fail to support the claims for a superiority of summer butter.

5.29. Animal versus Vegetable Fats. Certain fats, notably milk fat, are nutritionally more valuable than others because of their vitamin A value. But there is no clear evidence that, as sources of fatty acids, animal fats in general are superior to vegetable fats. In fact, the contrary is true in so far as the content of the EFA and vitamin E are concerned. Despite much study, no proof has been produced that the unique fatty-acid distribution in milk fat gives it a physiological advantage over other fats in a mixed diet. On the basis of rat experiments there is evidence that in the early weeks of life, when lactose is the sole carbohydrate ingested, butterfat is superior to vegetable oils in promoting growth; but even in this special case the evidence has been challenged. Data have also been reported indicating that butterfat and other animal fats are superior to certain vegetable oils as supplements to skim milk for calves, but here again other studies have failed to confirm these findings. It is now clear that the question here involved is one not of animal versus vegetable fats but of the degree of saturation of the fatty acids present. A review of the data shows that the reported deleterious effects resulted when highly unsaturated fats were fed but not when hydrogenated products or fats naturally low in unsaturated acids were employed. This conclusion is evident from the series of studies by Adams and coworkers,[14] which also provide a physiological explanation for the different results from the two types of fat. It was found that when corn oil or lard was fed, in addition to general symptoms of poor performance, there was a muscle involvement characteristic of muscular dystrophy and "white muscle disease" previously found to result from vitamin E deficiency (Sec. 8.19). No muscular lesions were noted when the corn-oil-fed group received a large supplement of vitamin E daily or in the groups receiving hydrogenated vegetable oils. It is postulated that the highly unsaturated oils greatly increase the dietary requirement for vitamin E, either by destroying the vitamin or by increasing the tissue requirements. Additional evidence for this explanation is presented in Sec. 8.19.

[14] R. S. Adams et al., Some effects of feeding various filled milks to dairy calves. Four subtitles, *J. Dairy Sci.*, **42**:1552–1592, 1959.

5.30. Special Nutritive Value of Fats as a Group. As far as we know at present, lipids are not specifically required in the diet except as a source of the essential fatty acids and of choline. Even here the requirements remain uncertain, in almost all cases, for farm animals. There is evidence, however, that the desirable intake of fat is not measurable solely by a need for these specific compounds. Fat promotes the absorption of both vitamin A and carotene, particularly the latter. Russell and coworkers[15] found that the absorption of carotene by hens, for example, was about 60 per cent of the intake in a ration containing approximately 4 per cent of fat, in contrast to a 20 per cent absorption on a ration extracted to 0.07 per cent of this nutrient. Fat also plays a role in the absorption of calcium. Fats supply two and one-quarter times as much energy as do carbohydrates. Thus, the higher the fat content of the ration, the greater energy value per pound. This fact is sometimes lost sight of.

While carbohydrates alone can supply the energy needs of the body, it is evident that under certain conditions, at least, these needs can be more efficiently met by supplying a part of the food energy in the more condensed form of fat. In the case of man at hard work, a liberal intake of fat is recognized as desirable, at least for the purpose of ensuring adequate energy consumption without excessive bulk. In reviewing the various experiments with rats, Mendel and Anderson[16] stated that an abundant intake of fat is much more effective for storing fat than an equicaloric intake of carbohydrates. It has also been shown that, within limits, increasing the fat content of the ration of growing pigs and fattening steers increases the feed efficiency beyond that which could be accounted for by the additional energy thus provided. Studies with chicks have shown that improved growth and energy utilization resulted from the isocaloric substitution of fat for carbohydrate in a purified diet. As is discussed later (Sec. 16.22), certain levels of fat are important in the dairy ration from the standpoint of maximum milk production.

According to studies by Forbes and associates at Pennsylvania State College, the greater than expected value of fat as a source of energy can be explained on the basis that, with equicaloric diets, increasing the fat component decreases the heat increment (Sec. 11.16). With fewer calories thus lost as heat, relatively more are available for production. Data illustrating this point are shown in Fig. 5.4 for rats fed high- and low-fat diets of equal calorie content. This chart is reproduced from

[15] W. C. Russell et al., The absorption and retention of carotene and vitamin A by hens on normal and low fat rations, *J. Nutrition,* **24**:199–211, 1942.

[16] Lafayette B. Mendel and W. E. Anderson, Some relations of diet to fat deposition in the body, *Yale J. Biol. Med.,* **3**:107–137, 1930.

—a publication by Swift[17] which reviews the Pennsylvania studies and discusses other aspects of the role of fat in the diet. As regards farm animals, the fact that it costs more to supply energy as fat than as carbohydrate may more than offset the higher efficiency of the fat source, but this is a question which needs further study, particularly since cost relationships are subject to change.

5.31. Fat Tolerance in Farm Animals. It is a common belief that the Herbivora have a low tolerance for fat, but the experimental evidence on this question is scanty. Certainly, the suckling is able to handle a relatively large amount of fat, since milk contains from 25 to 40 per cent of this nutrient on a dry-matter basis. Here we are reminded, however, that Holstein milk is more suitable for raising dairy calves than

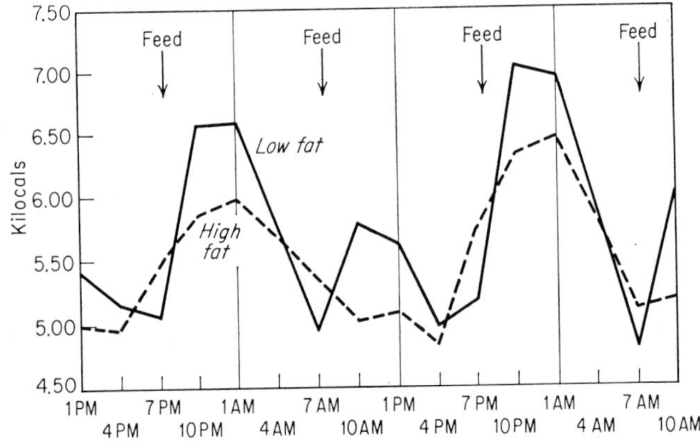

FIG. 5.4. Curves of heat production per 3-hour period of rats on diets of high and low fat content.

milk higher in fat. Beyond the milk-feeding stage, Herbivora receive in their normal rations only a small fraction of the fat which they consume as sucklings. While it is probable that certain levels may be expected to cause digestive disturbances and perhaps metabolic disturbances also, it seems unlikely that there need be any concern regarding such effects from any fat level occurring in the commonly fed rations. In fact, milking cows have been fed experimentally for several weeks, without any signs of trouble, on rations containing three times as much fat as they normally receive.

Certainly, the pig can tolerate rather high intakes of fat, and here no difficulty will arise with the usual feeds, except in respect to soft pork. Hens readily digest rations containing a percentage of fat representing a higher level than found in the commonly fed rations.

[17] R. W. Swift, The importance of fat in the diet, *Ann. N.Y. Acad. Sci.*, **56**:4–15, 1952.

SELECTED LITERATURE

Cunningham, H. M., and J. K. Loosli: The effect of fat-free diets on lambs and goats, *J. Animal Sci.,* **13**:265–273, 1954.

Dam, Richard, et al.: Studies of the effect of quantity and type of fat on chick growth, *J. Nutrition,* **68**:615–632, 1959.

Deuel, H. J., Jr.: Newer concepts of the role of fats and of the essential fatty acids in the diet, *Food Research,* **20**:21–91, 1955.

Hill, Eldon D., et al.: Effects of essential fatty acid deficiency in young swine, *Proc. Soc. Exptl. Biol. Med.,* **95**:274–278, 1957.

Hill, F. W., R. Dam, and L. B. Carew, Jr.: Special nutritive properties of fats in poultry rations, *Proc. Cornell Nutrition Conf.,* 1958, pp. 19–24.

Holman, Ralph T.: The ratio of trienoic:tetraenoic acids in tissue lipids as a measure of essential fatty acid requirement, *J. Nutrition,* **70**:405–410, 1960.

Keane, K. W., Eva M. Cohn, and B. Connor Johnson: Reproductive failure of rats on glyceryl trilaurate–containing diets and its prevention by certain natural fats, *J. Nutrition,* **45**:275–287, 1951.

Kramár, Jenö, and Victor E. Levine: Influence of fats and fatty acids on the capillaries, *J. Nutrition,* **50**:149–160, 1953.

Lambert, M. R., et al.: Lipid deficiency in the calf, *J. Nutrition,* **52**:259–272, 1954.

Shaw, J. C.: Ketosis in dairy cattle: a review, *J. Dairy Sci.,* **39**:402–434, 1956.

Shorland, F. B., and P. B. D. de la Mare: Studies on the fats of the bacon pig with reference to carcass quality. The effect of diet on the component fatty acids of the back fat, *J. Agr. Sci.,* **35**:33–38, 1945.

Viswanatha, T., J. E. Gander, and I. E. Liener; Interrelation of fat, carbohydrate and vitamin E in the diet of the growing rat, *J. Nutrition,* **52**:613–626, 1954.

Chapter 6

The Proteins and Their Metabolism

Since protein is the principal constituent of the organs and soft structures of the animal body, a liberal and continuous supply is needed in the food throughout life for growth and repair, and thus the transformation of food protein into body protein is a very important part of the nutrition process. This term protein is a collective one which embraces an enormous group of closely related but physiologically distinct members. Plant proteins differ from each other and from animal proteins; each animal species has its own specific proteins, and a given animal contains many different ones in its organs, fluids, and other tissues. In fact no two proteins seem to be exactly alike in their physiological behavior. From the standpoint of nutrition the important distinguishing feature of the various proteins is their amino acid make-up (Sec. 6.4).

6.1. Elementary Composition of Proteins. In common with the fats and carbohydrates, the proteins contain carbon, hydrogen, and oxygen. In addition they contain a large and fairly constant percentage of nitrogen. Most of them also contain sulfur, and a few contain phosphorus and iron. They are complex substances, colloidal in nature and of high molecular weight. The range of *elementary composition* of the more typical proteins is as follows:

	Per cent
Carbon	51.0 to 55.0
Hydrogen	6.5 to 7.3
Nitrogen	15.5 to 18.0
Oxygen	21.5 to 23.5
Sulfur	0.5 to 2.0
Phosphorus	0.0 to 1.5

6.2. Classification of Proteins. The various proteins cannot be identified or distinguished from each other by any simple chemical method,

The amino acids which have been identified in plant and animal proteins are classified according to the series of organic compounds in which they belong, and those in the aliphatic series are further classified according to the number of amino groups and carboxyl groups present. The classification of those which have received special attention in nutrition studies follows:

I. Aliphatic amino acids

A. Monoamino-monocarboxylic acids

```
CH2—COOH
|
NH2
```

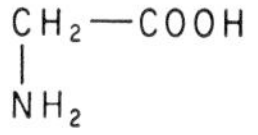

Glycine, $C_2H_5NO_2$
Amino-acetic acid

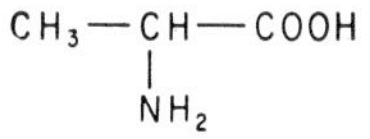

```
CH3—CH—COOH
    |
    NH2
```

Alanine, $C_3H_7NO_2$
α-Amino-propionic acid

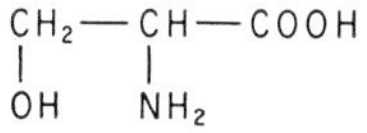

```
CH2—CH—COOH
|   |
OH  NH2
```

Serine, $C_3H_7NO_3$
α-Amino-β-hydroxypropionic acid

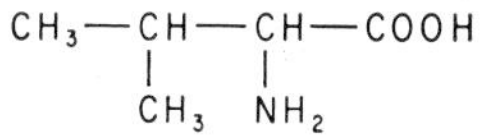

```
CH3—CH—CH—COOH
    |   |
    CH3 NH2
```

Valine, $C_5H_{11}NO_2$
α-Amino-β-methyl-butyric acid

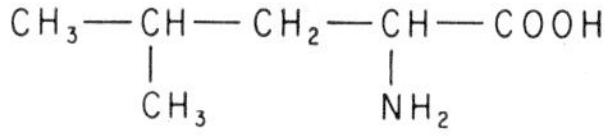

```
CH3—CH—CH2—CH—COOH
    |       |
    CH3     NH2
```

Leucine, $C_6H_{13}NO_2$
α-Amino-γ-methyl-valeric acid

```
CH3—CH2—CH—CH—COOH
        |   |
        CH3 NH2
```

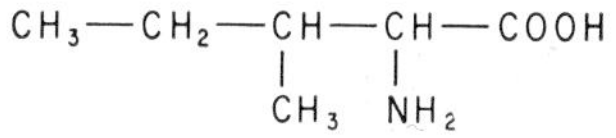

Isoleucine, $C_6H_{13}NO_2$
α-Amino-β-methyl-valeric acid

```
CH3—CH—CH—COOH
    |   |
    OH  NH2
```

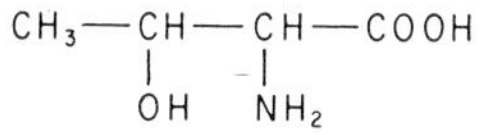

Threonine, $C_4H_9NO_3$
α-Amino-β-hydroxybutyric acid

B. Monoamino-dicarboxylic acids

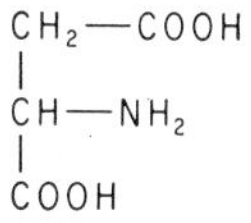

```
CH2—COOH
|
CH—NH2
|
COOH
```

Aspartic acid, $C_4H_7NO_4$
Amino-succinic acid

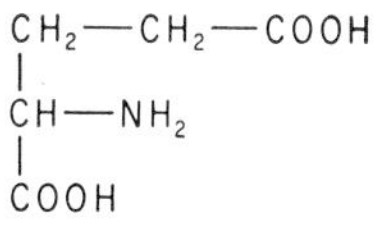

```
CH2—CH2—COOH
|
CH—NH2
|
COOH
```

Glutamic acid, $C_5H_9NO_4$
α-Amino-glutaric acid

C. Diamino-monocarboxylic acids

```
NH—CH2—CH2—CH2—CH—COOH
|               |
C=NH            NH2
|
NH2
```

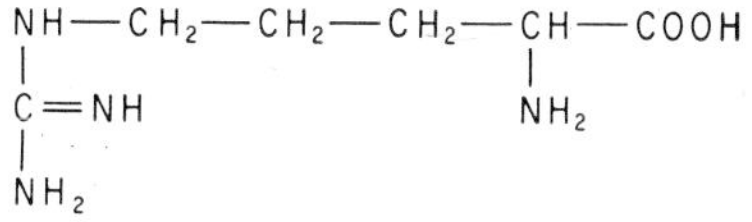

Arginine, $C_6H_{14}N_4O_2$
α-Amino-δ-guanidine-valeric acid

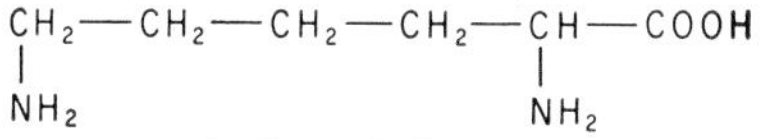

```
CH2—CH2—CH2—CH2—CH—COOH
|               |
NH2             NH2
```

Lysine, $C_6H_{14}N_2O_2$
α-ϵ-Diamino-caproic acid

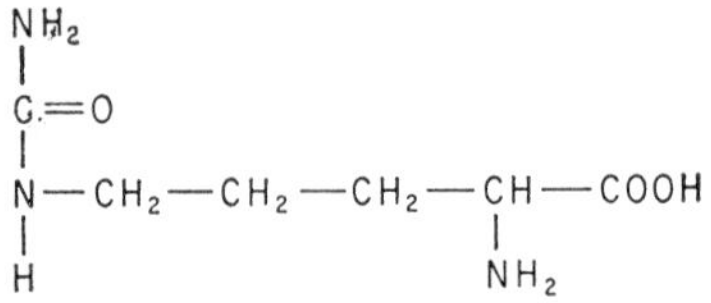

```
NH2
|
C=O
|
N—CH2—CH2—CH2—CH—COOH
|                 |
H                 NH2
```

Citrulline, $C_6H_{13}O_3N_3$
δ-Carbamido-α-amino-valeric acid

D. Sulfur-containing amino acids

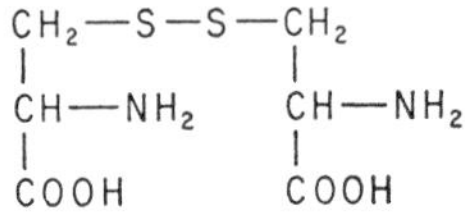

```
CH2—S—S—CH2
|       |
CH—NH2  CH—NH2
|       |
COOH    COOH
```

Cystine, $C_6H_{12}N_2O_4S_2$
Di (α-amino-β-thio-propionic acid)

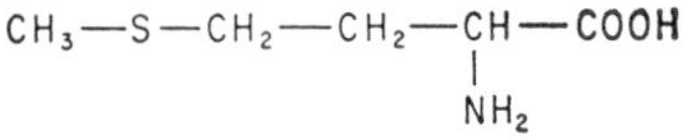

```
CH3—S—CH2—CH2—CH—COOH
              |
              NH2
```

Methionine, $C_5H_{11}NO_2S$
α-Amino-γ-methylthio-butyric acid

II. Aromatic amino acids

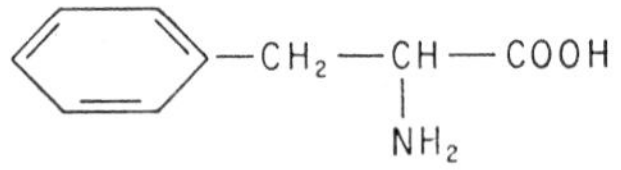

```
C6H5—CH2—CH—COOH
         |
         NH2
```

Phenylalanine, $C_9H_{11}NO_2$
α-Amino-β-phenyl-propionic acid

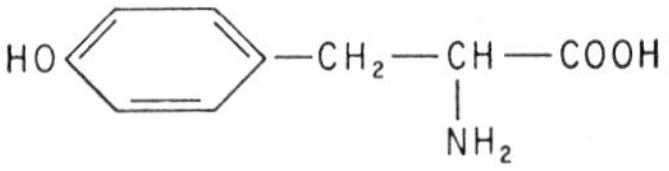

```
HO—C6H4—CH2—CH—COOH
            |
            NH2
```

Tyrosine, $C_9H_{11}NO_3$
α-Amino-β-parahydroxy-phenyl-propionic acid

III. Heterocyclic amino acids

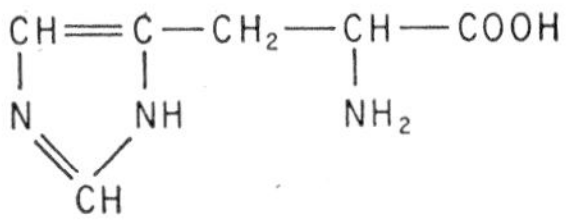

```
CH══C—CH2—CH—COOH
|   |     |
N   NH    NH2
 \\ /
  CH
```

Histidine, $C_6H_9N_3O_2$
α-Amino-β-imidazole-propionic acid

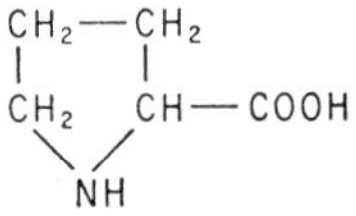

```
CH2—CH2
|   |
CH2 CH—COOH
 \ /
 NH
```

Proline, $C_5H_9NO_2$
Pyrrolidine-α-carboxylic acid

```
HO—CH—CH2
   |  |
   CH2 CH—COOH
    \ /
    NH
```

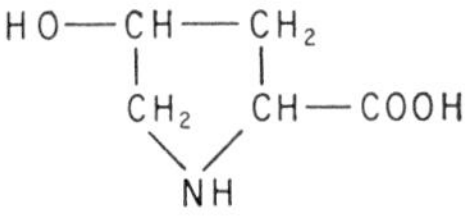

Hydroxyproline $C_5H_9NO_6$
Hydroxypyrrolidine-α-carboxylic acid

```
     CH
   //  \
HC      C——C—CH2—CH—COOH
|       ||  ||      |
HC      C   CH      NH2
  \\   / \ /
   CH    NH
```

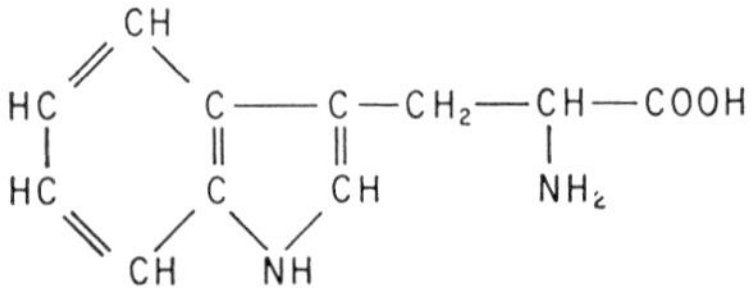

Tryptophan, $C_{11}H_{12}N_2O_2$
α-Amino-β-indolepropionic acid

It is noted that most of these amino acids are derivatives of the lower fatty acids. All, with the exception of glycine, are optically active in nature. The naturally occurring ones have the L form. Most of them are soluble in water. Since amino acids have both amino groups and carboxyl groups, they are considered to be amphoteric electrolytes, reacting as acids in the presence of bases and as bases in the presence of acids. Different amino acids have different isoelectric points.

The relative distribution of 12 of these amino acids in the body protein of different species, as determined by Williams and coworkers, is presented in Table 6.1. It is noted that the figures are very similar for the three species, tryptophan being the lowest for all and arginine, leucine, and lysine ranking at the top.

TABLE 6.1. AMINO ACID CONTENT OF BODY PROTEIN (GRAMS PER 16 GRAMS OF NITROGEN)*

Amino acid	Rat	Chicken	Pig
Arginine	5.89	6.71	7.12
Histidine	2.16	1.96	2.65
Isoleucine	3.49	4.12	3.84
Leucine	6.46	6.63	7.14
Lysine	7.61	7.46	8.55
Methionine	1.71	1.76	1.77
Phenylalanine	3.69	3.95	3.77
Threonine	3.87	4.02	3.79
Tryptophan	0.76	0.77	0.74
Valine	5.51	6.72	6.00
Tyrosine	2.88	2.49	2.59
Cystine	1.49	1.75	1.01

* Data from Harold H. Williams and coworkers, Estimation of growth requirements for amino acids by assay of the carcass, *J. Biol. Chem.*, **208**:277–286, 1954.

6.5. The Structure of the Protein Molecule. Our knowledge of the structure of proteins is due originally to the work of Emil Fischer who devised methods for uniting amino acids through their amino and carboxyl groups, with the elimination of water. As an example, the union of two molecules of glycine to form the dipeptide glycyl-glycine may be represented as follows:

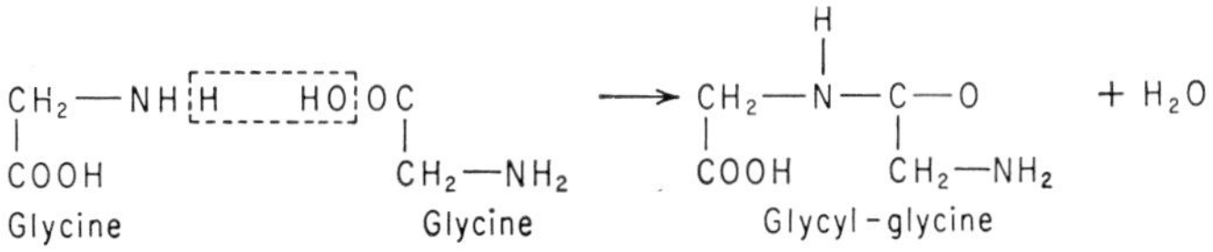

```
CH2—NH[H    HO]OC              ⟶  CH2—N(H)—C—O          + H2O
|                |                 |         |
COOH             CH2—NH2           COOH      CH2—NH2
Glycine          Glycine           Glycyl-glycine
```

Fischer succeeded in hooking together as many as 18 amino acids, and the complex synthetic polypeptides thus formed were found to have many properties in common with the proteins. Thus, on the basis of his and later work, it is considered that proteins are anhydrides of amino acids and that the principal linkage existing between the amino acids in the protein molecule is through the amino group of one acid and the carboxyl group of another. This type of union is referred to as the *peptide linkage:*

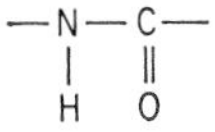

```
—N—C—
 |  ||
 H  O
```

All proteins have high molecular weights, but different ones show a wide range. The enzyme cytochrome *c* has a molecular weight of 15,600, and the tobacco mosaic virus, 60,000. Ovalbumin has some 400 amino acid units hooked together in a single polypeptide chain.

It is assumed that the proteins occurring in nature are built up from their constituent amino acids, but we have no knowledge as to the exact process. In the case of plants, including the lower forms such as yeast and bacteria, nitrates and ammonium salts are used as the initial nitrogenous compounds for protein synthesis. In the case of animals, however, the constituent amino acids must be available, with the exception of some which can be synthesized in the body from simpler compounds, as is discussed later.

6.6. Properties of Proteins. Proteins can combine chemically with both acids and bases. This is explained on the basis that they are amphoteric substances by virtue of containing free amino and carboxyl groups. Each protein has its characteristic isoelectric point at which the tendencies to acidic and basic dissociations are equal, and at this point the protein is most readily precipitated by salt solutions and by alcohol. This property is taken advantage of in the separation and purification of proteins.

In addition to forming chemical combinations, proteins in solution have colloidal properties. They do not pass through the membranes or gels which are used as the criteria for separating out colloidal particles, and many workers hold the view that proteins can bind ions physically by absorption as well as uniting with them chemically.

The different proteins vary as regards their solubility in water and various aqueous solutions, but none of them is soluble in the common fat solvents such as ethyl ether and petroleum ether. They can be precipitated from solution by a large variety of substances, including various neutral salts, such as sodium sulfate and magnesium sulfate. Large amounts of these salts are required to cause the proteins to precipitate, and the process is referred to as *salting out*. Salts of heavy metals are good precipitants, and so are strong mineral acids. Phosphotungstic acid, trichloracetic acid, and tannic acid are reagents commonly used in the laboratory for precipitating proteins.

The coagulation of protein probably involves a dehydration. It can be brought about by heat and by alcohol. In digestion it occurs as a result of enzymatic action. Proteins are such labile substances that their nutritive value may be altered by physical agents. Heat improves the nutritive value of the proteins of certain feeds but has the opposite effect in other cases (Sec. 14.24). The lability of proteins may be reflected in a decreased nutritive value in certain feeds on prolonged storage, depending on moisture content and other conditions.

6.7. The Chemical Determination of Protein. The direct determination of the various proteins which are present in a feed or tissue is an impracticable procedure. Thus the chemist takes advantage of the fact that nitrogen occurs in the different proteins in a fairly constant percentage—16 per cent on the average (Sec. 6.1). He analyzes for nitrogen and multiplies the result by the factor 6.25 ($100 \div 16$). While the average factor 6.25 is applied to feeds in general, specific factors may be used in the case of products for which the protein and nitrogen relations are definitely known. For example, it has been found that the combined proteins of milk contain approximately 15.7 per cent of nitrogen on the average, and hence the factor 6.38 is used. Wheat-flour protein, on the other hand, contains 17.5 per cent nitrogen, and thus the factor is 5.71. Specific factors are also employed for certain animal tissues. Jones[2] has published specific factors for 121 different proteins and foods.

The estimation of protein content from an analysis for nitrogen assumes that all of the nitrogen in the substance analyzed is in the form of protein. This is not strictly true for any feedstuff, and there are certain ones which contain a considerable amount of nitrogen in compounds other than protein. This fact was recognized by the early workers in animal nutrition, and methods were accordingly proposed for determining the *true protein* as distinguished from the crude protein obtained by multiplying the total nitrogen by a factor. The distinction, however, has largely lost its significance in so far as the protein values of feeds are concerned, for reasons which are detailed later (Sec. 6.14).

6.8. Nonprotein Nitrogen Compounds. The nonprotein compounds occurring in feeds include amides, amino acids, nitrogenous glucosides and fats, alkaloids, ammonium salts, and others. Of these, the amides and the amino acids are the only ones which occur to any considerable extent, and they are present in large amounts in only a few of the common feeds. They seem to be especially abundant where growth is rapid, and thus they may make up as much as one-third of the total nitrogen in pasture grass. The developing seed is high in nonprotein nitrogen at the start but low at maturity. A large part of the nitrogen in silage crops occurs in this form, due in part to their immaturity at harvest and in part to the fermentation processes which take place. Certain roots apparently have a considerable portion of their nitrogen stored in forms other than protein. Mature hays and the commonly fed concentrate mixtures of seeds and their by-products contain relatively little nonprotein nitrogen.

[2] D. Breese Jones, Factors for converting percentages of nitrogen in foods and feeds into percentages of proteins, *U.S. Dept. Agr. Circ.* 183, 1931. (Slightly revised, February, 1941.)

In addition to the nonprotein nitrogen compounds which occur in feeds, there are a number which are important in nutrition, either as intermediary or end products of protein metabolism or as essential and active constituents of various tissues and secretions.

Asparagine and *glutamine* are amides found in the free state in plants. They are the forms in which their corresponding amino acids, aspartic and glutamic, respectively, occur to a considerable extent in the protein molecule. Glutamine serves as a storage and transport mechanism in the body for amino groups. *Urea,* the diamide of carbonic acid, is the principal end product of nitrogen metabolism in mammals and in most fishes.

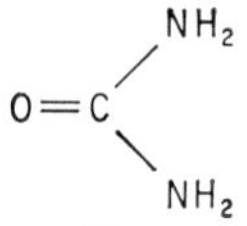

```
      NH2
     /
O=C
     \
      NH2
    Urea
```

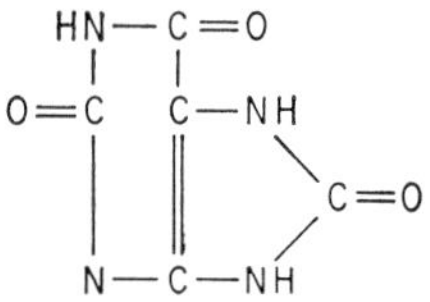

```
      HN—C=O
      |   |
    O=C   C—NH
      |   ||    \
      |   ||     C=O
      |   ||    /
      N—C—NH
      Uric acid
```

Uric acid is the principal end product of purine catabolism in man and of protein catabolism in birds and reptiles. Uric acid and urates are the principal nitrogenous excretory products in insects.

In mammals other than man and the monkey, the principal end product of purine catabolism is not uric acid but its oxidation product *allantoin,* $C_4H_6N_4O_3$.

Hippuric acid occurs in considerable amounts in the urine of all herbivorous animals and normally in much lesser amounts in the urine of other animals, including man. It is a combination of benzoic acid and the amino acid glycocoll, or glycine, and thus is named benzoylglycine. It is classed as a detoxication product in that benzoic acid,

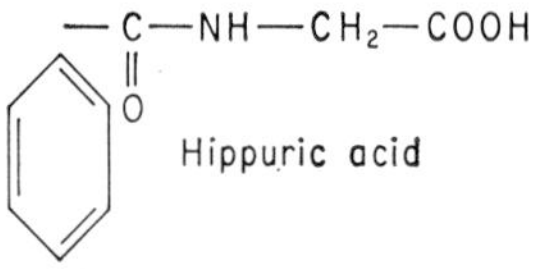

```
(C6H5)—C—NH—CH2—COOH
       ||
       O
      Hippuric acid
```

which cannot be utilized by the body and is in fact harmful, is transformed, by pairing it with glycine, into a harmless product which is readily excreted. The rations of herbivorous animals normally contain much larger amounts of hippuric acid precursors, such as benzoic acid and various related aromatic compounds, than is the case for Omnivora. In all species there are considerable variations in hippuric acid excretion according to the nature of the feed.

Creatine, methylguanidine acetic acid, occurs widely in the animal body, especially in muscle. It is excreted as its anhydride, *creatinine*, which is thus a normal constituent of urine. Creatinine excretion is a measure of the basal nitrogen catabolism, as is discussed later (Sec. 13.4). The relation between these two compounds is indicated by their formulas:

$$HN{=}C(NH_2)_2$$
Guanidine

$$HN{=}C(NH_2){-}N(CH_3){-}CH_2{-}COOH$$
Creatine

$$HN{=}C{-}N(CH_3){-}CH_2{-}C{=}O \text{ (ring closed through NH)}$$
Creatinine

Creatine occurs in muscle as an easily hydrolyzable phosphate, *phosphocreatine*, or *phosphagen*, which is decomposed in muscle activity (Sec. 17.2), serving as a source of "high-energy" phosphate bonds.

Glutathione is a tripeptide containing the amino acids cysteine, glutamic acid, and glycine, which plays a role in physiological oxidations.

AMINO ACIDS AND PROTEIN QUALITY

The recognition that the nitrogen present in the body had its origin in nitrogen compounds present in the food dates primary from the work of Magendie[3] published in 1816. After it became established that proteins were the nitrogen compounds essentially concerned, Magendie produced the first evidence that all proteins were not of equal value. In his famous "gelatin report" published in 1841, he showed that gelatin would not take the place of meat protein in the diet. Thirty-five years later Escher found that the nutritive value of gelatin for dogs could be improved by the addition of tyrosine. By 1905 it had become established, particularly as a result of the studies of Kauffmann, that tryptophan and cystine were also required as supplements to gelatin for the adequate protein nutrition of the dog. These various findings were the forerunners of the modern concept of the essential role of amino acids in nutrition.

In 1914 Osborne and Mendel[4] showed that certain proteins which resulted in nutritive failure in rats when used alone were rendered satisfactory by the addition of missing amino acids. These fundamental results, quickly followed by many others, including comparisons of differ-

[3] François Magendie (1783–1855), the great French physiologist, is recognized as the founder of the modern experimental method in animal-feeding experiments. He employed diets of pure carbohydrates and fats to prove that food nitrogen is essential. These studies were published under the title: Sur les propriétés nutritives des substances qui ne contiennent pas d'azote, *Ann. chim. et phys.*, (1) 3:66–77, 1816.

[4] Thomas B. Osborne and Lafayette B. Mendel, Amino acids in nutrition and growth, *J. Biol. Chem.*, **17**:325–349, 1914.

ent protein sources with chickens and hogs, led to the realization that the value of a given protein in nutrition is governed by its amino acid makeup. The body is unable to synthesize many of the amino acids which are present in its proteins, and thus the protein in the food must be of a nature which will supply them.

6.9. Essential and Nonessential Amino Acids. The modern advances in the field of amino acid nutrition date from 1930, when W. C. Rose of the University of Illinois began a brilliant series of studies, using a new technique which has given us specific information as to the acids which must be present in the food. By the use of diets designed to be otherwise adequate for the normal growth of rats, in which the sole source of nitrogen was supplied by amino acids, the effect of the addition or removal of each of the acids was studied. Thus, the Illinois workers were able to classify 10 as essential dietary constituents and the others as nonessential, as shown in Table 6.2, the details of which are referred

TABLE 6.2. CLASSIFICATION OF AMINO ACIDS WITH RESPECT TO THEIR GROWTH EFFECTS IN THE RAT*

Essential	*Nonessential*
Lysine	Glycine
Tryptophan	Alanine
Histidine	Serine
Phenylalanine	Cystine†
Leucine	Tyrosine‡
Isoleucine	Aspartic acid
Threonine	Glutamic acid§
Methionine	Proline§
Valine	Hydroxyproline
Arginine‖	Citrulline

* W. C. Rose et al., *J. Biol. Chem.*, **176**:753, 1948.

† Cystine can replace about one-sixth of the methionine requirement but has no growth effect in the absence of methionine.

‡ Tyrosine can replace about one-half of the phenylalanine requirement but has no growth effect in the absence of phenylalanine.

§ Glutamic acid and proline can serve individually as rather ineffective substitutes for arginine in the diet. This property is not shared by hydroxyproline.

‖ Arginine can be synthesized by the rat, but not at a sufficiently rapid rate to meet the demands of maximum growth. Its classification, therefore, as essential or nonessential is purely a matter of definition.

to later. Arginine was found to be a special case in that growth occurred in its absence but not at the normal rate. This meant that the body could synthesize this acid but not sufficiently rapidly to meet fully the needs for growth. Rose thus defined an essential amino acid as one which cannot be synthesized in the body at a rate required for normal growth. He found that, for maintenance, rats needed the same ones as for growth, with the exception of arginine. These pioneer studies are summarized in a review article by Rose[5] published in 1938.

The investigations with rats stimulated work with other species. Dogs were found to have the same needs. A series of studies in the Department of Poultry Husbandry at the University of California showed that for rapid growth chicks require the same list of amino acids as rats, plus glycine. Like arginine in the case of the rat, glycine can be synthesized by the chick, but not at a sufficiently rapid rate to meet the manifold needs for rapid growth, notably for the synthesis of uric acid, the end product of protein catabolism in birds. Adult chickens do not require glycine. Arginine continues to be needed after growth has ceased, differing from the case of the rat.

Pigs require the same ten amino acids for growth as do rats. Some data are also available for the growth of mice and turkeys and for egg production by the hen. Studies with chicks and pigs, as well as with rats, have also established quantitative requirements, as is discussed in later chapters. In the case of cattle and sheep any dietary need for specific amino acids is of markedly less importance because of their synthesis in the rumen (Sec. 6.15).

Rose repeated with human subjects his pioneer studies with rats, involving experiments of much greater magnitude and difficulty than any previously carried on in this field. With diets containing pure amino acids as the sole sources of nitrogen, the dietary needs of each for maintenance were determined by the nitrogen-balance method (Sec. 11.1). It was found that man needs the same list for maintenance as the rat, with the exception of histidine, a total of eight. Rose and associates[6] have published a series of five papers describing these studies. The most surprising finding in these studies is the ability of man to get along without a dietary source of the heterocylic amino acid histidine, contrary to the findings with rats and chicks. One possible explanation is that intestinal synthesis by microorganism occurs, but there is no evidence that this takes place. It is also possible that the cells of man contain an enzyme causing histidine synthesis not present in the case of other species. There is evidence that the growing human needs histidine. Some authorities feel that this may be true for the adult also, though not demonstrable in the short period of a balance experiment. Since the formation in the body of the various nonessential amino acids is dependent on specific enzyme reactions, species differences in ability to syn-

[5] William C. Rose, The nutritive significance of the amino acids, *Physiol. Revs.*, **18**:109–136, 1938.

[6] W. C. Rose and associates, The amino acid requirements of man. V. The role of lysine, arginine and tryptophan, *J. Biol. Chem.*, **206**:421–430, 1954. See also earlier papers cited.

thesize a given metabolic essential are explainable on the basis of differences in enzyme systems present.

It is evident from the above discussion that there are certain qualitative differences as to the essential acids required by different species and for different functions in the same species. There are also quantitative differences per unit of body weight or of growth tissue formed. This is not unexpected, since species differ in their protein make-up. For a similar reason the proportions of the amino acids required by a given species may vary according to the protein product being formed, e.g., growth tissue or eggs in the case of poultry. All of these considerations mean that one cannot generalize from one species to another or one function to another as to either qualitative or quantitative requirements.

In studies of the nutritive value of the optical isomers of the essential amino acids it has been found that, for the most part, only the naturally occurring form (L-) is utilized. Here again there are species differences. These findings have significance in connection with the possible use of synthetic amino acids as supplements to rations, since the synthetic products are racemic mixtures.

Some workers use the terms indispensable and dispensable instead of essential and nonessential. Some list a third classification, semi-indispensable. This classification includes, in the case of the rat, arginine, which is not required for slow growth, and cystine and tyrosine because of their interrelations with methionine and phenylalanine, respectively, as previously discussed.

6.10. Synthesis of Nonessential Amino Acids. The terms essential and nonessential refer to a need in the diet. All the amino acids which are found in body protein are metabolic essentials for its synthesis in nutritional processes. Since body protein consists of nonessential amino acids to the extent of 40 per cent, the dietary and metabolic sources of them is obviously of large quantitative importance. They must be made available to the tissues to build body protein. Two of the acids need a specific essential acid for their formation. Methionine is required to provide the sulfur for cystine synthesis. Phenylalanine is needed for the formation of its hydroxy compound, tyrosine. Thus, while cystine and tyrosine are classed as nonessential, in their absence from the diet more methionine and phenylalanine are required accordingly, as is indicated in the footnotes to Table 6.2. These are the only two cases where essential acids are required to form nonessential ones. While other nonessential acids can arise similarly, simply providing an excess of the essentials is not an effective way of supplying all the nonessentials required for protein synthesis during rapid growth. There are other ways in which they may be formed. Amino groups from various sources can be united to a keto or hydroxy acid to form the corresponding amino acid. Thus, several amino acids are mutually interconvertible by

in a joint United States–Canadian report[11] and of roughages and cereal grains in a United States report by Miller.[12]

6.14. Crude versus True Protein. The previous discussion of protein quality indicates why this distinction has lost much of the nutritional significance originally attributed to it. Proteins as such are required to furnish the essential amino acids, except in the case of ruminants, but their values for this purpose vary widely in accordance with their amino acid make-up. On the other hand, nonprotein nitrogen compounds, such as amides and ammonium salts, can be effectively used by the body to form the nonessential amino acids. For ruminants, nonprotein nitrogen compounds can also serve to provide the essential acids as a result of microbiological synthesis (Sec. 6.15). In view of all these considerations, a distinction between crude and true protein of feeds (Sec. 6.7) seems no longer worthwhile. In this book, unless otherwise specifically stated, the term protein is used without qualifying adjective to express the value obtained by multiplying the total nitrogen by 6.25 (or some other stated factor). It should be borne in mind that the value so expressed includes other nitrogen compounds besides protein and that a more exact measure of the value of feed nitrogen for protein nutrition must at present be a biological rather than a chemical one. Actually the nonprotein nitrogen compounds make up a significant portion of the total in only a few feeds.

In calculating rations it has been a British practice to give the nonprotein nitrogen a 50 per cent value. Thus they use a value termed *protein equivalent*, obtained as follows:

$$\text{Protein equivalent} = \frac{\text{digestible crude protein} + \text{digestible true protein}}{2}$$

PROTEIN METABOLISM

The end products of protein metabolism in the digestive tract are largely amino acids produced by the action of proteolytic enzymes in the intestine. In cattle and sheep, however, microbiological processes in the rumen play a dominant role in protein nutrition.

6.15. Protein Metabolism in the Rumen. In the discussion of carbohydrate metabolism, it was pointed out that bacteria and other microorganisms play a large role in the breakdown of complex carbohydrates in the digestive tract, especially in the ruminants. As the bacteria multiply, they synthesize protein to construct their own bodies, obtaining the raw material from the ingested food. For this purpose they can utilize

[11] Joint United States–Canadian tables of feed composition, *Natl. Acad. Sci. Natl. Research Council Publ.* 659, 1959.

[12] Donald F. Miller, Composition of cereal grains and forages, *Natl. Acad. Sci. Natl. Research Council Publ.* 585, 1958.

amides, ammonium salts, and even nitrates, as well as protein itself. Bacterial protein so formed in the rumen is digested later in the stomach and intestine, and thus the microorganisms of the rumen play an important role in protein as well as carbohydrate nutrition.

The concept that microorganisms play a useful role in protein metabolism was put forward long before the specific importance of amino acids was appreciated. From a study of cellulose digestion Zuntz,[13] in 1891, expressed the view that rumen bacteria use by preference amides, amino acids, and ammonium salts instead of protein. Other studies led to the belief that the protein supplied by a given ration was augmented as a result of the formation of protein in the bodies of bacteria and protozoa which were later digested. These early observations were followed by many experiments indicating that the protein requirements of animals, especially Herbivora, could be met in part by such nonprotein nitrogen compounds as asparagine, urea, and even ammonium salts, and these findings were frequently explained on the basis that microorganisms intervened to transform these simple compounds into protein which was later digested and thus served the body.

The many contradictory findings reported kept the question open for nearly fifty years after the initial observations of Zuntz. In 1937 Fingerling and coworkers[14] produced clear evidence from nitrogen-balance studies with calves that urea can be utilized to supply a part of the protein needs for growth. Shortly thereafter, convincing growth studies with both calves and lambs were published in both Great Britain and the United States, and it was established that urea could be utilized for milk production by the dairy cow.

Investigations during the past dozen years have added greatly to the knowledge of protein metabolism in the rumen. Some of the ingested protein passes on and undergoes digestion in the stomach and intestine, but a large part of it is broken down by microorganisms in the rumen to amino acids and simpler nitrogen compounds, notably ammonia, which are in turn used by the microorganisms to build their own protein tissues. McDonald[15] found that when 94 per cent of the total nitrogen in a sheep's

[13] Nathan Zuntz (1847–1920) was a pioneer in the field of basal metabolism and in respiration studies with farm animals. He developed the first portable respiration apparatus. Trained as a physician, he early forsook medicine to become a teacher and investigator in physiology, first at Bonn and later at Berlin. He devoted himself particularly to work with farm animals and to basic problems related to their nutrition. His publications, numbering over 400, deal with a wide variety of physiological problems.

[14] G. Fingerling and coworkers, Ersatz des Nährungseiweisses durch Harnstoff beim wachseden Rinde, *Landw. Vers. Sta.* **128**:221–235, 1937.

[15] I. W. McDonald, The extent of conversion of food protein to microbial protein in the rumen of sheep, *Biochem. J.*, **56**:120–125, 1954.

ration was fed as zein, 40 per cent of it was used by rumen organisms to synthesize their own protein. He believes that the percentage conversion is higher with rations of natural feeds. The ingested nonprotein nitrogen compounds are also subject to breakdown with the formation of ammonia and volatile fatty acids. The ammonia produced either from protein or nonprotein compounds is in part used by the microorganisms in growth and in part absorbed from the rumen into the blood stream. Much of the absorbed portion is rapidly converted into urea and excreted. Some of the ammonia, however, may be utilized in the synthesis of nonessential amino acids by amination of appropriate carbon chains, and some of the urea reenters the rumen through the saliva. According to the studies of El-Shazly,[16] the volatile acids formed from the microbial breakdown of amino acids and other nonprotein nitrogen compounds appear to be C_2, C_4, and C_5 acids, the latter being principally branched-chain acids which, though absorbed, are probably not available for resynthesis of amino acids. This means that this microbial action is wasteful of the carbon chains as well as of ammonia.

TABLE 6.4. AVERAGE DAILY AMINO ACID BALANCE OF SHEEP*
(In grams)

Amino acid	Intake	Excreted		
		Urine	Feces	Total
Arginine	0.19	0.48	0.06	0.54
Histidine	0.05	0.18	0.02	0.20
Isoleucine	0.00	0.52	0.06	0.58
Leucine	0.15	0.61	0.08	0.69
Lysine	0.24	0.71	0.12	0.83
Methionine	0.03	0.21	0.02	0.23
Phenylalanine	0.05	0.48	0.04	0.52
Threonine	0.07	0.67	0.06	0.73
Tryptophan	0.01	0.13	0.01	0.14
Valine	0.14	0.69	0.08	0.77

* Data from J. K. Loosli et al., Synthesis of amino acids in the rumen, *Science*, **110**:144–145, 1949.

Specific evidence that microbial action in the rumen can synthesize from urea all of the 10 amino acids which are essential for rat growth has been obtained by Loosli and associates using a nearly protein-free, purified diet with lambs. The data, summarized in Table 6.4, show that

[16] K. El-Shazly, Degradation of protein in the rumen of sheep. I. Some volatile fatty acids, including branched chain isomers, found *in vivo*, *Biochem. J.*, **51**:640–647, 1952. II. The action of rumen microorganisms on amino acids, *ibid.*, **51**:647–653, 1952.

three to ten times as much of each amino acid was excreted as was fed. Since the lambs were gaining in weight and were in positive nitrogen balance, the excreted acids could not have come from tissue breakdown but must have been synthesized in the rumen. On the basis of analysis of rumen samples the concentration of the various amino acids in the rumen contents was estimated to be 9 to 20 times greater than in the feed. These data should not be interpreted to mean that the protein needs of ruminants can be met solely by urea or similar sources of nitrogen. Normal growth did not occur in the lambs in question. Since the data show that the sulfur containing amino acids can be synthesized from urea, it is evident that some source of sulfur must be utilized in the process. It has been shown by both tracer studies and by the balance technique that inorganic sulfur serves for this purpose.

The microbial protein formed in the rumen is digested in the stomach and intestines to the constituent amino acids. In so far as this protein arises from amides, ammonium compounds, and the like, a distinct gain in amino acids available to the body results. Further, studies have shown that this microbial protein is of high biological value as measured by rat growth studies. This means that through the intervention of microorganisms in the rumen, rations which are of poor protein quality as fed are enhanced in quality for body use. Essential amino acids which are deficient in the ration are supplied by bacterial synthesis. Thus we have the explanation as to why the protein quality of the ration as fed is much less important in the case of ruminants than nonruminants. On the other hand, the microbial action results in some losses also. Notably, some of the ammonia produced is absorbed from the rumen, converted to urea, and partially lost in the urine, as has been mentioned.

Recent studies have been concentrated on factors which will promote the maximum bacterial synthesis of protein in the rumen to provide for the more effective use of rations poor in protein quality and, particularly, of nonprotein sources of nitrogen such as urea. The practical objective is a cheaper ration. Like carbohydrate breakdown the character and extent of the rumen flora are dominant factors which in turn are governed by the nature of the ration. The bacteria must have a readily available source of energy for rapid growth. Starch, either as such or as supplied in starchy feeds such as cereals and potatoes, works best. Molasses or sugars are less satisfactory because they pass on out of the rumen too rapidly. On the other hand, cellulose is made available too slowly. The utilization of urea is much less on high-protein rations, particularly where soluble proteins are present. Under conditions where protein synthesis by microorganisms is less active, there is a larger amount of ammonia produced in the rumen and absorbed from it. While rations low in protein and high in starch are most favorable to protein synthesis, this is not true as far as the breakdown of higher carbohydrates by rumen organisms is concerned (Sec. 4.19). This means that the maximum microbial activity for both purposes cannot be achieved with the same ration and that, from the standpoint of learning how both energy and protein nutrition in the ruminant can best be served, there is a case for studying carbohydrate breakdown and protein synthesis with the same rations.

While it has been proved by several studies that urea can replace a part of the protein in properly selected rations for growing cattle and sheep without loss of production, there is a limit to the amount that can be used because excess is toxic due to the ammonia formed, particularly under rumen conditions where this formation is rapid. With rations containing plenty of starch, urea can safely replace, on a nitrogen basis, up to a quarter or a third of the protein in rations for dairy cows, beef cattle, and lambs. Other nitrogen compounds that are less soluble than urea and from which ammonia is released more slowly would have an advantage in this respect. Trials have been conducted with various commercially ammoniated feeds such as molasses, beet pulp, and oat hulls, but the extent of their usefulness in comparison with urea remains uncertain. Particularly in the interest of making maximum use of nonprotein nitrogen compounds as feed ingredients, much more study is needed to learn how to promote the maximum use of ammonia for bacterial synthesis and keep its absorption at a minimum.

A comprehensive and critical review of urea as a protein replacement has been published by Reid.[17]

6.16. Enzymic Protein Digestion. The digestion of proteins to amino acids by enzymes secreted in the tract has long been understood. With the modern studies of the dominant role of amino acids in protein nutrition, the importance of some digestion variables, not previously appreciated, have come to be realized. There may be a differential digestion of the acids, both as to rate and extent, which has nutritional significance not indicated by the percentage digestibility of the protein as a whole. If a given essential amino acid is digested to a lesser extent than the over-all value, the quality of the protein ingested is lessened accordingly. If there is a marked lag in the digestion of such an amino acid, compared with the others, protein quality is unfavorably affected because of the "time factor" in protein synthesis, discussed later (Sec. 6.20). These differences in digestibility can result from structural differences in the proteins as they naturally occur in the feed and from various processing treatments. The data in Table 6.5, taken from a study by Kuiken, illustrate this point. Studies have also shown that a given amino acid may differ markedly in its digestibility according to feed

[17] J. T. Reid, Urea as a protein replacement: a review, *J. Dairy Sci.*, **36**:955–996, 1953.

source. These findings indicate that availability to the body must be taken into account in estimating the nutritive value of the amino acid mixture found in a feed by analysis.

TABLE 6.5. DIGESTIBILITY OF AMINO ACIDS IN COTTONSEED MEAL BY RATS*

Amino acids	Hydraulic meal, %	Solvent extracted meal, %
Arginine	95	98
Histidine	85	96
Isoleucine	72	84
Leucine	72	90
Lysine	71	88
Methionine	67	88
Phenylalanine	81	94
Threonine	72	86
Tryptophan	83	93
Valine	73	90
Total Nitrogen	77	92

* K. A. Kuiken, Availability of the essential amino acids in cottonseed meal, *J. Nutrition,* **46**:13–25, 1952.

6.17. Fecal Nitrogen. The nitrogenous compounds excreted in the feces consist in part of undigested or unabsorbed food nitrogen and in part of another fraction, called *metabolic fecal nitrogen.* This metabolic fraction comprises substances originating in the body, such as residues of the bile and other digestive juices, epithelial cells abraded from the alimentary tract by the food passing through it, and bacterial residues. Strictly speaking, however, the nitrogen in bacterial residues must be considered to have come originally, in part at least, from the food. The existence of this fecal metabolic nitrogen, as distinguished from undigested nitrogen, is shown by the fact that the feces excreted on a nitrogen-free diet always contain nitrogen compounds. The reason for making the distinction is that the two fractions have different origins and that the distinction is made use of in measuring the biological value of proteins in nutrition (Sec. 14.17).

While the amount of the undigested fraction is determined by the digestibility of the nitrogenous portion of the ration, the size of the metabolic fraction is independent of this factor and is governed in part by the total amount of dry matter consumed and its digestibility and in part by body size. That metabolic nitrogen output increases with the food intake is easily understandable from the fact that the higher the intake, the greater the secretion of digestive juices and the greater the wear and tear on the lining of the tract. The influence of body size is shown by observations that at the same level of food intake the larger animal excretes more metabolic nitrogen. This effect is explainable on the basis that some of the nitrogenous constituents of the bile, and possibly of other digestive secretions, represent true excretions of body metabolism unrelated to food intake. One would expect these excretions to be proportional to body size. The relative influence of food intake and of body size upon the amount of metabolic nitrogen has been critically studied by Schneider[18] working in Mitchell's laboratory, and this investigator presents an extensive review of the subject. The preponderance of the evidence to date indicates that food intake, particularly its indigestible fraction, has the predominant influence.

It is evident that, at a given level of food intake, the higher the digestibility of its protein, the larger is the proportion of the total fecal nitrogen which is represented by the metabolic fraction. In the case of a man eating a highly digestible diet, the fecal nitrogen is principally metabolic. At the other extreme, the metabolic nitrogen may be only a small fraction of the total fecal output in the case of Herbivora consuming a ration of low protein digestibility. To the extent that the metabolic nitrogen is a function of total food intake, lowering the proportion of protein in the ration results in a decrease in the undigested nitrogen relative to the total fecal output.

There is no reliable method for separating the metabolic from the undigested nitrogen in the feces. The output of metabolic nitrogen can be determined with a nitrogen-free ration or with rations containing small amounts of proteins which are known to be practically 100 per cent digested. Figures so obtained for the metabolic nitrogen per unit of dry-matter intake are used to calculate the metabolic fraction produced from rations which result in the excretion of undigested nitrogen as well, notably in the Thomas-Mitchell method of determining the biological value of proteins (Sec. 14.17). Using this procedure the metabolic nitrogen has been found to be approximately 0.1 g. for rats, pigs, and man per 100 g. dry matter consumed, and 0.5 g. for ruminants. The latter figure is smaller with rations low in roughage, but greater where roughage alone is fed.

In 1927 Titus[19] introduced a technique with steers, involving the plotting of the total nitrogen intake as a function of the total nitrogen excretion, with rations of varying protein content but of constant total food intake. He extrapolated the straight line thus obtained to the point of

[18] Burch Hart Schneider, The relationship of the metabolic nitrogen of the faeces to body weight and to food intake for rats, *Biochem. J.*, **28**:360–364, 1934.

[19] H. W. Titus, The nitrogen metabolism of steers on rations containing alfalfa as the sole source of the nitrogen, *J. Agr. Research*, **34**:49–58, 1927.

zero protein intake to arrive at the estimated metabolic nitrogen excretion for the food intake in question. The method has been found a reliable one for various species, including the rat, dog, pig, and sheep. Data supporting this conclusion are presented in the paper by Mitchell and Bert,[20] which also reports a study confirming the validity of the direct determination of metabolic fecal nitrogen.

6.18. Apparent and True Digestibility of Protein. The recognition that the fecal nitrogen consisted in part of compounds other than those coming from the food early led to the proposal to determine the true digestibility of protein by considering only the undigested fraction, as distinguished from apparent digestibility which was based on the total output. The previous discussion has indicated that there is no accurate method for quantitatively determining the two fractions. While such a distinction is desirable in certain experimental work, it does not have any important significance in feeding practice. The excreted metabolic nitrogen represents a loss which must be taken account of and assessed against some body process. Although it is independent of the nitrogen component of the food, it is related to the food intake as a whole and it is a loss which occurs in the course of the digestion of this food. It is more appropriately assessed against digestion than against any other body function. Thus the figures for the digestibility of protein commonly determined and employed represent apparent digestibility, though generally spoken of without this qualifying term.

6.19. The Disposal of Absorbed Amino Acids. The nitrogenous digestion products enter the blood stream from the intestine, mainly at least, as amino acids. Small amounts of ammonia and of the simpler peptides are also absorbable. Eventually the absorbed amino acids are disposed of in one of the following ways:

1. They may be synthesized into tissue proteins and other nitrogen-containing tissue constituents. Such a synthesis includes the formation of the protein and other nitrogenous compounds of secretions, notably of milk. It also involves the replacement of tissues and products used up in the "wear and tear" of body processes. Here are included the enzymes, the activity of some of which is very sensitive to protein deficiency, hormones, and others. In some cases the demand is for one or two specific amino acids; for example, phenylalanine and tyrosine are the sole precursors of the hormones thyroxine and adrenalin. Synthesis takes priority over deaminization in so far as there are structural needs and the amino acids are suitable in amount and kind for the purpose.

2. They are deaminated. One form of deamination has been men-

[20] H. H. Mitchell and M. H. Bert, The determination of metabolic fecal nitrogen, *J. Nutrition,* **52**: 483–497, 1954.

tioned—transamination. All amino acids undergo oxidative deamination with the formation of a keto acid, for example:

$$\underset{\text{Alanine}}{CH_3—\underset{\underset{NH_2}{|}}{CH}—COOH} + O \longrightarrow \underset{\text{Pyruvic acid}}{CH_3—\underset{\underset{O}{\|}}{C}—COOH} + NH_3$$

The keto acids serve as a source of energy for the body. Some of them follow the path of carbohydrate metabolism and can either be used to form glycogen and glucose or be immediately broken down to carbon dioxide and water. Other keto acids enter the path of fat metabolism and thus are also subject either to complete catabolic oxidation or to synthesis into body fat. In mentioning that some amino acids follow the path of carbohydrates and others the path of fat, it should be noted that there is an intermingling in the citric acid cycle (Sec. 4.26). The ammonia resulting from deaminization is changed to urea, or uric acid in the case of birds, and excreted, except as some of it may be used in the synthesis of the nonessential amino acids. The formation of urea from ammonia is a reaction for which ornithine [$NH_2—(CH_2)_3—CHNH_2—COOH$] is essential. This compound combines with two molecules of ammonia and one of carbon dioxide to form citrulline. The latter is converted into arginine, which is in turn hydrolyzed into urea and ornithine. Since ornithine is regenerated, a cycle results which is referred to as the *urea cycle*.

Actually the course of amino acid metabolism is much more complicated than previously outlined. Further, the nitrogenous compounds in the body, like the fats, exist to a certain extent in a dynamic state. Certain amino acids undergo reformation as well as deaminization. Certain body proteins also undergo breakdown and resynthesis. This is particularly true of liver protein which has been found to have a half-life of seven days. The great mass of muscle protein is metabolically inert, however, contrary to conclusions reached when the dynamic state of protein was first established by isotope studies. The various papers dealing with this topic have been reviewed by Borsook and Deasy.[21]

The mechanism of protein synthesis from amino acids is unknown. In vitro, it can be accomplished by the same enzymes which hydrolyze protein, and thus the synthesis is sometimes considered as a reverse phase of proteolysis. But the conditions under which it can be made to take place in vitro are vastly different from those which are met in the body, and thus the actual body process is far from being explained. In the adult animal which is producing no special nitrogenous product, such as milk,

[21] Henry Borsook and Clara L. Deasy, The metabolism of proteins and amino acids, *Ann. Rev. Biochem.*, **20**:209–226, 1951.

eggs, wool, or even a fetus, the need for protein synthesis is limited almost entirely to the requirements for the replacement of worn-out tissues; for, differing from the case for carbohydrates and fat, protein, as such, cannot be stored by the adult organism except to a very limited extent. Thus, any excess of amino acids eventually follows path 2 above. Not only is this true for the absorbed acids as a whole, but it is true also for specific ones present in an excess relative to others which are essential for protein synthesis. In rations containing protein of low biological value, therefore, an extensive loss of absorbed amino acids as such inevitably occurs irrespective of whether the needs of protein synthesis are completely met. The carbon chains are utilized for energy purposes as previously mentioned.

The previous discussion indicates that the excretory products of amino acid catabolism are primarily urea or uric acid, carbon dioxide, and water. In addition the urine contains small amounts of nitrogen as hippuric acid, ammonium salts, creatinine, and other compounds. Certain amino acid structures are not completely broken down. For example, the ring of tryptophan is excreted in the feces as indole and skatole. There is also a small excretion of amino acids as such in the urine. This excretion is not related to the amount or biological value of the protein fed. Thus, it has no special nutritional significance.

6.20. The Time Factor in Protein Synthesis. Research has established that the efficiency and extent of protein synthesis are governed by the completeness and balance of the amino acid mixture currently presented to the tissues. This fact is explainable on the basis that amino acids are not stored in the body as such and thus that incomplete mixtures are promptly catabolized rather than being held in the tissues for the arrival of the missing acids. Factors which may cause variations in the times and rates at which specific amino acids reach the tissues influence the extent of protein synthesis accordingly. Several studies with rats have shown that if a food or amino acid mixture deficient in an essential acid is fed at a given time and the deficient acid fed 6 hr. or more later, protein synthesis is less than when the deficient acid is included in the initial feeding. This means that time differences in ingestion are reflected in time differences in arrival at the tissues, which in turn lessen the extent of the synthetic activity. There is experimental evidence that the findings with rats occur in other species. In the case of pigs Eggert and coworkers[22] were unable to demonstrate an effect by a 24-hr. interval between feedings of protein supplements to a corn diet, but there was a decrease in nitrogen retention with a 36-hr. interval.

The rat-feeding experiments have been interpreted to mean that all

[22] R. G. Eggert, M. J. Brinegar, and C. R. Anderson, Delayed supplementation of corn diets with growing swine, *J. Nutrition*, **50**:469–477, 1953.

the amino acids must be present at the site of synthesis in greater than fasting levels for synthesis to occur. Borsook and Deasy,[23] however, doubt this interpretation in view of the experiments which they review showing a rapid and extensive incorporation of single amino acids into protein, both in vivo and in vitro. In any case, it does not seem likely that this experimentally demonstrated effect on protein synthesis is important in practice for either pigs or chickens because of the systems of feeding customarily employed. No comparable effect would be expected in the case of cattle and sheep in view of the different nature of the protein metabolism which occurs in the digestive tract in ruminants.

Even though the rations ingested at a given time provide a complete and balanced amino acid mixture for nonruminants, differences may occur in the rates and completeness of digestion of the individual acids (Sec. 6.16) with a consequent change in the mixture currently absorbed and presented to the tissues. This is a possibility which needs to be borne in mind in planning and interpreting the results of certain studies dealing with the protein efficiency of feeds and rations, although it may not be of importance in feeding practice.

6.21. Protein Reserve; Plasma Proteins. The previous statement that the adult organism cannot store protein requires qualification. During a period of inadequate protein nutrition, protoplasm may be broken down to meet certain other nitrogen needs of the body, and it may also be broken down to supply energy after a prolonged period of inadequate food intake. With the restoration of an adequate diet, additional protein will be retained in the adult body until the losses are made good. Further, exercise can result in increased muscle size in the adult, and this must mean some increase in protein content. In addition to these special cases of protein retention, it is recognized that a liberal protein intake regularly tends to result in a small increase in the body which is variously referred to as *protein reserve*, or *deposit protein*, and by other terms. On the other hand, the increment thus built up tends to disappear on a low-protein diet. The proof of the existence of this protein reserve, which actually consists of nonprotein nitrogen compounds as well, rests upon nitrogen-balance studies.

While this protein store is not at all comparable in magnitude to the fat depots, it is more important currently because it is the source from which *plasma proteins*, as well as hemoglobin, are manufactured. The principal proteins of the blood plasma are serum albumin, serum globulin, and fibrinogen. Each has specific functions and must be constantly regenerated from the protein reserve. When this reserve becomes depleted in anemia, through fasting or as a consequence of a diet low in protein, hypoproteinemia results. Thus, a low plasma-protein level, not

[23] Borsook and Deasy, *loc. cit.*

attributable to specific disease, is indicative of inadequate protein nutrition. The most sensitive indicator is a drop in serum albumin.

Since antibodies are produced from serum globulin, however, protein undernutrition that results in hypoproteinemia is linked with the occurrence of infectious diseases. This link has been definitely established experimentally, resulting in the conclusion that adequate protein nutrition is important from the standpoint of resistance to infection. Many enzyme systems also decrease in activity as the protein reserves are depleted.

The interrelationships between the protein reserve, hemoglobin, and the plasma proteins have been clearly set forth by Whipple.[24] A diagram

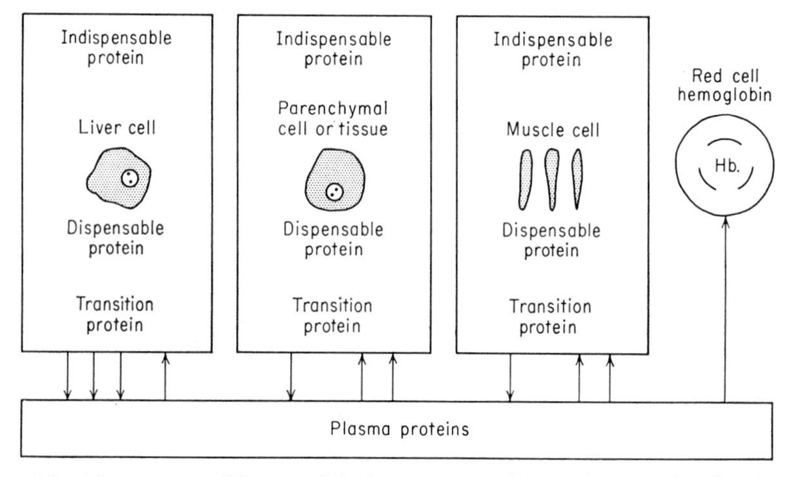

FIG. 6.1. Dynamic equilibrium of body proteins. (*From G. H. Whipple, Am. J. Med. Sci.*, **203**:477–489, 1942.)

reproduced from this article is given in Fig. 6.1. As here represented, the liver cell contains protein which is *indispensable* to its structure and stored protein which is *dispensable* and can be released to form the plasma. The protein currently on its way in or out of the liver cell is designated as *transition* protein. Note that the flow between cells and plasma is reversible. Whatever the mechanism, it is agreed that the protein molecule as such can pass through cell surfaces. The diagram shows that plasma protein is the source of hemoglobin, a lack of which results in anemia (Sec. 7.26).

6.22. Endogenous and Exogenous Catabolism. In 1905 Folin[25] put forth the theory that there are two forms of protein catabolism, essentially

[24] George H. Whipple, Hemoglobin and plasma proteins: their production, utilization and interrelation, *Am. J. Med. Sci.*, **203**:477–489, 1942.

[25] Otto Folin, A theory of protein metabolism, *Am. J. Physiol.*, **13**:117–138, 1905.

independent and quite different from each other: a variable one which he called *exogenous*, dependent on the level of protein consumed, and a constant type, the *endogenous catabolism*, related to body size and other body factors. According to this theory the endogenous catabolism represents metabolic processes which are the essential characteristic of living cells, exemplified by the nitrogen excretion on a nitrogen-free, otherwise adequate diet. It reflects metabolic processes which are essential to life, and the end products thus excreted tend to be constant, per unit of body size, unaffected by the character or amount of the food protein. The endogenous nitrogen excreted represents a loss which must be made good by dietary protein in order to maintain the integrity of the nitrogenous tissues of the body. The exogenous catabolism, on the other hand, reflects the breakdown of absorbed dietary nitrogen compounds which are not synthesized into body protein.

This theory of Folin was early challenged by certain workers, and the arguments against its validity have been reviewed by Borsook and Dubnoff.[26] It is at least subject to reinterpretation as a result of the recognition of the dynamic state of body proteins and amino acids. While only a small fraction of this protein appears to be involved in the dynamic state, the endogenous nitrogen is the excess left over as anabolic and catabolic processes come into balance. It is not merely the result of a minimum "wear-and-tear" protein catabolism. Thus, while any sharp distinction between endogenous and exogenous nitrogen, as set forth by Folin, may be no longer valid, it seems very doubtful that the dynamic state significantly changes the end results of catabolism.

This question is an important one for students of nutrition because one method of arriving at the maintenance requirement of protein (Sec. 13.15) and also the most widely used method of determining the biological value of protein (Sec. 14.17) assume the reality of Folin's endogenous catabolism. In this connection Mitchell,[27] who has been largely responsible for developing both of these methods, has come to the conclusion, from his own studies and from reviewing the work of others both pro and con, that the Folin concept remains valid, that there are no well-demonstrated findings to the contrary, and that results of isotope studies have clarified but not destroyed the basic concept. His conclusion appears justified. The questions here involved are discussed further in the later sections, referred to above, where the use of endogenous nitrogen measure is described.

It is important to bear in mind that the term endogenous as here

[26] H. Borsook and J. W. Dubnoff, The metabolism of proteins and amino acids, *Ann. Rev. Biochem.*, **12**:183–189, 1943.

[27] H. H. Mitchell, The validity of Folin's concept of dichotomy in protein metabolism, *J. Nutrition*, **55**:193–207, 1955.

used refers to the urinary excretion. The metabolic fecal nitrogen (Sec. 6.17) also comes from body sources rather than from food protein, but it is a loss incident to the digestion process and not to the essential cellular activity for which Folin coined the term endogenous. Since most physiologists restrict the term endogenous to the urinary losses of body origin, whether nitrogen or minerals, this is the usage followed in this text. To avoid confusion, the term metabolic fecal nitrogen is included where the fecal losses of body origin are also being taken into account as an endogenous loss.

6.23. Minimum and Optimum Protein Intake. The question as to whether a level of protein in excess of the minimum required to meet the protein needs of the body is advantageous or disadvantageous has been long debated in the field of human nutrition, and it has implications for animals also. Under the influence of Liebig,[28] who erroneously believed that protein was broken down to furnish the energy for muscular work, the importance of large intakes of proteins was greatly overemphasized for many years following the middle of the last century. Gradually, as a result of research, the pendulum swung to the other extreme marked by the publication in 1904 by Chittenden[29] of experiments supporting the view that minimum intakes favored health and bodily vigor. Chittenden's views were by no means universally accepted, and today most authorities favor intakes in excess of what may be considered the minimum requirements.

We have seen that a liberal protein intake tends to cause a high level of "deposit protein" in the tissues. The desirability of maintaining the protein reserves has been discussed (Sec. 6.21). On the other side, it is recognized that protein in excess of what the body can use tends to be wasted in so far as its specific functions as protein is concerned, since it cannot be stored in any but very limited amounts but must be catabolized. Further, there are those who feel that excess protein is definitely harmful, stating that its catabolism and the excretion of urea place an unnecessary and undesirable burden on the body, particularly

[28] Justus von Liebig (1803–1873) was the foremost organic chemist of his time and is frequently spoken of as the founder of agricultural chemistry. He was the father of the modern methods of organic analysis, and with him began the accumulation of knowledge regarding the composition of foods, tissues, feces, and urine not available to earlier nutrition workers. He wrote several books dealing with the relations of organic chemistry to agriculture and to animal economy which are well worth reading by the modern student.

[29] Russell H. Chittenden (1856–1943) served for forty years as professor of physiological chemistry at Yale University, where he made many outstanding contributions to the modern science of nutrition and inspired a host of students who have continued his work. An account of his protein studies is given in his book Physiological Economy in Nutrition, Frederick A. Stokes Company, Philadelphia, 1904.

on the kidneys. There are many experiments showing the harmful effect of the excessive feeding of specific amino acids. On the other hand, there is ample evidence that the body can metabolize rather high levels of proteins in complete diets for long periods without deleterious effects on production or on the body itself.

Some of the differences of opinion relative to the optimum level of protein intake have doubtless arisen from failure to recognize the bearing of variations in protein quality. The minimum intake which proves adequate for a specific combination of proteins will be neither adequate nor optimum for a combination of lower biological value. It is now apparent that some of the superior results reported for high-protein diets in the earlier literature were owing to the presence of unrecognized B-vitamins, notably B_{12}, in the animal sources used, which were not adequately supplied in the basal ration.

It seems clear that, at least during the growth period, the body can function normally over a rather wide range of protein intake above the minimum. Since marked differences in quality exist among commonly fed rations, at least for certain species, the intake in practice should be more liberal than the experimentally determined minimum with a specific combination. Further, it should be sufficient to maintain the protein reserves. There is also evidence (Sec. 11.16) that a liberal intake is desirable from the standpoint of the most effective use of the ration as a whole. But that there are stimulating or other definite, though intangible, beneficial effects from a *luxus consumption* appears very doubtful.

SELECTED REFERENCES

Belasco, I. J.: New nitrogen feed compounds for ruminants: a laboratory evaluation, *J. Animal Sci.*, **13**:601–610, 1954.

Dunn, Max S., and associates: Percentages of twelve amino acids in blood, carcass, heart, kidney, liver, muscle, and skin of eight animals, *Univ. Calif. (Berkeley) Pubs. Physiol.*, **8**:293–325, 1949.

Holmes, P., R. J. Moir, and E. J. Underwood: Ruminal flora studies in the sheep. V. The amino acid composition of rumen bacterial protein, *Australian J. Biol. Sci.*, **6**:637–644, 1953.

Johns, A. T.: Joint studies of protein and energy nutrition in the rumen, *New Zealand J. Sci. Technol.*, **37**:323–331, 1955.

Leverton, Ruth M., Mary R. Gram, and Marilyn Chaloupka: Effect of the time factor and calorie level of nitrogen utilization of young women, *J. Nutrition*, **44**:537–545, 1951.

Lewis, D.: Amino-acid metabolism in the rumen of the sheep, *Brit. J. Nutrition*, **9**:215–230, 1955.

McNaught, Mary L., and coworkers: Utilization of nonprotein nitrogen in the bovine rumen. VIII. Nutritive value of the proteins from preparations of dried rumen bacteria, rumen protozoa, and brewer's yeast for rats, *Biochem. J.*, **56**:151–156, 1954.

Rose, W. C.: Half-century of amino acid investigations, *Chem. Eng. News,* **30**:2385–2388, 1952.

———, Minor J. Coon, and G. Frederick Lambert: The amino acid requirements of man. VI. The role of the caloric intake, *J. Biol. Chem.,* **210**:331–342, 1954.

——— and Eldon E. Rice: The significance of the amino acids in canine nutrition, *Science,* **90**:186–187, 1939.

Schneider, Burch H.: The subdivision of the metabolic nitrogen in the feces of the rat, swine, and man. *J. Biol. Chem.,* **180**:845–856, 1949.

Tillman, A. D., and R. W. Swift: The utilization of ammoniated industrial by-products and urea by sheep, *J. Animal Sci.,* **12**:201–212, 1953.

Vickery, Hubert Bradford, and Carl L. A. Schmidt: The history of the discovery of the amino acids, *Chem. Revs.* **9**:169–318, 1931.

Chapter 7
The Inorganic Elements and Their Metabolism

The discussion in Chap. 2 has indicated that the body contains a large number of mineral elements which occur both in combination with each other and in combination with the organic constituents. While the physiological importance of some of them was recognized over one hundred years ago, our specific knowledge of their nutritional significance is due primarily to research carried out during the present century.

7.1. Essential Mineral Elements. Today we recognize that the following mineral elements perform essential functions in the body and thus must be present in the food: calcium, phosphorus, sodium, potassium, chlorine, magnesium, iron, sulfur, iodine, manganese, copper, cobalt, and zinc. The proof that each of these elements is essential rests upon experiments with one or more species. In these experiments symptoms produced by diets adequate in all nutrients except the mineral in question have been prevented or overcome by adding that mineral to the diets. All the elements previously mentioned have not been tested with all species, but it is highly probable that there is no exception to the need for all of them by all higher animals.

Evidence is increasing that fluorine, molybdenum, selenium, and chromium can perform useful functions in the body, which may entitle them to be classified as essential elements. This evidence is discussed later in the chapter, as the minerals in question are taken up.

There are two dozen or more other mineral elements regularly found in animal tissues. Some are undoubtedly present merely because they occur in the food and thus are retained in part rather than being excreted. On the other hand, some probably perform essential functions as yet undiscovered. The proof that a given element is essential depends upon feeding a ration so low in that element that structural or functional injury results. It is not possible to prepare any ration absolutely free from any mineral element, and thus proof of the need of those which may be required only in traces is difficult or impossible to establish. This explains why many remain in the doubtful column. The comparatively recent discovery that $\frac{1}{10}$ mg. of cobalt daily can restore to health sheep that otherwise die on pasture in certain areas of the world, despite failure to prove the element essential in earlier animal experiments with purified diets, is a case in point.

As our knowledge of enzymic processes became more specific during recent years, it has come to be recognized that certain mineral elements needed only in traces function either as constituents or as activators of enzymes (Sec. 3.8). Thus, it must be considered that some elements not now definitely classed as essential may actually be required for enzyme action. It has become apparent that much more study needs to be given to several elements which have thus far received little attention both to their possible essentiality and to their content in feeds. The previously mentioned discovery with respect to cobalt has served to disprove the earlier viewpoint that, even if some of the elements thus far considered unessential are actually needed in traces, their universal presence in feeds would probably take care of any need in practice. Further, it has come to be realized that interrelationships among certain minerals in the diet, as well as the actual amounts, govern both their usefulness and also their harmful effects. These various considerations are discussed in more detail later in this chapter as the minerals in question are taken up.

7.2. Area Deficiencies and Excesses of Mineral Elements. In the case of several of the essential minerals, the initial knowledge of their need and of the symptoms resulting from their deficiency in the ration was gained by observations with grazing animals. Thus, phosphorus deficiency was first established as a result of the correlation of the symptoms with the low-phosphorus content in the herbage resulting from a corresponding deficiency in the soil. A pioneer study here is the one by Theiler and associates.[1] They showed that large losses which occurred in both growing and adult cattle on the range were due to a very low content of the element in the herbage as a result of a deficiency in the soil, a situation that has since been noted in other parts of the world including various areas in the United States. This and similar observations have led to surveys of the occurrence of animal troubles that might be correlated with specific soil deficiencies. Bee-

[1] Arnold Theiler, H. H. Green, and P. J. du Toit, Phosphorus in the live stock industry, *Union S. Africa J. Dept. Agr.*, **8**:460–504, 1924.

son[2] of the U.S. Plant, Soil, and Nutrition Laboratory has reviewed the worldwide literature dealing with this general subject. Beeson[3] has also reported a study of the occurrence of diseases in the United States resulting from deficiencies or excesses of minerals in the soil. A map from this publication is reproduced in Fig. 7.1. The extent of the importance in feeding practice of the various soil deficiencies here indicated is discussed later as each mineral is taken up.

7.3. Ash. The mineral elements as a group are determined in a feed or animal tissue by burning off the organic matter and weighing the residue, which is called ash. Such a determination tells nothing about the specific elements present, and the ash may include carbon from organic matter as carbonate when base-forming minerals are in excess. The determination is used in the conventional feed analysis to provide a figure which can be added in with others to arrive at the nitrogen-free extract by difference (Sec. 4.14). The ash may be used as a starting point for the determination of the percentages of the specific elements present, the information in which we are interested from the standpoint of mineral nutrition. But it must be remembered that an analysis of the ash tells us nothing as to the combination in which a given mineral occurs either in a body tissue or in a feed. When the organic matter is oxidized, the minerals present in organic combination are changed to an inorganic form. Many of the minerals in the body function primarily as specific organic and inorganic combinations, and in the case of the food also, the combination is important in so far as the usefulness of certain elements is concerned. For example, the primary need for sulfur in the food is as a constituent of the amino acids cystine and methionine. No information as to the amount of the element so combined is furnished by determining the sulfur content of the ash of the ration. Thus the nutrition chemist must resort to special methods which give him specific information as to the forms in which certain mineral elements occur in the body tissues and in foods, rather than relying on a determination of the ash and its ingredients.

7.4. General Functions of Mineral Elements. The essential elements serve the body in many different ways. As constituents of the bones and teeth, they give rigidity and strength to the skeletal structures. They are also constituents of the organic compounds, such as protein and lipids, which make up the muscles, organs, blood cells, and other soft tissues of the body. Their roles in enzyme systems have been men-

[2] Kenneth C. Beeson, The mineral composition of crops, with particular reference to the soils in which they were grown: a review and compilation, *U.S. Dept. Agr. Misc. Pub.* 369, 1941.

[3] Kenneth C. Beeson, The relation of soils to the micronutrient element content of plants and to animal nutrition, in Trace Elements, Academic Press, Inc., New York, 1958, pp. 67–79.

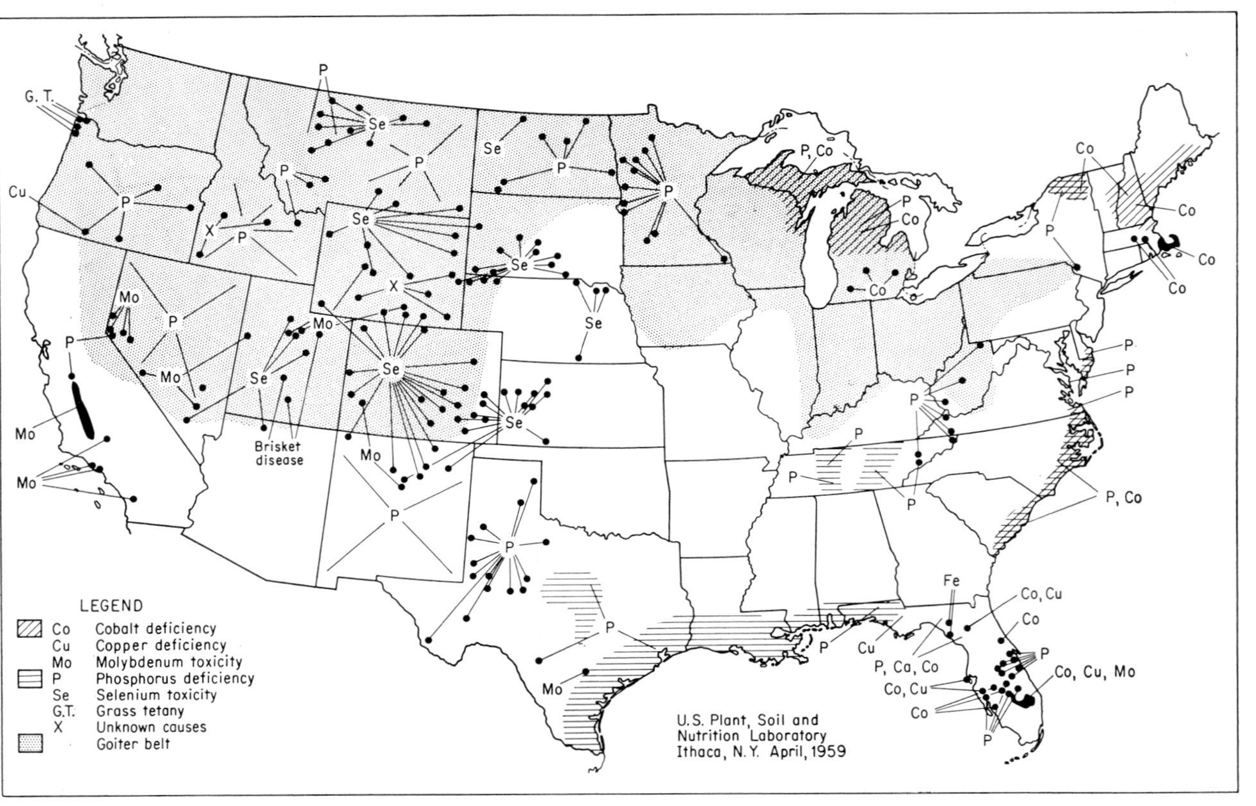

FIG. 7.1. Mineral deficiencies in the United States.

tioned. Further, they serve a variety of functions as soluble salts in the blood and other body fluids. Here they are concerned in the maintenance of osmotic relations and acid-base equilibrium and exert characteristic effects on the irritability of muscles and nerves. Many of their vital functions are due to an ionic interrelationship which finds expression in the terms "antagonistic action" and "balanced solution." For example, a certain balance between calcium, sodium, and potassium in the fluid which bathes the heart muscle is essential for the normal relaxation and contraction which constitute its beating. In addition to these general functions in which several minerals may take part, each essential one has various specific roles.

CALCIUM AND PHOSPHORUS

Over 70 per cent of the ash of the body consists of calcium and phosphorus. These two elements are discussed together because they are closely associated with each other in metabolism. They occur in the body combined with each other for the most part, and an inadequate supply of either in the diet limits the nutritive value of both. As early as 1842, it became recognized through the work of Chossat[4] with pigeons that poor bone developed on a diet low in calcium. When fed wheat alone, the birds died after 10 months, and on autopsy, the bones were found very much depleted. Calcium carbonate prevented the trouble. Chossat used chickens, rabbits, frogs, eels, lizards, and turtles in later studies. During the next twenty years, studies in both France and Germany showed that skeletal development in various species of farm animals was dependent upon the supply of calcium and phosphorus in the ration and that the deficiencies could be corrected by feeding bone meal and other sources of minerals. Early in the present century, experimental work in the field became particularly active, and with the discovery of vitamin D in 1922 a great impetus was given to studies of the metabolic processes involved.

7.5. Interrelation of Calcium, Phosphorus, and Vitamin D. Adequate calcium and phosphorus nutrition is dependent upon three factors: a sufficient supply of each element, a suitable ratio between them, and the presence of vitamin D. These factors are interrelated. While an adequate supply of the elements is the first essential, they are more effectively utilized when they are present in a certain ratio to each other. A ration containing 10 parts of calcium to 1 of phosphorus will not provide for efficient assimilation even though the phosphorus is present in what is normally a sufficient amount. The same is true where this re-

[4] M. Chossat, Note sur le système osseux, *Compt. rend. acad. sci.*, **14**:451–454, 1842.

lation between the elements is reversed. While the desirable calcium-phosphorus ratio has been defined as one lying between 2:1 and 1:2, adequate nutrition is possible outside these limits. The optimum ratio varies somewhat according to the levels of the elements. With plenty of vitamin D in the ration, the ratio becomes of less importance, and more efficient utilization is made of the amounts of the elements present. In the entire absence of the vitamin, assimilation is poor even though the other factors are optimum. The relative importance of these various factors differs considerably in different species and according to the physiological function in question. In the present discussion only incidental mention is made of vitamin D, since the role of this nutrient is taken up later in Chap. 8.

7.6. The Composition of Bone. Approximately 99 per cent of the calcium and 80 per cent of the phosphorus of the body are present in the bones and teeth. Though somewhat variable according to age, state of nutrition, and species, normal adult bone may be considered to have the following approximate composition: water, 45 per cent; ash, 25 per cent; protein, 20 per cent; and fat, 10 per cent. The organic matrix of bone in which the mineral salts are deposited consists of a mixture of proteins, of which the principal one is ossein. The water content of bone decreases with age, and the fat is variable according to the nutritive state, since the bone marrow serves as a fat depot; thus ash content is expressed most frequently on the basis of the moisture-free, fat-free bone. In mammals the ash is made up approximately as follows: calcium, 36 per cent; phosphorus, 17 per cent; and magnesium, 0.8 per cent. There are small amounts of several other minerals.

The exact chemical structure of bone has not been clearly established. Bone gives a diffraction pattern similar to that of the mineral apatite, the unit structure of which contains $3Ca_3(PO_4)_2 \cdot CaF_2$. It appears, however, that the bone mineral exists largely as hydroxy apatite:

$$3Ca_3(PO_4)_2 \cdot Ca(OH)_2$$

which is an extremely hard, difficultly soluble compound. Bone contains considerable amounts of carbonate and citrate and small amounts of magnesium, sodium, potassium, chlorine, fluorine and traces of other elements. Just how these constituents occur in the basic structure remains in debate. For a detailed discussion of the structure of bone, the student is referred to the paper by McLean.[5]

There is little variation in the elementary composition of bone ash. The calcium and phosphorus always occur in approximately a 2:1 ratio. Since bone ash consists almost entirely of calcium and phosphorus salts

[5] Franklin C. McLean, The ultra structure and function of bone, *Science,* **127**:451–456, 1958.

and since the relative amounts of these elements show little variation, the ash content of bone is commonly used as the measure of its state of calcium and phosphorus nutrition. Taylor and coworkers[6] found no consistent difference between the calcium, phosphorus, magnesium, and sodium contents of 15 bones of the skeletons of pullets. This finding means that one bone may be selected for analysis as being representative of the skeleton as a whole.

The nature of the diet, however, can affect somewhat the mineral relationships in bone, even though the ash content is not appreciably changed. Magnesium is somewhat higher than normal in rachitic bone and lower in magnesium deficiency (Sec. 7.19). These various changes need further study as measures of variations in bone quality not detectable by other means.

Teeth are similar to bone in chemical composition and in mineral relationships, but characteristic differences exist between the enamel, dentine, and pulp. The enamel is the hardest substance in the body and has the lowest water content, approximately 5 per cent. It contains only 3.5 per cent of organic matter.

7.7. Calcium and Phosphorus in Soft Tissues. The 1 per cent of body calcium which occurs outside the bones is widely distributed throughout the organs and tissues, where it exists, at least in part, in the colloidal state. The large amounts of phosphorus which are found elsewhere than in the bones are present mostly in organic combinations such as phosphoprotein, nucleoprotein, phospholipids, phosphocreatine, hexose phosphate, and others. Phosphate is a component of many enzyme systems. The discussions of phosphorus compounds in earlier chapters have indicated their distribution and functions and serve to show the many roles which the element plays in the organism other than as a structural element in bone. Phosphorus makes up 0.15 to 0.2 per cent of the soft tissues of the body.

7.8. Calcium and Phosphorus in Blood. The blood cells are almost or entirely devoid of calcium, but the serum, in health, contains from 9 to 12 mg. per 100 ml. in most species. In the laying hen, a much higher level occurs during egg production. Two types of serum calcium are distinguished, *diffusible* and *nondiffusible*, differentiated by a membrane impermeable to colloids. Most of the nondiffusible calcium is bound to protein. The diffusible fraction, which makes up 60 per cent or more of the total, is present largely as compounds of phosphate and bicarbonate and is the part which has been of principal significance in calcium and phosphorus nutrition. Isotope studies have shown that ingested calcium is found nearly equally distributed between the free and the protein-bound fraction. It is apparent that an equilibrium exists

[6] T. G. Taylor, J. H. Moore, and F. Hertelendy, *Brit. J. Nutrition*, **14**:49–57, 1960.

between the ionic and the protein-bound forms and redistribution between the two states is a continuing process. Thus the distinction between the two forms may have only minor metabolic significance.

The level of diffusible calcium is not necessarily higher in active metabolism. In addition to its function in bone deposition, the serum calcium is essential for the clotting of the blood and is concerned in the maintenance of acid-base equilibrium. It also plays a role in the physiological balance of basic ions (Sec. 7.61).

While the primary source of blood calcium is obviously the food, its level is not readily influenced by the dietary intake, though there are species differences in this respect. Various physiological factors tend to maintain a constant level, despite high intakes on the one hand or marked body losses on the other. The most important factor is a hormone secreted by the parathyroid glands which functions as need exists by mobilizing calcium from the bones (Sec. 7.10). If the parathyroids are removed or fail to function, the blood level drops and *tetany* occurs. This is a hyperirritability of the neuromuscular system which in severe cases results in convulsions. If the glands are abnormally active, as occurs in certain diseases, an excessive mobilization of calcium takes place with a consequent demineralization of the bones. There is an excessive loss of calcium from the body, principally in the urine. Blood calcium is low in "milk fever," but a low dietary intake is not the cause. It seems probable that the parathyroid glands fail to mobilize blood calcium rapidly enough to meet the drain at parturition which results from the onset of active milk secretion. Blood calcium may be low in rickets, particularly if accompanied by tetany.

Whole blood contains from 35 to 45 mg. of phosphorus per 100 ml., most of which is in the cells. The element occurs in a variety of forms, principally organic combinations. From the standpoint of mineral nutrition, our main interest lies in the inorganic phosphorus which occurs in the plasma, although it is evident that an interchange of phosphate between organic and inorganic forms continually occurs. In health its level generally lies between 4 and 9 mg. per 100 ml., depending upon the age and species. The level is higher at birth than at maturity, the most rapid decline occurring early in life. The maintenance of the inorganic phosphorus level of the blood is governed by the factors which promote calcium and phosphorus assimilation. The kidneys appear to play an important role in maintaining phosphorus balance. A low level occurs commonly in rickets.

The phosphorus compounds in the blood currently serve in phosphorylations which take place in the course of the metabolism of the sugars, as has been referred to. The calcium and phosphorus levels in the blood are important indicators of the state of nutrition of these elements, but in this connection, it should be remembered that their levels represent a balance between several opposing factors: absorption, excretion, deposition, and mobilization. Normal levels do not guarantee a normal state of bone nutrition.

7.9. Absorption and Excretion of Calcium and Phosphorus. Irrespective of the forms in which calcium and phosphorus are ingested, their absorption is dependent upon their solubility at the point of contact with the absorbing membranes. This applies both to the soluble compounds in the feed and also to the insoluble ones which are rendered soluble in passing down the digestive tract. The absorption of both calcium and phosphorus is thus favored by factors which operate to hold them in solution. An acid medium tends to prevent the formation of the insoluble and thus unabsorbable tricalcium phosphate. Lactose, which promotes an acid reaction in the digestive tract, favors absorption, and assimilation is thereby improved. Certain factors influence the absorption of one element but not the other. Large intakes of iron, aluminum, and magnesium interfere with the absorption of phosphorus by forming insoluble phosphates. An experimentally produced "beryllium rickets" is due to the effect of the beryllium in rendering phosphorus insoluble. Oxalates and phytates decrease the absorption of calcium as is discussed later (Sec. 7.15). Fatty acids may form insoluble calcium soaps which are assimilated with difficulty, yet a certain amount of fat seems to favor the absorption of this element. A great excess of either calcium or phosphorus interferes with the absorption of the other, a fact which helps to explain why a certain ratio between them in the diet is desirable for their best absorption. With a large excess of either element, the other one tends to become tied up as the insoluble tricalcium phosphate. One function of vitamin D is the promotion of phosphorus and calcium absorption, as is detailed later.

Differing from the organic nutrients previously discussed, a determination of apparent digestibility as measured by the difference between the amounts in the feed and feces is of no value as an indicator of the useful calcium and phosphorus. The reason for this is that the feces are a path of excretion of the minerals which have been absorbed and metabolized and thus served the body, as well of those which have escaped absorption. This fact has long been recognized, but our knowledge of the quantitative relations involved has been made much more specific by the use of the modern isotope techniques. These techniques provide for a distinction between the fecal fraction which is a metabolic excretion, the endogenous fraction, and the part representing the intake which was not absorbed. The method is illustrated by the experiment of Kleiber and coworkers.[7] A milking cow eating 11 kg. of air-dry feed showed an apparent digestibility of phosphorus of 12 per cent, based on an analysis of the intake and fecal outgo. By injection of P^{32} it was shown that 43 per cent of the total fecal output was endogenous and thus that the true digestibility was approximately 50 per cent. Later studies with lambs have shown a considerably higher true digestibility. Other studies with ruminants have shown that the major portion of the calcium found in the feces is endogenous.

The urine is also a path of calcium and phosphorus excretion. The distribution between the urine and feces varies with the species and is somewhat influenced by dietary and age factors. In all species the feces is the principal path for calcium. The same is true for phosphorus in the case of Herbivora, but the urine is the principal path for Carnivora, and the output is about equally divided between the two channels in the case of man. A variety of phosphorus compounds, chiefly phosphates, occur in the urine, of which approximately 6 per cent is in organic form. While not applicable to most animals because of the absence of sweat glands, it is interesting to note that, according to studies by Mitchell and Hamilton,[8] in profuse sweating in man substantial percentages of the total calcium and phosphorus excretions are found in the perspiration.

The term *net absorption* is used to denote the amount of calcium and phosphorus which remains in the body. It is determined by a balance experiment which measures the intake in the feed and the outgo through both urine and feces. It is particularly useful as a measure of the adequacy of calcium and phosphorus nutrition during growth. Within limits, the total net absorption increases with intake, but on the other hand, the lower the intake, the greater the efficiency of absorption.

7.10. Deposition and Mobilization of Calcium and Phosphorus. The bones serve not only as structural elements but also as storehouses of calcium and phosphorus which may be mobilized at times when the assimilation of these minerals is inadequate to meet body needs. Thus the mineral metabolism of bone involves not only the deposition of calcium and phosphorus during growth but also processes of storage and mobilization which occur throughout life. As an aid to an understanding of how these various processes take place, a diagram of a longitudinal section of bone is given in Fig. 7.2.

The growth of bone in length takes place at the junction of the epi-

[7] Max Kleiber and coworkers, Radio-phosphorus (P^{32}) as tracer for measuring endogenous phosphorus in cow's feces, *J. Nutrition,* **45**:253–263, 1951.

[8] H. H. Mitchell and T. S. Hamilton, The dermal excretion under controlled environmental conditions of nitrogen and minerals in human subjects, with particular reference to calcium and iron, *J. Biol. Chem.,* **178**:345–361, 1949.

physis and diaphysis. The cartilage in between is a temporary formation which grows by the multiplication of its own cells and continues to be replaced at both surfaces by calcified bone. When the cartilage ceases to regenerate and is entirely replaced by bone itself, the epiphysis unites with the diaphysis and growth ceases. This is referred to as the closing of the epiphysis. In the process of ossification, cartilage is converted into ossein and then calcified. The zone where this is taking place is referred to as the proliferation zone of cartilage, or the zone of provisional calcification. It is the area which is examined in the "line test" (Sec. 8.14) used as a measure of the state of calcium and phosphorus nutrition. Bone formation also occurs under the periosteum.

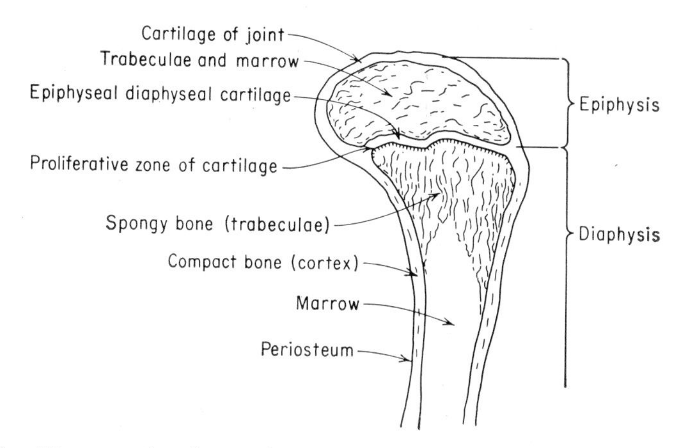

FIG. 7.2. Diagram of a longitudinal section of a growing bone. (*Courtesy of Katharine Hummel, Cornell University.*)

At first the only bone formed is of the spongy type. An internal reconstruction is responsible for the formation of the more complex structure called compact bone.

As distinguished from the shaft, the trabeculae are lacelike structures comprising the principal site in which a reserve of calcium and phosphorus is deposited for mobilization to meet needs not currently supplied by the diet. This function of the trabeculae has been clearly portrayed by the detailed studies of Bauer, Aub, and Albright.[9] These structures are located close to the epiphyseal ends of the bones where the blood supply is greatest. They provide the calcium mobilized by the parathyroid to maintain the level in the blood. During heavy lactation, they are drawn upon to meet a part of the requirements for the minerals

[9] Walter Bauer, J. C. Aub, and Fuller Albright, Studies of calcium and phosphorus metabolism. V. A study of the bone trabeculae as a readily available reserve supply of calcium, *J. Exptl. Med.*, **49**:145–161, 1929.

secreted in the milk (Sec. 16.29) and they also may be drawn upon in pregnancy. This depletion of the reserves involves no physiological harm, since they can be readily restored with an adequate diet during periods when the body needs for calcium are less, e.g., during the dry period for the dairy cow.

The above discussion implies a more static condition of the bone minerals than actually exists. Isotope studies have shown that there is a continuous interchange of calcium and phosphorus between the blood and bone and between various parts of the bones. The rate of exchange varies from region to region but is most active in the case of the spongy bone. Thus, the calcium and phosphorus in the body are in a dynamic state, similar to the situation for fat and protein previously described, and the net result of the interchange determines the nutritional status with respect to a given physiological need. In contrast to the skeleton, the calcium and phosphorus of the teeth are very little subject to mobilization and replacement. Once formed the teeth are comparatively little influenced by either the metabolic needs for these minerals or their supply in the ration.

Like the structure of bone itself, the physiochemical changes involved in the deposition of its calcium salts remain a puzzle, despite much study. There are several theories about the nature of these reactions but none which seem to provide an adequate, or at least generally accepted, explanation. Clearly, ossification is not an inert form of precipitation, or else it could normally occur anywhere in the body. First of all, there must be an appropriate supply of calcium and phosphate ions at the sites of calcification. It is agreed that certain "local factors," such as enzymes, are also essential. Both alkaline phosphatase and acid phosphatase have been found in bone tissue. The presence of other anions and cations, besides those of calcium and phosphorus, and the pH of the system influence the type of bone salt formed. There is increasing evidence that vitamin D plays a role in deposition as well as in absorption of calcium and phosphorus. It would appear that the reactions involved in deposition must be readily reversible in view of the dynamic state previously discussed.

7.11. Rickets. It is evident from the previous discussion that a failure of normal calcium and phosphorus nutrition may occur at any time of life when the supply of the elements and the factors concerned in their assimilation, notably vitamin D, are not adequate to meet functional needs. In the adult the failure is reflected in a negative balance of the minerals, and in growth the balance data show inadequate retention. At both stages there is a decreased ash content of the bones. Their consequent weakening may eventually result in certain external symptoms, such as lameness and fractures, which are alike at all ages, though, during the formative stage, abnormalities of growth which result in misshapen bones are the more common. There are, however, marked differences in the bone pathology, particularly histological, according to the stage of bone development and also according to the specific nutritional deficiency primarily concerned. Therefore various terms are used to designate different failures of calcium and phosphorus nutrition. Unfortunately there is a lack of uniformity in the use of these terms.

In its broadest sense, rickets represents a disturbance of the mineral metabolism in such a way that the calcification of the growing bone does not take place normally. This is the sense in which the term is used in this book. The formation of the organic cartilaginous matrix takes place, but calcium and phosphorus are not deposited in it. There is a lowering of the level of inorganic phosphorus or calcium or both and an increase in phosphatase, in the plasma. The blood picture varies according to the specific dietary deficiency involved. Some authorities limit the use of the term rickets, or *true rickets,* to the specific bone pathology found in very early growth, involving changes which are produced experimentally on a low-phosphorus-high-calcium diet deficient in vitamin D and which are accompanied by a low blood phosphorus. There is a widening of the epiphyseal-diaphyseal cartilage, an excessive production of osteoid tissue which accounts for the enlargement of the ends of the long bones, and other characteristic histological changes. But bone abnormalities can develop at any time during growth. They can occur at any time because of a lack of calcium as well as of phosphorus and of the vitamin, and the blood picture may vary as regards the mineral relations. Though the specific bone pathology may differ, the broad definition of rickets includes all of these nutritive failures, recognizing, however, that tetany may also occur if the blood calcium becomes very low. Frequently the terms *low-phosphorus rickets* and *low-calcium rickets* are used where a distinction is made.

The failure of bone nutrition during growth results not only in an arrest of its normal development but also in various structural abnormalities. There is an enlargement of the ends of the bones which shows itself in a beading of the ribs and certain other bones. In severe and prolonged failure of adequate nutrition, the tension of the muscles pulls the weakened bones out of shape and the weight of the body causes the leg bones to buckle and even to fracture. Rapid growth accelerates the development of rickets, probably caused in part by the demands of muscle formation for phosphorus.

Rickets is very common in calves and pigs. In calves its occurrence is revealed in decreased growth, stiffness of gait, enlarged and painful joints, arching of the back, and, as an extreme symptom, the birth of weak or deformed calves. A low blood calcium appears to be a more marked and regular finding than low phosphorus. In swine, retarded growth, enlarged joints, and bone deformities which may produce posterior paralysis are the most evident physical symptoms. In pigs low blood phosphorus is a characteristic finding, but on low-calcium rations the blood calcium may be low also. In lambs enlarged joints which are frequently painful, stiffness, and irregular gain are common. The occurrence of the disease in this species has been described by Duckworth and associates.[10] Rickets has also been reported in horses, chickens, dogs, and several other species. In all of them retardation of growth, inadequate calcification, and bone malformations result.

7.12. Osteomalacia. The term osteomalacia is commonly used to denote a failure of calcium and phosphorus nutrition in the adult bone, and it is so used in this book. A mobilization of calcium and phosphorus salts from the bones of the adult, exceeding the reserve supply, results in a breakdown of the structural portion. This excessive mobilization may be caused by an overfunctioning of the parathyroid or by some other pathological condition, but it is caused most frequently by a continued body demand for calcium and phosphorus which is greatly in excess of the supply being assimilated. Most of the acute cases occur during pregnancy and lactation when, owing to an inadequate diet, excessive demands are made upon bones already depleted. Any adult animal which continually fails to receive calcium and phosphorus nutrition adequate for its needs must gradually deplete its bones. Whether this occurs to the point where the bones break down or production becomes lessened depends upon the extent of the deficiency.

A striking depletion of the bones which resulted in broken pelves in dairy cows continuously fed on calcium-deficient roughages has been described by Becker, Neal, and Shealy.[11] A similar condition caused by phosphorus deficiency has been reported from South Africa and elsewhere. Osteomalacia in horses on a low-calcium-high-phosphorus ration has been reported by Phillippine workers. The trouble has been reported in sheep, beef cattle, swine, and other species. A characteristic feature of the trouble is a negative calcium and phosphorus balance. The blood may be low in one or both of the minerals. If very low in calcium, there may be tetany also. Provided it is not too far advanced, osteomalacia responds to treatment by correcting the dietary deficiency which is responsible for the inadequate calcium and phosphorus nutrition of the bones. Clearly, the necessity of giving attention to bone nutrition

[10] J. Duckworth, W. Godden, and W. Thomson, The relation between rates of growth and rickets in sheep on diets deficient in vitamin D, *J. Agr. Sci.*, **33**:190–196, 1943.

[11] R. B. Becker, W. M. Neal, and A. L. Shealy, Effect of calcium-deficient roughages upon milk production and welfare of dairy cows, *Florida Agr. Expt. Sta. Tech. Bull.* 262, 1933.

does not end with the close of the growth period. An active metabolism continues throughout life, and for a normal productive life of breeding stock and lactating animals, this nutrition must be such as to ensure that the bones do not become depleted, even though acute symptoms of osteomalacia do not occur. An accelerated mobilization of bone minerals and a decreased utilization of food calcium complicate the problem of

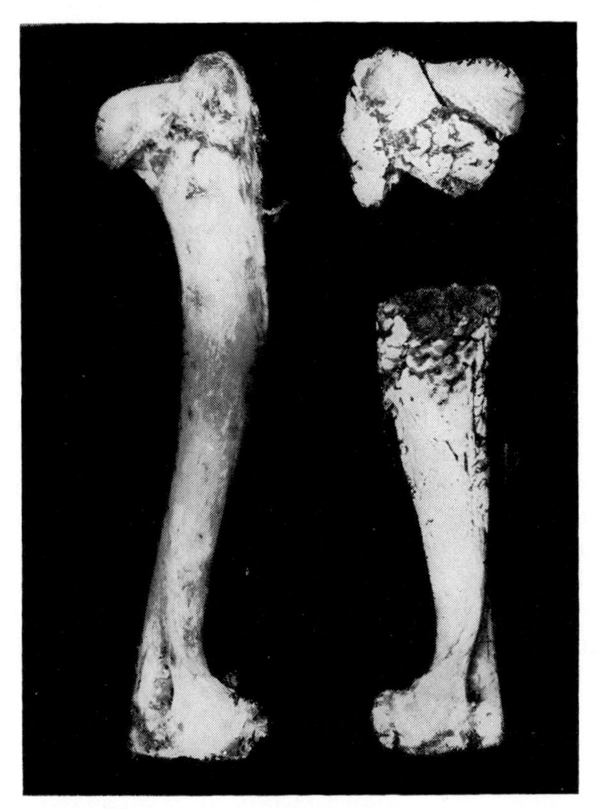

FIG. 7.3. Bones removed from an old dog on autopsy. The one on the right shows failure to heal following a fracture. (*Courtesy of C. M. McCay, Cornell University.*)

maintaining the bone structure in old age. For this reason also bones which accidentally break in old age are slow, or even fail, to heal (Fig. 7.3).

Like rickets, osteomalacia is a term used in somewhat different senses by different authorities. In reading accounts of investigations dealing with either of these troubles, it is important to note how the terms are being used. *Osteoporosis* is another term that has a rather variable meaning. Those who consider the low-phosphorus variety as the only true rickets have employed it to denote the histology where low calcium is primarily involved. In man the term is used to denote the result of a defective synthesis of the protein matrix of bone which commonly occurs in old age, with a resulting decalcification. What specific nutritional factors may be involved remain uncertain. *Aphosphoresis* and *acalciosis* denote, respectively, a condition due to a lack of phosphorus and a condition due to a lack of calcium. The role of vitamin D in these variously named troubles is discussed later (Sec. 8.11).

7.13. The Effects of High Intakes of Calcium. Deleterious effects on over-all nutrition can result from excessive intakes of calcium. By "excessive" is meant levels markedly higher than body requirements. Within an appropriate calcium-phosphorus ratio the effects noted have been due to an unfavorable influence on the assimilation of other mineral nutrients rather than to an action of calcium per se. Particularly when the intake of magnesium, iron, iodine, manganese, zinc, or copper is borderline in terms of needs, deficiency symptoms of the borderline element have been produced experimentally. The extent of the practical importance of these findings for farm animals has not been established. Experimental results showing that increasing the calcium content of the diet well above requirements without concurrently increasing the zinc results in a severe parakeratosis in swine and that high levels of calcium and/or phosphorus in the rations of swine and poultry intensify the effect of manganese deficiency are cases in point. A further discussion of the effects of relatively excessive levels of calcium is presented later as the minerals in question are taken up. In general, it would appear that harmful effects may occur in practice from rations containing calcium markedly in excess of body needs unless attention is given to ensuring liberal intakes of those minerals which, otherwise, may become relatively deficient.

Experiments dealing with this general problem have been reviewed by Davis.[12]

7.14. The Calcium and Phosphorus Content of Feeds. The different concentrates and roughages vary widely in their content of calcium and phosphorus. Certain combinations furnish a sufficient supply of these minerals, while others are deficient. Thus an important aid in providing for adequate calcium and phosphorus nutrition is a general knowledge of the composition of the common feeds. This knowledge enables the feeder to consider minerals, as well as protein and total digestible nutrients, in making up his rations and provides him with the information for determining when supplementary sources of these elements are needed.

The relative amounts of calcium in certain typical feeds are shown in

[12] George K. Davis, Effects of high calcium intakes on the absorption of other nutrients, *Federation Proc.*, **18**:1119–1123, 1959.

Fig. 7.4. For comparative purposes the values for skim milk and corn silage are given on a dry basis. The cereal seeds are all low in calcium. Legume seeds, notably soybeans, are higher, and the same is true for the oil meals. All seeds and their products, however, must be classed as poor sources of calcium in terms of the requirement of the animal body. Grass hays, such as timothy, are also poor in contrast to legume hays, which are rich. On a dry basis, skim milk exceeds grass hays in calcium content. Much richer than any of the feeds shown in the chart, however, are the animal by-products containing bone, such as tankage, meat scrap, and fish meal. A 60 per cent protein tankage will furnish

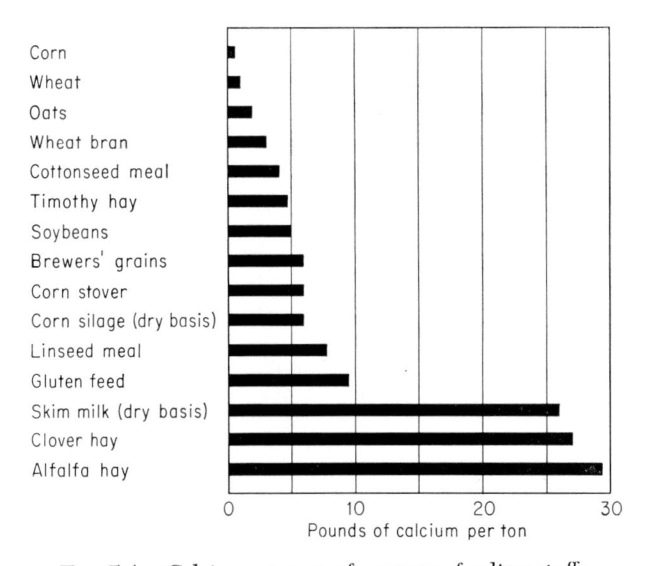

FIG. 7.4. Calcium content of common feeding stuffs.

four or five times as much calcium as will legume hay or skim milk and twenty times as much as will vegetable protein concentrates such as the oil meals.

As is shown in Fig. 7.5, these same feeds present a very different picture in phosphorus content. Here the seeds are uniformly higher than the roughages, and seed by-products, such as wheat bran and the oil meals, are especially rich in phosphorus. Skim milk is the only feed included in the charts which can be classed as rich in both calcium and phosphorus. The bone-carrying animal by-products are also very rich in both elements. Tankage supplies more than twice as much phosphorus as any feed shown in Fig. 7.5. The milled flours are lower in both calcium and phosphorus than the whole seeds.

While the data presented in Figs. 7.4 and 7.5 are useful to show the differences between the various kinds of feeds, they must not be considered to be exact values, because the calcium and phosphorus contents of feeds, especially the roughages, are variable according to the nature of the soil on which they are grown, the fertilizer used, and the water relations. Timothy hay grown on fertile soil may contain two or three times as much calcium as that grown on a worn-out acid soil. On the other hand, legume hays require a soil rich in lime for satisfactory growth, and thus, while they show some variation according to soil, they can always be relied upon as rich sources of calcium. All hays are highly variable in phosphorus content according to the supply available

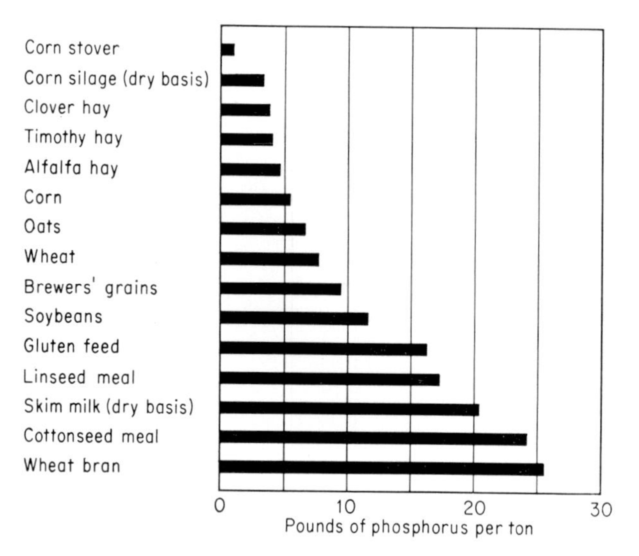

FIG. 7.5. Phosphorus content of common feeding stuffs.

in the soil and to other factors. Thus, the feeder must know something about the mineral content of his roughage in order to tell the exact conditions under which he needs a mineral supplement. General statements that one type of hay always needs a supplement while another type never does cannot always hold. Pasture grass is subject to even larger variations than dry roughage because the species of the grasses is a large factor and because climatic conditions also play a role.

On the basis of the survey reported by Collins and associates,[13] it may be calculated that, aside from a few limited areas, the water consumed provides an insignificant amount of calcium in terms of body needs.

[13] W. D. Collins, W. L. Lamar, and E. W. Lohr, The industrial utility of public water supplies in the United States, 1932, *U.S. Geol. Survey Water Supply Paper* 658, 1934.

7.15. Availability of Calcium and Phosphorus of Feeds. The possibility that the availability of calcium and phosphorus may vary considerably according to their chemical combination or physical association with other compounds in feeds must be recognized. There is little specific knowledge on this point, however.

Much research has centered around the question of the availability of phosphorus present as *phytin*, or *phytic acid*. The latter compound is an acid hexaphosphoric acid ester of inositol (Sec. 8.60). It occurs as salts of calcium, magnesium, etc., the complex being referred to as phytin. Half or more of the phosphorus of most mature seeds and their products, notably wheat bran which is a rich source, is so combined. Thus, the question of its availability is an important one in animal nutrition. There is no simple answer.

As a result of many studies, some of which have produced seemingly contradictory results, it is now clear that the answer is different for different species and also varies according to the level of vitamin D in the ration. There is clear evidence that ruminants can utilize phytin phosphorus satisfactorily. Reid and coworkers[14] found that in sheep ingested phytates were completely hydrolyzed in the alimentary tract, primarily in the rumen. Several studies have shown that this form of phosphorus is less well utilized than the inorganic form by rats, chickens, dogs, pigs, and man, but that a liberal supply of vitamin D partially corrects the lower utilization. This correction appears to be nearly complete for rats but much less in the case of chickens. Gillis and coworkers[15] found with chicks that in vitamin D deficiency, phytin phosphorus was not appreciably utilized and that with adequate vitamin D it was only 10 per cent as effective as disodium phosphate. Other studies have shown that laying hens fed rations adequate in the vitamin utilized calcium phytate or feed phytin about one-half as effectively as inorganic phosphates. How vitamin D specifically acts in improving the utilization of phytin phosphorus is not clear.

It is clear that, in those species which utilize phytin phosphorus less effectively than the inorganic form, phytin is incompletely broken down in the digestive tract. Both dietary *phytase* and microbiological activity appear to be concerned in the extent of this breakdown. Experiments with dogs and man have produced evidence that undigested phytate precipitates calcium, preventing its absorption and thus resulting in poorer bone calcification. On the other hand, in the reports of the experiments with rats and chickens a lessened supply of absorbable phosphorus

[14] R. L. Reid and coworkers, The utilization of phytate phosphorus by sheep, *Australian Vet. J.*, **23**:136–140, 1947.

[15] M. B. Gillis, K. W. Keane, and R. A. Collins, Comparative metabolism of phytate and inorganic P^{32} by chicks and poults, *J. Nutrition*, **62**:13–26, 1957.

is stressed. It seems reasonable to believe that species differences are here involved. While the end results can be definitely measured for all species in terms of bone calcification, the differences in intermediate metabolism which may be concerned are particularly difficult to study because of the interrelations of calcium, phosphorus, and vitamin D.

Both rat and human experiments have shown that the availability of the calcium of certain leafy materials is impaired by the presence of oxalic acid. The acid precipitates the calcium and prevents its absorption. In the case of spinach, for example, there is usually enough oxalic acid present to render all of its calcium unavailable. On the other hand, the calcium of kale, which contains practically no oxalic acid, is nearly as well assimilated as that of milk. It is unsafe, on the basis of the present evidence, to generalize from these results regarding effects on farm animals. One report has indicated that no interference with calcium assimilation occurs in cattle, and this observation was explained on the basis that oxalic acid is broken down in the rumen. On the other hand, there is a report of decalcification in sheep grazed on feed high in oxalic acid. It has also been reported that halogeton, a weed containing 20 to 25 per cent of soluble oxalates, which heavily infests certain range grazing areas, has caused injury under certain conditions. This problem is discussed in the bulletin by Cook and Stoddart.[16] Both the oxalic acid content of feeds and its significance in the metabolism of various species need further study.

7.16. Phosphorus Deficiency and Appetite. A deficiency of phosphorus has a specific effect in causing a loss of appetite and even a depraved appetite, frequently referred to as "pica," which is exhibited in the eating of bones, wood, clothing, and other materials to which the animal may have access. The animal becomes very emaciated. This condition is most frequently met in grazing animals in areas where the soil, and thus the forage, is very low in phosphorus. It may also occur in barn feeding, and here a lack of vitamin D may also be involved. Very large losses have occurred among grazing animals in different parts of the world as a result of this severe phosphorus deficiency, even where the forage was abundant and nutritionally adequate in other respects. Many of the deaths have resulted from diseases to which the weakened animals become especially susceptible, notably from infections contracted by eating decaying bones of animals which had died. Bone meal or other rich sources of phosphorus are now being effectively used to prevent these losses.

The fact that phosphorus deficiency results in a severe emanciation has raised the question as to whether there is a poorer utilization of the small

[16] C. Wayne Cook and L. A. Stoddart, The halogeton problem in Utah, *Utah Agr. Expt. Sta. Bull.* 364, 1953.

amount of food consumed. In studying this question with dairy cattle, Riddell, Hughes, and Fitch[17] found no decrease in digestibility, but there was evidence of a higher energy metabolism. From a critical experiment with beef heifers, Kleiber, Goss, and Guilbert[18] concluded that loss of appetite was the main factor but that there was a slightly lower efficiency of energy utilization.

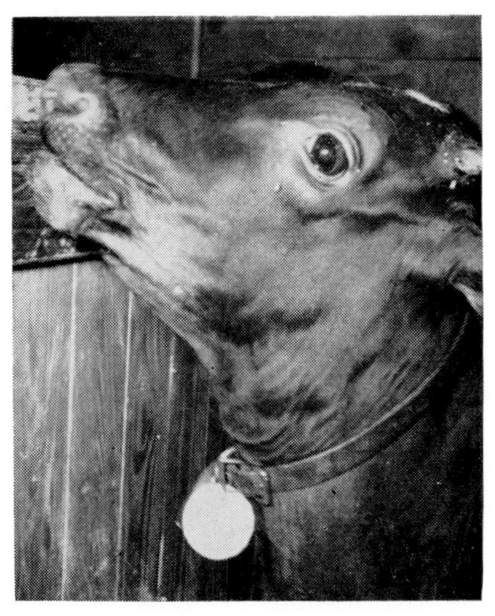

FIG. 7.6. Phosphorus-deficient calf chewing wood. (*Courtesy of S. E. Smith, Cornell University.*)

7.17. Calcium and Phosphorus Supplements. In selecting rations for their calcium and phosphorus content, consideration should first be given to supplying the minerals, in so far as possible, by choosing those feeding stuffs which are rich in the elements needed. However, the farmer must build his rations around the available feeding stuffs on his own farm, and it may not be practicable for him to make up his rations so that they will be rich in the needed minerals. Wherever it is not practicable or possible to provide for adequate mineral nutrition by an appropriate combination of the feeding stuffs available, mineral supplements should be used.

The qualities which determine the feeding value of a supplement are content of calcium and phosphorus, fineness of division, and freedom from harmful impurities. The analyses of commonly available calcium and phosphorus supplements are:

	Calcium, %	Phosphorus, %
Steamed bone meal	31.3	14.4
Dicalcium phosphate	23.5	18.7
Defluorinated phosphates	29 to 36	12 to 15
Ground limestone	38.5	

The chemical composition of these supplements varies according to the purity of the raw material and the method of processing. Standard

[17] W. H. Riddell, J. S. Hughes, and J. B. Fitch, The relation of phosphorus deficiency to the utilization of feed in dairy cattle, *Kansas Agr. Expt. Sta. Tech. Bull.* 36, 1934.

[18] Max Kleiber, Harold Goss, and H. R. Guilbert, Phosphorus deficiency metabolism and food utilization in beef heifers, *J. Nutrition,* **12**:121–153, 1936.

products should have a composition approximating that represented by the figures given in the table. The figure for ground limestone is representative of the high-calcium products available. Dolomitic limestones have much smaller and variable contents of calcium.

Many studies have shown that the minerals of these supplements are readily utilizable by both animals and man. Assuming that no harmful substances are present in the supplements and that the latter are in a suitable physical condition, all may be considered to be of approximately equal value per unit of calcium and phosphorus present. Though insoluble in water, they are similar in value to soluble salts of the minerals because, as previously explained (Sec. 7.9), it is the solubility at the point of absorption that counts. As regards chemically prepared salts, orthophosphates are readily available, but the meta- and pyrophosphates are of very limited availability, at least for chickens. The calcium in complex iron calcium silicates has also been found to be unavailable. Phosphoric acid has been found to be a highly available source of phosphorus for swine and cattle.

7.18. Rock Products. *Defluorinated Phosphates.* The calcium and phosphorus of raw rock phosphate and of superphosphate are absorbable, but the feeding of these products is harmful because of the fluorine present (Sec. 7.54). Spurred on particularly by wartime needs, processes were developed for removing this fluorine, and thus the production of "defluorinated phosphates." The calcium and phosphorus contents of these phosphates are given as ranges, reflecting the variations in the various products according to source of raw material and method of manufacture. Defluorinated superphosphate contains more of both minerals than does defluorinated rock phosphate, as is to be expected. Dicalcium phosphate can be made from either bone or rock, but where the latter source is used, the fluorine must be removed. The term "defluorinated" does not guarantee a safe product, because safety depends on the extent of the removal of fluorine, and products vary in this respect. The maximum fluorine content which is allowable in a mineral supplement for different species is discussed later (Sec. 7.54).

Various defluorinated phosphates have been tested experimentally with rats, chickens, pigs, and calves. Several have been found satisfactory, having a calcium and phosphorus availability equal to that of steamed bone meal or dicalcium phosphate. Some products have given poorer results, however. The differences in availability are attributable in large part to the amounts of pyrophosphate and metaphosphate present. These forms are less available than the usual ortho form. The temperature at which the fluorine is eliminated is a large factor in determining the relative amounts of the different forms in the final product. Much information along these lines is to be found in the reports of a collaborators' study.[19] In general, the products available today are better than those studed at that time, however.

Colloidal phosphate, or soft rock phosphate, frequently offered for feeding purposes, is a mixture of fine rock and clay. *Phosphatic limestone* is a product having a composition similar to a mixture of limestone and rock phosphate. Both the colloidal phosphate and the limestone product have nearly as much fluorine per unit of phosphorus as does the rock and, thus, are not satisfactory phosphorus supplements unless defluorinated.

Curacao phosphate is a special rock phosphate naturally low in fluorine (0.4 per cent). It contains approximately 33 per cent of calcium and 14.5 per cent of phosphorus, both of which are highly available to animals.

MAGNESIUM

Though present in the body in a much smaller amount, the magnesium is closely associated with calcium and phosphorus, both in its distribution and in its metabolism. Approximately 70 per cent of the body supply is in the skeleton, the remainder being found widely distributed in the various fluids and other soft tissues. Approximately one-third of the supply in the bones is subject to mobilization for soft-tissue use when the intake is inadequate. Depending on the species and individual, blood serum normally contains 2 to 5 mg. of the element per 100 ml. The considerable percentage which is found elsewhere than in the bones indicates that its distribution in the body as a whole follows that of phosphorus rather than of calcium. In fact, though the calcium content of the entire body is many times that of magnesium, the soft tissues actually contain much more of the latter. Like calcium and phosphorus, magnesium is excreted in both the urine and feces. The major output is found in the feces.

As well as serving as an essential constituent of bones and teeth, magnesium is required for various body processes, notably as an activator of various enzymes. Magnesium has been ascribed a helpful role in rickets by some investigators and a harmful role by others. It may well exert a variable effect here depending on the level of intake and the calcium-phosphorus ratio.

7.19. Symptoms of Magnesium Deficiency. In 1926 Leroy of France showed that magnesium is essential for the growth of rats. Later, Kruse,

[19] H. R. Bird and associates, Nutritive evaluation of defluorinated phosphates and other phosphorus supplements. II. Defluorinated phosphates as phosphorus supplements for chicks, *J. Assoc. Offic. Agr. Chemists*, **28**:118–129, 1945; N. R. Ellis and associates, III. Utilization experiments with rats, *J. Assoc. Offic. Agr. Chemists*, **28**:129–142, 1945.

Orent, and McCollum described the specific symptoms. Lowering the magnesium content of the diet to 1.8 p.p.m. resulted, in rats, in vasodilation, hyperirritability, convulsions, and death. In the main the same symptoms occurred in dogs. A characteristic blood finding was a lowered magnesium content but normal calcium and phosphorus. This picture led the investigators to call the trouble "magnesium tetany," thus distinguishing it from the usual tetany in which a low blood calcium is characteristic. Later workers with rats found a decrease in the ash content of the bone, reflecting a large loss of magnesium and some loss of calcium and phosphorus as well. Clinical and neurological changes similar to those found in the rat have been reported for the chick. Pigs on magnesium-deficient rations become irritable, show a reluctance to stand, lose equilibrium, go into tetany, and eventually die.

A tetany in calves, characterized by a low blood magensium with normal calcium and phosphorus, was reported by Duncan, Huffman, and Robinson[20] of the Michigan Experiment Station. The calves were reared for extended periods either on milk alone, a food which is rather low in magnesium, or on milk plus special supplements which contained little or none of the element. These observations were confirmed by other workers using purified diets very low in the element. In calves showing the typical symptoms, the magnesium in the blood serum is frequently as low as 0.1 mg. per 100 ml. compared with a normal of around 2.5 mg. This lowering of the blood level is preceded or accompanied by a large loss from the bones. On post-mortem examination the calves which died on the Michigan experiment revealed marked calcium deposits in the arteries, myocardium, and skeletal muscles. In a similar study, Blaxter and coworkers,[21] using a purified diet low in magnesium, produced a deficiency in calves which was characterized by a large drop in blood magnesium but no effect on calcium and phosphorus metabolism. There was tetany and a depletion of bone magnesium, but no pathological calcifications in the endocardium or vascular system. It seems possible that differences in the magnesium concentration in the two diets and also in the relative levels of calcium and phosphorus (Sec. 7.21) resulted in calcification of the soft tissues in one experiment and not in the other.

The findings with calves have focused attention on a disease of cattle called "grass tetany," or "grass staggers." This disease has been reported from Holland and New Zealand as a sickness that occurs in fresh cows within a week or two after they are turned out to pasture.

[20] C. W. Duncan, C. F. Huffman, and C. S. Robinson, Magnesium studies in calves. I. Tetany produced by a ration of milk, or milk with various supplements, *J. Biol. Chem.*, **108**:35–44, 1935.

[21] K. L. Blaxter, J. A. F. Rook, and A. M. MacDonald, Experimental magnesium deficiency in calves. I. Clinical and pathological observations, *J. Comp. Pathol. Therap.*, **64**:157–175, 1954.

Less definite reports have appeared as to its sporadic occurrence in the United States. According to the early studies by Sjollema[22] of the disease in Holland, the physical symptoms and the lowered blood level are similar to those of magnesium tetany and there is a similar frequency of fatal outcome. The pasturage on which the cows developed the disease was not unusually low in magnesium, however. New Zealand workers have reported that animals suffering from the disease and having a low blood magnesium respond to the administration of salts of the element. In the United States physical symptoms characteristic of grass tetany and locally referred to as wheat poisoning, because of the nature of the pasture, have been reported in cattle and sheep in the Texas panhandle and adjacent areas. Sometimes the blood has been found low in magnesium and also calcium, sometimes not. In general the supply of these minerals in the grass has appeared adequate. It seems clear that all the troubles referred to as grass staggers, or grass tetany, cannot be attributed to a simple magnesium deficiency. There is some evidence that hormonal disturbance is involved in certain cases. Faulty mineral interrelations in the feed may also be concerned.

7.20. Body Needs and Feed Supplies. While studies indicate that there are some species differences, it appears that the magnesium requirement of farm animals for growth is of the order of 0.06 per cent of the dry ration, assuming that the calcium and phosphorus intakes are adequate but not excessive. Most of the commonly fed roughages and concentrates contain at least 0.1 per cent of magnesium on a dry-matter basis, and many have three or four times this figure. Thus, assuming that the needs of other species are similar to those of calves and chicks, it would seem likely that the commonly fed rations of farm animals can be relied upon to supply an adequate amount without supplementation.

7.21. Interrelations of Magnesium with Calcium and Phosphorus. It has been shown with laboratory animals, notably the guinea pig and cotton rat, that, with diets adequate in magnesium and other nutrients, increasing the calcium or phosphorus or both results in symptoms of magnesium deficiency. With borderline intakes of magnesium the effects are much more marked on the production of calcification in the soft tissues and also on growth. The physiological explanations for these effects are not clear. There is evidence of decreased absorption or increased excretion of magnesium, or both. Quite evidently, high calcium and phosphorus intakes have the practical effect of increasing the minimum magnesium requirement for the species studied. Whether the findings discussed above hold for farm animals and have practical importance for them accordingly remains unknown. An early finding with laboratory

[22] B. Sjollema, On the nature and therapy of grass staggers, *Vet. Record,* n.s., **10:** 425-431, 450–453, 1930.

animals showed that the injection of magnesium causes a large loss of calcium in the urine with accompanying pathological symptoms and that magnesium interferes with calcification in vitro. These findings raised the question whether the high level of magnesium in certain water supplies and, particularly, the feeding of dolomitic limestone as a calcium supplement might not adversely affect calcium assimilation in practice. Some positive evidence for this view was suggested by early work.

It has become apparent, however, from several carefully controlled studies with different species that, when the magnesium is ingested instead of injected, there is a much smaller loss of calcium or no loss at all, due to a selective absorption which prevents most of the magnesium from entering the blood stream. It also appears that the extent of the absorption and thus of the deleterious effect on calcium retention is governed by the amount of calcium and phosphorus, particularly the latter, in the ration. When these two elements are present in liberal amounts, the harmful effect of the magnesium is slight or nil. Palmer, Eckles, and Schutte,[23] for example, showed that the ingestion of magnesium sulfate by cattle on a low-phosphorus diet results in serious and continuous losses of calcium which are overcome by increasing the phosphorus content of the ration.

Experiments with pigs, chickens, and rats, using rations liberal in phosphorus, have shown that dolomitic limestone is a satisfactory source of calcium for bone formation despite its magnesium content. Thus it appears that, provided both calcium and phosphorus are plentifully supplied, the ingestion of at least a moderate excess of magnesium, either in a mineral supplement or in water or other foods, will not markedly disturb calcium retention though it may tend to increase the requirements for calcium and phosphorus in the ration.

A review of the experiments bearing on the discussion in this section and on related interrelationships is to be found in the paper by O'Dell.[24]

SODIUM, POTASSIUM, AND CHLORINE

Differing from the minerals previously discussed, these minerals occur largely in the fluids and soft tissues. They function in maintaining osmotic pressure and acid-base equilibrium, in controlling the passage of nutrients into cells, and in water metabolism in general. Nutritionally they are of minor importance in the sense that meeting body needs

[23] L. S. Palmer, C. H. Eckles, and D. J. Schutte, Magnesium sulfate as a factor in the retention of calcium and phosphorus in cattle, *Proc. Soc. Exptl. Biol. Med.*, **26**:58–62, 1928.

[24] Boyd L. O'Dell, Magnesium requirement and its relation to other dietary constituents, *Federation Proc.*, **19**:648–654, 1960.

presents no practical problem and dangers of excessive intakes exist only in special situations. There is a regular dietary need; however, because of limited storage, the current excess being rapidly excreted. The body has some ability to conserve its supply through lessened excretion when the intake is limited. A deficiency of any of these elements results in lack of appetite, a decline of growth, loss of weight and production in the adult, and decreased blood levels—general symptoms which reflect more specific physiological and pathological changes for each.

7.22. Sodium. The body contains approximately 0.2 per cent of sodium. Some of this amount is localized in the skeleton in an insoluble, rather inert form, but by far the larger proportion is found in the extracellular fluids where it undergoes a very active metabolism. The element makes up 93 per cent of the bases of the blood serum, and thus it is the predominant basic element concerned in neutrality regulation. Sodium seems to be absent from blood cells, but it does occur in considerable amounts in the muscles, where it is associated in some unknown way with their contraction. A lack of the element also lowers the utilization of digested protein and energy and prevents reproduction. In laying hens, a deficiency results in lowered production, loss of weight, and cannibalism.

Sodium salts are readily absorbed and circulate throughout the entire body. Excretion takes place through the kidneys as chlorides and phosphates. There is some loss in the perspiration, which, in man at hard work, particularly in warm weather, may represent by far the major portion of the total excretion. Sodium requirements for growth ranging between approximately 0.1 per cent and 0.2 per cent of the ration have been reported from studies with rats, chicks, pigs, and calves. The exact figure depends on the species and certain mineral relations in the diet. The commonly used feeds do not contain sufficient sodium to meet body needs, but this deficiency is more than covered by the practice of including common salt in the ration.

7.23. Potassium. The potassium content of the body is similar to the sodium content, but it exists primarily as a cellular constituent. Human-blood cells, for example, contain over twenty times as much of the element as does the plasma. Potassium plays a vital role in muscle, where its content is six times that of sodium. While blood plasma contains many times as much sodium as potassium, in milk the reverse is true. The reason for the very different distribution throughout the body of these two elements, which are so closely related chemically, is a mystery.

Potassium deficiency has been experimentally produced in several species. In addition to nonspecific gross symptoms, there is a lowered content of the element in the heart and other organs, heart lesions, tubular degeneration of the kidneys, and other pathological changes. As studied with rats, pigs, and chickens the potassium requirement markedly exceeds that of sodium. Reported figures range from approximately 0.2 per cent to approximately 0.3 per cent of the dry ration. The commonly fed rations of farm animals can be counted on to meet these requirements. Potassium, like sodium, is readily absorbed, and the excess over body needs is immediately excreted. This excretion normally takes place in the urine to the extent of 90 per cent, but profuse sweating diverts a large portion through this channel.

The fact that plant products contain many times as much potassium as of sodium early raised the question as to the significance of the *sodium-potassium* ratio in the diet. In 1873 Bunge,[25] on the basis of rather meager data, evolved the theory that an excessive intake of potassium impoverished the organism of sodium and chlorine. This theory was extended to explain the apparently larger requirement of Herbivora than of other species for common salt as being due to the great excess of potassium relative to sodium in leafy materials. Pasture grass, for example, may contain 18 times as much potassium as sodium. Modern controlled studies with rats and poultry have shown that there are certain interrelationships between sodium and potassium in metabolism; for example, at inadequate levels of either, the deficiency symptoms are aggravated by a large excess of the other. These findings are illustrated by the experiments of Burns and associates.[26] It seems apparent, however, that sodium-potassium antagonism is not a matter of practical importance in the feeding of farm animals.

7.24. Chlorine. Differing from sodium and potassium, chlorine is found in large concentrations both within and without the cells of the body tissues. Blood cells contain about one-half as much as the plasma. Approximately 15 to 20 per cent of the chlorine of the body appears to be in organic combination. The chlorides of the blood, principally sodium chloride, make up two-thirds of its acidic ions. This indicates their large role in acid-base relations. The gastric secretion contains chlorine as free acid and in the form of salts. The body has a certain capacity to store chlorine in the skin and subcutaneous tissues. Its excretion follows that of sodium and potassium. The body's requirement is approximately half of that for sodium.

7.25. Common Salt. The age-old practice of including salt in the diets of both man and animals means that most of the sodium

[25] Gustave von Bunge (1844–1920), trained both in chemistry and in medicine, had a long and outstanding career as a teacher and investigator, serving for many years as professor of physiological chemistry at Basel. He made many contributions to the knowledge of the nutrition of minerals, notably iron, and wrote a textbook, Physiologie des Menschen, which contains a wealth of information for the modern student.

[26] C. H. Burns, W. W. Cravens, and P. H. Phillips, The sodium and potassium requirements of the chick and their interrelationship, *J. Nutrition,* **50**:317–329, 1953.

and chlorine is both ingested and excreted in this form. Since salt serves as a condiment as well as a nutrient, the intake tends to be highly variable and frequently in excess of needs. Its use as a condiment has physiological support in evidence that it stimulates salivary secretion and promotes the action of diastatic enzymes. When the intake is at a minimum, the body makes an adjustment whereby the output of sodium and chlorine in the urine nearly ceases. In contrast, large intakes involve a correspondingly large excretion, the water requirement being increased accordingly. The kidney is the regulating organ which, through its secretory activity, controls the concentration of electrolytes in the blood.

In 1905 Babcock[27] reported a long-time study of the role of salt in the dairy ration. He found that cows receiving no salt exhibited an abnormal appetite for it after two or three weeks, but that a much longer time elapsed, even a year, before any ill effect on health was noted. Eventually there was a loss of appetite, an unthrifty condition, and a marked decline in weight and milk yield. These symptoms appeared first in the higher producers, and the breakdown most frequently occurred at calving or shortly after the height of milk flow. The feeding of salt produced rapid recoveries in animals showing acute symptoms. The long period which elapsed before health was affected by salt deprivation illustrates the ability of the body to husband its supply of sodium and chlorine, reducing their excretion to a minimum, when the intakes are very small.

This early study was confirmed and extended, over fifty years later, by Smith and Aines[28] in a much more comprehensive experiment with higher-producing cows. Sodium was found to be the primary deficiency. Its level in the blood plasma remained unchanged in cows receiving no salt, but the urine content dropped almost to zero within a month. The sodium, chloride, and potassium contents of milk remained unchanged. The supplemental salt ($NaCl$) required for lactating cows producing about 11,000 lb. of milk per year was estimated to be about 30 g. per cow per day in addition to that in the feeds used, involving a total sodium requirement of about 21.3 g. daily. The condition of one of the salt-deficient animals, reflecting a large loss of body weight and gaunt appearance, is shown in Fig. 7.7.

The human kidney may excrete as little as 1 g. or as much as 40 g. of sodium chloride per day, depending on the intake. Given normal kidneys and an appropriate water intake, large amounts can be excreted without harm. Excessive intakes, however, result in water retention in the body, causing edema. These results have been reported in chicks on rations

[27] S. M. Babcock, The addition of salt to the ration of dairy cows, *Wisconsin Agr. Expt. Sta. Ann. Rept.* 22, pp. 129–156, 1905.

[28] S. E. Smith and P. D. Aines, Salt requirements of dairy cows, *Cornell Agr. Expt. Sta. Bull.* 938, 1959.

containing little more than 3 per cent of salt. Growing sheep have been found to tolerate much higher levels.

The salt requirement is greatly increased under conditions which cause heavy sweating because of the large loss in this secretion. Miners have been noted to lose 2½ kg. of sweat per hour, containing 2 g. of sodium chloride. If large amounts of water are drunk under these conditions, cramps result. The cramps disappear on drinking water containing salt. On a low-salt diet, however, the body gradually makes an adjustment

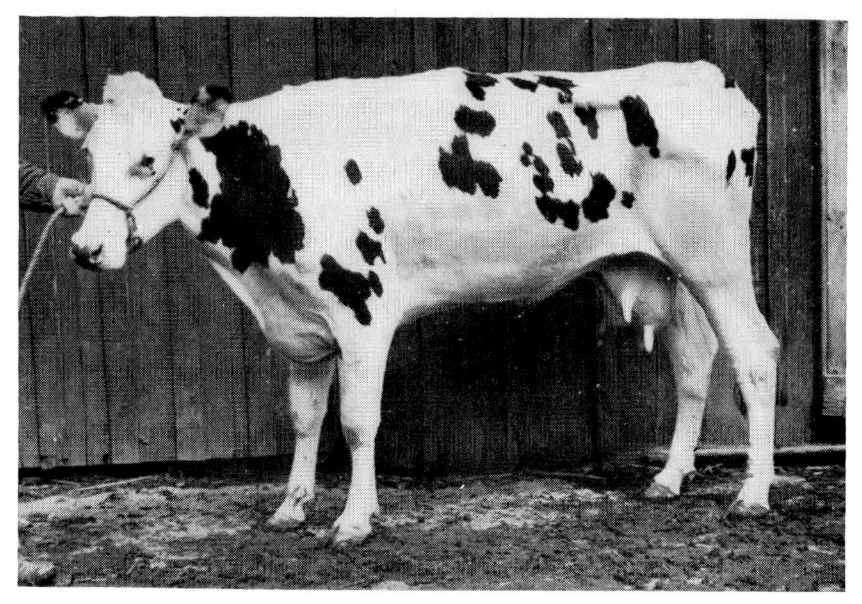

FIG. 7.7. Extreme salt deficiency in a lactating cow. (*Courtesy of S. E. Smith, Cornell University.*)

whereby the concentration in the sweat, as well as in the urine, is gradually decreased. Equilibrium between intake and outgo is thus established at a much lower level than is possible initially.

IRON

Although the body contains only about 0.004 per cent of iron, this element plays a central role in life processes. As a constituent of the respiratory pigment hemoglobin, iron is essential for the functioning of every organ and tissue of the body. It occurs as an iron-porphyrin nucleus, known as heme, not only in hemoglobin but also in proteins that are components of cytochrome *c*, peroxidase, catalase, and other enzymes. Thus, iron is a constituent of oxygen carriers and of oxidizing catalysts or enzymes. Over half of the iron present in the body is in the form of hemoglobin. Some is present in another protein, myoglobulin. In addition, a variable store is located in the liver and, secondarily, in the spleen and kidneys. Since the red cells and their hemoglobin are constantly being destroyed and replaced, iron obviously undergoes a very active metabolism. Its synthesis into hemoglobin occurs throughout life, as well as during the growing period, when the total blood supply is being augmented.

7.26. Hemoglobin Formation; Anemia. The blood cells which contain the hemoglobin are formed in the bone marrow, the process being referred to as hemopoiesis. These red corpuscles are continuously undergoing destruction and replacement. Their average life span is 127 days, according to isotope studies with rats. In the course of their destruction, the hematin of the hemoglobin is split into an iron compound, bilirubin, and other pigments which are carried to the liver and secreted in the bile. Iron released by the normal blood-cell destruction can be used again to form hemoglobin, practically without loss. In certain diseases, however, this destruction may be accelerated, and iron formed by toxic destruction cannot be reutilized. If the cells are not renewed as rapidly as they are destroyed, or if the increase in the number of cells which are required to enlarge the blood supply with growth does not occur, *anemia* results. The condition of the blood in this respect is commonly determined by measuring its hemoglobin content. The normal content for most mammals lies within the range 10 to 18 g. per 100 ml. of blood, depending on species, sex, and age. In severe anemia the value may drop to one-half or even one-third of the normal.

While the reduced hemoglobin content of the blood in anemia results primarily from a reduction in the number of red cells, there are also certain changes in the size and hemoglobin content of the cells. Thus, anemias are referred to as *microcytic*, *normocytic*, or *macrocytic* in accordance with cell size, and as *hypochromic*, *normochromic*, or *hyperchromic* in accordance with their color index. The usefulness of these various terms in characterizing the different anemias that can result from malnutrition or specific diseases will become evident in later discussions. Deficiencies of protein, iron, copper, and certain vitamins can result in anemias, most of which differ in morphological type. There are also species differences for a given deficiency. Anemia may result from an interference with or cessation of the production of hemoglobin, from a block in cell maturation, from increased destruction, or from blood loss. Various specific nutrients play a role in hemoglobin production and cell maturation, and thus the term *nutritional anemia* has a broader significance than earlier attributed to it. In addition to the anemias which result from dietary or pathological causes, there are hereditary anemias such as "sickle-cell anemia" in man and other types identified in animals.

7.27. Iron-deficiency Anemia. The anemia resulting from iron deficiency, like that produced on a low-protein intake, is obviously due to a lack of a building stone necessary for hemoglobin formation. In pigs and chickens iron deficiency results in hypochromic, microcytic anemia; in calves the microcytic, normochromic type has been reported. Anemia may occur at any time of life when the available supply of the mineral becomes deficient relative to the needs for hemoglobin formation. It is particularly likely to develop in certain species during the suckling period, since milk is very low in iron. Our knowledge of iron nutrition during this period is due particularly to the early work of Bunge and Abderhalden. A comparison of the mineral constituents of milk and of the newborn showed that, while the other constituents were in similar concentrations, the percentage of iron in the milk ash was only one-sixth of the figure for the iron in the ash of the newborn. It was also found that there was a much larger percentage of iron present at birth than later in life. The explanation was therefore made that nature provides for the iron requirements of the suckling largely by means of a store in its body at birth which may be drawn upon for blood formation and other essential functions during the period when milk is normally the principal or sole food. Bunge found that the guinea pig, which normally commences to eat leafy material within a day after birth, is born without any special store of iron.

This provision of nature for iron nutrition in the suckling does not always prove adequate. The store in the newborn is influenced by the diet of the mother during gestation. If the birth occurs prematurely, there is a smaller store because most of the storage occurs late in gestation. If the number of young born is larger than usual for the species, for example, twins in humans and extra-large litters in hogs, the individual's supply tends to be smaller. Even if the store is normal, a long nursing period without supplementary iron-rich food may exhaust it. The reserve of the human young is usually exhausted before the end of the sixth month. These factors are responsible for many cases of nutritional anemia in babies. In farm animals, the trouble occurs as a practical problem only in the case of pigs. In both species the anemia can be prevented by the feeding of iron and a trace of copper to the sucklings. It does no good to feed the mineral to the lactating mother, for the iron content of milk cannot be increased in this way. A detailed description of this anemia in suckling pigs and its treatment is given later (Sec. 14.41). While iron-deficiency anemia has been produced experimentally in lambs and calves by restricting them to a milk diet, in practice the disease is not met in these species because they early begin to eat supplementary food which supplies the needed iron.

7.28. Iron Absorption and Conservation. Iron is absorbed primarily from the small intestine, but some may be taken up from the stomach. Many studies have shown that, once iron is absorbed, it is tenaciously held by the body and not excreted to any appreciable extent. This means that, after the stores are filled, the adult animal, apart from blood loss or other pathological condition, needs little iron in its ration except for productive purposes. Both gestation and egg production call for substantial intakes, as is discussed later (Chap. 15). Given an adequate supply in its food, the animal normally regulates iron absorption in accordance with its needs. Studies using Fe^{59}, for example, have shown that there is an increased absorption during gestation to meet the needs for fetal growth. It has been postulated that the regulation of iron absorption is mediated through the iron protein complex *ferritin*, a compound which contains some 20 per cent of iron. It is explained that, as iron enters the intestinal mucosa, it unites with the protein *apoferritin* to form ferritin, and that as ferritin reaches an equilibrium with the iron reserves, further absorption is greatly decreased. The control is clearly not absolute, however.

The availability of the iron differs according to its food source. The probable reason is that the mineral occurs in a number of forms differing in the ease with which their iron is liberated in the digestion tract. In foods rich in phytic acid the iron is less available because it is precipitated as the insoluble phytate in the intestine. While chemical methods for estimating the availability of iron have been used, it is now recognized that a metabolic balance (Sec. 11.2) is the more reliable procedure. Hemoglobin regeneration in animals rendered anemic is also employed as a measure. Many such studies have been made with laboratory animals and humans, but few with farm animals. Since these studies indicate that important species differences exist, no general classification of foods as regards available iron can be made.

7.29. The Iron Value of Foods. Aside from milk, most of the feeds for animals contain very liberal amounts of iron relative to the need by the body. Leafy materials are rich sources, and so are many seeds. Since most of the iron in cereal seeds is in the outer coatings and germ, milling results in increasing the supply to animals but in decreasing it in so far as man is concerned. In so far as farm animals, including chickens, are concerned, their usual rations are so rich in iron that they can normally be counted upon to supply enough even though its availability is low. For example, a chick ration contains 30 to 50 mg. per pound in comparison with a tentative N.R.C. requirement[29] of 9 mg. On the other hand, benefits have been reported from adding iron to swine rations based on corn and soybean oil meal, without access to soil.

The largest metabolic demand for iron comes during high egg production, because eggs contain 1.1 mg. each. Probably the usual rations

[29] This term, as used here and later, refers to the requirements set up by the Committee on Animal Nutrition of the National Research Council (Sec. 12.2).

contain more than enough, but anemia has been reported in laying hens. The roughages which make up two-thirds of the ration of cattle and sheep, species which have lower requirements than pigs, commonly contain from 50 to 100 mg. of iron per pound. This should certainly ensure enough.

There have been reports, notably from Florida, of areas where the soil is so low in iron as to result in a deficiency in the forage and, thus, anemia in grazing animals. Later studies suggest, however, that other mineral deficiencies, such as cobalt or copper, may be primarily involved. From soil surveys one would not expect iron deficiency on any herbage producing a reasonably good yield. In general, there seems to be no need to supply additional iron to the rations of farm animals except for pigs on concrete. In fact, unneeded additions may be deleterious. Too much iron in the diet interferes with phosphorus absorption by forming an insoluble phosphate, and rickets may thus result on a diet otherwise adequate. The needs for iron of various species and functions are discussed in later chapters.

COPPER

As a result of a series of studies beginning in 1925, Hart and associates at the University of Wisconsin discovered that a small amount of copper is necessary, along with iron, for hemoglobin formation. It is not a constituent of hemoglobin, but it does occur as hemocuprein in blood cells. In certain invertebrates copper is present in hemocyanin that functions as an oxygen carrier.

7.30. Specific Functions of Copper. The role of copper in iron metabolism is incompletely understood. When copper is deficient in the diet, there is a decreased absorption of iron, a lowering of its total content in the body, a decrease in its mobilization from the tissues, and the development of a severe microcytic hypochromic anemia. The failure of injected iron to correct the anemia indicates that copper is essential for the utilization of iron in hemoglobin synthesis. It has been found to play a role both in hemoglobin synthesis and in red-cell maturation. It seems clear that copper exerts an influence on iron metabolism at the cellular level. The mineral is a constituent or activator of several enzymes, notably ascorbic acid oxidase, tyrosinase, cytochrome oxidase, and catalase. In pigs, cytochrome oxidase activity has been found greatly reduced in copper deficiency, and liver catalase is decreased to a lesser extent. Gubler and coworkers[30] have reported comprehensive

[30] C. J. Gubler, G. E. Cartwright, and M. M. Wintrobe, Studies on copper metabolism. XX. Enzyme activities and iron metabolism in copper and iron deficiencies, *J. Biol. Chem.*, **224**:533–546, 1957.

enzyme studies in copper and iron deficiencies in swine. Its presence in various enzyme systems also suggests that it has other basic functions besides its role in iron metabolism. This suggestion is borne out by the variety of symptoms which have been reported from copper-deficient areas or in controlled studies with herbivorous animals. Approximately half of the total body supply of copper is found in the muscle mass. Stores are also present in the bone marrow, liver, and to a lesser extent elsewhere. The total supply is only a very small fraction of the amount of iron found in the body. The body supply of copper is greatly lowered when the diet is deficient. Like iron, a large store of copper at birth serves the special purpose of providing for growth needs during the suckling period, for milk is very low in both elements.

7.31. Copper Deficiencies as Area Problems. More than a decade before the role of copper in hemoglobin formation was discovered, investigators in northern Europe were studying possible mineral deficiencies in the forage in areas where a wasting disease of cattle and sheep, called *lechsucht*, characterized by diarrhea, loss of appetite, and anemia, was common. In 1933 Sjollema established its cause as a copper deficiency by finding marked differences in the copper content of the forage in "healthy" and "sick" areas and by curing the trouble with copper therapy. Later Sjollema showed that in affected cows and goats the copper content of the blood falls to one-third of the normal concentration of 100 μg. per cent. The copper content of the liver, spleen, and hair was also decreased. It has also been established that a disease of lambs, referred to as *enzootic ataxia*, or "sway-back," and by other names and characterized by nervous symptoms, is caused by a deficiency of copper. The disease has been reported from several countries, and its prevention has been accomplished by feeding copper to the pregnant ewe. A chronic copper deficiency resulting from a low content in the herbage has also been reported responsible for a trouble in grazing cattle in Australia, known as "falling disease." This disease is characterized by staggering, falling, and instantaneous death. Troubles in cattle and sheep ascribed to copper deficiency have also been reported from South Africa, New Zealand, Scotland, and elsewhere. In the United States a wasting disease called "salt sick" was reported from Florida by Becker in 1931. It seems clear that a copper deficiency was involved, at least in some cases. Later studies indicate that copper deficiency is an important problem in certain other areas of the United States.

7.32. Symptoms of Copper Deficiency. These various reports of troubles ascribed to copper deficiency record a wide variety of symptoms differing somewhat from area to area and from species to species. The lowering of the copper content of the blood and liver is a rather constant finding, but anemia and scouring are not. The bleaching of the hair in cattle and the interference with normal wool growth in sheep have been widely reported. It has been established that copper deficiency interferes with the synthesis of keratin, the principal constituent of hair and wool. That copper deficiency results in a depigmentation of the hair was shown by Smith and Ellis,[31] as illustrated in Fig. 7.8. There was also a loss of hair and dermatosis. Marston and Lee[32] have shown

FIG. 7.8. A, rabbit reared on diet adequate in copper. B, rabbit showing graying of the hair resulting from copper deficiency. (*Courtesy of S. E. Smith, Cornell University.*)

that induced copper deficiency in sheep results in a marked decrease in the rate of wool growth and a change in its character. The depigmentation of black wool and the development of "stringy" or "steely" wool, characterized by limp, glossy fibers lacking the normal crimp, are reported

[31] Sedgwick E. Smith and G. H. Ellis, Copper deficiency in rabbits: achromotrichia, alopecia and dermatosis, *Arch. Biochem.*, **15**:81–88, 1947.

[32] H. R. Marston and H. J. Lee, Nutritional factors involved in wool production by Merino sheep. II. The influence of copper deficiency on the rate of wool growth and on the nature of the fleece, *Australian J. Sci. Research,* **1B**:376–387, 1948.

to be early symptoms. There is good evidence that these hair and wool changes reflect a failure of certain enzyme activities for which copper is essential. Specifically, the graying of black hair and wool represents a failure of melanin formation, a process for which the copper-containing enzyme tyrosinase is required.

The nervous symptoms in lambs referred to as *ataxia* have been widely reported and have been found to be associated with a low copper content of the ewe during pregnancy. Post-mortem studies have revealed nerve lesions in these lambs. The reported occurrences in cattle of abnormal gait, staggering, and falling have been referred to as nervous symptoms, but these physical symptoms vary in their appearance and severity from area to area, and it remains uncertain whether they all have the same basic cause.

Bone troubles have been described in lambs, cattle, pigs, chickens, and dogs, including symptoms such as lameness, swelling of the joints, and fragility of the bones. There is a failure of the deposition of bone in the cartilage matrix. The reported picture varies somewhat from area to area, and a simple copper deficiency cannot be considered the sole cause. In some areas low phosphorous is undoubtedly concerned. Davis, of Florida, however, has reported that on a copper-deficient muck soil, but with adequate intakes of calcium, phosphorus, and vitamin D, fragile bones of low ash content resulted. Diarrhea, anemia, hair changes, and nervous symptoms were present. In pigs fed a milk diet plus iron, lameness, rigidity of leg joints, and crooked front legs, along with anemia and hair changes, have been reported.

It has now become evident that other minerals are also involved in many of the area troubles reported. In some cases a combined copper and cobalt deficiency is concerned (Sec. 7.35). In others an excess of molybdenum, as is discussed later (Sec. 7.58), is an important factor in the occurrence of the symptoms observed. Sulfate may also be indirectly involved. These relationships help explain why a copper content in the forage which prevents troubles in one area proves inadequate in another. It has also been suggested that is some forages copper occurs in complexes of reduced availability. Studies seeking to clarify this complicated picture of copper deficiency and related troubles and, thus, to identify more clearly the specific effects of a deficiency of a given mineral are now in progress in several laboratories. An excellent review of these various area troubles and of the problems awaiting solution are presented in several chapters of the book edited by McElroy and Glass.[33]

7.33. Requirements and Feed Supply. On the basis of studies with men, dogs, and rats, the copper requirement for the prevention of anemia

[33] William D. McElroy and Bentley Glass, Copper Metabolism: A Symposium on Animal, Plant and Soil Relationships, sponsored by McCollum-Pratt Institute of Johns Hopkins University, Johns Hopkins Press, Baltimore, 1950.

is considered to be about one-tenth that of iron. Such an intake provides the amount of copper that is needed along with iron to prevent anemia in suckling pigs (Sec. 14.41). The daily copper requirement appears to be of the order of 50 mg. for cattle, 5 mg. for sheep, and 5 p.p.m. in the dry matter of the rations of swine. In areas where uncomplicated copper deficiency occurs 5 to 8 p.p.m. in the dry herbage produce healthy animals. The lower level figures out around 50 mg. per day for cattle and 5 mg. for sheep. In other areas the need for considerably higher levels has been reported. Salt licks containing 0.25 to 0.5 per cent copper sulfate, $CuSO_4 \cdot 5H_2O$, have been found effective in preventing troubles in grazing animals in areas where the herbage is deficient. Otherwise, there appears to be no need for copper supplements for cattle or sheep. According to the report of the N.R.C. Committee on Animal Nutrition, 4.5 mg. per pound of feed is adequate for baby pigs. Similarly the Committee's report for poultry tentatively lists 0.9 per pound of feed as the requirement for chicks.

While some feeding trials have shown benefits from feeding copper to pigs under practical conditions, others have not been able to demonstrate any benefit. The requirement for copper is modified by molybdenum, phosphorus, and probably other factors, thus explaining the responses to copper supplements in some experiments and not in others. In the United States commonly fed rations that are satisfactory in other respects provide an adequate supply, except in areas where copper is clearly deficient or molybdenum present in excess amounts. Further studies are called for, however, to ascertain whether the severe area symptoms reflect a deficiency that is actually much more widespread in a form too mild to be definitely recognized. The indiscriminate use of copper supplements, in mineral mixtures or otherwise, is to be avoided, because high intakes are toxic. The feeding of 30 mg. per day over an extended period caused hemolytic jaundice in sheep, according to Australian studies.

COBALT

Cobalt is a later addition to the list of mineral elements that are recognized to be essential for animal growth and health. The knowledge of its essential role developed as a result of long-time studies of certain peculiar wasting diseases of grazing animals, known by different names in different areas throughout the world but having similar symptoms that suggested a common cause. Each disease was early recognized to be limited to certain areas of the country in question, and prevention and cure by transferring the animals from "sick" to "healthy" areas were successfully practiced long before anything definite was known about the cause. The discovery of a lack of cobalt, resulting from its deficiency in the soil and thus in the herbage grazed, was reported independently in 1935 by Filmer and Underwood and by Marston and Lines, working in Australia. The history of the various area troubles and of the experimental studies carried out to establish their cause has been reviewed by Marston[34] in a publication which also presents a similar story with respect to copper and molybdenum.

Following the reports from Australia, cobalt-deficient areas were discovered elsewhere. In the United States they have been noted in Florida, western Canada, Michigan, Wisconsin, New Hampshire, New York, and North Carolina. Other areas are suspected. According to the reports from Canada and New Hampshire, cobalt deficiency can occur on dry, winter rations as well as on pasture. As a result of later studies, such as those reported from South Australia by Lee,[35] it is now recognized that some of the area troubles earlier attributed to a lack of cobalt represent a combined cobalt and copper deficiency. A similar situation occurs in Florida.

7.34. Symptoms of Cobalt Deficiency. The symptoms in cattle and sheep are similar to those of general malnutrition. The animals become listless, lose appetite and weight, become weak and anemic, and finally die. Uncomplicated cobalt deficiency has been experimentally produced in sheep (Fig. 7.9), and its pathology studied. The anemia is of the normocytic, normochromic type, thus differing from that occurring in iron or copper deficiency. Careful studies of organs and tissues at autopsy have provided little basis for the accurate diagnosis of cobalt deficiency. General inanition, a fatty degeneration of the liver, and deposits of hemosiderin (a breakdown product of hemoglobin) in the spleen are commonly found changes. Wool growth is retarded, and the fibers are weak. As is explained later, a lowering of the vitamin B_{12} content of the blood appears to be a specific symptom. The only certain diagnosis of cobalt deficiency rests upon the response of the animal to cobalt feeding. This response is rapid. Appetite picks up in about a week, and weight gains follow, but the remission of the anemia occurs more slowly, indicating that it may be a secondary effect.

7.35. Physiological Role of Cobalt. The specific role of cobalt in preventing the area troubles previously described long remained a mystery. Attempts to produce the deficiency symptoms in laboratory animals failed. The belief arose that the mineral must play a role in bacterial growth in the rumen. This was borne out by findings that in deficient animals marked alterations in the numbers and types of bacteria occurred, which were not caused by the lowered feed intake. The mystery was solved as a result of the discovery of vitamin B_{12} an anti-

[34] Hedley R. Marston, Cobalt, copper and molybdenum in the nutrition of animals and plants, *Physiol. Revs.*, **32**:66–121, 1952.

[35] H. J. Lee, Cobalt and copper deficiencies affecting sheep. I. Symptoms and distribution, *J. Agr. of S. Australia*, **54**:475–490, 1951.

anemic and growth factor, which was found to contain cobalt in its molecule. This vitamin is a metabolic essential for all species studied, but it is not a dietary essential for cattle and sheep because it is synthesized adequately by rumen organisms, provided an appropriate supply of cobalt is present. Thus, the long observed cobalt-deficiency trou-

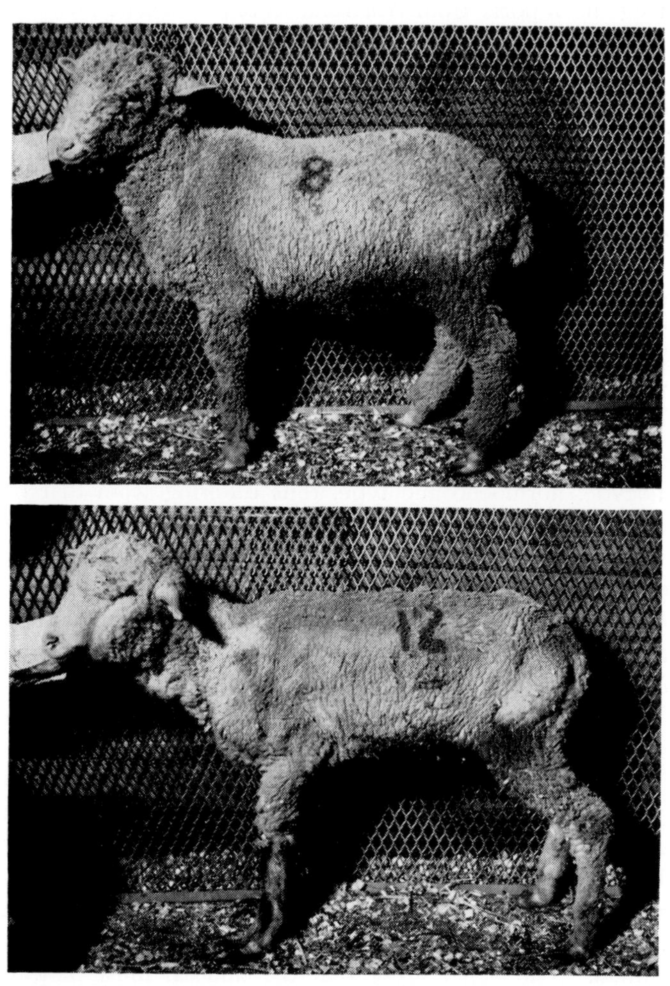

FIG. 7.9. Sheep No. 8 reared on a diet adequate in cobalt. Sheep No. 12 reared on cobalt-deficient diet. (*Courtesy of S. E. Smith, Cornell University.*)

ble in ruminants is actually a vitamin B_{12} deficiency, for this vitamin is not present in the plant products which comprise their feed. This conclusion has been reached as a result of several experiments. It has been shown that cobalt-deficient sheep have a very low vitamin B_{12} content in the blood compared with normal animals, that injecting the vitamin alleviates the cobalt-deficiency symptoms whereas injecting the mineral itself does not, and that there is little B_{12} in the rumen contents of animals showing cobalt deficiency compared with the situation in normal animals.

These findings explain why no essential role for cobalt has been demonstrated in the case of swine or poultry. They require vitamin B_{12} in their food. There is evidence that intestinal synthesis of the vitamin can occur to a limited extent, and this, of course, requires cobalt. There have been reports of benefits from adding cobalt to practical rations of swine, which is explainable on the basis that the rations were borderline in the vitamin and that some intestinal synthesis took place. Davis and coworkers[36] have shown that cobalt stimulates chick growth on a ration deficient in B_{12}, but not otherwise.

The possibility that cobalt may play some metabolic role in addition to its function as a constituent of the vitamin cannot be excluded on the basis of present knowledge. Evidence for the possibility has been suggested by certain in vitro enzyme studies and by findings regarding copper and cobalt interrelationships. It seems clear, however, that the major, if not the entire, role of cobalt in animal nutrition is as a constituent of vitamin B_{12}. The physiological role of this vitamin is discussed later.

7.36. Cobalt Requirements and Content in Feeds. While cobalt deficiency in ruminants is essentially a vitamin B_{12} deficiency, the most practical way of preventing or curing the trouble in situations where it otherwise may occur is to add cobalt to the ration. The evidence of the quantitative needs for cobalt rests on studies of its content in the herbage where troubles occur. It has been reported that the dry matter of grass of healthy areas contains around 0.1 p.p.m. of cobalt on the average compared with figures from 0.04 to 0.07 p.p.m. for "sick" areas. Assuming that 0.1 p.p.m. may be considered as the requirement, this would indicate a daily intake of approximately 0.1 mg. per 100 lb. body weight. Such a minute intake as this has actually restored sick animals to health.

Aside from the pasture grass and roughages produced in the areas where cobalt deficiency has been definitely identified, feeds in general appear to contain more than the 0.1 p.p.m. of cobalt that is considered essential. This is not true, however, in the case of milk and certain samples of corn and possibly other grains. Analytical data obtained by reliable methods are far too few to provide any adequate picture of the cobalt content of our feed supplies. Certainly, in those areas where cobalt deficiency has been identified, the simplest way of ensuring its prevention in the future is to feed a cobalt supplement to sheep and cattle. For this purpose 0.5 oz. of cobalt sulfate per 100 lb. of salt fed

[36] R. L. Davis, G. M. Briggs, and H. J. Sloan, Effect of cobalt in diet of the chick, *Proc. Soc. Exptl. Biol. Med.*, **82**:175–177, 1953.

free-choice should suffice. For milking cows cobalt sulfate can be added to the grain mixture at the rate of 2 g. (1/15 oz.) per ton. Large intakes of cobalt are toxic, but there is a very wide margin between the harmful and the essential levels.

Smith and Loosli[37] have published a comprehensive review of cobalt and vitamin B_{12} in ruminant nutrition. Beeson[38] has reviewed the literature on the occurrence of cobalt in soils and forages concerned in the production of the deficiency disease. Further studies are urgently needed of the cobalt content of feed crops grown in various areas, both to obtain a better picture of the adequacy of the general feed supply and also to help locate other possible areas of deficiency.

IODINE

The mature animal body is estimated to contain less than 0.00004 per cent of iodine, but if this minute amount is not maintained through the food, disaster results. More than half of this iodine is in the thyroid gland, and it is in connection with the functioning of this gland that the body's need for iodine occurs.

7.37. The Thyroid Gland. This gland consists of two parts lying on each side of the trachea at its upper end. In the case of an adult man it weighs about 1 oz. It produces an internal secretion which contains the hormone thyroxine, isolated by Kendall in 1914 as a crystalline product containing about 65 per cent of iodine. Thyroxine is an iodine-containing amino acid present as the protein thyroglobulin. Diiodotyrosine is also present in this protein. The formulas for these two compounds are shown below:

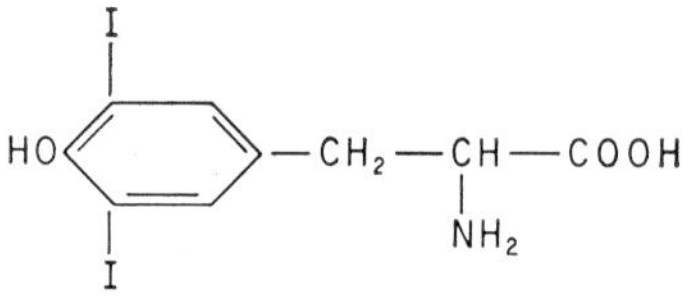

Diiodotyrosine

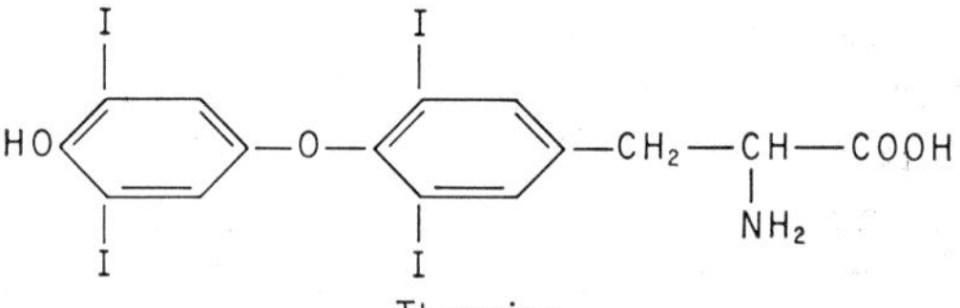

Thyroxine

[37] S. E. Smith and J. K. Loosli, Cobalt and vitamin B_{12} in ruminant nutrition: a review, *J. Dairy Sci.*, **40**:1215–1227, 1957.

[38] Kenneth C. Beeson, Cobalt: occurrence in soils and forages in relation to a nutritional disorder in ruminants: a review of the literature, *U.S. Dept. Agr. Inform. Bull.* 7, 1950.

If the diet contains tyrosine or its precursor phenylalanine, these compounds can be synthesized in the body, provided the needed iodine is present.

The removal of the thyroid early in life results in all species in a stunting of physical, mental, and sexual development. In adult animals the hair and skin show premature aging, and mental and physical sluggishness may develop. In all cases there is a lowered basal metabolism (Sec. 13.1). It is probable that the primary function of the thyroid gland is to control the metabolic rate through the output of its hormone and that the more evident effects of thyroid deficiency are a result of a failure of this control. Most of the iodine that occurs in the tissues and fluids of the body other than the thyroid is probably in thyroxine, serving its function in the control of metabolism.

The administration of thyroxine and of iodine-containing proteins stimulates body processes, notably milk and egg production. On the other hand, certain specific compounds such as thiourea and thiouracil suppress the gland's action and metabolic processes, thus promoting increased fattening. The application of these physiological effects to feeding practice is discussed later (Secs. 14.7, 16.3).

7.38. Symptoms of Deficiency. Goiter is an enlargement of the thyroid gland. Medical men recognize two types: simple or endemic goiter, which is caused primarily by a lack of iodine, and exophthalmic goiter, which involves other structures of the body besides the thyroid gland. Simple goiter is much the more common type, and it is the one with which we are concerned in nutrition. It develops as a result of a failure of the thyroid tissue to supply enough secretion, owing either to a reduced supply of iodine for its manufacture or to an increased demand for the secretion by the body. It is a compensatory hypertrophy, i.e., an enlargement involving the formation of more tissue in an effort to supply more secretion. The demand for thyroxine varies in accordance with the activity of the body functions it controls, and thus, given a fairly constant supply of iodine in the diet, simple goiter is most likely to develop during periods of greatly increased need. In the human these critical periods are pregnancy and puberty. In farm animals, however, goiter usually shows itself in the young at birth as a result of a deficiency of iodine in the rations of the mother during gestation. The young thus affected are born weak or dead. On a deficient diet the pregnant mother is not able to supply the fetus with enough iodine. The danger is thus increased in the case of multiple births.

In calves, lambs, and kids the enlargement of the gland is very evident in the newborn. In pigs the most outstanding symptom of the deficiency is hairlessness. They are bloated and have thick skins and puffy necks. In foals the only symptom may be extreme weakness at birth, resulting in an inability to stand and suck. A limited amount of data indicates that "navel ill" in foals may be lessened by feeding iodine to brood mares, but further evidence is required. Birds and fish as well as mammals have enlarged thyroids as a result of iodine deficiency. Animals born alive with a well-developed goitrous condition usually fail to survive or remain weaklings. No treatment has been found particularly effective. Studies of goiter troubles in humans have clearly established that, while iodine is effective as a preventive it may be harmful rather than beneficial as a treatment after the goiter has developed. While the nutrition scientist is concerned with prevention, treatment belongs entirely to the field of medicine.

Though a lack of iodine is the primary cause of simple goiter, it is recognized that other factors may contribute, notably the high-calcium content of the water in many goitrous regions. In addition, there are specific goitrogenic substances in certain foods, notably various members of the Brassica family, peanuts, and soybeans. These foods contain specific substances which slow down the thyroxine-secreting activity of the gland. Srinivasan and coworkers[39] have reviewed earlier studies and reported experiments of their own showing that peanuts are goitrogenic for the rat. They later found the active principle to be the glucoside, arachidoside. Mild goitrogenic efforts have been produced experimentally in both rats and chickens by feeding soybeans and counteracted by small amounts of additional iodine. The antithyroid principle is partially removed or destroyed in processing the beans to produce the low-fat meal. The continuous feeding of large doses of iodide is goitrogenic in the laying hen and also to the developing chick embryo in the eggs thus produced, according to Wheeler and Hoffmann.[40]

7.39. Iodine Deficiency an Area Problem. The need for additional iodine in the rations of farm animals, as well as of humans, exists primarily in certain areas where the soil and thus the water and food crops are low in this element. There are various regions throughout the world where goiter troubles of varying degrees are very common in all species unless additional iodine is fed, and there are others where the trouble is entirely unknown. In the United States, the goiter areas are primarily in the Northwest and in the Great Lakes region. It is estimated that, before iodine feeding was practiced in Montana, goiter caused an annual loss of many thousand pigs. Records from other areas

[39] V. Srinivasan, N. R. Moudgal, and P. S. Sarma, Studies of goitrogenic agents in foods. I. Goitrogenic action of groundnut, *J. Nutrition*, **61**:87–95, 1957.

[40] Robert S. Wheeler and Edmund Hoffmann, Goitrogenic action of iodide and the etiology of goiters in chicks from thyroprotein-fed hens, *Proc. Soc. Exptl. Biol. Med.*, **72**:250–254, 1949.

show that serious losses in the sheep and cattle industries occurred which were largely prevented following the discovery of the lack of iodine as the causative factor. There are borderline regions in which goiter occurs only occasionally. When the usual iodine intake is little above the minimum requirement, an enlarged physiological demand by an individual may be responsible for the occasional troubles. A barely sufficient intake may be changed to an inadequate one by a change in the make-up of the ration.

Hundreds of years before iodine was discovered, people living in goitrous areas learned the usefulness of certain products, now known to be rich in iodine, as a preventive of goiter. The value of sea salt in comparison with certain inland deposits was early recognized. Our real understanding of the problem is comparatively recent, as indicated by the fact that the discovery by Baumann of iodine in the thyroid gland was not made until 1896.

7.40. Iodine Requirements. We do not have specific knowledge of the minimum iodine requirements of the various species, but we do know the levels that are at least high enough to prevent goiter. These levels lie within the range of 0.002 to 0.004 mg. per kilogram of body weight. The report of the N.R.C. Committee on Animal Nutrition lists a requirement of 0.5 mg. per pound of feed for starting chickens and breeding hens, and 0.2 mg. for growing chickens and laying hens. Since goiter troubles in cattle, sheep, and hogs are associated primarily with reproduction, their specific needs for iodine are discussed in Chap. 15. Although it appears that these needs must be greatest during reproduction, iodine is obviously required throughout life to keep the thyroid gland functioning normally. The appearance of goiter may result as an advanced stage of deficiency. On this basis the continued feeding of an additional supply might be considered desirable in areas of severe iodine deficiency. There is some evidence from certain areas that additional iodine improves growth in various species, but this evidence is not entirely convincing. It has also been reported that, with sows fed in dry lot in an area borderline with respect to the occurrence of goiter, additional iodine lessens the number of pigs dead at birth or which die in the first week, although there was little physical evidence of iodine deficiency. Recommendations for year-round feeding are usually put on an insurance basis or are suggested as the simplest way of making certain that the needs of breeding stock are taken care of in areas where goiter is very common. The amounts fed should be limited to recommended levels, for excesses can cause harm.

7.41. Iodine Supplements. Where the occurrence of goiter shows that attention to iodine nutrition is needed, the most practical method is the use of some special source such as iodized salt or sodium or potassium iodide. The addition of 0.0076 per cent iodine to the salt represents the customary and effective level. None of the common feedstuffs, with the exception of fish meal made from salt-water fish, can be relied upon to be rich in iodine. Dried kelp, a sea plant, is rich in the element, and so is cod-liver oil. While special advantages are sometimes claimed for organic sources of iodine, the preponderance of the evidence indicates that the cheaper inorganic iodides are equally satisfactory. When massive doses of iodine are given as a therapeutic agent, an organic source has the advantage of slower absorption and less risk of harm from overdosage, but in the amounts needed to prevent goiter, this is not a factor. Iodized salt loses its iodine rather readily under certain conditions because of the catalytic action of impurities present. Thus, after storage it may be an unreliable source of iodine unless stabilized. Some processes have been developed for accomplishing this stabilization. Iodized salt in mixed feeds is less subject to deterioration because the presence of proteins and unsaturated fats tend to stabilize the iodine. Both human and animal experiments have tested the usefulness of salt iodized with potassium iodate as a product of higher stability than where iodide is used. Davidson and coworkers[41] have shown that salt blocks containing KIO_3 retained a much higher percentage of iodine when fed in the manger or subjected to outside exposure than did a product containing a commercial iodide complex.

Any required addition of iodine need not be supplied every day, because the thyroid has a considerable capacity to store the element. This is illustrated by the fact that goiter has been prevented in children in goitrous areas by feeding sodium iodide periodically for a month and repeating twice yearly.

SULFUR

The body contains approximately 0.15 per cent of sulfur. This element occurs almost entirely in organic compounds, notably in proteins in which it is present as the sulfur-containing amino acids cystine and methionine. Wool contains approximately 4 per cent of sulfur present as these acids. The body also utilizes these acids in the manufacture of the two sulfur-containing regulators of its metabolism, glutathione and insulin. It is clear that the sulfur needs of the body are primarily a matter of amino acid nutrition. Two vitamins, thiamine and biotin, contain sulfur, but these vitamins are not made inside the body proper of any species. Sulfur is present in inorganic form in chondroitin sulfate, a constituent of cartilage. The blood contains small amounts of

[41] W. M. Davidson, M. M. Finlayson, and C. J. Watson, Stability of various iodine compounds in salt blocks, *Sci. Agr.*, **31**:148–151, 1951.

sulfate. Thiocyanate ions are also present in blood, as well as in the saliva and other secretions.

Both the feces and urine are paths of sulfur excretion. In the urine three forms occur: inorganic sulfates, the principal fraction, which represent the final stage of oxidation of organic sulfur; ethereal sulfur, which is present in complex detoxication products; and neutral sulfur, which occurs as cystine, taurine, thiosulfates, and other compounds. Since excreted sulfur arises primarily from protein catabolism, there is a rather constant ratio between it and the nitrogen in the urine. There is evidence that the excretion of neutral sulfur is proportional to the basal metabolism.

It is evident from the above discussion that the sulfur needs of the body call for it in the form of organic complexes, notably amino acids, rather than in inorganic form. Mention has been made, however, of the fact that rumen bacteria can utilize the latter to build the sulfur-containing amino acids. Benefits have been demonstrated in ruminants from adding either elemental sulfur or sulfate to purified rations low in sulfur and having a part of the protein replaced by urea. On the other hand, several experiments have failed to find any advantage from adding inorganic sulfur to practical rations.

With rations containing their nitrogen largely in the form of urea and consisting of feeds grown on low-sulfur soils, one would expect that the addition of inorganic sulfur would prove advantageous. Studies using S^{35} have shown that the sulfate form can be used by the body to synthesize chondroitin sulfate. It has been reported that S^{35} injected into laying hens was found in the albumin of the egg in organic form, in part as cystine. A cystine-sparing action for growing chicks has also been reported. These effects in poultry appear to be small quantitatively. The various findings mentioned in this paragraph indicate that inorganic sulfur does play a role in nutrition, but, except when there is a substantial need for the rumen synthesis of protein, the effect is a small one compared with the role of that supplied as amino acids. A special case, however, in which the sulfate ion is of importance is its influence in lessening molybdenum toxicity (Sec. 7.57).

MANGANESE

Manganese occurs in the body principally in the liver, but it is also present in appreciable amounts in various other organs and in the skin, muscle, and bones. Despite the very small total supply in the body, this element has several essential functions and its consideration is of practical importance in animal nutrition.

7.42. Functions in Growth and Reproduction. In 1931 Kemmerer, Elvehjem, and Hart reported that the addition of traces of manganese to cow's milk supplemented with iron and copper had a favorable effect on the growth of mice and on ovulation. A month later Orent and McCollum reported extensive studies with rats, dealing primarily with reproduction. On a manganese-low diet, sexual maturity was delayed and ovulation was irregular. If conception occurred, the young were born weak or dead and their bodies contained less than half as much manganese as those born from mothers normally fed. In the male a diet devoid of the element causes a degeneration of the germinal epithelium. Thus the essentiality of manganese was established for these laboratory animals, and later studies extended the finding to other species. In the case of swine, Plumlee and coworkers[42] found that, when female pigs were weaned at 9 lb. and fed a low-manganese ration through growth, gestation, and lactation, the following results were obtained: reduced skeletal growth, irregular oestrus cycles, resorption of fetus or birth of small, weak pigs, poor udder development, and almost complete absence of milk. The need of poultry for manganese for growth and reproduction has also been established.

Ataxia, involving incoordination and loss of equilibrium, in the surviving offspring of manganese-deficient animals has been reported in the case of rats, chicks, and pigs. It is an irreversible defect.

7.43. Manganese and Bone Development. In 1936 Wilgus and associates reported evidence that manganese is markedly effective in reducing the incidence of *perosis*, or "slipped tendon," a malformation of the leg bones of growing chicks, thus providing the first specific information regarding the prevention of a long-known and serious trouble in practice. In this trouble the hock joints become swollen and the Achilles tendon slips from its condiles. The initial findings were confirmed by others, and further studies showed that a shortening of the leg bones was involved. Definite changes in the physical and chemical structure of the bones were noted. Manganese did not always prove 100 per cent effective, however, and support was thus furnished for an earlier view that some organic factor was also involved. In 1940 clear evidence was produced that choline, in addition to manganese, is necessary to prevent perosis in birds. Just how choline acts is not clear, but its action has no apparent connection with its role in fat metabolism (Sec. 5.14). It appears from present studies that other B-vitamins may also be concerned. The high-calcium and -phosphorus rations normally fed to poultry are a contributing cause of the occurrence of perosis, probably by interfering with manganese absorption, for they also aggravate the

[42] M. P. Plumlee and coworkers, The effects of manganese deficiency upon the growth, development and reproduction of swine, *J. Animal Sci.*, **15**:352–367, 1956.

adverse effect of a low-manganese intake on growth. The gross and histological lesions of perosis are described in detail by Wolbach and Hegsted.[43]

Bone malformations, grossly most evident as crooked front legs, have also been produced in rabbits by feeding a diet low in manganese, as are illustrated in Fig. 7.10. The humeri are shorter than normal and lower in ash, density, and breaking strength. There are also marked histological changes. Crooked legs and enlarged hocks have been produced in pigs on manganese-deficient rations. In the studies where the crooked legs were noted, the ration was high in calcium and phosphorus. In

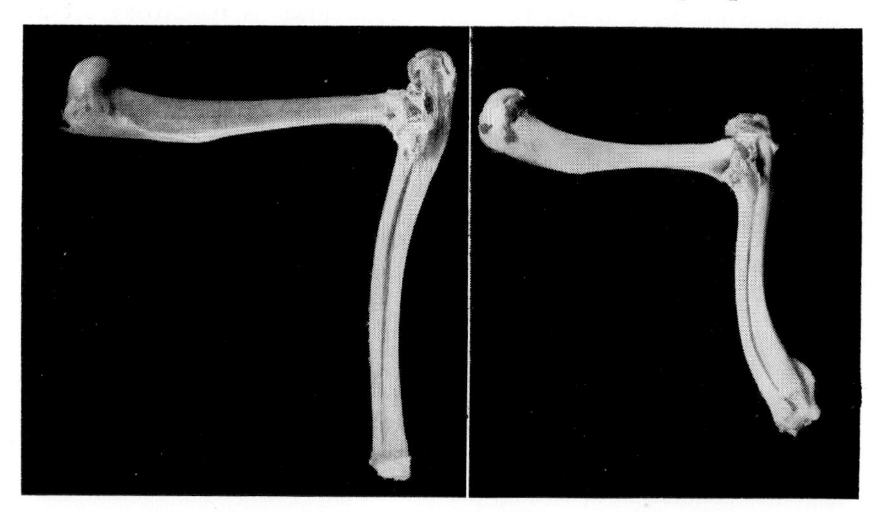

FIG. 7.10. Front leg bones from a control (left) and a manganese-deficient (right) rabbit. Note the bending of the radius and ulna and the shortness of the bones of the manganese-deficient rabbit. (*Courtesy of S. E. Smith, Cornell University.*)

rats fed a manganese-low diet, bone changes appear in the second generation.

Just how manganese functions in bone formation is not clear, but there is evidence that it is concerned in enzyme activity. It has been found that bone phosphatase is markedly lower than normal in perosis and in experimental manganese deficiency. Bentley and Phillips[44] have shown from in vitro studies that the amount of phosphate esterified by chick liver homogenates is reduced on manganese- or choline-deficient diets. Manganese plays a major enzymic role as a cofactor in oxidative phosphorylation.

[43] S. Burt Wolbach and D. Mark Hegsted, Perosis: epiphyseal cartilage in choline and manganese deficiencies in the chick, *Arch. Pathol.*, **56**:437–453, 1953.

[44] O. G. Bentley and P. H. Phillips, The effect of manganese deficiency in the chick on the uptake of inorganic phosphate by liver homogenates *in vitro, Arch. Biochem. and Biophys.*, **32**:338–346, 1951.

7.44. Requirements and Feed Supplies. Quantitative data on the needs by farm animals are meager, except in the case of poultry. The N.R.C. Committee has stated a requirement of 25 mg. per pound of feed for chicks and 15 mg. for breeding hens. These levels have been set high enough to meet the situation when the ration is very high in calcium and phosphorus also, as a result of the liberal inclusion of bone-carrying feeds. It has become common practice to add a manganese supplement to poultry rations, primarily as an insurance measure.

For swine the N.R.C. Committee reports that by increasing the manganese intake from 5.4 to 18 mg. per pound of feed, growth and feed efficiency were improved. The requirement is tentatively set at 18 mg. Growth has been reported satisfactory at considerably lower levels. Corn, which forms the basis of many swine rations, is very low in this mineral (2.3 mg. per pound). Rations based on corn and soybean oil meal have been found to contain around 11 mg., and such rations might be improved by a manganese supplement. Other practical rations contain much higher levels of the element. The N.R.C. report states that no significant benefit in terms of reproduction and lactation have been obtained by adding manganese to a ration containing 5.4 mg. per pound.

From studies with dairy cattle, Bentley and Phillips[45] report that 20 p.p.m. in the diet (9 mg. per pound) would appear to be a satisfactory level to meet requirements with a margin of safety. For beef cattle, the N.R.C. report states that, while requirements are uncertain, they appear to be met by 2.7 to 4.5 mg. per pound of air-dry ration. Since most roughages contain 20 to 65 mg. per pound and concentrates, other than corn, 7 to 20 mg., it seems clear that manganese needs are always adequately supplied in the usual cattle rations and that no supplement is called for. The same considerations probably apply to sheep.

There is no problem of toxicity from moderate excesses of manganese, but 125 p.p.m. have been found to depress hemoglobin synthesis in baby pigs. This apparently represented a manganese-iron antagonism since additional iron overcame the depression. Growth was depressed by 1250 p.p.m.

ZINC

The zinc content of the body is only approximately 3 mg. per cent. The highest concentrations are found in the epidermal tissues, such as skin, hair, and wool, but traces also occur in the bones, muscles, blood, and various organs. The mineral is present in milk and, in a much higher concentration, in the colostrum. The initial studies of Bertrand

[45] O. G. Bentley and P. H. Phillips, The effects of low manganese rations on dairy cattle, *J. Dairy Sci.*, 34:396–403, 1951.

and Berzon, in 1922, indicating that this element played an essential role, have been confirmed and extended by others in experiments with both rats and mice. On a nearly zinc-free diet, growth was retarded and hair development was interfered with. These early findings, plus the identification of zinc in certain enzyme systems, led to the conclusion that the element is an essential one for all species, but several years elapsed before specific information on farm animals was obtained.

7.45. Zinc Deficiency in Farm Animals. After a detailed description by Kerncamp and Ferrin in 1953 of a dermatitis in swine, designated as parakeratosis, Tucker and Salmon[46] in 1955, reported that a zinc deficiency was concerned. This report was rapidly confirmed by other workers. The disease is characterized by specific skin lesions, retarded growth, and other symptoms. The trouble is aggravated by excess calcium intakes. Studies dealing with the interrelationship are reported by Hoefer and coworkers.[47] The gross symptoms are illustrated in Fig. 7.11.

In 1958 at least three different laboratories described the symptoms of zinc deficiency in the chick. The prominent symptoms reported were slow growth, shortened and thickened long bones, and poor feathering, with keratosis resulting when the deficiency was severe. It has also been noted that the deficiency results in lower hatchability and embryonic anomalies. Excess calcium is apparently an aggravating factor in this species as well. No reports of zinc deficiency in cattle and sheep have been noted.

The specific biochemical lesions responsible for the symptoms of zinc deficiency remain unknown. There is a decrease in the trace amounts of the mineral normally found in the body. Zinc functions in several enzyme systems, notably the respiratory enzyme carbonic anhydrase, which is found in the red blood cells and elsewhere in the body, which plays an essential role in eliminating carbon dioxide, and which contains 0.3 per cent of zinc. The element can serve as an activator of alkaline phosphatase. There is some evidence that it plays a role in keratinization and calcification. It is evident that zinc functions at the enzyme level, and this appears to be true also for the antagonizing effect of calcium.

7.46. Zinc Requirements and Feed Supplies. Quantitative data on zinc requirements are limited. The N.R.C. report for swine specifies a requirement of 23 mg. per pound of feed, with the notation that higher levels may be needed when excess calcium is present. The correspond-

[46] Howard F. Tucker and W. D. Salmon, Parakeratosis or zinc deficiency disease in the pig, *Proc. Soc. Exptl. Biol. Med.*, **88**:613–616, 1955.

[47] J. A. Hoefer and coworkers, Interrelationships between calcium, zinc, iron and copper, *J. Animal Sci.*, **19**:249–259, 1960.

ing report for poultry gives a figure for starting chicks only, namely, 20 mg. per pound of feed. Analyses of poultry feedstuffs indicate that chick and broiler rations contain 18 to 27 mg. per pound, suggesting that some of the rations fed may be borderline in this nutrient. There is evidence that some practical swine rations may benefit from a zinc supplement.

Several times the levels recommended as requirements have been fed to pigs and poultry without any observed toxic effect. In rats, however,

FIG. 7.11. Parakeratosis. (*Courtesy of R. W. Luecke of Michigan Agricultural Experimental Station.*)

a large excess of zinc results in an anemia which is overcome by the feeding of additional copper. Apparently zinc interfered with the function of copper in the formation of iron-porphyrin compounds, hence the anemia. This is another example of interrelationships at the enzyme level.

CHROMIUM AND BROMINE

7.47. Chromium. Schwarz and Mertz[48] have reported that chromium in the trivalent form is needed in the rat to maintain the maximum rate of utilization of excess sugar. In depleted animals sugar is still utilized,

[48] Klaus Schwarz and Walter Mertz, Chromium III and the glucose tolerance factor, *Arch. Biochem. Biophys.*, **85**:292–295, 1959.

but at a reduced rate. Whether chromium is part of an organic factor is not known. So far no other deficiency symptoms or evidences of impaired health or function have been noted. Further work seems needed to confirm and expand the observations, in other laboratories and with other species, before chromium can be considered an essential mineral element.

7.48. Bromine. In 1956 two reports were published indicating that bromine is a useful element. One report dealt with an increase in chick growth; the other reported that the element counteracted the growth inhibition in mice caused by feeding iodinated casein. No further reports have been published, and thus any role this element may have in nutrition remains uncertain.

ALUMINUM, SILICON, AND BORON

7.49. Aluminum. All plants and animals contain traces of aluminum. Thus far no evidence has been produced that it is an essential constituent of body tissues, and its presence is explainable on the basis that it is passively taken up and retained owing to its universal presence in foods. Experimentally it has been shown that intakes which are large enough to combine with a substantial part of the phosphorus of the diet render the latter unabsorbable and results in a lowering of the plasma phosphate, a decrease in bone ash, and rickets. Such an effect is not to be feared from natural foods, since they contain, at most, only a few parts per million of the element. The biological role of aluminum has been recently reviewed.[49]

7.50. Silicon. All animal tissues which have been examined have been found to contain silicon in varying amounts. It is present in the blood serum of farm animals as 1 to 2 mg. per 100 ml. Wool contains from 0.02 to 0.08 per cent, but this variation apparently has no relation to wool quality and no definite correlation with intake. Silica is present in the ash of feathers and may help maintain their rigidity. No one has been able to demonstrate that the element plays any essential role in the body, and thus its occurrence is generally regarded merely as an accumulation resulting from its universal occurrence in foods, particularly those of vegetable origin.

Mature roughages are especially rich in silicon, since their cellulose is infiltrated with the element. Samples of timothy hay have been reported to contain as much as 0.7 per cent. The mineral metabolism studies of Forbes and Beegle[50] revealed an extensive metabolism of

[49] Anonymous, The biological role of aluminum, *Nutrition Revs.*, **15**:23–25, 1958.

[50] E. B. Forbes and F. M. Beegle, The mineral metabolism of the milch cow, *Ohio Agr. Expt. Sta. Bull.* 295, 1916.

silicon in the dairy cow. In many instances the intakes equaled those of sodium, chlorine, and phosphorus. Most of the ingested element was recovered in the feces, but the balance studies recorded some storage in almost all cases, frequently 3 to 5 g. daily. Only very small amounts were found in the urine, the feces being by far the principal channel of excretion.

7.51. Boron. The findings of the large importance of traces of boron in plant growth have stimulated a study of its possible role in animal nutrition. In comprehensive experiments by different workers, however, diets supplying as little boron as 0.16 mg. per kilogram body weight have had no deleterious effects on growth, reproduction, or lactation in rats. Neither is there any evidence for its need by other species.

TOXIC MINERALS

While some of the minerals previously discussed have been noted to be harmful in excess, those minerals and compounds included under the present heading are of importance in nutrition primarily because of their occurrence in harmful levels in natural feeds or mineral supplements.

7.52. Fluorine: Its Harmful Effects. While fluorine is found in various parts of the body, notably in the hair, its regular occurrence in the teeth and bones at maturity to the extent of 0.04 to 0.06 per cent or more is of primary interest to the nutritionist. Here it exists in an apatite form as an integral part of the structure. Although this regular occurrence and certain specific evidence discussed later suggest that fluorine may be an essential dietary constituent in minute amounts, its primary significance in animal nutrition is concerned with definitely harmful effects resulting from excessive intake. In large doses fluorine is an acute poison. The harmful effects that are of practical importance in livestock feeding, however, are the result of the continuous ingestion of comparatively minute amounts in fluoride-containing water or in rations supplemented with mineral phosphates high in the element. While most of the ingested fluorine is excreted by the kidneys, there is a gradual accumulation in the bones and teeth and, to a much lesser extent, in soft tissues.

The bones lose their normal color and luster, become thickened and softened, and the breaking strength is decreased. Bony outgrowths from the surface, called exostoses, occur. The fluorine content of the bone increases many times, and its magnesium content also increases, but there is a decrease in carbonate. The total ash content is lowered by high levels of intake. There are also characteristic histological changes. The effects upon the teeth are similar, though they mainfest themselves somewhat differently, particularly in certain species. In the rat the enamel loses its glistening yellow color and becomes chalky and brittle. The permanently growing incisors do not wear away normally, and either the upper or lower incisors become elongated. These changes are illustrated in Fig. 7.12, which also shows the thickening of the skull bones resulting from fluorine feeding. In hogs and cattle, defects in the enamel are produced and the teeth become soft and worn down until in some cases the pulp cavities are exposed. The teeth become sensitive to cold water, and food consumption is interfered with.

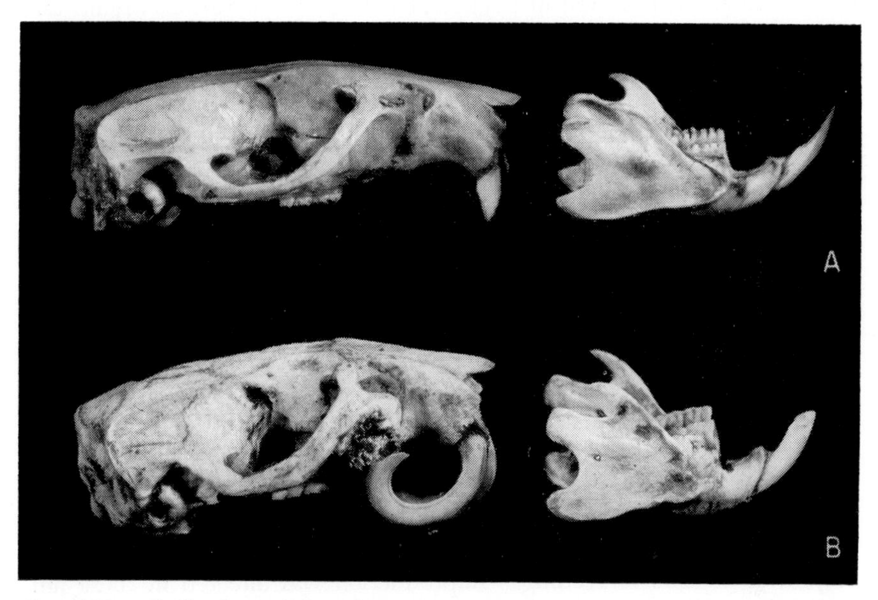

FIG. 7.12. Skulls of rats fed on diets with and without fluorine. Top, normal skull. Bottom, thickened skull with elongated and chalky upper incisors caused by excessive fluorine intake.

In children an excessive fluorine intake is responsible for the development of mottled enamel. This condition is characterized by the presence of chalky-white patches on the surface of the teeth. Frequently the entire tooth surface is dull white in color, and the enamel becomes pitted and may chip off. Secondarily, the teeth may become stained, showing a coloration which varies from yellow to black. Mottled teeth are structurally weak owing to an interference with the normal development of the enamel. Mottling is chiefly a defect of the permanent teeth which results during their formation. Normally formed teeth do not become mottled later. In the permanently growing teeth of the rat, however, bleaching may be produced at any time during life. The fact that mottling will occur in children who regularly drink water containing as little as 2 to 5 p.p.m. of fluorine illustrates how small an amount may cause this change. Mottled enamel occurs in cattle and sheep in areas where the water is high in fluorine, and erosion of the teeth can result, as reported for cattle in Texas by Neeley and Harbaugh.[51]

While injuries to the bones and teeth are the initial or the most evident effects of fluorine, higher intakes or long-continued feeding interfere with food consumption, growth, reproduction, and lactation. Of course, the wearing down of the teeth interferes with food consumption, and this, in turn, with growth and production. There are generalized toxic effects, however, reflected in degenerative changes in various organs and soft tissues. The form in which fluorine is fed has an influence on its toxicity. Sodium fluoride is more toxic than calcium fluoride and certain other insoluble products. There are species differences in susceptibility. The chicken will tolerate a considerably higher level than other farm animals.

Fluorine is a cumulative poison. Short-time experiments in which no harmful effect is noted are not reliable measures of the safety of a given level in feeding practice. At first the fluorine merely accumulates in the bones and teeth without evident harm, and considerable time elapses before structural injury becomes evident. The avidity of the bones and teeth for fluorine tends to protect the soft tissues against excessive concentrations. As the bones become saturated, however, the greater part of the absorbed fluorine is free to produce its general toxic effects on the organs and soft tissues. Wisconsin workers found that while the deleterious effects of higher levels were evident much earlier, an intake of rock phosphate which provided approximately 0.008 per cent of the total dry matter fed to dairy cows had a marked effect on production only after 3 years of feeding. Reproduction was affected in these animals. Later Wisconsin experiments by Suttie and coworkers[52] showed that a lower level of intake (50 p.p.m.) did not generally reduce milk production over a 5½-year period but that symptoms of fluorine toxicosis developed. With certain cows, sustained intakes at average levels of 1.5 mg. and a peak intake of 1.7 mg. or more fluorine per kilogram body weight led to a reduction in milk yield, primarily as a result of anorexia. As reported in a later paper, the animals receiving 50 p.p.m. stored 10 times as much fluorine in their bones as did the controls.

Hobbs and associates[53] have published the results of a very extensive study of the effect of different levels of fluorine fed over periods ranging

[51] K. L. Neeley and F. G. Harbaugh, Effects of fluoride ingestion on a herd of dairy cattle in the Lubbock, Texas, area, *J. Am. Vet. Med. Assoc.*, **124**:344–350, 1954.

[52] J. W. Suttie, R. F. Miller, and P. H. Phillips, Effects of dietary NaF on dairy cows. II. Effects on milk production, *J. Dairy Sci.*, **40**:1485–1491, 1957.

[53] C. S. Hobbs and associates, Fluorosis in cattle and sheep, *Tennessee Agr. Expt. Sta. Bull.* 235, 1954.

up to 4½ years to cattle and sheep. The data show that the maximum intake which can be tolerated without a decrease in appetite and in rate of gain, and without other deleterious effects, depends on the length of the feeding period. The bulletin contains many data from digestion and metabolism studies, production records, bone analyses, and teeth examinations. In general, the findings support the recommendations of Mitchell and Erdman (Sec. 7.53) as to safe levels for practice.

The acute effects which result from relatively high levels over a short feeding period are shown by the study of Comar and associates[54] with pigs using Ca^{45}. An addition of 1000 p.p.m. to a practical ration resulted, over a period of 75 days, in reduced appetite and a decrease in body growth and skeletal growth. This paper presents autoradiograms indicating how excess fluorine affects bone structure.

7.53. Safe Levels of Fluorine Intake. It is evident that the safe level varies with the species, the duration of the feeding period, and the source of the fluorine. An authoritative discussion of the questions here concerned, based on a review of the various feeding experiments which have been published, is to be found in the summary by Mitchell and Erdman.[55] These authors state that 0.01 per cent of fluorine as rock phosphate in the total dry matter of the rations of cattle, sheep, or hogs, 0.035 per cent for chicks, and 0.053 per cent for laying hens represent the maximum safe intakes. Somewhat higher levels may be safe over short periods. For feeding over the economic life of breeding and lactating animals Mitchell and Erdman would reduce the intakes of cattle and sheep to 0.005 per cent of the dry ration. They feel that the safe levels stated above for the various species should be 50 per cent lower where highly soluble fluorides are fed.

7.54. Practical Aspects of Fluorine Toxicity. Aside from the special situation in areas where the water is high in fluorine, our practical interest in this fluorine problem from the standpoint of farm animals lies in the fact that certain mineral supplements may contain excessive amounts. Rock phosphate contains 3.5 to 4 per cent of fluorine, and thus even 1 per cent of it in the concentrate mixture would provide an intake approximately 10 times the permissible level previously mentioned. Products made from rock, such as acid phosphate and dicalcium phosphate, as normally manufactured, are also far too high in fluorine for safe use. In fact, it was the employment of rock phosphate and its products as mineral supplements that first demonstrated the fluorine problem in feeding practice. As has previously been mentioned (Sec.

[54] C. L. Comar and associates, Effects of fluorine on calcium metabolism and bone growth in pigs, *Am. J. Anat.*, **92**:361–389, 1953.

[55] H. H. Mitchell and Marjorie Erdman, The fluorine problem in livestock feeding, *Nutrition Abstr. & Revs.*, **21**:787–804, 1952.

7.18), processes have now been developed for defluorinating rock phosphate and its products to make them safe for animal feeding. According to the Official Publication of the Association of American Feed Control Officials for 1959, the term "defluorinated" shall not be used in connection with the name of any phosphate product containing more than 1 part of fluorine (F) to 100 parts of phosphorus (P).

Bone meal, a calcium and phosphorus supplement, contains 0.03 to 0.04 per cent of fluorine, an amount that is below the permissible level when the product is fed as 1 per cent of the concentrate mixture for cattle or sheep. Despite its widespread use over many years in experimental studies as well as in practice, no evidence of fluorine injury from the use of bone meal as a mineral supplement has been noted. The Association of American Feed Control Officials has set forth the following tentative regulations regarding the fluorine content of mineral substances:

> The fluorine content of any mineral or mineral mixtures that are to be used directly for the feeding of domestic animals shall not exceed 0.30 per cent for cattle; 0.35 per cent for sheep; 0.45 per cent for swine; and 0.60 per cent for poultry.
>
> Soft phosphate with colloidal clay, rock phosphate, or other fluorine bearing ingredients may be used only in such limited amounts in feeding stuffs so that they will not raise the fluorine of the total concentration of the (grain) ration above the following amounts: for cattle 0.009 per cent of fluorine; for sheep 0.010 per cent of fluorine; for swine 0.014 per cent of fluorine; and for poultry 0.035 per cent of fluorine.

While fluorine occurs in most of the common feedstuffs, in general, the level does not exceed 1 or 2 p.p.m. Considerably higher values have been reported for certain fish meals, as is to be expected in view of their bone content. The question as to whether phosphate manuring constitutes a hazard by reason of an increased fluorine content in the crops so fertilized has been answered in the negative. Studies have shown, however, that under some conditions the vegetation on soils highly fertilized with rock phosphate may be contaminated by soil fluoride as a result of rain splashing or wind.

A practical problem of fluorine toxicity exists in areas nearby industrial plants, such as smelters and defluorinating plants, which give off fluoride dust, or soot, or gases into the atmosphere. The fluorides settle on the growing crops and the gases may be absorbed. Thomas,[56] who has presented an excellent review of this problem, states, for example, that only a fraction of a part per million of hydrogen fluoride in the air can result in concentrations of 200 p.p.m. or more in certain growing

[56] Moyer D. Thomas, Gas damage to plants, *Ann. Rev. Plant Physiol.*, 2:293–322, 1951.

crops. Many cases of fluorine injury to cattle and sheep have resulted from the eating of forage grown nearby plants which are contaminating the atmosphere with solid or gaseous fluorine compounds. Mitchell and Erdman[57] state that fluorosis has been observed in grazing animals on forage contaminated with only 25 to 50 p.p.m.

7.55. Is Fluorine an Essential Element? Evidence that, despite its harmful effects at higher intakes, the ingestion of minimum amounts of fluorine may be distinctly beneficial has come from observations with respect to tooth decay in man and experimental animals. It has been definitely shown by both epidemiological and experimental studies that, where the water supply contains 1 to 2 p.p.m., in contrast to lower levels, the incidence of dental caries is decreased during the period of tooth development. Thus, as a public health measure, many municipalities are adding 0.7 to 1 p.p.m. of fluorine to water supplies which otherwise contain much smaller traces. This added level does not result in mottled enamel or any other deleterious effect observable in long-time studies. Clearly, fluorine, as here ingested, is to be classed as a useful mineral for the lessening of dental caries.

The question whether fluorine is an essential dietary constituent has been investigated with rats, using diets designed to be as low as possible in the element. In general, only negative results have been obtained. Using a diet exhaustively purified and estimated to contain no more than 0.007 p.p.m. of utilizable fluorine, Maurer and Day[58] fed rats through three generations and into the fourth, one group receiving redistilled water and the other group the same water plus 2 p.p.m. of fluorine. No differences in health or weight gain could be noted between the two groups. It is possible that fluorine may have some undiscovered beneficial action in traces other than its effect in lessening dental caries, but from the standpoint of animal feeding, its harmful effect is the one of practical importance.

7.56. Selenium. This element has comparatively recently been found to be responsible for a peculiar disease of livestock long known to exist in certain regions of the world. In the United States, it occurs in some areas of the plains region, notably South Dakota, and is known locally as "alkali disease," or "blind staggers." In chronic cases there is a loss of hair from the mane and tail in horses and from the tail in cattle and a general loss of hair in swine. The hoofs slough off, lameness occurs, food consumption decreases, and death may occur by starvation. These external symptoms are accompanied by marked pathological changes, notably liver injury, which are revealed on autopsy.

[57] Mitchell and Erdman, *loc. cit.*

[58] Richard L. Maurer and Harry G. Day, The nonessentiality of fluorine in nutrition, *J. Nutrition,* **62**:561–573, 1957.

As a result of studies begun in 1929, Franke, chemist of the South Dakota Experiment Station, traced the cause of the disease to crops grown in localized soil areas. This finding led to a cooperative study with the U.S. Department of Agriculture which resulted in the discovery of selenium as the specific factor. Various food crops may contain toxic levels of the element as a result of the amounts present in the soil in the

FIG. 7-13. Selenium poisoning. (*Courtesy of O. E. Olson, South Dakota Agricultural Experiment Station.*)

areas in question. The soil may contain as much as 40 p.p.m., but any soil which contains more than 0.5 p.p.m. is potentially dangerous. Both the forage and the grains contain toxic levels. Different plants vary greatly in the amounts they take up, but the concentration in the plant is generally much greater than in the soil. On a soil containing 9 p.p.m. of selenium certain crops have been found to contain as much as 1200 p.p.m. Chronic toxicity is caused by rations containing as little as 8.5 p.p.m. of selenium. Acute cases of poisoning have been reported from levels of 500 to 1000 p.p.m. Young animals are especially susceptible, and growth is retarded with levels too low to cause other evident symptoms. In swine levels as low as 10 p.p.m. have been found to lower the conception rate and result in a higher percentage of pigs dead at birth or weak and smaller in size, according to the studies of Walstrom and Olson.[59]

Reproduction troubles have also been noted in sheep and poultry. This selenium injury is not limited to animals, for human cases have also been reported. White flour milled from wheats grown in a seleniferous area may contain toxic levels. Selenium occurs in the milk and eggs from cows and hens fed rations containing the element.

Many studies with both laboratory and farm animals have been made in an endeavor to counteract selenium toxicity. Certain protein sources, notably linseed oil meal, exert some protective action. The oil meal is less protective for cattle than for swine or rats. Studies have shown that various compounds exert a favorable effect experimentally, but, in general, they have been found to have only a very limited practical application. The incorporation of arsenicals of the organic type into swine rations has proved helpful. Sulfate alleviates the growth depression in rats and chicks, but does not lessen the liver damage which is the critical pathological effect. Sulfate, used as a fertilizer, also lessens selenium uptake by plants, but this does not appear to be of any practical importance as a control measure. In summary, no satisfactory practical solution has been found for the livestock suffering from selenium poisoning in the areas concerned. An excellent review of the background of the selenium problem and an account of studies with range cattle are presented by Dinkel and associates.[60]

7.57. Selenium as a Useful Element. Studies beginning about 1950 established that brewer's yeast contained an unidentified factor which would prevent dietary liver necrosis in rats and exudative diathesis, a hemorrhagic disease in chicks, and that the factor was different from vitamin E, which would also present these troubles. Continuing research established the fact that the unidentified factor, designated as factor 3 by Schwarz who was the pioneer in the rat studies, is a selenium compound. Only minute traces of the element are required, the amount in the case of exudative diathesis being approximately 0.1 p.p.m. Thus selenium became recognized as a useful dietary ingredient, as well as a harmful one. The experiments which were concerned in this very interesting development up to 1960 are reviewed by Schwarz.[61]

Continuing studies have shown that selenium is helpful in preventing

[59] R. C. Walstrom and D. E. Olson, The effect of selenium on reproduction in swine, *J. Animal Sci.*, **18**:141–145, 1959.

[60] C. A. Dinkel and coworkers, Agricultural research at the Reed Ranch field station, *South Dakota Agr. Expt. Sta. Circular* 135, 1957.

[61] K. Schwarz, Factor 3, selenium and vitamin E, *Nutrition Revs.*, **18**:193-197, 1960.

some of the other troubles in which vitamin E is also effective, notably white muscle disease in lambs and calves and heart and skeletal muscle dystrophy in mink. The prevention of liver necrosis and muscle dystrophy in swine has also been reported. It is evident, however, that the mineral has not been found effective in preventing resorption sterility in rats and encephalomalacia in chicks (Sec. 8.19). Active studies are continuing to ascertain what physiological roles selenium may play apart from its relationship with vitamin E. It has been reported to improve growth in chicks on rations adequate in the vitamin. New Zealand workers[62] have reported that the periodic feeding of trace amounts of selenium has lessened the mortality and improved the growth of grazing lambs and calves suffering from a peculiar disease, characterized by unthriftiness, occurring in certain areas of the country.

7.58. Molybdenum. A trouble in cattle referred to as *teartness* and known for over a hundred years to be definitely associated with certain pasture areas in England and not with others was identified in 1938 by Ferguson and associates as a molybdenum toxicity. The trouble was found to affect ruminants, particularly calves and cows in milk. The prominent physical symptoms were extreme diarrhea with consequent loss in weight and production. Molybdenum was discovered to be the cause of the trouble by analyses of the forage from unhealthy and normal areas and by its experimental production with sodium molybdate. The trouble was observed where the forage contained 0.002 per cent or more of the element. Later, potentially toxic levels in the soils and herbage and the actual occurrence of molybdenosis were found in various areas in the world, including Florida, California, and Manitoba in North America. The symptoms reported generally included diarrhea, emaciation, anemia, and stiffness. Molybdenum toxicity has been found to be a practical problem only in grazing animals and apparently only in limited areas, but its toxicity to other species, notably rats, rabbits, chicks, and pigs, has been demonstrated by feeding experiments.

The early English workers noted that the symptoms they observed were similar to those reported for cattle in copper-deficient areas in Holland. They were led to adminster copper sulfate to affected animals and found that it cured the diarrhea. This result was obtained despite the fact that the forage contained levels of copper considered adequate. It became apparent that a copper-molybdenum interrelationship was involved. A new area of study was opened accordingly. It was shown with both laboratory animals and ruminants that feeding excess molyb-

[62] C. Drake, A. B. Grant, and W. J. Hartley, Selenium in animal health. II. The effect of selenium on unthrifty weaned lambs, *New Zealand Vet. J.*, 8:7–10, 1960; R. D. Jolly, A preliminary experiment on the effect of selenium on the growth rate of calves, *New Zealand Vet. J.*, 8:13, 1960.

denum brought on the physical symptoms of copper deficiency and interfered with copper metabolism. The addition of copper restored the animals to normal. In Herbivora, a molybdenum content ranging from 2 to 25 p.p.m. in the growing forage was found to increase the copper requirement. The bone changes noted in copper deficiency were aggravated where the molybdenum content of the forage was high. In laboratory animal experiments the symptoms of chronic molybdenum poisoning and of copper deficiency were found similar. These various studies led to the tentative conclusion that molybdenosis was primarily the result of a relative copper deficiency or, expressed another way, that copper deficiency as seen in the field resulted from an excess intake of molybdenum. Later studies have shown that the interrelationship is much more complicated than this.

The sulfate content of the ration is a determining factor, as established by a series of studies by Dick of Australia.[63] In experiments with sheep it was found that increasing the sulfate intake counteracts molybdenosis. The molybdenum content of the blood and tissues is reduced, and its urinary excretion is increased. Somewhat similar findings have been reported in the rat and chick. This effect of the sulfate ion appears to be a specific one. It is now apparent that studies on molybdenum toxicity are of very limited value unless the sulfate content of the ration is taken into account.

There are other dietary factors which have been found to be involved in molybdenosis. It is evident that a low phosphorus content of the forage contributes to the severity of some of the bone troubles reported. Additional methionine has been found to alleviate the harmful effects of molybdenum toxicity in the rat. An interrelationship between molybdenum and zinc has also been demonstrated. Studies have shown that excessive intakes of molybdenum alter certain enzyme systems, and there is evidence that this affects copper metabolism at the cellular level. The specific biochemical mechanisms remain unknown.

The previous very brief discussion of molybdenum and its interrelationships indicates that there are many questions remaining to be answered. A comprehensive review of the many papers dealing with this general field has been published by Miller and Engel.[64] The various studies here reviewed also serve to illustrate the increasing evidence that both the requirements for essential minerals and the toxic levels of harm-

[63] A. T. Dick, Preliminary observations on the effect of high intakes of molybdenum and of inorganic sulfate on blood copper and on the fleece character of crossbred sheep, *Australian Vet. J.*, **30**:196–202, 1954. Molybdenum and copper interrelationships in animal nutrition, in W. D. McElroy and B. Glass (eds.), Inorganic Nitrogen Metabolism, Johns Hopkins Press, Baltimore, 1956, pp. 445–473.

[64] Russell F. Miller and R. W. Engel, Interrelations of copper, molybdenum and sulfate sulfur in nutrition. *Federation Proc.*, **19**:666–671, 1960.

ful ones are governed in part by the levels in the ration of certain interrelated ones.

7.59. Molybdenum as an Essential Nutrient. While the problem of excess molybdenum is the one of practical importance, evidence that this element is an essential one in traces has come from the finding that it is a constituent of the enzyme xanthine oxidase. This enzyme, which plays an essential role in purine metabolism, is found in liver and intestinal tissue and probably others, and also in milk. Details regarding this role of molybdenum are reported in the papers by Richert and Westerfeld[65] and by DeRenzo and associates,[66] whose work was primarily responsible for this brilliant discovery. Molybdenum has been reported to be essential for chicks and poults fed purified diets, but negative results have been obtained with rats. A species difference might be expected on the basis that the chick has a large need for xanthine oxidase for uric acid formation in contrast to the rat, in which, like other mammals, the principal end product of nitrogen metabolism is urea. A nutritional role of molybdenum in the growth of lambs has been reported and explained on the basis of a stimulating action on rumen organisms. While present evidence indicates that molybdenum should be classed as an essential nutrient, it seems highly probable that any need by farm animals is always met by their usual rations.

7.60. Nitrates. In 1937 Newsom and coworkers of Colorado reviewed a series of reported cases of acute symptoms and death in cattle following the ingestion of oat hay or straw and referred to as *oat-hay poisoning.* The physical symptoms noted were trembling, staggering gait, rapid respiration, and prostration. Detailed studies of cases in Wyoming were later reported by Bradley and coworkers.[67] Among the post-mortem findings recorded was the significant one that most of the hemoglobin had been converted to methemoglobin, explaining the physical symptoms noted. Chemical analyses of 15 samples of oat hay and straw fed where deaths had occurred revealed a potassium nitrate content of 2.2 to 7.3 per cent, whereas other oat hay contained only a trace. Since nitrite, rather than nitrate, was known to form methemoglobin, and since there was no nitrite present in the hay, Bradley and coworkers concluded that the nitrate must have been converted into nitrite in the digestive tract. Support for their conclusion is to be found in earlier studies by Seekles and Sjollema, who introduced potassium nitrate into the rumen of cattle and got symptoms of nitrite poisoning as indicated

[65] Dan A. Richert and W. W. Westerfeld, Isolation and identification of the xanthine oxidase factor as molybdenum, *J. Biol. Chem.*, **203**:915–923, 1953.

[66] Edward C. DeRenzo and associates, Identification of the xanthine oxidase factor as molybdenum, *Arch. Biochem. and Biophys.*, **45**:247–253, 1953.

[67] W. B. Bradley, H. F. Eppson, and O. A. Beath, Livestock poisoning by oat hay and other plants containing nitrate, *Wyoming Agr. Expt. Sta. Bull.* 241, 1940.

by the formation of methemoglobin. Forage poisoning ascribed to a high nitrate content has been reported from several areas in the United States and elsewhere in the world. Losses in weight and milk production and noninfectious abortion have been noted as sublethal effects in dairy cattle. The trouble appears to be of sporadic occurrence, and other factors besides nitrate content may be involved. Many feel that the problem has become more serious with the increased use of nitrogen fertilizers on forage crops. Corn stalks as well as oat hay were early found responsible for nitrate poisoning. More recently, other forages, such as corn silage, sorghum silage, and alfalfa hay, have been implicated. In addition to the harmful effects resulting when forage high in nitrate is fed, a hazard arises from the fact that nitrogen oxide gases, poisonous to man and animals, can be produced in the silo when nitrate is present in large quantities in the silage crops. This production takes place immediately after ensiling.

Uncertainty exists about what level of nitrate ingestion should be considered the minimal lethal dose (M.L.D.). Bradley and coworkers, in the publication previously cited, found the M.L.D. for calves to be 25 g. of KNO_3 per hundred pounds of animal, as determined by stomach-tube administration. Prewitt and Merilan[68] found that the M.L.D. was in excess of 30 g. per hundred pounds when administered to calves in gelatin capsules or in skim milk. It would seem that administration with the feed, instead of by stomach tube, should provide the more appropriate test in the case of ruminants. While nitrate poisoning is of most concern in the case of cattle and sheep, cases in horses have been reported. Robinson of New Zealand noted a special case of nitrate poisoning in pigs resulting from the formation of nitrite from nitrate in the cooking of the mangels fed.

The nitrate problem is excellently discussed by Crawford and Kennedy[69] in an article which reviews much of the previous work.

SOME PHYSIOLOGICAL EFFECTS OF MINERALS AS A GROUP

The previous discussions have shown that with certain elements their quantitative reactions to each other are important as well as their absolute amounts in the diet. Some of the interrelationships here concerned may be of real practical significance in view of the wide variations in the quantitative distribution of the various mineral elements, both essential and nonessential, in feed crops, particularly forages.

[68] R. D. Prewitt and C. P. Merilan, Effects of potassium nitrate on dairy calves. *J. Dairy Sci.*, **41**:807–811, 1958.

[69] R. F. Crawford and W. K. Kennedy, Nitrates in forage crops and silage: benefits, hazards, and precautions, *Cornell Misc. Bull.* 37, 1960.

There are also physiological effects resulting from the relations among the minerals as a group or from their intakes as a whole which require some consideration.

7.61. Acid-base Balance in the Ration. It has been noted that the pH of the blood and other body fluids must be held in a very narrow range for health and normal function. In contrast, the food ingested may exhibit wide ranges of potential acidity or alkalinity, depending upon the amounts of the various mineral elements present. Thus the question of the influence of the acid-base balance, more specifically designated as acid—alkali-ash value, of the diet upon metabolism has received much study. This balance is determined by calculating the equivalent in normal acid of the acid-forming minerals, chlorine, phosphorus, and sulfur, and figuring the equivalent in normal alkali of the base-forming elements, sodium, potassium, calcium, and magnesium. Calculated in this way the potential acidity of wheat exceeds its potential alkalinity by the equivalent of 12 ml. of normal acid per 100 g. It is an acid-forming food. On the other hand, alfalfa has a net potential alkalinity of 93 ml. and is, therefore, a base-forming food. In general, seeds and their by-products are acid-forming, while roughages are base-forming. High-protein diets tend to be acid-forming owing especially to the sulfur present. The acid—alkali-ash value of a ration can be calculated from the figures for its ingredients.

In figuring this value, no account is taken of organic acids. Citrus fruits contain considerable amounts of these acids, but they are base-forming foods. Organic acids are not taken into consideration, because, for the most part, they are oxidized or otherwise metabolized in the body and thus do not function as acids in the fluids.

It is recognized that highly acid-forming diets decrease the alkali reserve of the blood and may result in the excretion of fixed bases, even from the bones. It has been shown, however, that the body is able to tolerate a moderate excess of acid-forming elements without harm. In farm animals most of the experiments in which this question has been studied by the ingestion of mineral acids have indicated that the animals have effective means of taking care of them. The production of ammonia from urea provides a particularly effective agency for the neutralization of acid without increasing protein catabolism or loss of fixed base. The urine of Herbivora is generally alkaline, reflecting the fact that their ration is usually base-forming. The urine of Carnivora is commonly acid, and that of Omnivora is either acid or alkaline, depending on the nature of the diet.

The feeding of large amounts of silage which has developed a high acidity does not cause any serious physiological disturbance because the acidity is due to organic acids which for the most part are readily oxidized. In the case of silage preserved with mineral acids, however, as is the case with the AIV (A. I. Virtanen) process and with the use of phosphoric acid, the situation is different. Particularly when such silages are fed for several months with little or no other roughages, the protective mechanism of the body may not suffice. It has thus become common practice to add calcium carbonate as a neutralizer where AIV silage is thus fed. In the case of phosphoric-acid silage, the need for neutralization is somewhat less, but the addition of the carbonate is recommended here where hay which is part legume is not fed also. Legume hay has a higher net alkali-ash value than grass hays. Of course, the amount of acid added to the silage and the character of the crop, whether legume or nonlegume, are also factors governing the need for neutralization. This general problem is reviewed in connection with the studies reported by Lepard and associates.[70]

7.62. Saline and Alkaline Waters. The water supplies for animals in certain regions have such high concentrations of various salts as to interfere with growth, lactation, and reproduction. This problem has been critically studied by Heller,[71] and the studies have produced some very valuable data on the tolerance of animals to specific salts and to large intakes of minerals in general. The waters studied were heavily saturated with chlorides and sulfates of sodium, calcium, and magnesium and contained minor quantities of carbonates, bicarbonates, and other ions. It was found that the damage depended more on the total amount of salts present than on any specific one, thus representing an osmotic effect rather than an injury from any particular ion. The maximum concentration of soluble salts which could be safely tolerated appeared to lie between 1.5 and 1.7 per cent. Alkalies were more injurious than neutral salts. Chlorides were less harmful than sulfates, and organic salts less harmful than inorganic. Magnesium chloride was more injurious than the calcium or sodium salt. Sheep were more resistant to injury than cattle, and cattle more than hogs. More recent studies by Heller have indicated that the cause of the injury is not due to any influence on the pH of the intestinal tract, digestibility, or nitrogen retention.

SELECTED LITERATURE

Anonymous: Multiple origins of muscular dystrophy in lambs, *Nutrition Revs.*, **19**:41–42, 1961.

Boda, J. M., and H. H. Cole: Calcium metabolism with special reference to parturient paresis (milk fever) in dairy cattle: a review, *J. Dairy Sci.*, **39**:1027–1054, 1956.

[70] O. L. Lepard and associates, The effect of phosphoric acid silage on the acid-base balance in dairy cows, *J. Dairy Sci.*, **23**:1013–1022, 1940.

[71] V. G. Heller, Saline and alkaline drinking waters, *J. Nutrition*, **5**:421–429, 1932; The effect of saline and alkaline waters on domestic animals, *Oklahoma Agr. Expt. Sta. Bull.* 217, 1933.

Comar, C. L., and associates: Comparison of two isotope methods for determination of endogenous fecal calcium, *J. Nutrition,* **50**:459–467, 1953.

Conrad, J. H., and W. M. Beeson: Effects of calcium level and trace minerals on the response of young pigs to unidentified growth factors. *J. Animal Sci.,* **16**: 589–599, 1957.

Cunningham, H. M., J. M. Brown, and A. E. Edie: Molybdenum poisoning of cattle in the Swan River Valley of Manitoba, *Can. J. Agr. Sci.,* **33**:254–260, 1953.

Duckworth, J., and R. Hill: The storage of elements in the skeleton, *Nutrition Abstr. & Revs.,* **23**:1–17, 1953.

Ellis, W. C., and coworkers: Molybdenum as a dietary essential for lambs, *J. Animal Sci.,* **17**:180–188, 1958.

Hegsted, D. Mark, Clement A. Finch, and Thomas D. Kinney: The influence of diet on iron absorption. II. The interrelation of iron and phosphorus, *J. Exptl. Med.,* **90**:147–156, 1949.

Krueger, Hogo: The Wulzen calcium dystrophy syndrome in guinea pigs, *Am. J. Phys. Med.,* **34**:185–209, 1955.

Kunkel, H. O., K. H. Burns, and J. C. Camp: A study of sheep fed high levels of potassium bicarbonate with particular reference to induced hypomagnesemia, *J. Animal Sci.,* **12**:451–458, 1953.

Lofgreen, G. P.: The availability of the phosphorus in dicalcium phosphate, bonemeal, soft phosphate and calcium phytate for wethers, *J. Nutrition,* **70**:58–62, 1960.

McClymont, G. L., and associates: Sodium chloride supplementation of high grain diets for fattening merino sheep, *Australian J. Agr. Research,* **8**:83–90, 1957.

Matrone, Gennard, R. H. Hartman, and A. J. Clawson: Studies of manganese-iron antagonism in the nutrition of rabbits and baby pigs, *J. Nutrition,* **67**:309–317, 1959.

Meyer, J. H., and associates: Sodium, potassium, and chlorine content of feeding stuffs, *J. Animal Sci.,* **9**:153–156, 1950.

———: The tolerance of sheep to high intakes of sodium chloride, *J. Animal Sci.,* **13**:443–449, 1954.

Muth, O. H., et al: White muscle disease (myopathy) in lambs and calves. VI. Effects of selenium and vitamin E on lambs, *Am. J. Vet. Research,* **20**:231–235, 1959.

Patton, A. R.: Silicon content of wool in relation to dietary silicon, *Arkansas Agr. Expt. Sta. Bull.* 375, 1939.

Peirce, A. W.: Studies on fluorosis of sheep. II. The toxicity of water-borne fluoride for mature grazing sheep, *Australian J. Agr. Research,* **5**:545–554, 1954.

Plumlee, M. P., and coworkers: The availability of the phosphorus from various phosphatic materials for swine, *J. Animal Sci.,* **18**:73–88, 1958.

Smith, R. H.: Calcium and magnesium metabolism in calves: plasma levels and retention in milk-fed calves, *Biochem. J.,* **67**:472–481, 1957.

Smith, W. H., M. P. Plumlee, and W. M. Beeson: Zinc requirements for growing swine, *Science,* **128**:1280, 1958.

Thomas, W. E., and associates: The utilization of inorganic sulfates and urea nitrogen by lambs, *J. Nutrition,* **43**:515–523, 1951.

Ullrey, D. E., and coworkers: The requirements of the baby pig for orally administered iron, *J. Nutrition,* **70**:187–192, 1960.

Underwood, E. J.: Mineral metabolism, *Ann. Rev. Biochem.,* **28**:499–526, 1959.

Whiting, F., and associates: The sulphur requirements of mature range ewes, *Can. J. Agr. Sci.,* **34**:261–268, 1954.

Chapter 8
The Vitamins

A century and a quarter ago Prout[1] stated that there were three great staminal or proximate principles—a saccharine principle, an oily principle, and an albuminous principle—which provided the essential nutritive constituents of all organized bodies. Until early in the present century these principles, which later became known as the carbohydrates, fats, and proteins, were considered to be adequate to meet all the nutritive needs of the body other than its mineral requirements. Then came the discovery that there were other organic dietary essentials, previously unrecognized because needed in only minute amounts, which were not supplied by the early known principles. These are the nutrients which we class as vitamins. Knowledge as to the chemical nature of these dietary essentials lagged far behind the discovery of their nutritional importance, and thus, in the absence of any chemical basis for classifying them, they were grouped together and the term *vitamine*, coined by Funk in 1912 to designate a single one, was taken over to cover the group. From a physiological and nutritional standpoint, there are many advantages in considering the vitamins as a group, but it should be borne in mind that most of them are unrelated chemically and that the group name has no chemical significance.

Over the years since the first vitamin was discovered, our knowledge in this field has greatly advanced. New ones have been reported from time to time, their physiological functions have been worked out, and their chemical nature has been established. There are some 15 vitamins for which the information is sufficiently complete and definite that their existence is generally accepted, but much more needs to be learned

[1] William Prout, Chemistry, Meteorology and the Function of Digestion, Bridgewater Treatise, William Pickering, London, 1834. Prout (1785–1850), an English physician, was a profound student of the relations of chemistry to physiology. He discovered hydrochloric acid in the gastric juice, showed that the snake excreted its nitrogen as uric acid, and demonstrated that the developing chick takes calcium from the shell to build its bones.

about them. There are several others which have been proposed as the result of various experiments. It is unlikely that all of them are distinct essentials. On the other hand, the probability that there are still undiscovered vitamins must be recognized. A textbook on nutrition can deal only with those which are well established by a substantial amount of generally accepted evidence. For a knowledge of the status of others which have been proposed, the student must consult the voluminous literature in this field, and as is true for an up-to-date knowledge of the subject of vitamins in general, he must follow the new contributions as they appear in the various journals. He will find this no easy task, and he will also come to realize that complete knowledge of the subject of the vitamins lies far in the future.

A generally recognized vitamin is one that has been proved an essential dietary constituent for one or more species. Some vitamins are metabolic essentials, but not dietary essentials, for certain species, because they can be synthesized readily from other food or metabolic constituents. Thus, while vitamin C has been proved a metabolic essential for many species, it is a dietary essential only in the case of man, guinea pigs, and monkeys, because the other animals are able to provide their needs through synthesis. Various B-vitamins are essential for normal ruminant metabolism and yet are not needed in the food because of bacterial synthesis in the rumen. While metabolic needs are similar, dietary needs for the vitamins differ widely among species. No generalizations can, therefore, be made regarding the nutritive requirements of farm animals for the vitamins as a group. Neither can generalizations be made with respect to feed sources. Each vitamin has a somewhat different distribution from the others in terms of the materials which make up the food supply. Our knowledge here must be specific even as is the case for the requirements of the different animals.

The vitamins now recognized as distinct dietary essentials are differentiated chemically and on the basis of their physiological functions, particularly as indicated by the metabolic and other symptoms of their deficiency. Chemical evidence is required to make certain that a distinct essential is being dealt with, but in the case of several of the vitamins there are different, though closely related, chemical compounds that have the same physiological effects. Thus, there are some 10 sterols that have vitamin D activity.

8.1. Development of the Vitamin Concept. Though the incidence of some of them has doubtless increased in modern times owing to changes in dietary habits, the specific diseases which we now know to be due to the absence of the recently discovered vitamins date far back in history. Scurvy has been a scourge of various peoples at least since the time of Hippocrates (400 B.C.), while beriberi was apparently known to the

Chinese hundreds of years earlier. Though the specific evidence is comparatively recent, it is clear that, by the trial-and-error method, various individuals and peoples gradually learned that certain of these troubles were associated in some way with the nature of the diet and that specific foods were helpful in their treatment. The very early use by the Chinese of substances rich in vitamin A as remedies for night blindness, now known to be caused by a lack of this vitamin, is evident from the recent studies of these old remedies. In 1747, Lind, a British naval surgeon, showed that the juice of citrus fruits was a cure for scurvy. Cod-liver oil was used as a specific for rickets long before anything was known about the cause of this disease.

During the nineteenth century, many isolated observations were made which gradually led up to the discovery of vitamins as the causes of these disorders now called deficiency diseases. Prior to 1816, Magendie[2] observed in a dog what was undoubtedly xerophthalmia, in an experiment constituting a forerunner of the purified-diet method which was responsible one hundred years later for the discovery of vitamin A. In the latter part of the century, several men made observations which led them to suggest that there were other dietary essentials besides the early recognized proximate principles, but these unorthodox suggestions at first received little attention. In 1881, Lunin reported studies made in Bunge's laboratory showing that mice would not grow on an artificial mixture made up of the proximate principles of milk. He expressed the view that there might be "unknown substances" essential for life in addition to proteins, fats, carbohydrates, and salts.

During the last decade of the century, Eijkman, a physician working in the Dutch East Indies, was led to study polyneuritis in birds in view of its similarity to beriberi in man. He found that the disease was caused by an exclusive diet of polished rice and cured by adding the polishings. He also noted that beriberi in prisoners eating polished rice tended to disappear when a less highly milled product was fed. In these various studies, published in 1897, he was clearly dealing with the factor which later became known as vitamin B. The studies of Eijkman were extended by Grijns, another Dutch scientist who made important contributions to the early knowledge of vitamins. Prior to the work of Eijkman, Takaki, director-general of the Japanese Navy, sent two ships in 1887 on a nine-month voyage to test the effect of dietary additions on the incidence of beriberi. Of the crew which received mostly polished rice and dried fish, 60 per cent developed the disease, while in the other ship, where this diet was supplemented with more meat, vegetables, and milk, only 14 cases occurred among the 276 men. At that time the

[2] François Magendie, Sur les propriétés nutritives des substances qui ne contiennent pas d'azote, *Ann. chim. et phys.*, (1)3:66–77, 1816.

beneficial effect was erroneously ascribed to the larger amount of protein in the diet.

With the opening of the twentieth century, the earlier work of Lunin with artificial diets was repeated by others, notably by Pekelharing of the University of Utrecht, who was familiar with the course of the studies in the Dutch East Indies and by Hopkins in England. Again it was concluded that the proximate principles would not suffice. As stated by Hopkins[3] in 1906: "No animal can live on a mixture of pure protein, fat, and carbohydrate, and, even when the necessary inorganic material is carefully supplied, the animal still cannot flourish. The animal body is adjusted to live either upon plant tissues or other animals, and these contain countless substances other than protein, carbohydrate and fats." He coined the term *accessory food factors* for these substances.

From 1907 to 1913, Holst and Frölich of the University of Christiana carried out their classic investigation on scurvy. They were directed to investigate scurvy in Norwegian sailors. They showed that guinea pigs developed this disease on cereals and bread and that it was cured by small amounts of fresh cabbage or carrots. They concluded that scurvy was due to the absence of a specific chemical factor, which was destroyed by cooking. They demonstrated a relationship between human and guinea pig scurvy.

Following work published in 1909 by Stepp showing the necessity of some constituent contained in the lipid fraction of certain natural foods, definite proof of the existence and specific physiological function of vitamin A was furnished in 1913 by the independent investigation of McCollum and Davis[4] and of Osborne and Mendel.[5] This specific knowledge resulted from carefully controlled experiments by the purified-

[3] Frederick Gowland Hopkins was born in England in 1861 and trained as chemist. His activities in the field of biochemistry and nutrition began in 1898 at Cambridge University and continued there until his death in 1947. Early in his career he isolated and identified tryptophan and showed that zein could be improved nutritionally by adding this amino acid to it. This and other early work led to his conclusions regarding the "accessory food factors" as substances essential for the prevention of deficiency diseases. For this pioneer concept of the existence of the vitamins he received in 1939, jointly with Eijkman, the Nobel prize in medicine.

[4] E. V. McCollum and Marguerite Davis, Necessity of certain lipins in the diet during growth, *J. Biol. Chem.*, **15**:167–175, 1913. Elmer V. McCollum was born in 1879 and received his B.A. and M.A. from the University of Kansas and his Ph.D. from Yale University. He began his teaching and research career as instructor in agricultural chemistry at the University of Wisconsin in 1907 and moved in 1917 to Johns Hopkins University as professor of biochemistry, where he worked until he became Professor Emeritus in 1946. His research resulted in the discovery of vitamin D as well as vitamin A and in many other fundamental contributions which have caused him to be recognized as an outstanding pioneer in the modern science of nutrition.

[5] Thomas B. Osborne and Lafayette B. Mendel, The influence of butter-fat on growth, *J. Biol. Chem.*, **16**:423–437, 1913.

diet method (Sec. 10.3). Dating from 1913, the extension of the knowledge of vitamins proceeded very rapidly.

In this brief statement of the historical background of the vitamin concept, only a few of the men concerned in its development have been mentioned. The discussion suffices to show that many scientists throughout the world contributed and that it is impossible to name any one person or group as the discoverer of this far-reaching concept. Such is the often-repeated story in scientific investigations. Links in the chain of facts are supplied and gradually put together by various workers over a period of years. Finally some one man may complete the chain, and a discovery is announced; but he may deserve no more, and sometimes even less, credit than others who made the previous observations which he used and extended in making the final contribution.

8.2. Fat-soluble and Water-soluble Vitamins. McCollum proposed the names *fat-soluble A* for the factor found in butter and *water-soluble B* for the one concerned with beriberi as descriptive terms, since the first was extractable from foods with fat solvents and the second with water. On a similar basis, the antiscorbutic vitamin was later called water-soluble C. Though these descriptive adjectives were eventually given up, they are still frequently used as general terms in classifying the vitamins. Thus the fat-soluble vitamins include A, D, E, and K, while the members of the B complex, C, and others are classed as water soluble.

In the present chapter, these various vitamins are discussed as regards their physiological effects, chemical nature and properties, and distribution in feeds. The specific requirements for growth, lactation, and other body functions are discussed in later chapters. Principal attention is given to those vitamins which have been demonstrated to be of practical importance in the feeding of farm animals.

VITAMIN A

All animals require a dietary source of vitamin A. The vitamin does not occur as such in plant products but rather as its precursor, carotene. This compound is commonly spoken of as *provitamin* A because the body can transform it into the active vitamin. This is the way in which the vitamin A needs of farm animals are met, for the most part, because their rations consist mainly or entirely of foods of plant origin. The combined potency of a feed, represented by its vitamin A and carotene content, is referred to as its *vitamin A value*.

8.3. Physiological Function and Symptoms of Deficiency. Vitamin A is combined with a protein in visual purple, a compound that breaks down in the physiological process of sight, as a result of a photochemical reaction. A deficiency of the vitamin, in terms of the needs for the resynthesis of visual purple, results in night blindness, which is a symptom in all animals. The deficiency first manifests itself as a slow dark adaptation and progresses to total night blindness. In man the measurement of this physiological response after exposure of the eye to a calibrated source of light is used in estimating quantitative needs for the vitamin. The reactions which take place in vision and the role played by vitamin A are shown in Fig. 8.1.

There are various other eye symptoms that vary markedly among species, some of which represent secondary infections. Xerophthalmia,

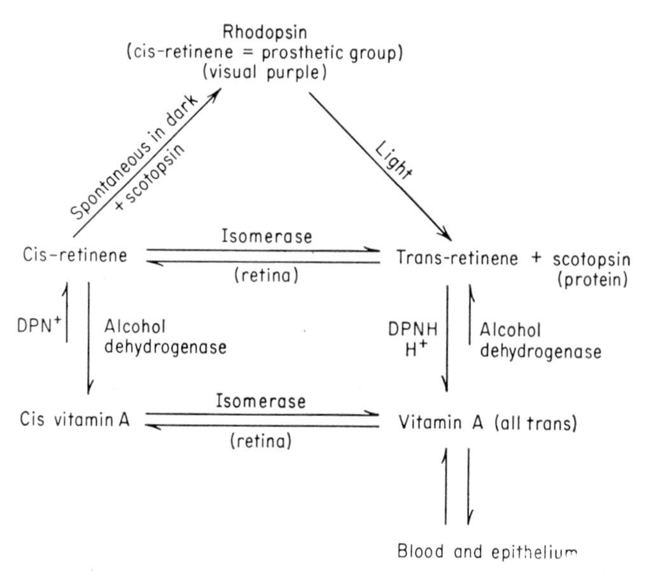

FIG. 8.1. Vitamin A and vision. (*Adapted from George Wald, Am. Scientist,* **42:** 73–95, 1954.)

an advanced stage of vitamin A deficiency noted particularly in children and rats, is characterized by a dry condition of the cornea and conjunctiva, cloudiness, and ulceration. It is not a common symptom in other animals, although corneal changes occur. Copious lacrimination is a more prominent eye symptom in cows (Fig. 8.2). In the case of chickens, on the other hand, the secretions of the tear glands dry up, and an infection may then occur, resulting in a discharge that causes the lids to stick together. At least some of these symptoms develop as a result of basic epithelial changes caused by a deficiency of the vitamin.

Wolbach and Howe[6] were responsible for discovering a generalized

[6] S. B. Wolbach, and P. R. Howe, Tissue changes following deprivation of fat-soluble A vitamin, *J. Exptl. Med.,* **42:**753–777, 1925; Vitamin A deficiency in the guinea-pig, *Arch. Pathol. Lab. Med.,* **5:**239–253, 1928.

pathological effect of the absence of the vitamin. They found that the normal epithelium in various locations throughout the body became replaced by a stratified, keratinizing epithelium. This effect has been noted in the respiratory, alimentary, reproductive, and genitourinary tracts, as well as in the eye. This keratinization lowers the resistance of the epithelial tissues to the entrance of infective organisms. Thus

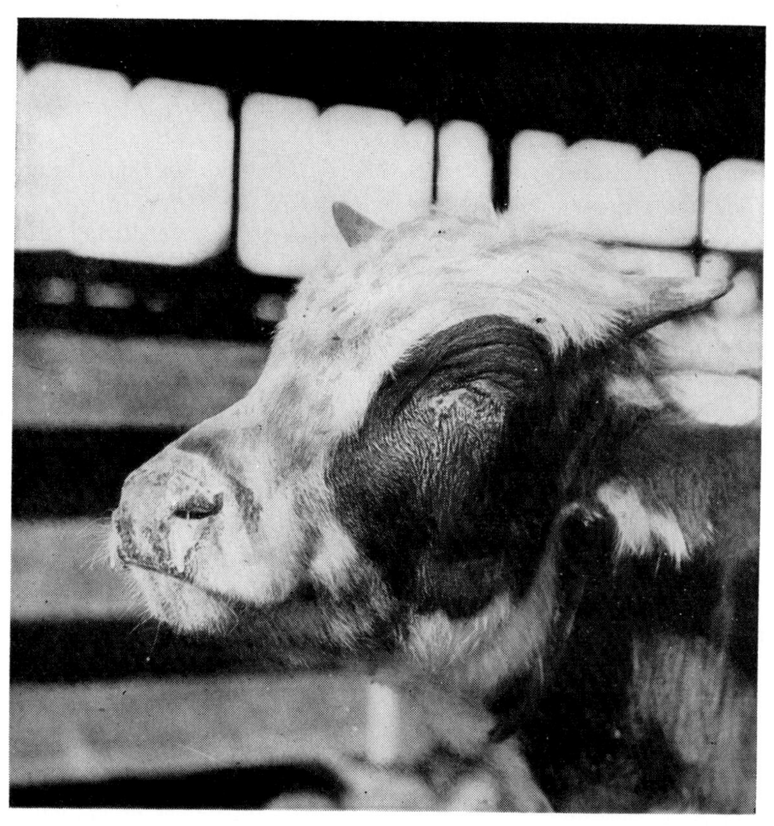

FIG. 8.2. Advanced stage of eye lesion in vitamin A deficiency. (*Courtesy of S. W. Mead, University of California.*)

respiratory troubles, such as colds and sinus infections, tend to be more severe in vitamin A deficiency. A diet adequate in the vitamin is necessary to help maintain the normal powers of resistance, but additional intakes will not increase resistance to infections which enter through the epithelium. Aside from its curative effect on xerophthalmia, which may be secondary to a bacterial invasion, there is no evidence that the administration of the vitamin after an infection has become established will shorten its course or lessen its severity.

These observations do not mean that this keratinization of the epithelium is of little importance. There are many troubles, noninfective in character, which increase following its occurrence. This is true for certain gastrointestinal disturbances such as diarrhea. The formation of kidney and bladder stones is favored because the damaged epithelium interferes with the normal secretion and elimination of the urine and the sloughed keratinized cells may form foci for the formation of stones. There is a specific interference with reproduction caused by this altered epithelium which is of great importance, as is discussed later (Sec. 15.13). Jungherr and coworkers[7] found that squamous metaplasia in the parotid gland was an early change in vitamin A-deficient calves and that it proved useful in diagnosing a deficiency.

Vitamin A is concerned in the normal development of bone through a control exercised over the activity of the osteoclasts and osteoblasts of the epithelial cartilage. The bones are altered in shape during growth, as is clearly illustrated by the studies of Mellanby.[8] The teeth are also affected. A failure of the spinal and some other bones to develop normally results in turn in pressure on the nerves and in their degeneration. For example, a blindness in calves results from a constriction of the optic nerve caused by a narrowing of the bone canal through which it passes. Avitaminosis A can result in deafness in dogs, owing to an injury to the auditory nerve. Bone changes may also be responsible for the muscle incoordination and other nervous symptoms shown by A-deficient cattle, sheep, and swine. They may be also concerned in the increase in cerebrospinal fluid pressure shown by Moore[9] and coworkers to be characteristic of the deficiency. While the pathological basis is unknown, several studies have shown that a lack of vitamin A causes congenital malformation in certain soft tissues. Examples are the birth of pigs without eyeballs, as studied by Hale,[10] and hydrocephalus in rabbits, reported by Lamming.[11]

8.4. Chemical Nature of Vitamin A and Carotene. Chemical isolation and identification early became a goal of vitamin research because of the recognized importance of working with pure substances of known composition, rather than with concentrates containing many other chemical compounds besides the vitamin under study. In view of the enormous difficulties involved in isolating substances which are complex in nature,

[7] E. L. Jungherr and coworkers, Parotid gland lesions in experimental bovine vitamin A deficiency, *J. Dairy Sci.*, **33**:666–675, 1950.

[8] E. Mellanby, Vitamin A and bone growth: the reversibility of vitamin A-deficiency changes, *J. Physiol.*, **105**:382–399, 1947.

[9] L. A. Moore and coworkers, Carotene requirements for Guernsey and Jersey calves as determined by spinal fluid pressure, *J. Dairy Sci.*, **31**:533–538, 1948.

[10] Fred Hale, Pigs born without eyeballs, *J. Heredity*, **24**:105–106, 1933.

[11] G. E. Lamming, Hydrocephalus in young rabbits associated with maternal vitamin A deficiency, *Brit. J. Nutrition*, **8**:363–369, 1954.

present in only minute amounts, and rather unstable, it is not surprising that our knowledge of the chemical nature of the vitamins lagged far behind their discovery. Remarkable progress has been made during the last thirty years, with the result that today we have fairly complete information regarding most all of these essentials.

Vitamin A is a nearly colorless substance having the formula $C_{20}H_{30}O$. It does not occur as such in plant materials, but rather as its precursors, certain carotenoid pigments which are converted into the vitamin in the animal body. The development of the knowledge as to the relationship between vitamin A and carotene and as to their chemical nature represents a highly interesting chapter of vitamin research, which illustrates the course of such studies.

In 1914 McCollum and Davis found that the vitamin was contained in the unsaponifiable fraction of milk fat, and later studies confirmed its identity as an unsaponifiable constituent extractable by lipid solvents. In 1919 Steenbock called attention to the fact that among vegetable foods vitamin A potency was associated in a rather remarkable way with yellow color, and shortly thereafter, he and his associates published many data demonstrating this association. They went so far as to suggest that carotene was the source of the vitamin. This view was not accepted by other workers, and Steenbock came to recognize that the vitamin was not carotene itself because certain potent sources of the vitamin were colorless. It was ten years before the riddle was solved.

In the meantime studies in various laboratories gradually built up the body of information which provided the answer. Drummond and his associates used an old color reaction for cod-liver oil as a basis for developing a test which provided a method for the detection and estimation of vitamin A. The test involved the production of a brilliant blue color by arsenic trichloride. Later the test was modified by Carr and Price by the substitution of antimony trichloride for the arsenic compound, and the tests is known today as the *Carr-Price reaction.* The spectrograph (Sec. 3.15) also came into use for studying the nature of the vitamin, and its content in fish-liver oils was found to be correlated with a selective absorption with a maximum at 328 mμ. Both the color reaction and the absorption spectrum proved very useful in the later studies which resulted in the identification of the vitamin and in demonstrating its relationship to carotene.

Renewed beliefs in this relationship caused von Euler and associates in Stockholm to conduct carotene-feeding experiments. They obtained a definite growth response when the pigment was added to a vitamin A-deficient diet. In 1930 Moore[12] produced proof that the animal body trans-

[12] Thomas Moore, Vitamin A and carotene. I. The association of vitamin A activity with carotene in the carrot root, *Biochem. J.*, **23**:803–811, 1929.

formed carotene into vitamin A. He fed rats on a diet which resulted in the symptoms of deficiency. Some of the animals were then killed, and their livers found devoid of A. The rest of the animals were fed carotene with a resulting disappearance of the deficiency symptoms, and on autopsy, their livers were found rich in the vitamin.

Meanwhile halibut-liver oil had been found an especially concentrated source of the vitamin, and fractionation methods were applied to it to isolate the active substance. These methods brought success by 1932 in the isolation, by Karrer and his associates in Switzerland and by Drummond and his coworkers in England, of a very active fraction which was identified as an unsaturated alcohol having the formula $C_{20}H_{30}O$. Karrer proposed the structural formula given below which shows the compound to have a β-ionone ring and an unsaturated side chain.

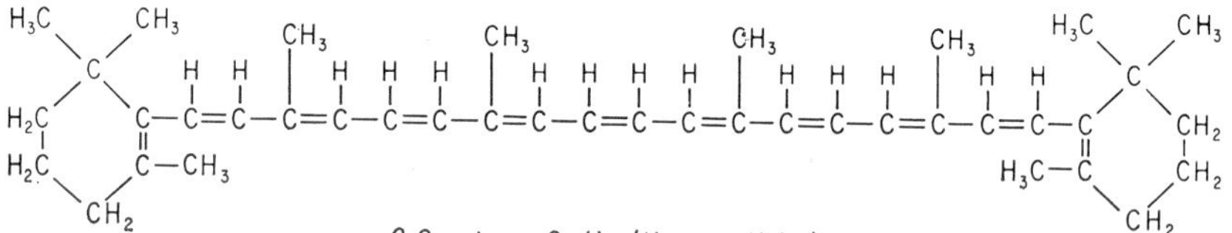

β-Carotene, $C_{40}H_{56}$ (Karrer, Kuhn)

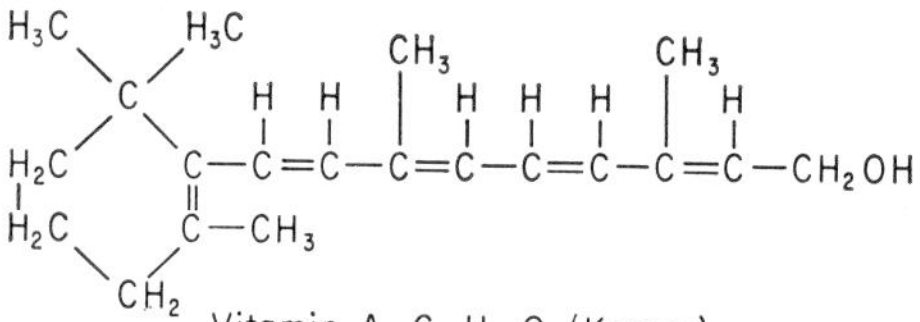

Vitamin A, $C_{20}H_{30}O$ (Karrer)

There followed the brilliant researches by Karrer, by Kuhn in Germany, and by others which established the chemical structure of the highly complex hydrocarbon carotene, which was previously known to have the empirical formula $C_{40}H_{56}$. Several isomeric forms of carotene were isolated, and their structural formulas worked out. All were reddish-yellow crystalline compounds, which differed, however, as regards optical activity and the wavelength at which maximum color absorption occurred. It is now recognized that there are four different carotenes which have vitamin A activity, viz., α-, β-, and γ-carotene and cryptoxanthine. The last is a hydroxy-β-carotene and is the principal form found in yellow corn. Most of the carotene of other feeds is in the β form. Vitamin A contains a β-ionone ring, and β-carotene contains two of these rings, while γ-carotene contains only one, as shown by their formulas. The mechanism of the conversion of β-carotene to vitamin A, which involves cutting the molecule in half, is not fully understood. It is considered that carotene is changed to retinene by oxidation. The retinene is in turn reduced to vitamin A by alcohol dehydrogenase. The vitamin A activity of β-carotene is substantially greater than α-, γ-, or hydroxy-β-carotene.

Vitamin A exists only in the animal kingdom. Here it occurs both as the free alcohol and also as esters of the higher fatty acids and is related to unsaturated acids. Later it was discovered that there is another form of vitamin A, referred to as vitamin A_2 to distinguish it from the common form A_1, previously described. A_2, which was isolated from fresh-water fish, has not been crystallized, but it is distinguished from A_1 by its maximum absorption at 345 to 350 mμ in contrast to 325 to 328 mμ for A_1. It has a lower activity than A_1.

8.5. Stability of Vitamin A and Carotene. Differing from the nutrients previously considered, the vitamins as a class are susceptible to destruction in varying degrees by certain physical and chemical agents which may become operative in the course of some of the processes to which feeds are subjected. The same is true during storage under certain conditions. The different vitamins vary greatly in their susceptibility to the action of these agents. Both carotene and vitamin A are destroyed by oxidation, and this is the most common cause of any depreciation which may occur in the potency of sources of them. The process is accelerated at high temperatures, but heat without oxygen has a minor effect. Butter exposed in thin layers in air at 50°C. loses all its vitamin A potency in 6 hr., but in the absence of air there is little destruction at 120°C. over the same period. Cod-liver oil in a tightly corked bottle has shown activity after 31 years, but it may lose all of its potency in a few weeks when incorporated in a feed mixture stored under the usual conditions. The distribution of the oil over the feed particles provides a large surface for oxidative action, and this process is accelerated by the presence of prooxidants in any rancid fats present. Certain metals also, especially the trace-mineral elements, catalyze the destructive action. The effective prevention of rancidity and of destruction of vitamin A activity presents a practical problem in mixed rations, as is shown by the studies of Kamstra and associates.[13] The carotene in alfalfa meal is much more stable than carotene in oil under these conditions.

Large losses of carotene take place in the curing of roughages and in their later storage. Bernstein and Thompson[14] have shown that the destruction of carotene in leaves is partly enzymic and partly photochemical. Enzymatic destruction requires oxygen, is greatest at high temperatures, and ceases after complete dehydration. The photo-

[13] L. D. Kamstra, A. W. Halverson, and A. L. Moxon, Effect of trace minerals and other dietary ingredients upon carotene stability in stored poultry diets, *Poultry Sci.*, **32**:352–356, 1953.

[14] Leon Bernstein and John F. Thompson, Studies on the carotene-destroying processes in drying bean leaves, *Botan. Gaz.*, **109**:204–219, 1947.

chemical action increases with decreasing moisture content in curing but slows down as this content reaches 20 to 30 per cent. Walsh and Hauge[15] have shown that the same type of reactions occur in alfalfa. In curing and preserving forages both the enzymatic and the photochemical destruction must be controlled to produce roughages high in carotene (Sec. 8.10). Corn has been reported to lose as much as 60 per cent of its carotene on seven months' storage. With both carotene and vitamin A the nature of the associated substances and the temperature and moisture conditions have a marked influence on the rate of destruction.

The cooking processes commonly used in human food preparation do not cause much destruction to the vitamin potency. Hydrogenation of fats lessens their vitamin A value, and thus the commercial products prepared for culinary purposes commonly contain none of the vitamin, though it may have been present in the original material. Saponification does not destroy the vitamin if oxidation is avoided.

8.6. Metabolism of Vitamin A and Carotene. The first step in the utilization of carotene and vitamin A is absorption. This absorption varies, particularly for carotene, according to the nature of the diet and the species. Differences in digestibility of food sources are reflected in variations in the amounts of the provitamin available for absorption. Fats promote the absorption of both A and carotene, and emulsifying agents may have an additional effect. Some of the ingested provitamin is destroyed in the intestine. The presence of vitamin E, an antioxidant, in the ration lessens this destruction. The effects of these variable factors have been studied with various feed sources and species. One cannot generalize from the results, however, as applied to farm animal nutrition, other than to note that the utilization of the vitamin A value of the ration may be low in many situations because of limited absorption. For therapeutic use certain vitamin A preparations in aqueous solution have been found more absorbable than in the usual oily medium.

In order to serve the body, carotene must be converted to vitamin A. For a long time it was assumed, without definite evidence, that this conversion took place in the liver. Studies by Wiese, Mehl, and Deuel,[16] confirmed by others, have shown that in the rat ingested carotene is converted to vitamin A in the intestinal wall. Similar conversion has also been reported for the pig, calf, goat, and chicken. In rats, sheep, goats, and swine carotene is not absorbed into the blood stream, except in traces. In contrast, the blood of cattle and horses contains substan-

[15] Kenneth A. Walsh and S. M. Hauge, Carotene—factors affecting destruction in alfalfa, *J. Agr. & Food Chem.*, **1**:1001–1004, 1953.

[16] Catherine Elisabeth Wiese, John W. Mehl, and Harry J. Deuel, Jr., Studies on carotenoid metabolism. VIII. The *in vitro* conversion of carotene to vitamin A in the intestine of the rat, *Arch. Biochem.*, **15**:75–79, 1947.

tial amounts of carotene when these animals are fed a ration rich in the provitamin. Guernsey cattle have higher plasma carotene than other breeds of cattle on similar feed, and more is secreted in the milk, accounting for its yellower color. In these species only part of the carotene in the feed is converted into vitamin A in the intestinal wall. Some of the provitamin is absorbed unchanged and stored in the liver and fatty tissues of the body.

Studies by Bieri and Pollard[17] and by others have shown that water-soluble carotene injected into the blood stream was changed into vitamin A. Conversion was not impaired after ligation of the bile duct, removal of the small intestines, or removal of 60 to 75 per cent of the liver. These results suggest that various body tissues are able to convert carotene to vitamin A. Thus, it now seems clear that body reserves of carotene can be converted to vitamin A to serve in metabolism.

The vitamin A level of the blood does reflect the nutritional status with respect to this vitamin. This level is governed by the extent of the liver stores, discussed later, as well as by the current intake. While the determination of plasma vitamin A is being increasingly used as a measure of adequacy of intake, the question of the significance which can be attached to the results in various species in terms of current and previous intakes of the vitamin and its precursor requires much further study.

8.7. Relation of Vitamin A to X-Disease. Extensive loss of cattle has occurred from a disease called X-disease, or hyperkeratosis, which exhibits symptoms similar in many respects to severe vitamin A deficiency. During the decade of 1942 to 1952 hyperkeratosis was observed in 32 states of the United States and in a number of European countries. Olafson[18] first described the disease in detail as characterized by thickening of the skin, profuse lacrimination and salivation, depression, and loss of appetite and condition. Growth of young cattle is retarded or stopped. Males become sterile because of failure of sperm formation owing to changes in germinal epithelium of the testes. Females often abort, and the ovaries become small and inactive. Extensive microscopic lesions are seen. Death of cattle frequently occurs, and surviving animals remain unprofitable for long periods. Several groups of workers reported extremely low plasma vitamin A values in cattle showing symptoms of X-disease. Feeding large doses of vitamin A increased the plasma vitamin A, but the values fell rapidly when therapy was discontinued. When carotene was fed plasma carotene values rose, but there was no elevation of plasma vitamin A, suggesting an interference

[17] J. G. Bieri and C. J. Pollard, Studies of the cite of conversion of β-carotene injected intravenously into rats, *Brit. J. Nutrition,* **8**:32–44, 1954.

[18] Peter Olafson, Hyperkeratosis (X-disease) of cattle, *Cornell Vet.,* **37**:279–291, 1947.

with the conversion of carotene to vitamin A. Decreased tocopherol levels in the plasma of cattle with X-disease have been observed. Goats, sheep, swine, mice, rats, and chickens, animals which normally have little or no carotene in the blood plasma, are all much more resistant to the disease than cattle.

Hyperkeratosis is caused by highly chlorinated naphthalenes, as was shown by Bell[19] and several others. This interesting story is reviewed by Hansel and McEntee.[20] As a result of these research findings chlorinated naphthalenes have been largely eliminated from lubricating oils and other materials that have direct contact with cattle and with all livestock feeds. No recent outbreak of the disease has been reported in the United States.

8.8. Vitamin A Storage. Some vitamins are stored in the body in large amounts; others to only a very limited extent. The liver is a large storehouse of vitamin A, as has been shown for cattle by the studies of Guilbert and Hart.[21] The total storage of carotene and vitamin A in the liver and depot fat of cows which had access to a carotene-rich ration throughout life was estimated to be 0.6 to 0.7 g. for the younger animals and up to 3.6 g. in aged cows. From 67 to 93 per cent of the storage was in the liver. In this organ most of the storage was in the form of the vitamin itself, while in the fat depots carotene predominated. A cow whose reserves were depleted was fed approximately 15 g. of carotene in freshly cut alfalfa during a period of 13 days and stored about 400 mg. It is evident that the rate of storage with a high intake can greatly exceed the rate of depletion on a vitamin-deficient diet. Guilbert and Hart found that over 200 days elapsed before the livers of animals which had previously received feeds rich in carotene were completely depleted of the vitamin and its precursor. In studies with rats, Davies and Moore[22] have shown that the adult is able to store, with massive doses, enough vitamin A in its liver to supply its theoretical requirement for a century but that these superfluous stores are eliminated at a very rapid rate until a state of stable storage is reached.

The storage of vitamin A, or its precursor in those species which absorb carotene, or both, appears to be a function of all species. It has a large

[19] Wilson B. Bell, The relative toxicity of the chlorinated naphthalenes in experimentally produced bovine hyperkeratosis (X-disease), *Vet. Med.*, **48**:135–140, 1953.

[20] W. Hansel and K. McEntee, Bovine hyperkeratosis (X-disease): a review, *J. Dairy Sci.*, **38**:875–882, 1955.

[21] H. R. Guilbert and G. H. Hart, Storage of vitamin A in cattle, *J. Nutrition*, **8**: 25–44, 1934; Minimum vitamin A requirements with particular reference to cattle, *ibid.*, **10**:409–427, 1935.

[22] Alan W. Davies and Thomas Moore, Vitamin A and carotene. XII. The elimination of vitamin A from the livers of rats previously given massive doses of vitamin A concentrate, *Biochem. J.*, **29**:147–150, 1935.

practical importance in nutrition because it provides a means whereby reserves can serve during periods of dietary scarcity, and it eliminates the necessity of a constant daily supply of the vitamin or its precursor in the diet. A quantity sufficient to protect a rat for several months can be given in a single dose. Animals on good pasture can store extensive reserves to help meet their needs during the winter feeding period when their rations may be deficient. This large capacity to store the vitamin must be taken account of in studies of requirements in order to make sure that intakes which appear adequate for a given function are not being supplemented by reserves stored up prior to the period of observation. The measurement of the liver store of vitamin A at slaughter or in samples obtained on biopsy is a useful technique in studies of vitamin A status and requirements.

Eaton and associates[23] have shown that in dairy calves approximately four months of age, fed a depletion ration devoid of vitamin A activity, the plasma vitamin A level decreases in a linear manner until values of 4.0 μg. per 100 ml. are reached. Calves exhibiting such low plasma values for two consecutive weeks were shown to be depleted of liver stores of vitamin A. The linear decrease in plasma vitamin A makes it possible to estimate the time needed to deplete animals of liver reserves.

8.9. Quantitative Determination of Vitamin A Value. The improvement and standardization of methods for the quantitative estimation of the vitamin A value of foods constitute a very active field of research at the present time. Biological, chemical, and physical methods are being employed. Since the procedures are constantly being modified, the description of the methods in use will be limited to a statement of the principles involved.

The biological method measures the total potency whether due to the vitamin itself or to its precursor or to both, while certain others determine only one of these substances. The most commonly used one is the rat-growth method. The food to be tested is fed at several levels to different groups of young rats, as a supplement to a vitamin A-free diet which has caused growth to cease. The growth response is then compared with that produced in a similar group of rats receiving as a supplement a standard source of the vitamin, either carotene or vitamin A acetate. In this way the amount of the feed under test which gives the same response as the standard supplement is determined, and the potency is expressed in units per gram. The standard is a solution of vitamin A acetate in vegetable oil. The vitamin A activity of a food is expressed in International Units (I.U.). One I.U. is defined as the activity of 0.3 μg. of

[23] H. D. Eaton and associates, Effect of vitamin A depletion on liveweight, plasma and liver vitamin A and microanatomy in young calves, *J. Dairy Sci.*, **34**:386–395, 1951.

crystalline vitamin A alcohol (0.344 μg. of vitamin A acetate). β-carotene is the standard for provitamin A, 0.6 μg. being equivalent in activity to 0.3 μg. of vitamin A. Another biological method of assay measures the storage of the vitamin in the liver of rats after a depletion period. A third method is based on the fact that, on a vitamin A-deficient diet, rats show a persistence of cornified cells in the vagina which disappear on the addition of the vitamin to the diet.

Nonbiological assays for carotene are available for measuring separately the amounts of the various carotenoids, taking advantage of differences in physical properties. The chromatographic method, involving separation of the biologically active carotenoids from the total carotenoid pigments and their photometric measurement, is the most widely used procedure. The results are expressed as micrograms of β-carotene per gram of product. Each plant product presents a special problem in extracting the pigments and in their separation. Failure to recognize this fact has resulted in many unreliable values in the literature. Special problems are met in applying the colorimetric or spectrophotometric procedure to butter, which contains both vitamin A and carotene and also added coloring material. Details cannot be here given, as to either these various procedures or their limitations.

For certain species, the rat-assay method overvalues the actual vitamin A potency of a food that contains much of this potency in the form of carotene, because the rat utilizes carotene to a greater degree than does the species in question. In the case of man an I.U. of carotene is considered to be only one-half to one-third as valuable, depending on its food source, as an I.U. of vitamin A. Guilbert found that it took approximately twice as many I.U. of carotene as of vitamin A to prevent night blindness in cattle and that the ratio was wider at the higher levels needed for storage and reproduction. The pig and sheep also utilize carotene less efficiently than does the rat. In the case of poultry, however, both forms of the vitamin have been found equal per I.U. The errors here involved in using rat-assay values or in applying the relationship found in the rat assay to determining the vitamin A values of plant products fed to farm animals are obvious. For this reason it is becoming an increasing practice to state animal requirements both as carotene and as vitamin A and to express the carotene and vitamin A content of feeds separately, both in micrograms. This makes it possible to calculate how the needs of a given species can be met in terms of a specific feed supply, as is illustrated in later chapters where requirements are discussed.

8.10. Vitamin A Value of Feeds. The richest sources of vitamin A are the fish oils. Some swordfish-liver oils contain as many as 250,000 units of vitamin A per gram. Halibut-liver oil may run even higher. Thus both are many times more potent than cod-liver oils. Products from the same species, however, may be highly variable in potency, and thus, in their manufacture for use as vitamin A supplements, they are subjected to a biological assay in order that the user may be assured of a certain minimum potency. Among the common foods of animal origin, milk fat, egg yolk, and liver are rated as rich sources, but this is not the case if the animal from which they come has been receiving an A-deficient diet for an extended period. Since the vitamin is present in the fat, skim milk contains very little.

In the nutrition of farm animals, we are primarily interested in the potency of plant products. Though the yellow color is masked by chlorophyll, all green parts of growing plants are rich in carotene and thus have a high vitamin A value. Good pasture always provides a liberal supply, and the kind of pasture plant, whether grass of legume, appears to be of minor importance. At maturity, however, leaves contain much more than stems, and thus legume hay is much richer in vitamin content than timothy or other grasses. With all hays and other forage, the vitamin value decreases after the bloom stage, and much of the carotene is destroyed by oxidation in the process of field curing. Russell[24] found that there may be a loss of more than 80 per cent of the carotene of alfalfa during the first 24 hr. of the curing process. It occurs chiefly during the hours of daylight, owing to photochemical activation of the destructive process. Hays which are cut in the bloom stage or earlier and cured without exposure to rain or to too much sun retain a considerable proportion of their carotene content, while those which are cut in the seed stage and exposed to rain and to the sun for extended periods lose it almost entirely. Under similar conditions of curing, alfalfa and other legume hays are much richer than grass hays because of their leafy nature, but a poor grade of alfalfa may have less than a good grade of timothy.

In the artificial curing of hay with a "hay drier," there is only a slight loss of carotene because of the rapidity of the process. Russell and coworkers found the machine-dried product to have two to ten times the value of field-cured alfalfa. Severe heating of hay in the mow or stack reduces the vitamin content, and there is a gradual loss in storage so that old hay is poorer than new. Owing to their higher initial content machine-dried hays are subject to larger percentage losses than field-cured. Losses as high as 60 per cent have been reported from July to November, but they were found much smaller during the colder months. Temperature is the major factor causing variations in loss during storage.

[24] Walter C. Russell, The effect of the curing process upon the vitamin A and D content of alfalfa, *J. Biol. Chem.*, **85**:289–297, 1929.

The extent of carotene losses which occur under practical conditions is shown by the report of Shepherd and associates,[25] as illustrated in Fig. 8.3.

The degree of greenness in a roughage is a good index of its carotene content. The data in Table 8.1 are useful to indicate the order of the differences found among various roughages differing as to color, kind, and other factors. Published average values as to carotene content can serve only as approximate guides in feeding practice because of the many factors affecting the actual potency of individual samples as fed.

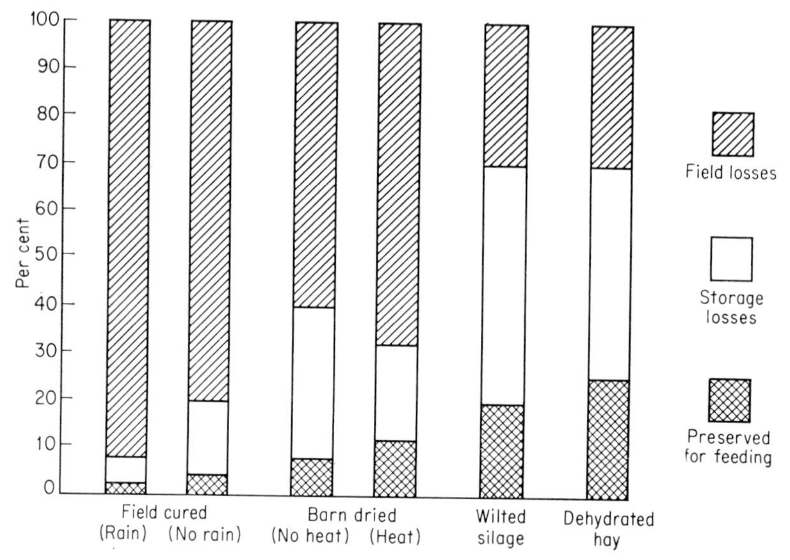

FIG. 8.3. Percentage of carotene lost in the field and during storage of alfalfa hay and silage. (*Courtesy of J. B. Shepherd, U.S. Department of Agriculture.*)

Aside from yellow corn and its by-products practically all of the concentrates used in feeding animals are devoid of the vitamin or nearly so. The potency of yellow corn is only about one-eighth that of good roughage. Roots and tubers as a class supply practically no vitamin A, but carrots are a very rich source and so are sweet potatoes, as might be expected from their yellow color. Pumpkins and squash also supply considerable amounts. The green leafy vegetables used in human nutrition are rich.

Tankage, meat scraps, and similar animal by-products have little if any

[25] J. B. Shepherd and associates, Experimental harvesting and preserving alfalfa for dairy cattle feed, *U.S. Dept. Agr. Tech. Bull.* 1079, 1954.

vitamin A potency. Certain fish meals are fair sources, but variation in the raw material and in the methods of processing which may entirely destroy any potency originally present, make generalizations here of no value.

TABLE 8.1. ESTIMATED CAROTENE CONTENT OF FEEDS IN RELATION TO APPEARANCE AND METHODS OF CONSERVATION*

Feedstuff	*Carotene, mg. per lb.*
Fresh green legumes and grasses, immature	15 to 40
Dehydrated alfalfa meal, fresh, dehydrated without field curing, very bright green color	110 to 135
Dehydrated alfalfa meal after considerable time in storage, bright green color	50 to 70
Alfalfa leaf meal, bright green color	60 to 80
Legume hays, including alfalfa, very quickly cured with minimum sun exposure, bright green color, leafy	35 to 40
Legume hays, including alfalfa, good green color, leafy	18 to 27
Legume hays, including alfalfa, partly bleached, moderate amount of green color	9 to 14
Legume hays, including alfalfa, badly bleached or discolored, traces of green color	4 to 8
Nonlegume hays, including timothy, cereal, and prairie hays, well cured, good green color	9 to 14
Nonlegume hays, average quality, bleached, some green color	4 to 8
Legume silage	5 to 20
Corn and sorghum silages, medium to good green color	2 to 10
Grains, mill feeds, protein concentrates, and by-product concentrates, except yellow corn and its by-products	0.01 to 0.2

* Compiled by H. R. Guilbert, University of California, and reproduced with his permission.

Lard was used for years as a vitamin A-free source of fat in diets for experimental animals until it was demonstrated that large intakes would prevent vitamin A deficiency in rats. Ames and Harris[26] were able to identify this "lard factor" as true vitamin A. Variations in the vitamin A content of lard as influenced by diet have not been studied.

VITAMIN D

Only a few years after vitamin A was discovered, it became clear, through the work of Mellanby in England with dogs, that a dietary defi-

[26] Stanley R. Ames and Philip L. Harris, Identification of the so-called "lard factor" as true vitamin A, *Science*, **120**:391–393, 1954.

ciency was concerned in rickets. The proof that it was due to a distinct vitamin was furnished by McCollum and associates[27] in 1922. This proof was obtained by oxidizing cod-liver oil until vitamin A was destroyed, as shown by the inability of the oil to cure xerophthalmia, and then by demonstrating that the oxidized oil was still effective in curing rickets.

8.11. Physiological Functions and Symptoms of Deficiency. In view of the circumstances of the discovery of vitamin D as well as the fact that cod-liver oil had long been known to be effective in the cure of rickets, the term *antirachitic factor* naturally arose. It is evident from previous discussions (Sec. 7.11) that, however the term is defined, rickets is a disturbance of calcium and phosphorus metabolism and that the mineral relations in the diet as well as the vitamin are involved. There can be no calcification without calcium and phosphorus. On the other hand, the vitamin has a nutritional significance in addition to its relation to this disturbance of bone growth.

Undoubtedly vitamin D is always required for the normal calcification of the growing bone, but the amount needed varies with the mineral relations in the diet and also with the species. More is required when the amount of either element or the ratio between them is suboptimum. But no amount will compensate for severe deficiencies of either mineral. Theiler,[28] for example, has shown that rickets develops in calves on a low-phosphorus ration despite a very large supply of D in the form of radiant energy (Sec. 8.12). The species differences are illustrated by the fact that with adequate intakes of calcium and phosphorus a ration which contains only enough vitamin D to produce normal bone in the rat or pig will quickly cause the development of rickets in chicks. Surprisingly, the human baby is more like the bird in this respect than the other mammals mentioned. Turkeys and pheasants have higher requirements than chicks. An advanced stage of vitamin D deficiency is shown in Fig. 8.4. X-ray photographs of the width of the ulnar epiphyseal cartilage have been effectively used to detect the presence of rickets in calves and its severity. The method is described in the report by Thomas and associates.[29]

The necessity of vitamin D for normal calcification during growth has been demonstrated for many different species. The physical symptoms

[27] E. V. McCollum et al., Studies on experimental rickets. XXI. An experimental demonstration of the existence of a vitamin which promotes calcium deposition, *J. Biol. Chem.*, **53**:293–312, 1922.

[28] Arnold Theiler, The osteodystrophic diseases of domesticated animals. I. The structure of the bone; atrophy; osteoporosis, osteomyelitis, *Vet. J.*, **90**:143–158, 1934.

[29] J. W. Thomas, M. Okamoto, and L. A. Moore, The ulnar epiphyseal cartilage width in normal and rachitic calves and its use compared to other methods of detecting rickets, *J. Dairy Sci.*, **37**:1220–1226, 1954.

and bone and blood changes characteristic of inadequate calcification have been described (Sec. 7.11). The role of vitamin D in the adult animal appears much less important except during reproduction and lactation. Cases of human osteomalacia caused by a lack of vitamin D are frequently reported. Congenital malformations in the newborn result from extreme deficiencies in the diet of the mother during gestation, and the mother's skeleton is injured as well.

A lack of the antirachitic factor decreases egg production and hatchability, and the few eggs laid have thin shells and are easily broken.

FIG. 8.4. Advanced stage of rickets. (*Courtesy of W. E. Krauss, Ohio Agriculture Experiment Station.*)

The vitamin content of the eggs produced is influenced by the amount present in the diet of the hen. In view of the intense calcium and phosphorus metabolism that takes place in lactation, one would expect vitamin D to play a large role in milk secretion. This is not true in the case of the cow, as is discussed later (Sec. 16.35). Other species have been little studied. Apparently the vitamin is not readily secreted into milk, for massive doses in the feed are required to influence its concentration in this secretion. Ordinary levels of cod-liver oil are ineffective for this purpose.

Vitamin D aids calcium and phosphorus metabolism in a number of ways. Its over-all effect is to increase the net retention of the minerals. A primary way in which this is accomplished is by increasing the absorption of calcium from the intestine, as clearly shown by isotope studies. Such studies have also indicated a favorable effect on the deposition of lime salts in the bone. The kidney excretion of calcium and phosphorus is also influenced. The vitamin helps maintain the normal levels of these minerals in the blood. It also has an influence on the blood and bone levels of citrate which is concerned in some way with bone metabolism. The biochemical mechanisms, however, by which vitamin D acts, remains unknown. There is some basis for relating its effect on calcium and phosphorus metabolism to the activity of alkaline phosphatases which are present in bone, blood, and other tissues. Blood phosphatase increases in a deficiency of the vitamin, and its level has been used in detecting rickets. The level is restored to normal upon administering the factor. It has been reported that a water-soluble phosphorylated form of the vitamin activates alkaline phosphatase from bone, kidney, and intestine. Clearly, much more study is needed to clarify the specific functions of the vitamin and to harmonize conflicting views.

The body has some ability to store the vitamin, although to a much lesser extent than is the case for vitamin A. The principal stores of vitamin D occur in the liver, but it is also found in the lungs, kidneys, and elsewhere. While there is no large transfer to the fetus, a liberal intake during gestation does provide a sufficient store in the newborn to help prevent early rickets. For example, newborn lambs can be provided enough in this way to meet their needs for 6 weeks.

8.12. Vitamin D and Radiant Energy. While the value of sunlight in the treatment of rickets had been known for many years prior to the discovery of vitamin D, it was not until X-ray methods of diagnosis became available that positive proof was obtained of a specific effect on bone calcification. Using these methods Huldschinsky[30] demonstrated in 1919 that ultraviolet light caused the deposition of calcium salts in the bones of rachitic children and thereby cured the disease. Later work showed that sunlight was also effective.

When it became evident that both ultraviolet light and a factor present in cod-liver oil produced an identical effect in the healing of rickets, the question naturally arose as to why two such apparently unrelated factors could produce the same specific results. The answer was not long in coming. Following the studies of Goldblatt and Soames showing that the livers of irradiated rats possessed antirachitic properties, Hess of Columbia University and Steenbock of Wisconsin, independently and almost simultaneously, announced in 1924 that food materials which were ineffective in preventing rickets could be made antirachitic by exposing them to ultraviolet light. The original announcements were published

[30] K. Huldschinsky, Heilung von Rachitis durch künstliche Höhensonne, *Deut. med. Wochschr.*, **45**:712–713, 1919.

in detail by Hess and Weinstock,[31] by Steenbock and Black,[32] and by Steenbock and Nelson.[33] Several other papers quickly followed showing that a great variety of edible materials could be activated, that the same short wavelengths were here concerned as were effective in irradiating the body, and that the active substance was in the unsaponifiable fraction. These observations provided the working hypothesis that radiant energy cured rickets because it activated some precursor in the body to provide the active agent, that by similar action it produced in certain foods a similar agent which became effective upon ingestion, and that certain substances such as cod-liver oil naturally possessed this agent. Leads were thus provided for an attack on the problem of the chemical nature of the antirachitic factor.

8.13. Chemistry of Vitamin D. The knowledge that the active substance in materials made antirachitic by irradiation was in the nonsaponifiable fraction led to experiments with various sterols which resulted in the initial conclusion that cholesterol was the specific one activated. Later studies showing that irradiated ergosterol was much more active were responsible for the view that the activity of cholesterol was due to ergosterol as a contaminant. Several different kinds of evidence from various laboratories led to the conviction by 1928 that ergosterol was the precursor which became vitamin D through a molecular rearrangement brought about by the action of radiant energy. Attention was next directed to the very difficult task of isolating the active substance present in the resinous gum which resulted from the most effective irradiation of the crystalline ergosterol. Success was achieved by 1932. A group of English workers isolated from the mixture of sterols, which resulted from irradiation of ergosterol, a highly active crystalline substance which they named *calciferol*, and an essentially identical substance was simultaneously obtained by Windaus and associates in Germany. Calciferol, designated D_2, melts at 114 to 117°C. and is isomeric with ergosterol, which melts at 166°C. Ergosterol has three double bonds, while calciferol has four. Thus irradiation results in breaking one of the carbon-to-carbon linkages.

Further studies with different species and different sources of the vitamin led to proof that the original idea as to the activity of irradiated

[31] A. F. Hess and Mildred Weinstock, Antirachitic properties imparted to inert fluids and to green vegetables by ultra-violet irradiation, *J. Biol. Chem.*, **62**:301–313, 1924.

[32] Harry Steenbock and Archie Black, Fat-soluble vitamins. XVII. The induction of growth-promoting and calcifying properties in a ration by exposure to ultra-violet light, *J. Biol. Chem.*, **61**:405–422, 1924.

[33] Harry Steenbock and M. T. Nelson, Fat-soluble vitamins. XIX. The induction of calcifying properties in a rickets-producing ration by radiant energy, *J. Biol. Chem.*, **62**:209–216, 1924.

cholesterol was also correct. The active compound was isolated from fish-liver oil, and also prepared by irradiating 7-dehydrocholesterol. It was designated D_3. Its formula is shown along with that of D_2. Later

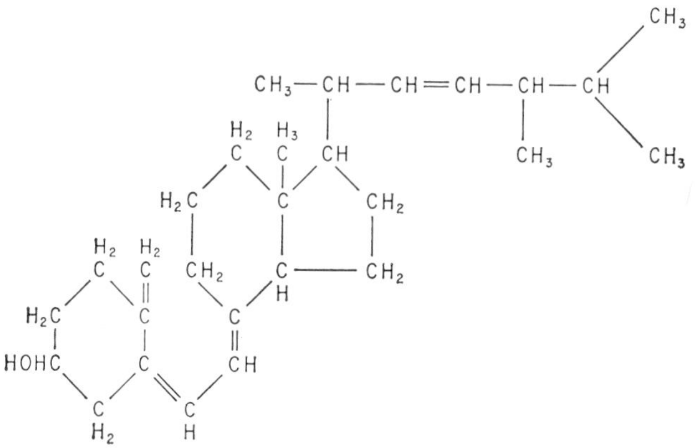

Calciferol (vitamin D_2), $C_{28}H_{44}O$
An active product of ergosterol

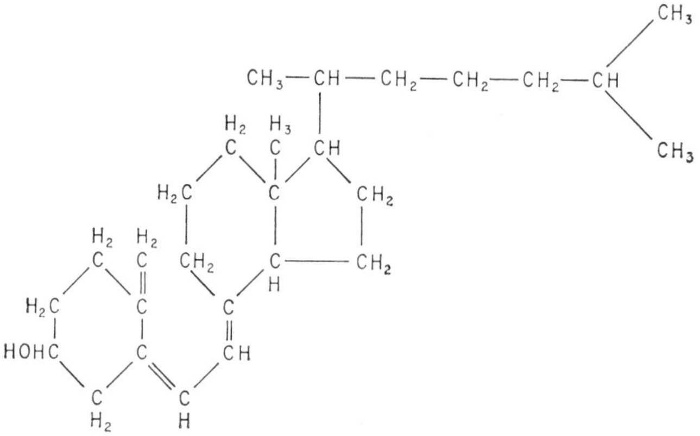

Vitamin D_3, $C_{27}H_{44}O$
Irradiated 7-dehydrocholesterol

other active compounds were discovered, and now it is known that there are at least 10 sterol derivatives that have vitamin D activity. Thus one speaks of the "multiple nature" of this vitamin. Only D_2 and D_3 are important, however, in terms of the normal food supply.

Vitamin D_2 is the form found in plant products, such as hay, after irradiation, in yeasts, and thus in vitamin D milk produced by yeast feeding (Sec. 16.36). Vitamin D_3 is the animal form found in fish oils, in irradiated milk, and in the body after irradiation. Both have the same antirachitic value for the rat, dog, pig, calf, and man, but D_3 is much more effective for the chick and turkey.

Under most conditions, both forms of vitamin D are much more stable than vitamin A, particularly to oxidation. There is a large destruction of D, however, in mixed feeds, under certain conditions, similar to that described for A (Sec. 8.5). An especially rapid loss has been found to occur when fish-oil concentrates or activated animal sterols are combined with minerals, particularly calcium carbonate, as a premix for storage and later inclusion in mixed feeds. Industrial practice has been changed accordingly to minimize these losses.

8.14. Vitamin D Assay. The antirachitic value of a food can be measured by chemical analysis of the bones or by X-ray methods or by the "line test." The last, originally developed by McCollum and associates,[34] is the one at present recommended by the U.S. Pharmacopoeial Vitamin Advisory Board. The deposition of calcium salts in the metaphyses of the distal ends of the radii and ulnae of growing rats is measured by the extent of the staining of sections by silver nitrate. Standard rats are first made rachitic on a basal ration, and then the substance to be tested is added in graded amounts to different groups and the calcification compared with that obtained in a group receiving a reference cod-liver oil of known potency. For the details of the test, the student is referred to the most recent announcement of the advisory board.

Except in the case of poultry, vitamin D potency is expressed in rat units per gram. Both the international unit and the U.S.P. unit are defined as the antirachitic activity of 0.025 μg. of crystalline vitamin D_3. Requirements for poultry are expressed in international chick units (I.C.U.). This unit is the activity produced in chicks by 0.025 μg. of crystalline vitamin D_3, the same reference standard used for the U.S.P. unit determined with rats.

8.15. Vitamin D in Foods. Of all the vitamins, the antirachitic has the most limited distribution in natural foods. Among animal products, eggs, especially the yolks, are a very good source, particularly where the diet of the hen is rich. Milk contains a variable amount in its fat fraction (5 to 40 U.S.P. units in cow's milk per quart), but neither cow's nor human milk contains enough to protect the baby against rickets. Other animal products are poor, as is to be expected from the fact that the storage of the vitamin in animal tissues is very limited. Certain fish meals, depending upon the nature of the raw material and its processing, contain fair amounts of the antirachitic factor.

Seeds and their by-products are practically devoid of the vitamin. The same is true for the living tissues of pasture grass and other growing forage crops. During the sun-curing of roughages, however, vitamin D

[34] E. V. McCollum and associates, Studies on experimental rickets. XVI. A delicate biological test for calcium-depositing substances, *J. Biol. Chem.*, **51**:41–49, 1922.

is formed under the action of radiant energy upon ergosterol or some other provitamin, and the principal source of the antirachitic factor in the rations of farm animals is thus provided. Legume hay which is cured in such a way as to preserve most of its leaves and green color contains considerable amounts. Alfalfa, for example, will range from 300 to 1000 I.U. per pound. Timothy and other grass hay contain less. Stemmy hay, lacking in leaves and color, which has been exposed to a minimum of sunlight may contain none, whether legume or nonlegume.

Machine-dried and barn-cured hay generally contains less than that which is properly sun-cured. Even hay dried in the dark immediately after cutting, however, has some of the vitamin present. This results because the dead or injured leaves on the growing plant are responsive to irradiation even though the living tissues are not. This fact is also largely responsible for the vitamin D found in corn silage. An extensive study of this general subject is reported by Moore and coworkers[35] which showed that either barn-cured hay or wilted silage could supply sufficient D to prevent rickets in calves reared out of sunlight. Thomas and Moore[36] have shown that the antirachitic value of the alfalfa crop increases with state of maturity because of the increase in dead leaves which were found very high in the vitamin. A cooperative study carried out at ten agricultural experiment stations, involving the determination of vitamin D in 65 roughage samples, has been reported by Wallis and coworkers.[37] The results, which showed wide and unpredictable variations for a given type of forage, are summarized as follows in I.U. per pound on an air-dry basis:

Forage	*I.U. per lb.*
Sun-cured hay	70 to 1440
Mow-cured hay	160 to 790
Winter range grass	89 to 270
Silage (wet basis)	70 to 110
Artificially dried roughages	80 to 280

Cod- and certain other fish-liver oils, as well as certain fish-body oils, are rich sources of vitamin D and thus are used in both human and animal nutrition to supplement the common foods which are deficient. More commonly, however, the much more concentrated products mentioned in the following paragraph are employed.

[35] L. A. Moore and coworkers, Comparative antirachitic value of field-cured hay, barn-dried hay, and wilted grass silage for growing dairy calves, *J. Dairy Sci.*, **31**: 489–499, 1948.

[36] J. W. Thomas and L. A. Moore, Factors affecting the antirachitic activity of alfalfa and its ability to prevent rickets in young calves, *J. Dairy Sci.*, **34**:916–928, 1951.

[37] G. C. Wallis, G. H. Kennedy, and Roy H. Fishman, The vitamin D content of roughage, *J. Animal Sci.*, **17**:410–415, 1958.

8.16. Enrichment of Foods in Vitamin D. Steenbock patented his discovery that certain foods could be enriched in the antirachitic factor by irradiation with ultraviolet light, assigning the patent to the University of Wisconsin. The process has found wide application and has proved an outstanding contribution to better nutrition. Activation is dependent upon the presence of a provitamin in the substance in question, and thus certain materials develop a high potency on irradiation, while others acquire little or none. The most potent products are obtained by irradiating the sterols that are subject to activation. Thus, irradiated ergosterol is produced and sold for human use in a variety of forms under the trade name "viosterol." Irradiated animal sterol, activated 7-dehydrocholesterol, is most frequently used in poultry feeds in view of the superior value of the D_3 form of the vitamin for this species. Yeast is rich in ergosterol, and thus its irradiation results in a potent source that has been used for other farm animals. Milk, which normally is not a rich source of the vitamin, can be irradiated to contain 400 U.S.P. units per quart, a level also obtainable by feeding irradiated yeast (Sec. 16.36).

Foods can also be enriched in the antirachitic factor by adding to them one of the concentrated sources previously mentioned. This is the procedure now generally used.

8.17. Sunlight and Vitamin D Nutrition. The previous statements that most of the commonly used feeds contain little or no vitamin D suggest that there must be a widespread need for supplements of the vitamin in feeding farm animals. This would be true were it not for the sun, which by irradiation produces vitamin D_3 from precursors present in the body. In sunlight, nature has provided for the deficiencies in most of her food products. The skin and sebaceous secretions contain the provitamin, and thus the activated substance is produced on and in the skin from which it is absorbed. That this absorption can take place is clear from the fact that rickets can be successfully treated by rubbing cod-liver oil on the skin. Animals also ingest some of the activated material present in the skin secretions in the process of licking the body. Irradiation is less effective on dark-pigmented skin. This has been shown to be true for white and black breeds of hogs as well as for people. Irradiation is more effective on exposed skin than through a heavy coat of hair.

The effectiveness of the sunlight is dependent upon the lengths and intensity of the ultraviolet rays which reach the body. It is ineffective through ordinary window glass because the latter does not allow sufficiently short wavelengths to pass through. The radiations which reach the earth contain only a small part of the ultraviolet range which has an antirachitic effect. The shortest wavelength which ever reaches the earth is 290 mμ, shorter ones being absorbed by the atmosphere. This shortest available wavelength reaches the earth only in summer and only in the tropics. The greater the distance the rays have to travel, the longer is the minimum wavelength which reaches the earth and the lesser the intensity of the effective radiations. Thus sunlight is more potent in the tropics than in the Temperate or Arctic zone, more potent in summer than in winter, more potent at noon than in the morning or evening, and more potent at high altitudes. These variations are of large importance in vitamin D nutrition. Animals which are on pasture during the summer never suffer from the lack of the antirachitic factor even though their diet is practically devoid of it. In the wintertime the story is different. At best, the animals are outside only a part of the time, there are generally fewer sunny days, and the sunlight which actually reaches the animal is much less effective than in summer. Under most conditions of practice in the latitude of the northern United States, it is unsafe to rely on exposure to sunlight to provide the antirachitic factor during the winter months, as has been definitely proved for pigs and calves.

Fortunately, especially for city dwellers, it is not necessary for the body to be in the direct sunlight in order that activation may take place. It can occur in the shadow on sunny days. "Skyshine" from the northern sky on bright days may be one-half to two-thirds as potent as direct sunlight. Rays reflected from snow and water are more potent than when direct. Clouds, smoke, and dust, however, greatly cut down the effectiveness of the light. The dust and smoke of cities are responsible for the much greater incidence of rickets in city children than occurs in the country.

8.18. Overdosage with Vitamin D. Experiments with massive doses of irradiated ergosterol have shown that a condition of "hypervitaminosis" can be produced characterized by hypercalcemia, the widespread deposition of calcium salts in the arteries and various organs and tissues; other pathological changes; and even death. Fortunately the range between the body requirements and the harmful dose is rather wide. There need be no fear from intakes of the vitamin which represent the maximum ever needed for normal calcification, but since harm can result from overdosage, it is important to bear in mind that excessive intakes may be injurious rather than beneficial. Harm can also result from overirradiation of the body in the case of man.

VITAMIN E (TOCOPHEROLS)

As a result of the stimulus to experimentation with purified diets which followed the discovery of the first vitamin, it was frequently observed that on certain diets, which were satisfactory for growth and health, rats failed to reproduce. Studies of the cause of this failure resulted in the discovery in the early twenties, by Evans of the University of California, Mattill of the University of Rochester, Sure of the University of Arkansas, and their associates, that there is a specific dietary factor essential for reproduction in the rat. Sure coined the name vitamin E, which is now known to consist chemically of tocopherols. Much has been learned in the past thirty years about the chemical nature of vitamin E and its distribution in foods, but despite many studies the knowledge of its physiological functions and need by various species remains in a very unsatisfactory state. Specific information regarding its significance in farm-animal nutrition is especially limited.

8.19. Physiological Functions and Symptoms of Deficiency. The very extensive studies of the physiological role of vitamin E have produced many important facts. The problem has proved to be much more complex than originally visualized, however, and the establishment of generalizations applicable to nutritional science and practice has been limited accordingly. On the basis of studies with several species this vitamin seems to be concerned in a large number of apparently unrelated body functions, but few of the various deficiency symptoms noted appear to be common to the different species. It has been definitely proved that vitamin E is essential for normal reproduction in the rat, both male and female. When the factor is absent from the diet of the female, death and resorption of the fetuses result. In the male, degenerative changes in the testes are produced. The injury of the male causes permanent sterility, while in the female later pregnancies are successful if the vitamin is supplied. If the deficiency in the female is not so great as to cause fetal death, it may nevertheless result in paralysis in the suckling young toward the end of the nursing period In the mouse, fetal death and resorption result from the deficiency, but, differing from the rat, no injury appears to be caused to the male. Testicular degeneration has been noted in hamsters, however. In poultry a deficiency results in low hatchability.

Many attempts to relate vitamin E to similar reproductive failures in other species have resulted in negative or contradictory results. Extensive experiments in the United States have failed to connect a deficiency of vitamin E with reproductive failure in cattle, sheep, or goats or to demonstrate that the reproductive performance on commonly fed rations can be improved by feeding concentrated sources of the vitamin. The situation may be different for pigs. These aspects are discussed later (Sec. 15.15).

Muscular dystrophy has been experimentally produced in various animals on E-deficient rations. The dystrophy is found primarily in the skeletal muscles, but sometimes also in the heart. The external symptoms of muscle weakness and paralysis are reflected in degenerative histological changes. Creatine excretion is increased. Vitamin E does not appear to be concerned in human muscular dystrophy, however. Cornell workers[38] showed that the vitamin can prevent and cure "stiff-lamb" disease, a trouble of sporadic occurrence in suckling lambs, characterized by stiffness and dystrophic lesions. The investigators were able to produce the symptoms experimentally by feeding the ewe a ration of alfalfa hay and beans and to cure them by administering tocopherols to the lambs. Several papers have dealt with the experimental production and cure of this trouble, which also occurs in calves and which is more specifically referred to as "white muscle disease." Mention has been made of the findings that selenium also prevents this disease (Sec. 7.57). These apparently related roles of vitamin E and selenium require further study.

Chronic vitamin E deficiency has been noted to produce, in rabbits, lambs, poultry, and cattle, electrocardiogram changes which are considered to reflect heart muscle injury. Sudden deaths have resulted in some cases, and histological examinations have showed atrophy and scarring of the muscle fibers. Several studies have shown that a deficiency of the vitamin in the diet of the chick results in nutritional encephalomalacia, characterized by an uncoordinated gait, prostration, and brain lesions. While experimental muscular dystrophy in rabbits and guinea pigs, produced by an E-deficient diet, is not accompanied by changes in the central nervous system, there is evidence that a chronic deficiency in rats affects both the muscular and the nervous systems. Exudative diathesis, a hemorrhagic disease of chicks, and dietary liver necrosis in rats are other troubles which are prevented by vitamin E and also by selenium, as previously mentioned. A basic effect of E deficiency is the hemolysis of red blood cells.

These many and diverse symptoms and pathological changes in vitamin E deficiency, many of them apparently unrelated, must have some common physiological link. As a result of various studies it is evident that the vitamin plays a fundamental role as an antioxidant, not only in the protection of certain dietary constituents from oxidative destruction, such as the lessening of carotene destruction in the intestine, but in body tissues as well. This has been shown to be true in experiments in which

[38] J. P. Willman et al., Prevention and cure of muscular stiffness ("stiff-lamb" disease) in lambs, *J. Animal Sci.*, **4**:128–132, 1945; F. Whiting, J. P. Willman, and J. K. Loosli, Tocopherol (vitamin E) deficiency among sheep fed natural feeds, *J. Animal Sci.*, **8**:234–242, 1949.

the feeding of synthetic antioxidants, such as methylene blue, has prevented various symptoms of E deficiency in rats and chicks which otherwise occurred. Present data do not justify the conclusion, however, that the vitamin functions solely as an antioxidant.

Vitamin E injury is aggravated by the presence of large amounts of unsaturated fats in the diet, particularly the highly unsaturated ones. This fact explains the early finding that excess intakes of cod-liver oil caused muscle dystrophy in lambs and other species because of the highly unsaturated acids thus fed. These findings are reviewed and extended by Moore and coworkers.[39] It is clear that highly unsaturated acids in the diet increase the vitamin E requirement. This has been found true for various species. Mention has been made (Sec. 5.29) that adding the vitamin to the diet corrected the dystrophy in young calves which resulted from the substitution of vegetable oils for butterfat in their diet. It is evident that this antagonistic effect of unsaturated acids is somehow related to the role of vitamin E as an antioxidant. Various explanations have been offered, but further studies are required to clarify the relationship.

The study of the functions of vitamin E is complicated by the fact that the body has a large ability to store it. This storage is distributed throughout the various organs and tissues. The extent of the store is shown by the fact that females born of mothers whose diets contained a liberal supply frequently have enough in their bodies at birth to carry them through a first pregnancy. Rats reared on natural foods rich in the factor and then placed on a deficient diet may produce three or four litters before exhausting their reserves. The vitamin E content of the body tissues can also be demonstrated by feeding these tissues to females which have failed as a result of a deficiency and noting the recovery that occurs. Storage doubtless complicates a study of questions now at issue as to the functions of the vitamin and its need by various species. Tocopherols pass through the placental membranes and also the mammary gland, and thus the diet of the female influences the store of the young at birth and the amount it gets from its mother's milk.

8.20. Chemistry of Vitamin E. The vitamin is found in the nonsaponifiable fraction of fats and oils, as is the case also with vitamin D. In 1936 Evans and associates isolated from wheat germ an alcohol having vitamin E activity, for which the term α-tocopherol was proposed. Two years later its structure, characterized by a chromane nucleus, was identified. Later, the three other naturally occurring isomeric forms, β, γ, and ζ, were found to be active also. There are other naturally

[39] T. Moore, I. M. Sharman, and R. J. Ward, Cod-liver oil as both source and antagonist of vitamin E, *Brit. J. Nutrition*, 13:100–110, 1959.

occurring forms, but they are inactive. Several active synthetic products have also been produced. Thus, vitamin E, like several others, has a

```
         CH3     H2
         |       |
         C       C
       //  \   /   \
HO—C        C       CH2                 CH3                  CH3                CH3
   |        ||      |     H   H   H   |      H   H   H   |     H   H   H   |
H3C—C       C       C——— C—C—C—C——— C—C—C—C——— C—C—C—CH
      \\   /  \   / |     H   H   H   H      H   H   H   H     H   H   H   |
         C       O  |                                                    CH3
         |          CH3
         CH3
```

Vitamin E (alpha-tocopherol)

multiple nature. The α form is much more active than the others, at least for the cure of resorption and sterility in the rat and for the prevention of dystrophy. The tocopherols are extremely resistant to heat but readily oxidized. They keep well in ordinary feeds and mixtures but are destroyed by rancid fats.

8.21. Vitamin E in Feeds. Vitamin E is assayed biologically by measuring the ability of graded amounts of the test feed to cause the birth of a normal litter from female rats of proved fertility which show failure during gestation on a vitamin-free ration. This procedure, described by Mason and Harris,[40] is very time-consuming and is being supplanted by chemical methods which are now available. Since the relative amounts of the various tocopherols making up the total vary in different feeds and since the α form is most active physiologically, its determination apart from the whole is of special importance. One method involves the determination of total tocopherols by molecular distillation; the separation of the β-, γ-, and other tocopherols by a chromatographic procedure; and the estimation of the α by difference. There are other procedures using paper chromatography.

As measured by bioassay or the determination of total tocopherols, it is evident that vitamin E is widely distributed in livestock feeds. It is abundant in whole cereal grains, particularly in the germ, and thus in the by-products containing the germ. Green forage and other leafy materials, including good-quality hay, are very good sources. Alfalfa is especially rich. Animal by-products supply only limited amounts, and milk and dairy products are poor sources. Eggs, particularly the yolk, make a significant contribution, depending, however, on the feed of the hen. Wheat-germ oil is the most concentrated natural source. Various other oils such as soybean, peanut, and particularly cottonseed are also rich. Unfortunately, most of the oil meals now marketed are devoid of

[40] K. E. Mason and P. L. Harris, Bioassay of vitamin E, *Biol. Symposia,* **12**:459–483, 1947.

these oils because of solvent extraction. A table showing both the total and the α-tocopherol values of feedstuffs is contained in the review by Ames.[41]

The wide distribution of vitamin E bears out the findings of experimental work that any need of farm animals should usually be met by the commonly fed rations. The vitamin E nutrition of farm animals has been reviewed by Blaxter and Brown.[42]

VITAMIN K

In 1929, Henrik Dam of Denmark fed chickens a purified diet in an attempt to determine whether they were able to synthesize cholesterol. He noted that the chickens that were kept on an ether-extracted diet became anemic and developed subcutaneous and intermuscular hemorrhages. This was the first observation of the symptoms that we now know to be attributable to vitamin K deficiency. Since the factor was found to be concerned with blood coagulation, the Danish workers (Dam and Shønheyder) proposed the name *vitamin K* from the Danish word for coagulation.

8.22. Physiological Functions and Symptoms of Deficiency. When vitamin K is deficient, the coagulation time of the blood is increased and the prothrombin level is decreased. The function of the vitamin is to maintain this level by means of its influence on prothrombin formation that takes place in the liver. The adequacy of vitamin K is determined by measuring the clotting time of the blood. Where the time is prolonged, either a decreased absorption or a decreased utilization of the vitamin is indicated. It is not known whether the vitamin catalyzes prothrombin synthesis or serves as a precursor. Though originally discovered in chicks, the symptoms of K deficiency have been reported in other birds (geese, pigeons, and ducks) and also in mice, rats, rabbits, and man under special conditions. While the vitamin is needed for the physiological functioning of all species, any dietary need may be unimportant in species other than birds because of bacterial synthesis in the digestive tract (Sec. 8.24).

Vitamin K has been found to have a definite value in human therapy (1) as a preoperative and postoperative measure to prevent risk of bleeding, (2) in cases where absorption is impaired as in obstructive jaundice because bile is necessary for the absorption of K, and (3) in hemorrhagic diseases of the newborn. The blood of infants at birth contains less than

[41] Stanley R. Ames, Role of vitamin E (α-tocopherol) in poultry nutrition and disease, *Poultry Sci.*, **35**:145–159, 1956.

[42] Kenneth L. Blaxter and Fred Brown, Vitamin E in the nutrition of farm animals, *Nutrition Abstr. & Revs.* **22**:1–21, 1952.

the usual amounts of prothrombin, and this deficiency increases for a time because the intestine of the newborn is sterile.

Vitamin K bears an interesting relation to "hemorrhagic sweet clover disease." This disease has been responsible for large animal losses. Studies have also shown that spoiled sweet clover contains dicumarol that decreases the blood prothrombin, resulting in the hemorrhages that are characteristic of the disease. More vitamin K will overcome this action by dicumarol. These findings have resulted from a series of brilliant studies by Link and associates of the University of Wisconsin. Dicumarol serves as an anticoagulant in medicine in certain situations, just as vitamin K under other conditions steps up the coagulating time. The action of dicumarol against the vitamin is similar to that of an antimetabolite (Sec. 8.29). A very interesting account of the observations and research which led to these important findings regarding dicumarol is given by Link.[43]

8.23. Chemistry of Vitamin K. It is now recognized that there are several different compounds, similar in structure, that have vitamin K activity. In 1939, as a result of the activities of several different workers, two such compounds were isolated as fat-soluble substances. The more active one, designated as K_1, was isolated from alfalfa and found to have the following structure:

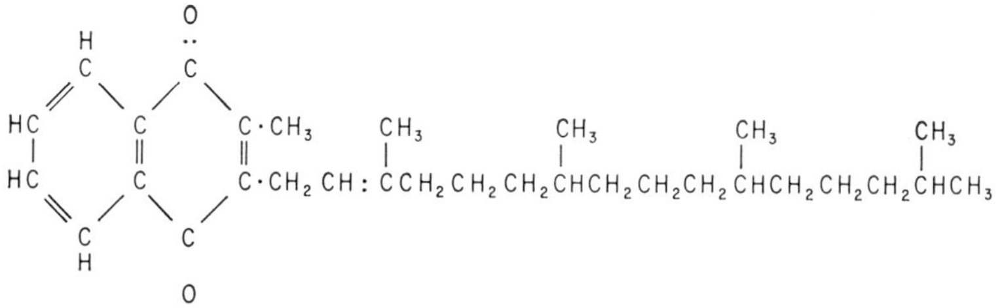

```
                 O
        H        ..
        C        C
      //  \    /   \
  HC        C        C·CH3     CH3           CH3             CH3              CH3
  |         ||       ||        |             |               |                |
  HC        C        C·CH2 CH: CCH2CH2CH2CHCH2CH2CH2CHCH2CH2CH2CHCH3
     \\   /   \    /
        C        C
        H
                 O
```

Vitamin K_1 (2-methyl-3-phytyl-1,4-naphthoquinone)

The second compound, designated as K_2, was isolated from fish meal. It contains the same quinone nucleus, but there are some differences in the side chain. More recently another active compound, K_3, was obtained from corn stigma. In addition, several synthetic naphthoquinones have been prepared that have vitamin K activity. 2-Methyl-1, 4-naphthoquinone, called *menadione*, is a synthetic product which is much more active than K_1. Some of the synthetic products are water-soluble, in contrast to the natural products that caused the vitamin to be classed originally as fat-soluble.

8.24. Bacterial Synthesis of Vitamin K. Like the case for amino acids (Sec. 6.15), microorganisms in the digestive tract play important roles in

[43] Karl Paul Link, The discovery of dicumarol and its sequels, *Circulation,* **19**:97–107, 1959.

the synthesis of certain vitamins and in modifying dietary needs accordingly. Vitamin K is the first example met in this chapter. Like most of the B-vitamins discussed later, vitamin K is synthesized by bacteria in the rumen. In cattle and sheep the rumen is the principal seat of the synthetic activity. In nonruminants, however, synthesis takes place in the large intestine, as was demonstrated by the following rat experiment. Animals in which the blood-clotting time was normal were fed sulfonamides which check bacterial action in the intestine. As a result the clotting time was slowed down and hemorrhages developed. These defects were then corrected by feeding or injecting the vitamin. While this experiment proved that intestinal synthesis took place, its practical significance has been greatly lessened by a later finding indicating that *coprophagy* (feces eating) may have occurred despite the fact that the rats were kept on wire screens. Many years ago it was proved that rats caged on litter obtained B-vitamins by feces eating. The vitamins were apparently synthesized in the tract below the zone of absorption, excreted in the feces, and then absorbed when the feces were eaten. Thus the practice was established of keeping experimental animals on wire screens to prevent this complication in vitamin feeding experiments. The practice was assumed to be successful until in 1957 Barnes and coworkers showed,[44] by the use of a new technique, that rats may eat 50 to 65 per cent of their feces even when maintained on wire screens. In a later experiment Barnes and Fiala[45] showed that, when rats were prevented by this new technique from feces eating, a vitamin K deficiency uniformly developed on a diet free of the vitamin. This did not occur when a dietary source of the vitamin was provided. These and other findings by Barnes and associates call for a reexamination of previous experiments with feces-eating animals from which it has been assumed that the techniques used prevented coprophagy and thus that the vitamins synthesized in the intestine from diets devoid of them were directly absorbed and thus served the body. This fact must be borne in mind in reading the later discussions in which the intestinal synthesis of vitamins is mentioned.

There are physiological reasons why one would not expect any large absorption of vitamins synthesized in the large intestine. The bacterial cells containing them are little subject to digestive action, in contrast to what happens in the small intestine where rumen organisms containing vitamins are broken down. Furthermore, absorption of nutrients in general from the large intestine appears to be limited because of the nature of the epithelial lining.

[44] Richard H. Barnes and coworkers, Prevention of coprophagy in the rat, *J. Nutrition,* **63**:489–498, 1957.

[45] Richard H. Barnes and Grace Fiala, Effects of the prevention of coprophagy in the rat. VI. Vitamin K, *J. Nutrition,* **68**:603–614, 1959.

These considerations do not affect the practical significance of conclusions previously drawn regarding the synthesis of vitamin K and various B-vitamins in the rumen. In the case of poultry little intestinal synthesis apparently occurs because of the short digestive tract.

8.25. Food Sources of Vitamin K. As far as is known there is no need for giving any special consideration to the vitamin K content of the rations of farm animals except in the case of poultry. The N.R.C. Committee has set a requirement of 0.24 mg. per pound feed for starting chicks. Rumen synthesis should meet any needs of cattle and sheep not supplied by their rations. All green, leafy materials, fresh or dry, are rich sources of the vitamin, and some other plant products contain substantial amounts. Liver, egg, and fish meal are good animal sources. Assay procedures have been worked out with chicks, based on the determination of the clotting time of the blood and using 1 μg. of menadione as the unit. The method is described by Almquist.[46]

THIAMINE (VITAMIN B_1)

The early work of Eijkman and others which established the fact that there is a specific dietary factor essential for the prevention of beriberi in man and polyneuritis in pigeons has been referred to. Further studies of this factor, which became known as water-soluble B and later simply as vitamin B, caused it to be recognized as essential for growth and for certain other physiological functions besides its antineuritic properties. As more critical investigations were made of its distribution in foods, chemical nature, and properties, the realization gradually developed, between 1925 and 1930, that vitamin B actually consisted of at least two factors differing as regards chemical nature and physiological effects. Thus what was formerly spoken of as vitamin B came to be called *the vitamin B complex*, or *group*. The term vitamin B (or B_1) was reserved for the antineuritic factor. The name *thiamine* was introduced when its chemical nature was established (Sec. 8.27). The vitamin is required in the metabolism of all species of animals and in plant metabolism as well. Higher plants synthesize it, and so do many of the lower forms. All animals, however, must have a dietary source, unless it is synthesized for them by microorganisms in the digestive tract—as is the case with ruminants (Sec. 8.28).

8.26. Physiological Functions and Symptoms of Deficiency. Thiamine functions as a constituent of cocarboxylase, a coenzyme of several enzyme systems, notably that concerned in the oxidative decarboxylation of pyruvic acid to a two-carbon compound. This is an essential reaction in the utilization of carbohydrates to provide energy for body

[46] H. J. Almquist, The assay of vitamin K, *Biol. Symposia*, **12**:508–523, 1947.

processes. If the reaction does not take place, pyruvic and lactic acids, intermediates in carbohydrate metabolism, accumulate in the blood and tissues and give rise to deficiency symptoms of the vitamin accordingly.

The classic diseases beriberi in man and polyneuritis in birds represent a late stage of the deficiency, resulting from a peripheral neuritis caused by the accumulation of intermediates of carbohydrate metabolism, as was first indicated by the studies of Peters and associates at Oxford. Other symptoms include a slowing of the heart beat (bradycardia), enlargement of the heart, edema, gastrointestinal troubles, and lack of appetite (anorexia). Muscle weakness, easy fatigue, and hyperirritability are less specific symptoms. There is a very marked effect on growth that is the result, at least in part, of loss of appetite. In swine the deficiency reveals itself particularly in a decrease of appetite and body weight, vomiting, a slow pulse, subnormal body temperature, nervous symptoms, and post-mortem heart changes. In chickens and turkeys there is a loss of appetite, emaciation, impairment of digestion, a general weakness, and frequent convulsions with polyneuritis as an extreme symptom. This characteristic trouble will develop in 9 to 12 days with day-old chickens on a thiamine-deficient diet. Recovery is amazingly prompt when the vitamin is given. In foxes the deficiency causes a characteristic disease, Chastek paralysis. Horses fed experimental diets low in B_1 and other B-vitamins have shown incoordination and other nervous symptoms which were alleviated by feeding thiamine, indicating that this species requires a dietary source of this vitamin. A lack of vitamin B_1 causes reproductive failure in both sexes. There is a larger requirement for lactation than for growth because of the increased metabolism involved.

While the symptoms listed above have been proved experimentally to result from B_1 deficiency, most of them are not specific for this deficiency alone. In pigs, for example, nervous symptoms result from deficiencies of vitamin B_6 and pantothenic acid as well as of thiamine. Symptoms noted in practice may represent multiple deficiencies. There is no question about the specificity of such symptoms as polyneuritis and Chastek paralysis, but these are terminal stages. The problem of identifying the early stages by any specific sign is an unsolved one for thiamine and for several other of the B-vitamins. It is recognized that the first lesions are biochemical and that tissue changes and physical symptoms are later effects. Thus, current research is endeavoring to find biochemical changes which may be considered diagnostic. With respect to thiamine, the urinary excretion is linearly related to the intake except at low levels, and use is made of this fact in the diagnosis of deficiency in man. A low level of excretion following a test dose is indicative of tissue depletion.

8.27. Chemistry of Thiamine. In 1926 the Dutch workers Jansen and Donath isolated vitamin B_1 in crystalline form and reported an empirical formula containing carbon, hydrogen, oxygen, and nitrogen. Later Windaus and coworkers prepared a crystalline product which was found to contain sulfur as well as the elements reported by Jansen and Donath. Other workers confirmed the presence of this additional element, and it was later found also in the crystals of the Dutch workers. In 1936 synthesis of the vitamin was accomplished by Williams and Cline,[47] and Williams[48] established the following structure:

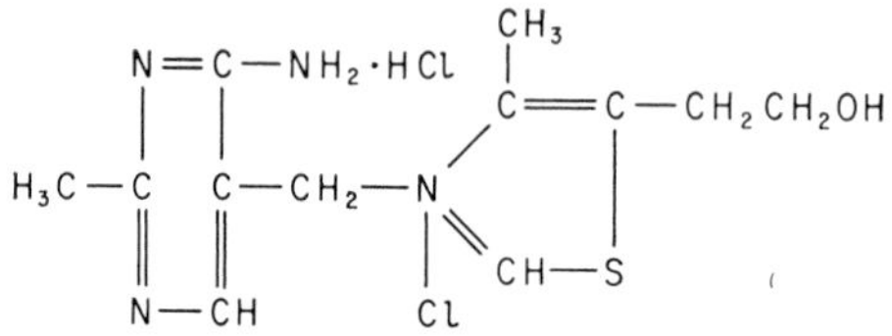

```
                                  CH3
          N=C—NH2·HCl             |
          |   |                   C==C—CH2CH2OH
          |   |                  /    |
   H3C—C   C—CH2—N                    |
          ||  ||          |\          |
          ||  ||          | \ CH—S
          N—CH           Cl
```

Thiamine hydrochloride (Williams, 1936)

It is noted that the vitamin consists of a molecule of pyrimidine and a molecule of thiazole. Cocarboxylase is a pyrophosphate of thiamine, synthesized in the body from thiamine and adenosine triphosphate (ATP). The enzyme systems containing thiamine are composed of a protein, diphosphothiamine, and magnesium. Thiamine is soluble in 70 per cent alcohol as well as water and is readily destroyed by heat, especially in the presence of alkali. In a dry state, it is stable at 100°C. for several hours, but moisture greatly accelerates the destruction, and thus it is much less stable to heat in fresh than in dry foods. Autoclaving destroys vitamin B_1, an observation which played an important role in the discovery that what was originally considered to be a single vitamin contains more than one factor.

8.28. Metabolism of Thiamine. The vitamin is absorbed from both the small and large intestine. It is carried to the liver where it is phosphorylated to form cocarboxylase. While a high level of intake may be reflected in a somewhat higher blood level, there is little storage in the body. Intakes in excess of current needs are rapidly excreted as such in the urine. This means that the body needs a regular supply and also that unneeded intakes are wasted. The pig is somewhat of an exception, however. For some reason which is not understood, its tissues contain several times as much thiamine as is the case with other species studied, and there is thus a store that can meet body needs on a thiamine-deficient diet for as long as two months.

Though thiamine is a metabolic essential for all species studied, it is not needed in the diets of ruminants because of microbial synthesis, a

[47] R. R. Williams and J. K. Cline, Synthesis of vitamin B_1, *J. Am. Chem. Soc.*, **58**:1504–1505, 1936.

[48] R. R. Williams, Structure of vitamin B_1, *J. Am. Chem. Soc.*, **58**:1063–1064, 1936.

fact established by the pioneer studies of Bechdel and coworkers.[49] In 1926 they reported that a ration which was so low in the vitamin B complex as to stop growth of rats and to cause their death in 2 to 5 weeks was adequate to grow calves normally to maturity and to permit reproduction. They concluded that either the growing calf must have a very low requirement compared with the rat or the vitamin was produced by synthetic action in the digestive tract. To study the question of vitamin synthesis during digestion in the cow, Bechdel and coworkers[50] made use of the rumen-fistula method originated over a century ago. They found that rats receiving a control ration supplemented with an extract of rumen contents from an animal receiving a ration deficient in the B complex made a much better growth than those receiving the vitamin-deficient control ration alone. These were the pioneer studies which have been followed by many others showing that thiamine and various other B-vitamins are synthesized in the rumen in sufficient amounts to meet body requirements. Proof that there is a metabolic need for the calf, as in other species, has been produced by Johnson and coworkers[51] in their experiments with newborn calves. In these animals in which a functional rumen had not yet developed, characteristic symptoms of thiamine deficiency were produced. Similar results have been obtained with newborn lambs. An excellent study of the metabolism of thiamine in the sheep, dealing with rumen synthesis and blood and urine levels, is presented by Austin.[52]

The bacterial synthesis of thiamine in the intestinal tract has been demonstrated. In the case of the horse considerable quantities of B_1 and other B-vitamins are produced in the cecum and in the large intestine, according to the studies of Carroll and coworkers.[53] The production of nervous symptoms which were alleviated by feeding thiamine indicated that the synthesis of this vitamin was not sufficient to meet metabolic needs. The bacterial synthesis of thiamine in the intestine of rats and man has also been demonstrated, but it is doubtful whether the amount thus produced and absorbed is large enough to make a significant contribution to body needs, except when the dietary intake is very low. Apparently the same is true for the pig and chick.

[49] S. I. Bechdel, C. H. Eckles, and L. S. Palmer, The vitamin B requirement of the calf, *J. Dairy Sci.*, **9**:409–438, 1926.

[50] S. I. Bechdel and coworkers, Synthesis of vitamin B in the rumen of the cow, *J. Biol. Chem.* **80**:231–238, 1928.

[51] B. Connor Johnson and coworkers, Thiamine deficiency in the calf, *J. Nutrition*, **35**:137–145, 1948.

[52] C. R. Austin, The metabolism of thiamin in the sheep, *Australian J. Exptl. Biol. Med. Sci.*, **25**:147–155, 1947.

[53] F. D. Carroll, Harold Gross, and C. E. Howell, The synthesis of B vitamins in the horse, *J. Animal Sci.*, **8**:290–299, 1949.

8.29. Antimetabolites of Thiamine. The term *metabolite* is used to denote any substance which is essential to the chemical process by which living cells are produced and maintained. Substances which block or inhibit the normal function of a metabolite are referred to as *antimetabolites* and also as *antivitamins* where a vitamin is the metabolite involved. Thiamine presents a case in point. In a diet which is adequate in thiamine for mice, the addition of pyrithiamine, which has the same structural formula as thiamine, except that the sulfur atom of the vitamin is replaced by the grouping —CH=CH—, will produce deficiency symptoms of the vitamin which can in turn be overcome by adding more thiamine. Other structurally related compounds have been noted to produce similar effects. It is considered that the antimetabolite competes with thiamine in the enzyme systems in which the latter functions and thus antagonizes its action. In such a case the antivitamin is referred to as the *analogue* of the vitamin. Later discussions will refer to substances which act similarly in the case of various B-vitamins.

The role of antimetabolites is not limited to vitamin nutrition. The broad field has been reviewed by Woolley.[54] This is a comparatively new field of knowledge, the practical importance of which remains largely to be determined through further research. This importance clearly depends on the extent to which antimetabolites, thus far largely identified by studies with pure compounds, may occur naturally in the feed supply.

An antagonistic action on thiamine of a different sort is represented by the occurrence in practice of Chastek paralysis in foxes and other animals fed raw fish. Here the causative agent is an enzyme, *thiaminase*, which splits the thiamine molecule into two components and thus renders it inactive. The case seems to be similar in the disease in horses referred to as "fern poisoning" or, "bracken poisoning." Following earlier evidence obtained with rats by Oregon workers that a factor antagonistic to thiamine was concerned, Evans and coworkers[55] experimentally produced the disease in horses by feeding a bracken hay ration and cured the symptoms, which were typical of thiamine deficiency, by the administration of the vitamin. It has been shown, however, that the causative agent in fern poisoning is not thiaminase but an antithiamine substance of nonenzymic nature.

8.30. Thiamine in Foods. Brewer's yeast is the richest known source of vitamin B_1. The factor is present in liberal amounts in a wide variety of foods. Whole cereal grains are rich sources. Since the vitamin is present primarily in the germ and seed coats, by-products containing the

[54] D. W. Woolley, Antimetabolites, *Science*, **129**:615–621, 1959.

[55] E. T. Rees Evans, Charles Evans, and H. E. Roberts, Studies on bracken poisoning in the horse, *Brit. Vet. J.*, **107**:364–371, 399–411, 1951.

latter are richer than the whole kernel, while highly milled flour is very deficient. Wheat germ ranks next to yeast. Lean pork, liver, kidney, and egg yolk are rich animal products. The content in lean pork can be doubled by increasing the thiamine intake of the pig. The content in hays decreases as the plant matures and is less in the cured than in the fresh product. The content is correlated with leafiness, greenness, and protein content. In general, good-quality hay is a substantial source, and in a dry climate there is practically no loss in storage. Milk is not a rich source, and pasteurization for 30 min. at 145°F. destroys 25 per cent of its content.

The fact that thiamine is water-soluble as well as unstable to heat results in large losses in certain cooking operations to which foods are subjected. There should be little concern about any lack of vitamin B_1 in the rations of farm animals in view of the generous supply in most of the feeds used. Further, rumen synthesis makes the question of feed supply of little or no importance in the case of cattle and sheep.

Feeds are assayed for thiamine by various procedures. The biological method measures the growth response in rats caused by the test substance under standardized conditions. This procedure is time-consuming and costly. A standard chemical method is based on the fluorescence produced by thiochrome, a compound that is formed from thiamine on oxidation. A commonly used microbiological method is based on the need of the vitamin for the growth of the fungus *Phycomyces blakesleeanus.* The basis of the method lies in the fact that the growth of the fungus is proportional to the amount of thiamine added over a low range of addition. A comparison of the amount of growth produced through the addition of known amounts of thiamine with the amount produced by the addition of specific amounts of the food to be tested provides a basis for estimating its vitamin content.

The official unit (I.U. and U.S.P.) is the biological activity of 3 μg. of pure thiamine hydrochloride. Thus, 1 mg. of thiamine equals 333 I.U. Food content is expressed in milligrams.

RIBOFLAVIN

Following the recognition that the original water-soluble B consisted of more than one factor, it was thought for a time that the effects not attributable to a lack of the antineuritic vitamin were owing to a deficiency of another single factor, designated G by some and B_2 by others. But soon it was learned that at least two factors were involved here also. Some confusing use of the letters followed. The situation became more complicated as evidence developed that there were more than two, and possibly several, factors concerned. Fortunately, one by one the different vitamins were identified chemically and given specific chemical names that have come into standard use.

The first factor identified was riboflavin. It is sometimes still referred to as G or B_2. The vitamin is required in the metabolism of all animals but not required in the rations of cattle and sheep because of bacterial synthesis in the rumen.

8.31. Physiological Functions and Symptoms of Deficiency. Riboflavin functions in the body as a constituent of several enzyme systems. The enzymes are flavoproteins and are commonly referred to as "yellow enzymes" because of the color imparted by the flavin group. One or more of the yellow enzymes is required along with coenzymes I or II (nicotinamide, Sec. 8.35) in the catabolism of glucose to provide energy for body processes. The action of these vitamins precedes that of thiamine previously described. Riboflavin is also a constituent of D-amino acid oxidase, which functions in the final stages of protein metabolism, and of xanthine oxidase, which is concerned in purine metabolism. In view of these basic roles of the vitamin in the release of food energy and the assimilation of nutrients, it is understandable why a deficiency is reflected in a wide variety of symptoms which are variable with the species. It is not possible to relate the symptoms, however, to the specific biochemical roles which have been established.

In 1929 Norris and associates described a peculiar type of leg paralysis in chicks which they considered to be the result of a lack of an unidentified vitamin. This paralysis was later shown to be the most characteristic symptom of riboflavin deficiency in this species. The chicks are first noted to be walking on their hocks with their toes curled inward ("curled-toe paralysis"). The legs become paralyzed, but the birds may otherwise appear normal. Diarrhea is another common symptom in chicks. In laying birds, a deficiency of riboflavin results in low egg production and poor hatchability. A deficiency in swine causes crooked and stiff legs, thickened skin, skin eruptions and exudates over the back and sides, lens opacities, and cataracts. Reproduction and lactation failures also result.

In man there are both skin and eye symptoms, such as roughened skin, furrows around the mouth (cheilosis), dermatitis, and "corneal vascularization."

While studies with newborn calves and lambs have shown that riboflavin is a metabolic essential for these species, bacterial synthesis in the digestive tract is adequate to meet body needs after the rumen has developed. Riboflavin synthesis occurs in the cecum of horses, but it is not sufficient to meet metabolic needs.

A decreased rate of growth and a lowered feed efficiency are common symptoms in all species affected. Neither of these symptoms nor the eye, skin, and nervous symptoms noted above can be considered specific signs of riboflavin deficiency. Various ones have been produced experimentally by deficiencies of other B-vitamins and even of certain amino acids. The only certain way at present of identifying a riboflavin deficiency seems to be to cause a remission of the symptoms in question by feeding riboflavin alone. The level of the riboflavin excretion in the urine is of some value in assessing the adequacy of the nutrition with respect to this vitamin. Red blood cell content appears to be a better measure, on the basis of human studies. Requirements are determined by adding graded levels of the vitamin to purified diets devoid of it using growth as the measure. The method is illustrated by the report of Miller and associates[56] which also records the physical symptoms and the gross and microscopic pathology resulting from a deficiency of the vitamin. It was concluded that the optimum requirement for baby pigs approximates 3.0 mg. per kilogram feed solids, although external, gross, and microscopic lesions were present only in animals receiving less than 2.0 mg.

8.32. Chemistry of Riboflavin. Milk was early recognized to be an excellent source of the original vitamin G, as measured by growth response. Observations that the growth effect exhibited by whey seemed to be associated with its greenish-yellow fluorescent pigment led to the isolation of this pigment, first called lactochrome and later *lactoflavin*, (Fig. 8.5) as the biologically active material. A similar compound was also isolated as hepatoflavin from liver and as ovoflavin from eggs. Later riboflavin was synthesized, and evidence was obtained for its identity with the naturally occurring products, both chemically and biologically. The advances here resulted particularly from the brilliant work of György, Kuhn, and associates in Germany, Karrer and coworkers in Switzerland, and von Euler and associates in Sweden. It is now accepted that the biologically active substance has the following structural formula:

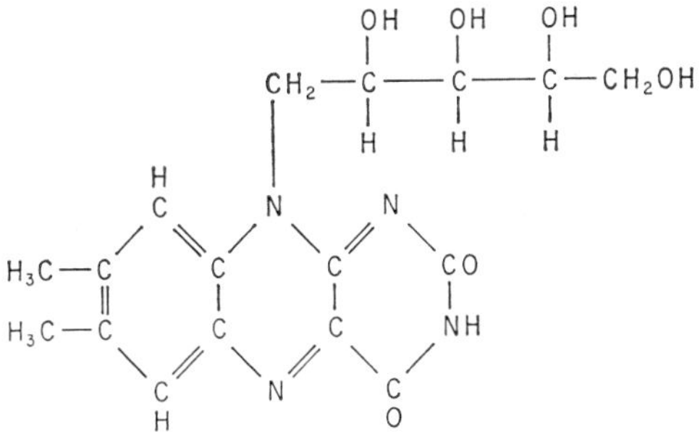

```
                      OH     OH     OH
                      |      |      |
               CH2 —  C  ——  C  ——  C — CH2OH
                |     |      |      |
                |     H      H      H
         H      |
         C      N          N
       /   \\  /  \      //  \
H3C — C      C      C         CO
      ||     |      |          |
H3C — C      C      C         NH
       \   //  \  //  \      /
         C      N       C
         H              O
```

Riboflavin, $C_{17}H_{20}N_4O_6$

[56] E. R. Miller and coworkers, The riboflavin requirement of the baby pig, *J. Nutrition*, **52**:404–413, 1954.

The compound consists of a dimethyl-isoalloxazine nucleus combined with the alcohol of ribose as a side chain. It may be obtained in the form of orange-yellow crystals which, in solution, have a greenish-yellow fluorescence. Riboflavin is only slightly soluble in water and is heat-stable in acid solution but readily destroyed in an alkaline medium. Visible light, particularly the blue and violet rays, quickly destroys it. Loss in milk during pasteurization and exposure to light is 10 to 20 per cent. Much larger losses can occur if the bottled milk is left standing

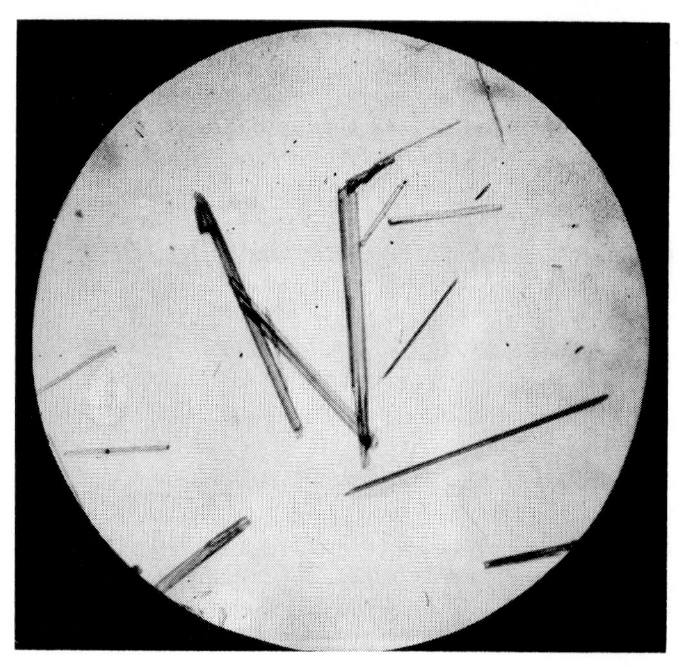

FIG. 8.5. Crystalline riboflavin. (*Courtesy of George C. Supplee.*)

in bright sunlight. Poultry mashes left exposed to direct sunlight for several days and frequently stirred are subject to some loss accordingly. There are at least three antivitamins of riboflavin, but they are not of practical importance so far as known.

8.33. Metabolism of Riboflavin. In addition to the rumen and cecal synthesis previously mentioned, intestinal synthesis has been demonstrated in rats and man. Its extent is markedly influenced by the nature of the carbohydrates in the diet. Under certain conditions enough is produced and absorbed to make a significant contribution to body needs. The vitamin is phosphorylated in the intestinal wall and carried by the blood to the cells of the tissues where it occurs as the phosphate or as a flavoprotein. Following a period on a riboflavin-deficient diet, a liberal intake of the vitamin results in some increase in the blood level and in the tissues. The total amount thus stored is small, however, and intakes above current needs are rapidly excreted in the urine. According to studies with pigs the riboflavin requirement is substantially higher at a low than at a high environmental temperature. There is no adequate physiological explanation for this finding.

8.34. Riboflavin in Foods. Milk is a rich source of the vitamin, especially the skim milk or whey fractions. This is one of their very important values in rations for pigs and poultry. Alfalfa hay is rich in riboflavin, and other green leafy forages are important sources also. Cereals and their by-products have a rather low content, in contrast to their supply of thiamine. Oil meals are much better sources, as are also certain meat by-products. Riboflavin concentrates prepared from whey, yeast, and the by-products of butyl alcohol fermentation are commonly used in poultry rations.

The riboflavin content of foods may be determined by rat or chick assays, but the more rapid microbiological or chemical methods are now more generally employed. The most commonly used microbiological method is based upon the growth response of *Lactobacillus casei*. There are various chemical methods that measure the fluorescence produced by riboflavin. Food content is expressed in milligrams.

NICOTINAMIDE (NIACIN)

Our knowledge regarding nicotinamide as a dietary essential grew out of the long-time search for a cure for pellagra, a disease that as late as 1935 was estimated to be taking several thousands of lives annually in Southern states. Outstanding pioneer studies covering several years were made by Goldberger of the U.S. Public Health Service, resulting in the conclusion in 1920 that the disease was caused by an ill-balanced diet. In 1925 he established significant resemblances between pellagra and black tongue in dogs, thus ushering in an era of research on the latter. In 1937 Elvehjem and coworkers[57] at the University of Wisconsin made the dramatic discovery that nicotinic acid, a compound that had remained idle on the chemist's shelf for many years, would cure black tongue. Proof that it would also cure uncomplicated human pellagra quickly followed. It became recognized as a dietary essential for pigs, chickens, monkeys, and other species. Nicotinamide was found equally useful and, in fact, the physiologically active compound. Thus, the vitamin is now properly called nicotinamide. Niacin and niacinamide are used as shorter names for nicotinic acid and its amide.

[57] C. A. Elvehjem and coworkers, Relation of nicotinic acid and nicotinic acid amide to canine black tongue, *J. Am. Chem. Soc.*, **59**:1767–1768, 1937.

8.35. Physiological Functions and Symptoms of Deficiency. In the body nicotinamide functions as a component of two coenzymes—diphosphopyridine nucleotide (DPN) and triphosphopyridine nucleotide (TPN). They act in conjunction with flavoprotein enzymes in cell respiration, and this function is believed to be basic to most of the physiological effects of the vitamin. They are essential for various reactions concerned with carbohydrate, lipid, and protein metabolism.

Pellagra in man is characterized by a fiery red tongue, ulcers of the mouth, dermatitis, loss of appetite, nausea, and other symptoms. Somewhat similar troubles are found in pigs and chickens. The need of pigs for nicotinic acid and the symptoms resulting from its deficiency were first established by the studies of Chick and associates in England and by Hughes of California. Loss of weight, diarrhea, vomiting, dermatitis, and normocytic anemia are commonly occurring symptoms. In chicks its deficiency is characterized by poor growth, mouth symptoms somewhat similar to those of black tongue in dogs, poor feathering, and occasionally a scaly dermatitis. On a niacin-low diet turkey poults develop an enlarged hock disorder. It is obvious that most of these symptoms are not specific.

The synthesis of the vitamin in the rumen of cattle and sheep has been demonstrated. A deficiency has been produced by Hopper and Johnson[58] in young calves on a low-tryptophan diet. The significance of the tryptophan level, which explains why niacin may not be a dietary requirement for various species on certain rations although it is always a metabolic need, is discussed later (Sec. 8.37).

8.36. Chemistry and Metabolism of Nicotinic Acid and Nicotinamide. The structural formulas of nicotinic acid and the physiologically active nicotinamide are shown below:

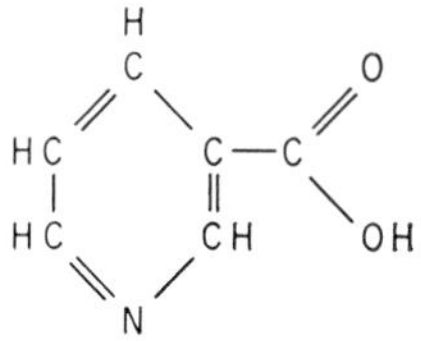

```
       H                          H
       C        O                 C        O
     //  \     //               //  \     //
   HC     C—C                 HC     C—C
   |      ||   \              |      ||   \
   HC     CH    OH            HC     CH    NH2
     \\   /                     \\   /
       N                          N
   Nicotinic acid              Nicotinamide
```

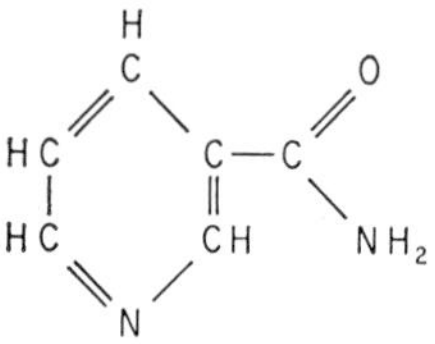

The formulas reveal that the compounds are derivatives of pyridine, explaining the previously mentioned names of the compounds in which the vitamin functions. Both the acid and amide are colorless crystalline substances readily soluble in water and alcohol. They are very resistant to heat, air, light, and alkali and, thus, are stable in foods. There are

[58] John H. Hopper and B. Connor Johnson, The production and study of an acute nicotinic acid deficiency in the calf, *J. Nutrition*, **56**:303–310, 1955.

a number of antivitamins which are similar in structure, such as 3-acetyl pyridine.

The principal excretory products in man, dog, rat, and pig are the methylated metabolites N′-methylnicotinamide and N′-methyl-6-pyridonenicotinamide. On the other hand, in Herbivora niacin does not seem to be metabolized by methylation, but large amounts are excreted unchanged. In poultry the excretory product is dinicotinylornithine. The measurement of the excretion of these metabolites is carried out in studies of niacin requirements and of niacin metabolism. Such studies are complicated by the fact that the kinds and relative amounts of these products vary with the species and level of niacin intake, as shown by Perlzweig and coworkers.[59]

8.37. Nicotinic Acid and Tryptophan Interrelationships. The consumption of corn was early associated with the occurrence of pellagra. Even after the vitamin was discovered and its low content in corn established, evidence persisted that corn had some positive role in connection with the disease. This idea was furthered by studies first published in 1945 showing that a high-corn diet increased the niacin need for dogs and chicks and caused a deficiency in rats not normally requiring a dietary source of the vitamin. The deficiency in rats was overcome by adding nicotinic acid or casein or tryptophan. Milk also helped correct the deficiency, an observation which was in line with the evidence that milk is effective in curing pellagra, though rather low in nicotinic acid. Other protein sources were also found effective. An interrelationship between protein and nicotinic acid needs was also established for pigs and chicks. As a result of further studies it became definitely established by 1947 that the effective proteins were those high in tryptophan and specifically that this amino acid served as a precursor for the synthesis of niacin in the body.

Many studies with rats have dealt with the question as to the site of this synthesis. There is considerable evidence, such as that by Ellinger and Kader,[60] that the synthesis can take place in the intestine. These investigators found that there was a much larger urinary excretion of the metabolite N′-methylnicotinamide where tryptophan was administered by stomach tube than when injected parenterally. When a sulfa drug was fed, the excretion of the metabolite decreased markedly and the feeding of tryptophan caused no increase in the excretion. There is also evidence that the synthesis can take place inside the body. This evidence

[59] W. A. Perlzweig, Fred Rosen, and P. B. Pearson, Comparative studies in niacin metabolism: the fate of niacin in man, rat, dog, pig, rabbit, guinea pig, goat, sheep and calf, *J. Nutrition*, **40**:453–469, 1950.

[60] P. Ellinger and M. M. Abdel Kader, The nicotinamide-saving action of tryptophan and the biosynthesis of nicotinamide by the intestinal flora of the rat, *Biochem. J.*, **44**:285–294, 1949.

is based on the observation that the parenteral administration of the amino acid causes increased output of the metabolites of niacin in the urine and more specifically on an experiment by Henderson and Hankes[61] showing that, despite the removal of the major portion of the intestinal tract, marked increases in the excretion of niacin metabolites occurred on the feeding of tryptophan. Synthesis occurs in the developing chick embryo.

Isotope studies have been used to demonstrate the synthesis of nicotinamide from tryptophan and explain the chemical pathway by which it occurs. Several steps are involved, and thiamine, riboflavin, and vitamin B_6 are essential, each acting at a given step in the pathway. It has been shown that rats, pigs, and chicks meet their entire niacin needs by synthesis, assuming an adequate supply of tryptophan in the diet for the purpose and also for protein synthesis. The latter function takes preference, however, at least in rats, and a deficiency of the vitamin can be induced by a diet relatively deficient in tryptophan for protein synthesis, as shown by the studies of Henderson and coworkers.[62] Approximately 60 mg. of tryptophan is required for the synthesis of 1 mg. of niacin in the body, as determined by rat studies. The quantitative relationship of the requirements of both for the pig is shown in the study by Firth and Johnson.[63]

Nicotinamide is clearly a metabolic need for all species. Ruminants have no dietary need, and the requirement for other species depends upon the extent of synthesis from tryptophan. It is evident that pigs and chickens on a liberal protein diet rich in tryptophan have a very low, if any, need for the vitamin. Human needs can also be met by tryptophan.

The establishment of this tryptophan-niacin interrelationship, together with the fact that corn protein is low in this amino acid, provided an explanation for the "pellagragenic" effect of corn. A further explanation is that much of niacin in corn is in a "bound form," unavailable to the rat, pig, or poultry without alkali treatment. The same is true for wheat, rice, and barley grains, as shown in the case of the rat by Chandhuri and Kodicek.[64] These findings obviously have a bearing on the practical usefulness of cereals as dietary sources of the vitamin.

[61] L. M. Henderson and L. V. Hankes, Effect of enterectomy on synthesis of niacin in the rat, *Proc. Soc. Exptl. Biol. Med.*, **70**:26–28, 1949.

[62] L. M. Henderson, O. J. Koepple, and Harriet H. Zimmerman, Nicotinic acid-tryptophan deficiency resulting from amino acid imbalance in non-casein diets, *J. Biol. Chem.*, **201**:697–706, 1953.

[63] J. Firth and B. Connor Johnson, Quantitative relationship of tryptophan and nicotinic acid requirements in the baby pig, *J. Nutrition*, **59**:223–234, 1956.

[64] D. K. Chandhuri and E. Kodicek, The availability of bound nicotinic acid to the rat, *Brit. J. Nutrition*, **14**:35–42, 1960.

8.38. Nicotinic Acid in Foods. The vitamin has a wide distribution among feeds, and thus a deficiency in the commonly fed rations of farm animals that need this factor seems unlikely. This viewpoint is supported by experimental observations. Animal and fish by-products, distiller's grains and yeast, various distillation and fermentation solubles, and certain oil meals are good sources. Leafy materials, especially pasture grass, are fair sources. Several of the cereals are fair sources, but the availability of the vitamin present is in question for reasons previously discussed.

The dog is used in assaying for nicotinic acid biologically, but this is a long and expensive procedure. Further, no biological method is exact because tryptophan interferes. Thus, various chemical, colorimetric, and microbiological methods have been developed. The last have proved to have the most general usefulness, notably the collaborative A.O.A.C.-U.S.P. method.[65]

VITAMIN B_6

In 1934 György separated the nonthiamine part of the B complex into riboflavin and a "complementary factor" which he named vitamin B_6 and defined as the factor "responsible for the cure of a specific dermatitis developed by young rats on the vitamin-free diet supplemented with B_1 and riboflavin." In 1938 Lepkovsky isolated the vitamin as crystals of his previously reported "factor I." Other workers announced the isolation during the same year. The structure of the vitamin was first explained by Kuhn and coworkers who gave it the name *adermin*. These same workers, along with Harris and Folkers of Merck and Company, deserve credit for the synthesis of the vitamin.

In view of the chemical structure of the compound here concerned, György proposed *pyridoxine* as the name for the vitamin, and this proposal was widely adopted. Later, however, two other compounds, *pyridoxal* and *pyridoxamine*, were identified. Thus, by official action of the Society of Biological Chemists and the American Institute of Nutrition, the original term B_6 is now the approved name for this vitamin, which, like several others, has a multiple nature. The vitamin is a dietary essential for the rat, pig, chick, dog, man, and other species, including microorganisms. Vitamin B_6 is a metabolic essential for ruminants as well as other animals, as indicated by studies with newborn calves, but after the rumen is developed, cattle and sheep have no need for a dietary source. In horses the vitamin is synthesized in the cecum.

[65] Esmond E. Snell, Microbiological methods in vitamin research, in Paul György (ed.), Vitamin Methods, Academic Press, Inc., New York, 1950, vol. 1, pp. 360–371.

8.39. Physiological Functions and Symptoms of Deficiency. Microbiological studies have shown that vitamin B_6 functions in several enzyme systems concerned in protein metabolism. In the form of phosphorylated pyridoxal it serves as a coenzyme (codecarboxylase) for enzymes which decarboxylate several amino acids. As phosphorylated pyridoxal, it also is a coenzyme for transaminases, which catalyze the transfer of the amino group of glutamic acid and certain other amino acids to keto acids. The vitamin also functions in a variety of other reactions concerned in the metabolism of amino acids. It is essential

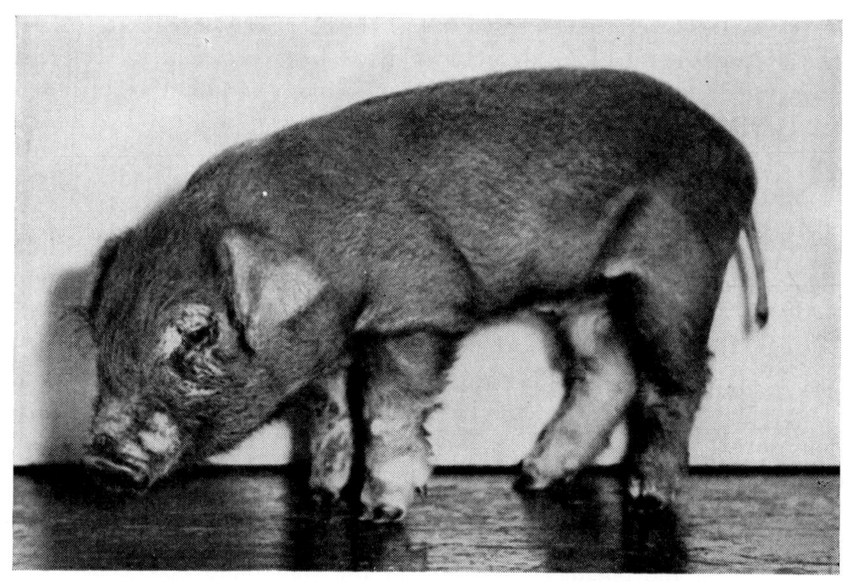

FIG. 8.6. Vitamin B_6 deficiency. (*Courtesy of R. W. Luecke, Michigan Agriculture Experiment Station.*)

for the complete metabolism of tryptophan. Otherwise the abnormal metabolite xanthurenic acid is formed and excreted. The level of xanthurenic acid excretion has been used as an indicator of the status of B_6 nutrition in the pig. B_6 is also concerned in some way with fat metabolism. A deficient animal is shown in Fig. 8.6.

The specific dermatitis (acrodynia) that characterizes vitamin B_6 deficiency in rats is not found in other species, but convulsions are a common symptom in all. In pigs the symptoms include a microcytic, hypochromic anemia; epileptic-like fits or convulsions; and slow growth. Nerve degeneration and hemosiderosis, the deposition of a dark-yellow iron pigment, are regularly found on autopsy. In chicks, abnormal excitability, jerky, aimless movements, and, later, convulsions occur, followed by complete exhaustion. Slow growth and suppressed appetite are accompanying symptoms. The experimental production of deficiency symptoms in pigs is described in the report by Lehrer and coworkers.[66] Among other functions, it is essential for the synthesis of arachidonic acid from linoleic acid (Sec. 5.28). As shown by rat studies, normal reproduction requires an adequate supply of the vitamin both prior to mating and during gestation.

The symptoms in animals have been produced experimentally with purified diets designed to be lacking in the vitamin and also with diets of natural feeds to which the antimetabolite desoxypyridoxine has been added. There is no evidence that deficiencies occur in farm animals on commonly fed rations, and their occurrence is not to be expected in view of the widespread distribution of the vitamin in feedstuffs. The symptoms cannot be considered specific for B_6 deficiency only. For example, lack of pantothenic acid produces similar skin and nervous manifestations.

8.40. Chemistry of Vitamin B_6. The formulas for the three naturally occurring free forms of B_6 are as follows:

```
         C—CH2OH                  C—CH2NH2                    C—C(=O)H
       /   \\                   /   \\                      /   \\
   HOC       C—CH2OH       HOC       C—CH2OH          HOC       C—CH2OH
    ||       |              ||       |                 ||       |
CH3—C        CH        CH3—C         CH           CH3—C         CH
      \     //               \     //                   \     //
         N                      N                          N
     Pyridoxine             Pyridoxamine                Pyridoxal
```

As is to be expected in view of their common role in metabolism, pyridoxine can be converted into the amine and the aldehyde. The latter two are reversibly converted into each other. The three compounds are all water-soluble and fairly stable to heat, but the sterilization of milk products results in a substantial loss.

8.41. Food Supply. Vitamin B_6 is widely distributed in feeds. Yeast, liver, muscle meat, milk, cereal grains and their by-products, and vegetables are all excellent sources. Many other products contain substantial amounts. Assays are carried out mostly by microbiological methods. Here it is essential either to use an organism that will respond to all

[66] W. P. Lehrer and coworkers, Pyridoxine deficiency in baby pigs, *J. Animal Sci.*, **10**:65–72, 1951.

three compounds, both free and combined, or to use different organisms in separate tests. Mice, rats, chicks, and dogs have also been used in assays. Miller and coworkers[67] have reported that the requirement for the baby pig lies between 0.75 and 1.0 mg. per kilogram feed. This paper details the physical symptoms of the deficiency and also blood changes, organ weights, and levels of xanthurenic acid excretion. The N.R.C. requirement for starting chickens is 1.3 mg. per pound of feed.

PANTOTHENIC ACID

In 1933, R. J. Williams and associates fractionated bios, a growth factor for yeast, and obtained a very potent acid fraction which they named pantothenic acid. When the chemical nature of this substance was definitely established, it became clear that it was the same factor concerned in a specific dermatitis condition in chicks, described by various workers. Now it is known that pantothenic acid is a dietary essential also in rats, dogs, pigs, turkeys, and other species. It is synthesized in the rumen of the cow and sheep to the extent that no need for a supply in their rations has been shown. Intestinal synthesis of pantothenic acid has been found to occur in all species studied. In the case of the rabbit and the horse it appears to be sufficiently extensive to meet body needs, at least in large part.

8.42. Physiological Functions and Symptoms of Deficiency. As a constituent of coenzyme A, (Co A), the vitamin plays an essential role in many basic biochemical reactions. The coenzyme functions in acetyl-Co A and in the acetylation of choline, sulfanilamide, and other compounds. Its combination with two-carbon fragments from fats, carbohydrates, and certain amino acids to form acetyl-coenzyme A is an essential step in their complete metabolism. The coenzyme enables these fragments to enter the citric acid cycle. It also plays an essential role in fat and cholesterol synthesis. The vitamin is, therefore, one of the essential components in the basic reactions concerned in the cellular oxidation of food materials. Indirect evidence indicates an essential role in fat and cholesterol synthesis. The manifold functions of Co A, only partially mentioned here, are reviewed by Lipmann,[68] who made pioneer discoveries in the field.

In view of the diverse functions of the vitamin, a variety of deficiency symptoms are to be expected. They include growth and reproductive failure, skin and hair lesions, gastrointestinal symptoms, and lesions of

[67] E. R. Miller and coworkers, The pyridoxine requirement of the baby pig, *J. Nutrition*, **62**:407–419, 1957.

[68] Fritz Lipmann (Chairman), Symposium on chemistry and functions of coenzyme A, *Federation Proc.*, **12**:673–715, 1953.

the nervous systems. The metabolic roles of the vitamin are interrelated with those of several other B-factors. In chickens there is first a retardation of growth and feather development. Next, the dermatitis appears. The eyelids become granular and stick together, and scabs appear around the mouth, and vent, and on the feet. Liver damage, changes in the spinal cord, and several other post-mortem findings are to be noted. Hatchability is decreased in adult birds. The condition produced in chickens is shown in Fig. 8.7. Pigs suffering from panto-

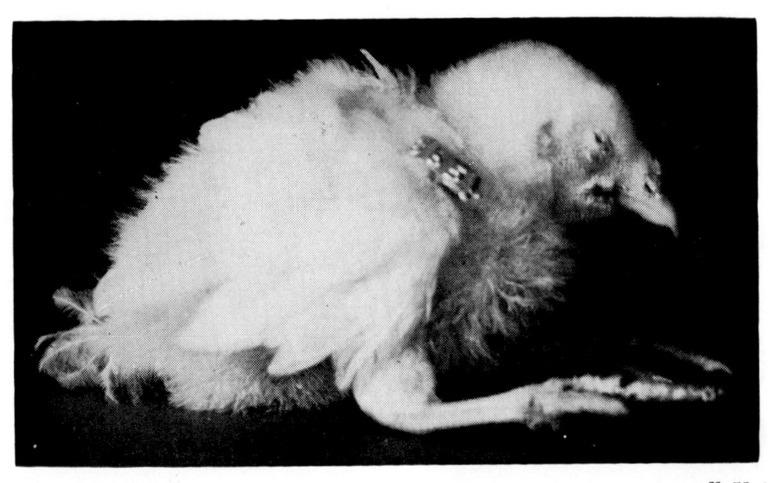

FIG. 8.7. Pantothenic acid deficiency. (*Courtesy of L. C. Norris, Cornell University.*)

thenic acid deficiency have a scurfy skin and thin hair, a brownish secretion around the eyes, gastrointestinal troubles, slow growth, and a characteristic goose-stepping (Fig. 8.8). Nerve degeneration and organ changes are found on autopsy. None of these physical symptoms can be considered specific for pantothenic acid deficiency alone. The various ones described have been noted on experimental diets lacking in the vitamin. There is also evidence that deficiencies may occur on practical rations. McKigney and coworkers[69] have reported such evidence using a low-protein (about 14 per cent) corn-soybean ration, fortified with minerals and vitamins except pantothenic acid. The ration contained, on analysis, approximately 6.7 mg. of pantothenic acid per kilogram. Growth was not affected, but various other deficiency symptoms were noted, which were prevented by adding the vitamin to the basal

[69] J. I. McKigney, H. D. Wallace, and T. J. Cunha, The influence of chlortetracycline on the requirement of the young pig for dietary pantothenic acid, *J. Animal Sci.*, **16**:35–43, 1957.

ration. Earlier work by others is reviewed in this publication. In the case of chickens there is no convincing evidence that commonly fed rations which are otherwise adequate need a pantothenic acid supplement.

A lack of pantothenic acid has been found to result in a premature graying of the hair in piebald rats, foxes, and dogs. Administration of the vitamin restores the hair to its natural color. The effect is not

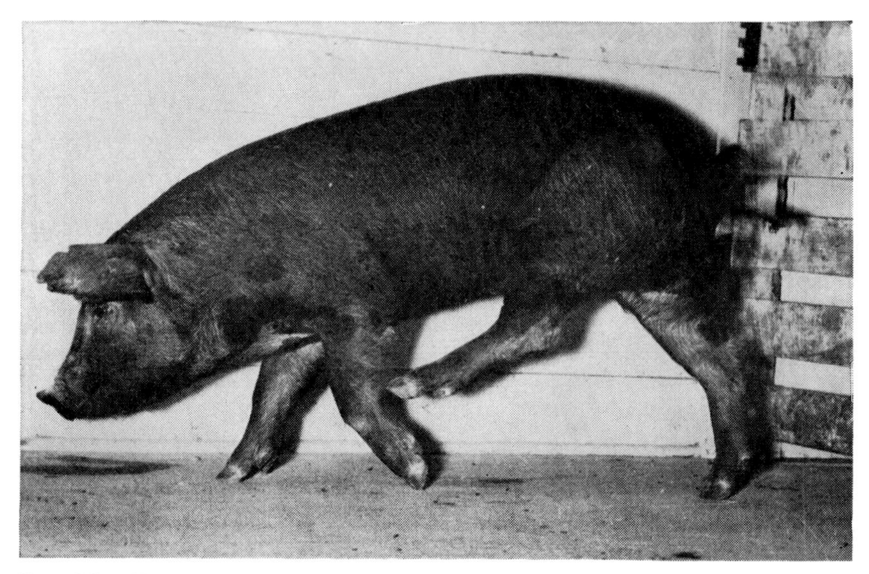

FIG. 8.8. Goose-stepping in pantothenic acid deficiency. (*Courtesy of R. W. Luecke, Michigan Agriculture Experiment Station.*)

specific because such a graying has been observed as a result of a deficiency of other factors. Neither pantothenic acid nor any other factor has been shown to be concerned in the graying of hair in man.

8.43. Chemistry of Pantothenic Acid. This vitamin is a peptide of β-alanine and 2,4-dihydroxy-3,3-dimethyl butyric acid.

$$\begin{array}{ccccccccccccc} & & CH_3 & & OH & & O & & & & & & \\ H & & | & & | & & \| & & H & & H & & H \\ HOC & - & C & - & C & - & C & - & N & - & C & - & C-COOH \\ H & & | & & H & & & & & & H & & H \\ & & CH_3 & & & & & & & & & & \end{array}$$

Pantothenic acid

It is obtained as its calcium salt, which is a white, relatively insoluble powder. There are various analogues of pantothenic acid which act as antimetabolites in antagonizing its growth effect on microorganisms. Coenzyme A contains the vitamin combined with adenosine 3′-phosphate, pyrophosphate, and β-mercaptoethylamine, as shown by the following formula:

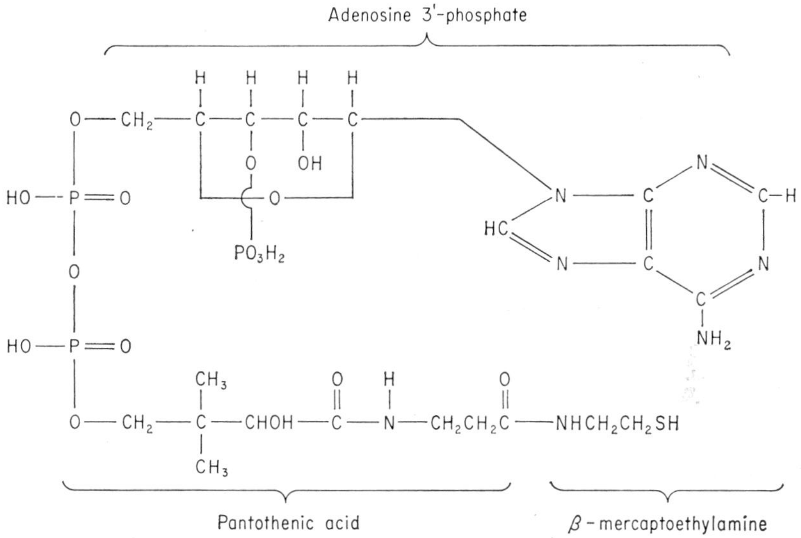

Adenosine 3′-phosphate

$$O-CH_2-\overset{CH_3}{\underset{CH_3}{C}}-CHOH-\overset{O}{\overset{\|}{C}}-\overset{H}{N}-CH_2CH_2\overset{O}{\overset{\|}{C}}-NHCH_2CH_2SH$$

Pantothenic acid β-mercaptoethylamine

Coenzyme A

8.44. Pantothenic Acid in Foods. The vitamin is widely distributed in foods of both animal and plant origin. A deficiency in the commonly fed rations of farm animals seems improbable. Alfalfa hay, peanut meal, cane molasses, yeast, rice bran, and wheat bran are especially rich in the factor. Cereal seeds and their by-products and many other feeds are good sources. In both plant and animal tissues the vitamin occurs very largely as coenzyme A, which is referred to as the "bound form." Bioassays are carried out with both rats and chicks. There are also microbiological procedures.

The N.R.C. requirement for chickens and breeding hens is 4.2 mg. per pound of feed. A somewhat higher requirement appears to be needed for swine.

BIOTIN

The history of the discovery of the physiological significance of biotin is the history of the merging of three lines of investigation, for a long time apparently unrelated. It well illustrates how scientific information develops. In 1936 Kögl and Tonnis in Germany announced the crystallization of a factor called *biotin* necessary for the growth of yeast. Later it was discovered to be identical with a growth factor, "coenzyme R," found essential in 1933 for the growth of nodule bacteria. In 1927 Boas in England had reported that the feeding of Chinese egg white to rats produced a typical dermatitis. Parsons of Wisconsin studied this "egg-white injury" in detail for several years, finding that there was a "protective factor" in certain foods, notably liver and kidney. In the meantime, György studied the chemistry of this protective factor and in 1937 applied the term "factor H" to it.

In 1938 György and du Vigneaud teamed up on the problem and in 1940 announced that vitamin H and biotin were identical, and they gave further proof later. Next it was announced by Eakin and by György and Eakin that egg-white injury resulted from its rendering dietary biotin unavailable, owing to a specific constituent, "avid-albumin," or "avidin." At the same time R. J. Williams announced the isolation from egg white of a substance rendering biotin inactive for yeast growth. Du Vigneaud isolated the vitamin in 1941 and determined its structure in 1942. Harris and coworkers of Merck and Company synthesized it in 1943. Thus a new metabolic essential for both animals and lower plants was discovered. In animal nutrition it presents a unique case in that its discovery rested on the identification of another previously unknown substance which, as a dietary constituent, combines with biotin in the intestine, preventing its absorption. Avidin is a protein which is a secretory product of the mucosa of the oviduct and thus found in the albuminous part of eggs.

8.45. Physiological Functions and Symptoms of Deficiency. Most of our knowledge of the basic metabolic functions of biotin has been obtained in studies with microorganisms. It is a constituent of various enzyme systems, some of which have been shown to function in animals as well as in bacteria. The vitamin is concerned in both carbon-dioxide fixation and decarboxylation. For example, it functions in the addition of carbon dioxide to pyruvate to form malate, and it decarboxylates oxalosuccinate to α-ketoglutarate. It functions in fat synthesis through the incorporation of carbon dioxide into isovaleric acid to form acetoacetate. The vitamin plays a role, at least in bacteria, in deaminating systems of certain amino acids occurring in both the free and a bound form.

Symptoms of biotin deficiency in several species have been produced by feeding raw egg white or by the use of biotin-free diets plus a sulfa drug to prevent intestinal synthesis. Dermatitis, loss of hair, and poor growth are found in all species. In chicks these symptoms have been produced on a biotin-low diet without the use of egg white or sulfa drugs and cured by supplying the vitamin. Biotin has also been found useful along with manganese, choline, and folic acid in preventing perosis (Sec. 7.43). In the mature fowl hatchability is decreased by its deficiency. Cunha and coworkers[70] have reported the experimental production of biotin deficiency in pigs by feeding egg white. The symptoms found were as follows: spasticity of the hind legs, cracks in the feet, and a dermatitis characterized by dryness, roughness, and a brownish exudate. None of these symptoms in chicks or pigs can be considered specific for differentiating biotin deficiency from those of certain other of the B-vitamins.

In cattle and sheep rumen synthesis apparently takes care of body needs adequately. There is a substantial intestinal synthesis of biotin in all other species studied, including man. The nature of the diet markedly influences the extent of this synthesis, as illustrated by the studies of Couch and coworkers[71] with hens.

8.46. Chemistry of Biotin. As determined by isolation and by synthesis, biotin is 2-keto-3,4-imadazilido-2-tetrahydrothiophenevaleric acid. It is an acid, as indicated by the carboxyl group in the side chain.

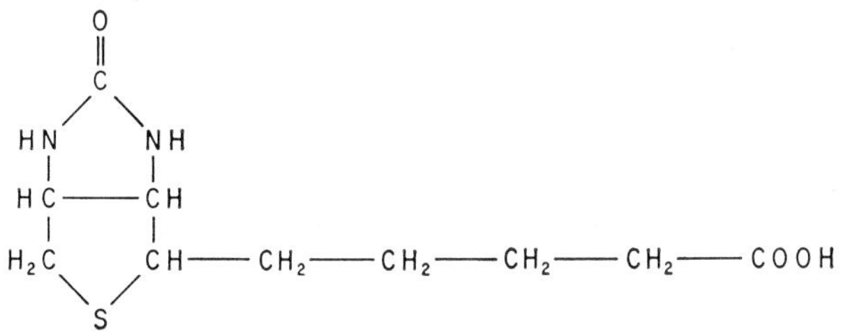

```
          O
          ||
          C
         / \
      HN     NH
      |       |
      HC------CH
      |       |
     H2C      CH----CH2----CH2----CH2----CH2----COOH
        \    /
          S
```

Biotin

It is a crystalline compound, very stable chemically but soluble in alcohol and water. Structurally related compounds have been found to have biotin activity for the growth of microorganisms, and thus there may be more than one compound that has activity in animal nutrition. There are also compounds which have antibiotin activity.

8.47. Biotin in Foods. Biotin is widely distributed in plant and animal nutrition and thus in feeds and foods generally, occurring in both the free and the combined form. Both bioassays with rats and chicks and microbiological assays are used to measure food content. The animal assay is a laborious procedure but readily measures both forms, whereas the microbiological methods, though short, require much care to obtain

[70] Tony J. Cunha, Dean C. Lindley, and M. E. Ensminger, Biotin deficiency syndrome in pigs fed desiccated egg white, *J. Animal Sci.*, **5**:219–225, 1946.

[71] J. R. Couch and coworkers, Effect of oats, oat products and fat on the intestinal synthesis of biotin in mature fowl, *J. Nutrition*, **37**:251–261, 1949.

complete extraction of the bound form. Yeast and organ meats are very rich sources. Biotin is concentrated largely in the seeds of plants, and thus whole grains are good sources. Molasses and milk also contain substantial amounts. Data on animal feeds are limited, but commonly fed rations should furnish substantial amounts in terms of any need. In the case of the chick, the only animal for which a quantitative dietary need has been established, the N.R.C. requirement has been set at 0.04 mg. per pound of feed. Rumen synthesis should supply any needs of cattle and sheep. There is no present evidence that deficiencies occur in practice in any farm animal.

CHOLINE[72]

Choline has been previously discussed as a constituent of the phospholipid lecithin, and its formula has been given (Sec. 5.14). The importance of phospholipids as constituents of cells and tissues throughout the body has long been recognized, but the knowledge that the choline component is a specific dietary essential under certain conditions is a comparatively recent development. While the fatty acids and glycerol of lecithin can arise from either fat or carbohydrate metabolism, choline must be supplied in the diet as such except to the extent that it can be synthesized within the body through the special process of transmethylation (Sec. 8.49).

8.48. Functions and Symptoms of Deficiency. Choline is a metabolic essential for building and maintaining cell structure. It also plays an essential role in fat metabolism in the liver, preventing the abnormal accumulation of fat (fatty livers) by promoting its transport as lecithin or by increasing the utilization of the fatty acids in the liver itself. Because of this role in preventing fat accumulation, the compound is referred to as a "lipotropic" factor. Choline is essential for the formation of acetylcholine, a substance which makes possible the transmission of nerve impulses. It plays a nonspecific role as a source of "biologically labile methyl groups" (Sec. 8.49) and a specific one in the prevention of perosis (Sec. 7.43).

Choline deficiency has been produced in rats, dogs, chickens, pigs, and other species. Slow growth is a nonspecific symptom. Fatty livers are produced for reasons mentioned above. In young rats the kidneys become hemorrhagic, owing presumably to a deficiency of choline for the phospholipid required to build cell structure at this critical growth

[72] Choline is discussed along with the vitamins of the B complex in accordance with common practice. It differs from them in being essential as a structural component of tissues rather than as a metabolic catalyst.

period. Best and Hartroft[73] made the important observation that, when young rats which have developed hemorrhagic kidneys as a result of a deficiency of choline and its precursors are placed on a normal diet, they later develop moderate to severe hypertension. As the authors suggest, these results are of general significance because they indicate that extensive and often fatal pathological changes during adult life may have their origin in a very short period of faulty nutrition at a very young stage.

The need for choline by chicks was first noted in connection with perosis. Several experiments have shown it essentiality for the growth of this species. Neumann and coworkers[74] have produced choline deficiency in the pig, using a purified diet. The pigs made only slow growth, were very unthrifty, lacked coordination in movements, and showed fatty infiltration of the liver on autopsy. A need by baby calves has also been shown.

8.49. Transmethylation. In 1935 it was shown that casein had a lipotropic effect, preventing or curing fatty livers in rats, and two years later this effect was found due to the amino acid methionine. These observations provided the background for a brilliant series of investigations by du Vigneaud and associates showing that methionine can furnish methyl groups which combine with ethanolamine to form choline, and that, in reverse, methyl groups from choline can unite with homocysteine to form methionine. Thus it was recognized that both choline and methionine contain "biologically labile methyl groups" which can be transferred within the body, the phenomenon being called transmethylation. In this way methionine can partially replace choline as a dietary essential, and choline plus homocysteine can replace the essential amino acid methionine. Later work showed that vitamin B_{12} (Sec. 8.55) is in some way concerned in transmethylation.

In view of these findings it is now recognized that the metabolic needs for choline can be supplied in two ways, either by dietary choline as such or by choline synthesis in the body through transmethylation which makes use of labile methyl groups. While these groups can be synthesized in the body, there is evidence, as set forth by du Vigneaud and associates,[75] that this synthesis cannot take place rapidly enough entirely to meet the needs of the young rat for growth. Thus these workers regard the labile methyl group as a dietary essential in the same sense that arginine is an essential amino acid for rat growth.

[73] Charles H. Best and W. Stanley Hartroft, Nutrition, renal lesions and hypertension, *Federation Proc.*, **8**:610–617, 1949.

[74] A. L. Neumann and coworkers, The choline requirement of the baby pig, *J. Nutrition*, **38**:195–231, 1949.

[75] Vincent du Vigneaud, Charlotte Ressler, and Julian R. Rachele, The biological synthesis of "labile methyl groups," *Science*, **112**:267–271, 1950.

The interrelations of methionine and choline in chick nutrition, which result from transmethylation, are illustrated by the studies of McKittrick,[76] who concluded that the choline required by the chick may be divided into two parts, an essential part and another part replaceable by methionine.

Other interrelationships of choline are indicated by the findings that deficiencies of biotin and folic acid are also concerned in the production of perosis and that vitamin B_{12} is involved in methyl synthesis.

8.50. Food Supply. All naturally occurring fats contain some choline, and thus it is supplied by all feeds which contain fat. Quantitative data for representative feeds are presented by McElroy, Rigney, and Draper.[77] Since the metabolic need for choline can be met in part by body synthesis, it seems unlikely that dietary deficiency is apt to occur in commonly fed rations. This is a matter that may need further study, however, particularly in view of the increasing removal of fat from the feed supply.

Obviously, the dietary requirement for choline depends on the level of methionine in the ration. In the case of baby pigs it has been reported that, with the methionine level at about 0.8 per cent, 0.1 per cent of choline is required. With sufficient methionine in the diet no choline is needed by the rat or pig, but this is not true for the chicken.

FOLIC ACID (FOLACIN) AND RELATED FACTORS

Folic acid is an antianemia factor which has several physiologically active derivatives. These various compounds first came into the literature as unidentified factors on the basis of their essentiality for the prevention of deficiency states in various animal species or for the growth of certain microorganisms. Thus, such names as "factor U," "vitamin M," "vitamin B_c," "B_c conjugate," "*Lactobacillus casei* factor," "SLR factor," "folic acid," and others originated. There was much confusion regarding these various unidentified factors until in 1943 the Parke-Davis group and the Lederle group isolated a crystalline compound from liver which proved to be the *L. casei* factor. Next the structure and synthesis of the compound was accomplished by the Lederle group and named pteroylglutamic acid. This is the compound now called "folic acid,"

[76] D. S. McKittrick, The interrelations of choline and methionine in growth and the action of betaine in replacing them, *Arch. Biochem.*, **15**:133–155, 1947; The interrelations of choline and glycine betaine in the growth of the chick, *ibid.*, **18**:437–448, 1948.

[77] L. W. McElroy, H. A. Rigney, and H. H. Draper, Choline content of live stock feeds used in Western Canada, *Sci. Agr.*, **28**:268–271, 1948.

or "folacin." It also represents the factors previously referred to as "vitamin M," "vitamin B_c," and "factor U." Other unidentified ones were found to be derivatives of it. A later discovered active derivative is the *citrovorum* factor. The same compound is also represented by the names "folinic acid" and "leucovorum."

8.51. Chemistry of Folic Acid. The *L. casei* factor, identified as mentioned above, has the following formula:

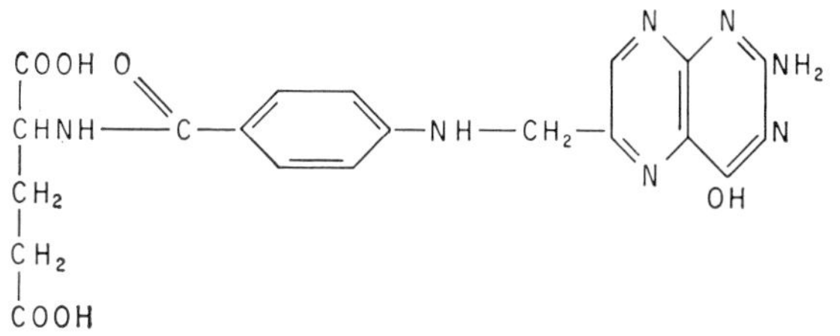

Liver *L. casei* factor (folic acid)

Reading from left to right it is seen that this compound consists of glutamic acid, paraaminobenzoic acid, and a pteridine nucleus, the last two making up pteroic acid. Thus the name pteroylglutamic acid was suggested. The shorter terms, folic acid and folacin, are now commonly used. Folinic acid is formyltetrahydrofolic acid, as shown by its formula:

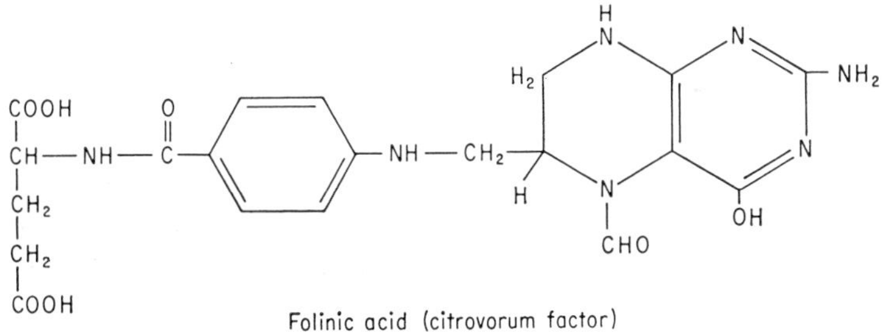

Folinic acid (citrovorum factor)

It performs all the functions of folic acid and is the more active form. The SLR factor, commonly known as rhizopterin, is formylpteroic acid. Folic acid and the citrovorum factor also occur combined with additional glutamic acid groups. These conjugated forms are active for those species having appropriate enzymes for splitting them. Thus, B_c conjugate is unavailable to microorganisms but becomes available on treatment with folic acid conjugases in pancreas or kidney.

Another active pterin is *xanthopterin,* which was isolated from butterfly wings by Hopkins in 1889. Twenty years ago German workers reported that this compound caused red cell formation in rats made anemic by goat's milk. Its effectiveness in curing an anemia in fish was later reported. These reports did not become explainable until later discoveries regarding folic acid were made.

Folic acid is a yellow crystalline solid, slightly soluble in water but unstable in acid solution. At pH 1 autoclaving destroys most of its activity. Its action is antagonized by many compounds structurally related to it, one of the most effective being 4-amino-pteroylglutamic acid, commonly called *aminopterin.*

8.52. Functions and Symptoms of Deficiency. Folic acid plays a basic biochemical role in the transfer of single-carbon units in various reactions, a role analogous to that of pantothenic acid in the transfer of two-carbon units. Thus, it functions in the interconversion of serine and glycine, in the synthesis of purines, in histidine degradation, and in the synthesis of certain methyl groups. Deficient purine synthesis results in a deficiency of nucleoprotein formation for blood-cell maturation, and the characteristic anemia develops accordingly.

Folic acid has been found to be a dietary essential for the monkey, chick, turkey, fox, mink, rabbit, mouse, and guinea pig. In the rat and pig a deficiency has not been produced except by the simultaneous feeding of sulfa drugs, indicating that intestinal synthesis is adequate to meet needs. Synthesis occurs in the rumen, but newborn lambs require a dietary supply, according to the work of Draper and Johnson.[78] In species in which deficiency symptoms are produced, there is a characteristic macrocytic, hyperchromic anemia called megaloblastic anemia. The red cells are large and immature and there are related changes in the bone marrow. *Leucopenia* (a reduced number of white cells) also occurs. In the chick, growth is retarded, poor feathering results, and depigmentation occurs in colored feathers. In humans the vitamin is used therapeutically to treat megaloblastic anemias of infancy and pregnancy and in sprue. It is also effective in treating the anemia but not the nervous symptoms of *pernicious anemia.*

An excellent review of the physiology of folic acid is to be found in an article by Jukes.[79]

8.53. Interrelations of Folic Acid and Other Vitamins. Several studies have shown the actions of folic acid and other vitamins to be interrelated in ways incompletely understood. Both folic acid and vitamin B_{12} appear to function in the synthesis or metabolism of the various compounds making up nucleic acids. For some years it has been known, as shown

[78] Harold H. Draper and B. Connor Johnson, Folic acid deficiency in the lamb, *J. Nutrition,* **46**:123–131, 1952.

[79] Thomas H. Jukes, Folic acid and vitamin B_{12} in the physiology of vertebrates, *Federation Proc.,* **12**:633–638, 1953.

initially by Schaefer and coworkers,[80] that folic acid has a sparing effect on the requirement of rats and chicks for choline. The effect is probably due to increased synthesis of methyl groups. An interrelationship with vitamin C is indicated by the finding that rats showing folic acid deficiency as a result of a diet containing sulfa drugs are benefited by feeding ascorbic acid. A relationship between folic acid and riboflavin has also been reported.

8.54. Feed Supplies and Requirements. Folic acid is widely distributed in plant and animal products. Green leafy materials and organ meats are rich sources. Cereals, soybeans, other beans, and various animal by-products are good sources. Milk contains the vitamin in limited amounts. From the previous discussion it is evident that the only farm animals found to require a dietary source are poultry. The requirements per pound of feed, as stated by the N.R.C., are 0.25 mg. for the chick, 0.11 for the laying hen, and 0.16 for breeding hens. These needs are readily met by good practical rations. The chick is the preferred animal for assaying feeds for the vitamin. Microbiological methods are also used.

VITAMIN B_{12}

For many years following the discovery that liver contained a substance which could cause a remission of pernicious anemia, scientists strove unsuccessfully to isolate from liver the *antipernicious anemia factor* (APA). When hope that folic acid was the factor proved unfounded despite its action on the specific type of anemia involved, activities were redoubled in other directions. Within two years success was achieved through the discovery of vitamin B_{12}, which proved to be both APA and also a long-sought growth factor for animals.

8.55. The Discovery of Vitamin B_{12}. The story of the discovery of this vitamin is a dramatic one made possible by the combined efforts of microbiologists, biochemists, nutrition scientists, and physicians working in various laboratories. In 1947 Mary Shorb of the Department of Poultry Husbandry of the University of Maryland reported the finding in liver extract of a factor (LLD factor) required by *Lactobacillus lactis* Dorner in concentrations bearing an almost linear relationship to the APA activity of the extract. Making use of this organism, Rickes and coworkers of Merck and Company culminated several years of experiments by announcing, in 1948, the isolation of a red crystalline compound from liver which West found highly active hematopoietically in pernicious

[80] A. E. Schaefer and coworkers, Interrelationship of folacin, vitamin B_{12} and choline: effect on hemorrhagic kidney syndrome in the rat and on growth of the chick, *J. Nutrition,* **40**:95–111, 1950.

anemia. The dose required by intramuscular injection was only a few micrograms. The Merck group proposed the name vitamin B_{12}. The compound was found to have a high LLD activity and thus was apparently identical with the factor of Shorb. Almost simultaneously with the report by the Merck group came the announcement by E. L. Smith of England of the isolation from liver of two red pigments, later crystallized, which were found clinically active in treating both the anemia and the nervous symptoms of pernicious anemia. One of these was later crystallized and found to be identical with vitamin B_{12}. Within a year clinical trials by four other groups of workers showed that crystalline B_{12} caused both hematological and neurological improvement in the disease. The above is a very incomplete story of the many contributions which resulted in the discovery of the long-sought APA factor.

8.56. Vitamin B_{12} and the Animal Protein Factor. As a result of studies by various workers it came to be recognized by 1945 that there was an unidentified factor (or factors) essential for the growth of chicks fed diets entirely of plant origin and that the missing nutrient could be supplied by fish meal, fish solubles, liver, meat scrap, and other animal products. The association of the unknown factor with animal protein sources was responsible for its designation as the *animal protein factor* (APF). It was also referred to as the "chick growth factor." The same factor was also found essential for hatchability. Cow manure was also found to contain the factor, and an organism was isolated from hen's feces that could synthesize a factor effective in promoting chick growth. Cary of the U.S. Department of Agriculture found that milk, commerical casein, and liver extract contained a "factor X" necessary for rat growth on purified diets containing all the known essentials, but having, as its protein component, casein which had been highly purified. With the isolation of vitamin B_{12} it was quickly found that this factor was required for chick growth and for hatchability and that under appropriate experimental conditions it could entirely replace sources of the APF.

8.57. Functions and Symptoms of Deficiency. Vitamin B_{12} is a metabolic essential for all animal species studied. Pernicious anemia in man is a B_{12}-deficiency state in the tissues caused by the failure of the absorption of the vitamin, due to a gastric abnormality. Injection of the vitamin alleviates the megaloblastic anemia and the nervous symptoms. Injections must be continued because the gastric abnormality is not corrected. This abnormality prevents any benefit from feeding the vitamin. This specific anemia does not occur in B_{12}-deficient animals. Decreased growth is the most evident symptom, as shown by studies with rats, mice, chicks, pigs, and others. Neumann and coworkers[81] have de-

[81] A. L. Neumann, B. Connor Johnson, and J. B. Thiersch, Crystalline vitamin B_{12} in the nutrition of the baby pig, *J. Nutrition*, **40**:403–414, 1950.

scribed the symptoms in pigs (Fig. 8.9). In addition to retarded growth, posterior incoordination and unsteadiness of gait resulted. Certain blood changes were noted, but no anemia. In hens, body weight and egg production are maintained despite a deficiency, but poor hatchability results. The newly hatched chicks show bone abnormalities similar to perosis. In rats a deficiency in the diet of the mother can result in hydrocephalus, eye defects, and bone defects in the newborn, as shown by Grainger and coworkers.[82] The vitamin is also essential for normal reproduction in pigs. In none of the animal species studied has anemia been noted on diets adequate except in B_{12}.

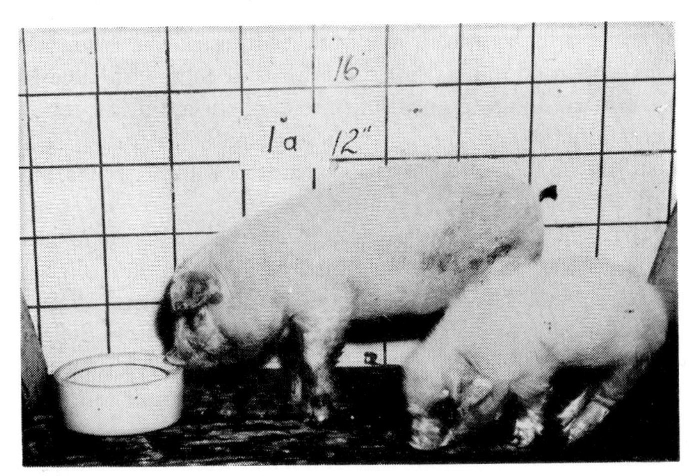

FIG. 8.9. Vitamin B_{12} deficient and normal baby pigs. (*Courtesy of B. Connor Johnson, University of Illinois.*)

B_{12} is a metabolic essential for cattle and sheep and is a dietary requirement in the young before the rumen becomes functional. The deficiency symptoms which have been noted in young calves are cessation of growth, poor appetite, and, in some cases, incoordination. Later the vitamin is synthesized adequately in the rumen provided that sufficient cobalt, a constituent of the vitamin, is available. In Sec. 7.35 it was pointed out that the major, if not the entire, role of cobalt is as a constituent of B_{12}. An excellent review of the various physiological studies dealing with this cobalt–vitamin B_{12} relationship in ruminants is presented by Smith and Loosli.[83] The feces of ruminants, assuming the intake of cobalt is adequate, contain large amounts of the vitamin, explaining the

[82] Robert B. Grainger, Boyd L. O'Dell, and Albert G. Hogan, Congenital malformations as related to deficiencies of riboflavin and vitamin B_{12}, source of protein, calcium to phosphorus ratio and skeletal phosphorus metabolism, *J. Nutrition*, **54**:33–48, 1954.

[83] S. E. Smith and J. K. Loosli, Cobalt and vitamin B_{12} in ruminant nutrition: a review, *J. Dairy Sci.*, **40**:1215–1227, 1957.

discovery of the "cow manure factor." Intestinal synthesis occurs in other species, which probably explains frequent failures to produce a B_{12} deficiency in pigs and rats on diets designed to be free of it. The deficiency can be readily produced in rats, however, when coprophagy is completely prevented, as shown by Barnes and Fiala.[84] The vitamin is undoubtedly a dietary essential for human growth, as well as for the treatment of pernicious anemia.

The specific biochemical functions of B_{12} remain little understood. It has been clearly established that the vitamin is required for methyl group synthesis from various one-carbon precursors, but it is not directly involved in transmethylation. There is evidence that it is concerned at some stage in purine synthesis. Several studies have suggested a role in the synthesis of amino acids into proteins, but more evidence is needed. Some role in carbohydrate and lipid metabolism has also been indicated. The vitamin functions in the body in some cofactor form. A review of the mechanisms of the action of B_{12}, as studied with rats, pigs, and chicks, is to be found in the paper by Johnson.[85]

As reviewed by Smith and Monty,[86] Australian workers have found that in B_{12}-deficient sheep there is an inability to metabolize propionic acid which is one of the major products of rumen fermentation. Experiments showed that the capacity of liver homogenates from deficient sheep to convert propionyl-Co A to succinate was greatly impaired. It was reported that this is considered to be the basic metabolic lesion of vitamin B_{12} deficiency in the ruminant.

8.58. Chemistry of Vitamin B_{12}. Shortly after the discovery of the vitamin it was found to contain carbon, hydrogen, oxygen, nitrogen, phosphorus, and cobalt and was recognized to have a very complex structure. The tremendous task of working out this structure was completed in 1955 through the concerted efforts of scientists at Cambridge and Oxford Universities in England and at Princeton University and the University of California at Los Angeles in the United States. Such diverse techniques as chemical and crystallographic analyses, electron density measurements, and those of electronic computers were used to accomplish the task. The reports of the different groups were published briefly in *Nature* (London) as two articles in 1955 and one in 1956. The articles bear the names of thirteen different authors, reflecting the large number of scientists involved. The size and international distribution of the overall group, and the diversity of techniques used, reflect the effectiveness of present-day team research.

[84] Richard H. Barnes and Grace Fiala, Effect of prevention of coprophagy in the rat. II. Vitamin B_{12} requirement, *J. Nutrition,* **65**:103–114, 1958.

[85] B. Connor Johnson, Studies of the mechanism of the action of vitamin B_{12} in animal nutrition, *Am. J. Clin. Nutrition,* **6**:34–49, 1958.

[86] Richard M. Smith and Kenneth J. Monty, Vitamin B_{12} and propionate metabolism, *Biochem. and Biophys. Research Communications,* August, 1959, pp. 105–109.

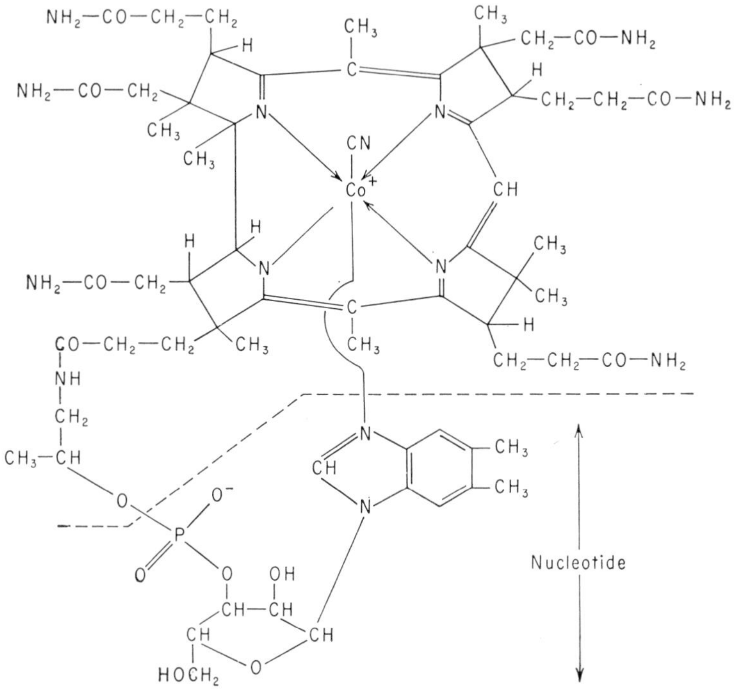

Vitamin B_{12} (cyanocobalamin) $C_{63}H_{88}O_{14}N_{14}PCo$

The formula* shows that the main part of this complex molecule has a cobalt atom in the center of a tetra-ring porphyrin structure. A cyanide group is attached to the cobalt atom, which is responsible for the name cyanocobalamin applied to vitamin B_{12}. It is noted that there is a nucleotide portion which is coordinated with the cobalt atom and joined to the ring structure through its phosphate group and amino-proponal. The cyanide group can be replaced by an hydroxyl group to form hydroxocobalamin, called B_{12a}. Similarly, replacement with a nitrite group produces nitrocobalamin, or B_{12c}. The three compounds, B_{12}, B_{12a}, and B_{12c}, referred to as the "cobalamins," are all active. In addition, several other compounds, referred to as "presudo" vitamins B_{12} or vitamin B_{12}-like factors, have been isolated or synthesized. *Coenzyme* B_{12} is a chemically modified form which is the functional form for certain reactions.

8.59. Requirements and Food Sources. For those species requiring a dietary source, the amounts needed are small compared with those of other vitamins. The N.R.C. requirements are stated as 0.004 mg. per pound of feed for chicks and 0.002 mg. for breeding hens. The requirements for a 10-pound pig are set at 0.01 mg., drop to 0.005 mg. at 50 pounds, and remain at this level for other weights including breeding

* Adapted from Hodkin et al., *Nature,* **178**:64–66, 1956.

stock. The needs of both species can be readily met by the inclusion of a part of the protein supplement as animal or fish by-products. Of course, the common practice of adding antibiotic feed supplements that contain fermentation residues to swine rations (Sec. 9.1) provides a liberal supply of vitamin B_{12} as well. Other feeds of plant origin are practically devoid of the vitamin. The occurrence in feed sources of a large number of B_{12}-like compounds with differing activities to different organisms and the fact that higher animals are very selective as to the form used make biological assays the methods of choice. Chicks and rats are the species commonly used. There are also microbiological methods.

OTHER VITAMINS OF THE B GROUP

8.60. Inositol. This compound occurs in plant products in the organic phosphorus substance phytin (Sec. 7.15). In the animal body it is a constituent of certain cephalins. It has the following formula:

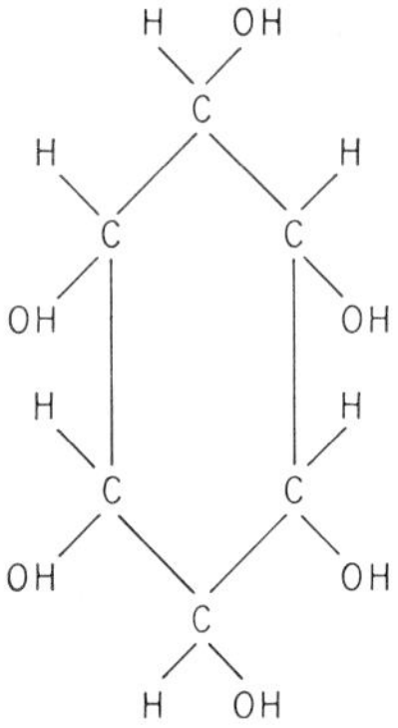

Inositol, $C_6H_{12}O_6$

In 1940 Woolley showed that inositol could prevent and cure a characteristic alopecia (deficient and patchy hair) in mice. Evidence for its usefulness otherwise is very limited despite much study. It has a lipotropic action in certain rat diets in which other vitamins may be deficient. Most workers feel that it is highly doubtful whether inositol is essential as such. It may merely be able to perform some of the functions of other vitamins. The symptoms of alopecia are very similar to those produced by a deficiency of B_6 or pantothenic acid. Relationships with biotin have also been established. Intestinal synthesis has been demonstrated. There is no evidence that inositol is needed in otherwise adequate rations of farm animals. Its occurrence in animal feeds is widespread, and thus commonly fed rations should supply it in abundance to meet any need which may exist.

8.61. Paraaminobenzoic Acid. This compound was originally discovered as a growth essential for microorganisms and later classed with the vitamins on the basis of its reported growth effects with chicks and lactation effects in rats. Clear evidence that it performs essential functions on otherwise complete rations is still lacking. It is an essential group in folic acid. Thus in a diet lacking in this vitamin paraaminobenzoic acid may provide intestinal bacteria with an essential building stone for folic acid synthesis. Because of its essentiality for the growth of certain microorganisms it may promote the synthesis of other B-factors in the intestine. In this connection it is interesting to note that paraaminobenzoic acid has the ability to reverse the bacteriostatic effects of sulfonamides. Here we have another example of antimetabolite action, explainable on the basis of similarity of structure:

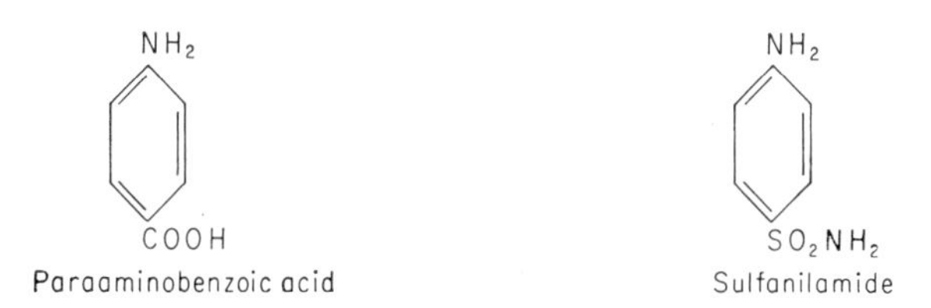

Paraaminobenzoic acid Sulfanilamide

8.62. Other Factors. At every stage of the development of our knowledge of vitamins certain factors have been under consideration which required further evidence as to their reality as new vitamins. Later some of them became established as new dietary essentials, while others were proved to be old factors in a new guise or scientific mistakes. So today we have a long list of factors which require more definite characterization. Some have been identified chemically, but no need by higher animals established. In the case of others, there is evidence of need by these animals but a lack of chemical characterization to prove that they are actually new factors.

Vitamin B_{13}, obtained from distiller's solubles, is a compound of unknown structure which appears to contain orotic acid (5-carboxyl-uracil) or yield it on decomposition. It has been found to stimulate the growth of rats, chicks, and pigs under certain conditions, but evidence remains uncertain whether it plays an essential role in an otherwise adequate diet.

Vitamin B_t is an essential growth factor for the meal worm, which has been identified as carnitine. It is widespread in vegetable and animal tissues, but there is no evidence for a dietary need by higher animals. *Lipoic acid* is a compound of known structure which occurs in living cells combined with thiamine and phosphate. It apparently is a nutritional requirement for the growth of certain microorganisms, but no such need for any animal species has been established.

It is evident that there are unidentified factors for chicks and poults, as indicated by impaired growth on purified diets containing all the known nutritive essentials, compared with the performance where certain special products or concentrates of them are added. Thus, we have such terms as "whey factor," "fish solubles factor," "grass juice factor," and others. None of them has been isolated and identified.

The literature contains many other names proposed by investigators to designate compounds considered to be new vitamins for one or more species. Thus, we have vitamin B_{14}, the vitamin T complex, L_1 and L_2 (lactation factors), the "hay factor," "grain factor," and others. While the information regarding some of them is more definite than for others, none are sufficiently well characterized at the present time to justify their discussion in a textbook dealing primarily with animal nutrition. Papers dealing with some of the factors mentioned in this section are listed at the end of the chapter.

VITAMIN C (ASCORBIC ACID)

Ascorbic acid is the vitamin that was designated as *water-soluble C*, or the *antiscorbutic factor*, about forty years ago. The metabolic need appears to be a general one among species, but a dietary need is limited to man, the guinea pig, and the monkey. The ability of the pig to meet its metabolic needs from birth to maturity by synthesis has been demonstrated by Braude and associates.[87]

8.63. Physiological Functions and Symptoms of Deficiency. The most clearly established functional roles of vitamin C are exhibited in connection with the formation and maintenance of intercellular material in the bones as well as in the soft tissues. A deficiency for this purpose results in the well-known symptoms of scurvy, such as swollen, bleeding, and ulcerated gums; loosening of teeth; weak bones; and fragility of the capillaries with resulting hemorrhages throughout the body. The widespread effects throughout the body of a deficiency of vitamin C reflects its basic role as a tissue catalyst, but the specific biochemical changes have only been partially characterized. It functions in hydroxylation reactions. Of special significance is its role in the formation of hydroxyproline, which is a constituent of collagen required for the maintenance of intercellular material. The vitamin has been ascribed a function in tyrosine metabolism and also in the conversion of folic acid to folinic acid.

There have been reports with rats and cattle that on vitamin A-deficient diets the ascorbic acid content of the tissues and blood plasma may be low and that a vitamin C deficiency may thus result in species not

[87] R. Braude, S. K. Kon, and J. W. G. Porter, Studies in the vitamin C metabolism of the pig, *Brit. J. Nutrition,* **4**:186–199, 1950.

normally having a dietary requirement. There is also much negative evidence, however, and thus claims for the practical importance of the positive findings remain to be established.

Ascorbic acid is stored to only a very limited extent in the body, and thus needs must be supplied regularly. The level in the plasma is a good measure of the current intake. The content in the white cells and platelets is an indicator of body stores. The urine excretion is used to measure the vitamin C status of the body and of its needs as indicated by the *saturation technique*. This technique is based on the fact that, when the body is depleted, an intake results first in storage and then in excretion. The intake which will keep the tissues saturated, as indicated by the urinary output, represents the maximum which can be considered of any value to the body. The determination of plasma or serum ascorbic acid is another method of estimating body status.

8.64. Chemistry of Vitamin C. Credit for the isolation of the compound we now call ascorbic acid is due to King of the United States and Szent-Györgyi of Hungary. The vitamin occurs in two forms, a reduced form that is readily oxidized to a dehydro form, as shown:

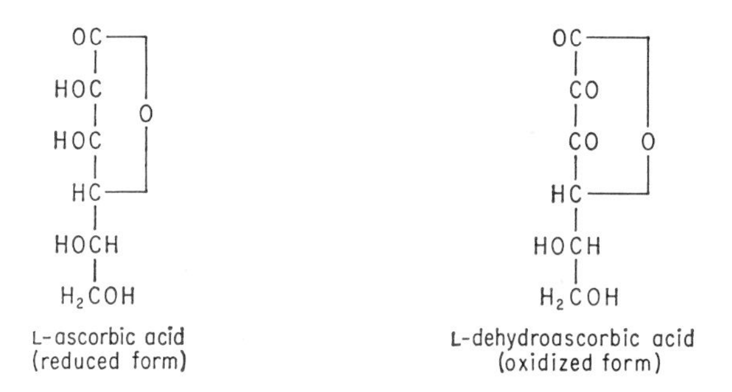

L-ascorbic acid (reduced form)

L-dehydroascorbic acid (oxidized form)

Both forms are biologically active. In foods the reduced form greatly predominates, but it may reversibly oxidize to the dehydro form. The latter can be further oxidized to diketogulonic acid, an inactive compound. This reaction is irreversible. This change takes place readily, and thus the vitamin is very susceptible to destruction through oxidation, a change that is accelerated by heat. The vitamin is more stable in an acid than an alkaline medium. It is not found in dried foods and is markedly destroyed by cooking, particularly where the pH is alkaline. Cooking losses also result because of its solubility. There are also losses in storage, particularly in certain foods.

Vitamin C is an antioxidant. This property is made use of in the addition of the vitamin in the canning of certain fruits to prevent oxidation changes which cause darkening. Glycoascorbic acid acts as an antimetabolite for vitamin C.

8.65. Vitamin C in Foods. The guinea pig assay provides the most reliable information as to the biological activity of sources of vitamin C, but it is a laborious and time-consuming procedure. Most of our knowledge of the ascorbic acid content of foods has been obtained by chemical methods, involving the reduction of the dye, 2,6-dichlorophenol-indophenol by the reduced form of vitamin C and measurement by titration or colorimetry. Special procedures are required where the oxidized form is also present. The vitamin C value of a food is commonly expressed in milligrams. One I.U. is the activity of 0.05 mg. of ascorbic acid. Citrus fruits, tomatoes, green leafy vegetables, potatoes, and certain other fruits and vegetables are the principal food sources. Milk is a substantial source as drawn, but much of the vitamin value is lost in pasteurization.

POLYPHENOLS (FLAVENOIDS)

In 1936 Szent-Györgyi announced that there is a substance in citrus fruits, different from vitamin C, which is essential to prevent fragility of the capillaries. The substance was designated as *vitamin P.* In the past twenty-five years several papers have shown that catechol, rutin, hesperidin, chalcone, and other nonspecific polyphenols, or flavenoids, which are widely distributed in fruits and vegetables can, under certain conditions, provide some protection against capillary fragility. There is evidence that some of these compounds may have some value as a supplement to limited C intake, particularly under conditions of stress. They have not been established as essential nutrients, however, and hence on the basis of present evidence none of them should be classed as a vitamin or confused with vitamin C. They have no known role in the nutrition of farm animals. The Joint Committee on Biochemical Nomenclature has recommended that the use of the term vitamin P be discontinued.

SELECTED LITERATURE

Vitamin A

Dowling, John E., and George Wald: Vitamin A deficiency and night blindness, *Proc. Natl. Acad. Sci.*, **44**:648–661, 1958.

Howell, C. E., G. H. Hart, and N. R. Ittner: Vitamin A deficiency in horses, *Am. J. Vet. Research,* **2**:60–74, 1941.

Hume, E. M., and H. A. Krebs: Vitamin A requirement of human adults: an experimental study of vitamin A deprivation in man, *Med. Research Council* (*Brit.*) *Spec. Rept. Ser.,* No. 264, 1949.

McGillivray, W. A., and N. A. Worker: The utilization of aqueous dispersions of carotene by rats and of carotene and vitamin A by lactating goats, *Brit. J. Nutrition,* **11**:47–56, 1957.

Vitamin D

Cramer, John W., et al.: A rachitogenic and growth-promoting effect of citrate, *Arch. Biochem. Biophys.*, **60**:58–63, 1956.

Hendricks, Jeannette B., Agnes Fay Morgan, and Ruth M. Freytag: Chronic moderate hypervitaminosis D in young dogs, *Am. J. Physiol.*, **149**:319–332, 1947.

Keener, H. A.: The effect of various factors on the vitamin D content of several common forages, *J. Dairy Sci.*, **37**:1337–1345, 1954.

Vitamin E

Bratzler, J. W., and associates: Effect of the dietary level of tocopherols on their metabolism in swine, *J. Nutrition*, **42**:59–69, 1950.

Draper, H. H., et al.: A study of the nutritional role of anti-oxidants in the diet of the rat, *Brit. J. Nutrition*, **12**:89–96, 1958.

Lalor, R. J., W. L. Leoschke, and C. A. Elvehjem: Yellow fat in the mink, *J. Nutrition*, **45**:183–188, 1951.

Maplesden, D. C., J. D. Harvey, and H. R. Brandon: Blood plasma tocopherol levels in a herd of beef cattle, *J. Nutrition*, **71**:77–84, 1960.

Maplesden, D. C., and J. K. Loosli: Nutritional muscular dystrophy in calves. II. Addition of selenium and tocopherol to a basal dystrophogenic diet containing cod-liver oil, *J. Dairy Sci.*, **43**:645–653, 1960.

Sturkie, P. D., and associates: The effects of dietary deficiencies of vitamin E and the B-complex vitamins on the electrocardiogram of chickens, *Am. J. Vet. Research*, **15**:457–462, 1954.

Thiamine

Draper, Harold H., and B. Connor Johnson: Thiamine deficiency in the lamb, *J. Nutrition*, **43**:413–422, 1951.

Hegsted, D. Mark, and Gwelda S. McPhee: The thiamine requirements of the adult rat and the influence on it of a low environmental temperature, *J. Nutrition*, **41**:127–136, 1950.

Miller, E. R., et al.: The thiamine requirement of the baby pig, *J. Nutrition*, **56**:423–430, 1955.

Miller, R. C., and associates: The influence of the thiamine intake of the pig on the thiamine content of pork with observations on the riboflavin content of pork, *J. Nutrition*, **26**:261–274, 1943.

Phillipson, A. T., and R. S. Reed: Thiamine in the contents of the alimentary tract of sheep, *Brit. J. Nutrition*, **11**:27–41, 1957.

Yudkin, Warren H.: Thiaminase, the Chastek-paralysis factor, *Physiol. Revs.*, **29**:389–402, 1949.

Riboflavin

Bessey, Otto A., et al.: The riboflavin economy of the rat, *J. Nutrition*, **64**:185–202, 1958.

Draper, Harold H., and associates: The riboflavin requirement of the Holstein calf, *J. Nutrition*, **46**:37–44, 1952.

Horwitt, M. K., and associates: Correlation of urinary excretion of riboflavin with dietary intake and symptoms of ariboflavinosis, *J. Nutrition*, **41**:247–264, 1950.

Mitchell, H. H., and associates: The riboflavin requirement of the growing pig at two environmental temperatures, *J. Nutrition,* **41**:317–337, 1950.

Nicotinamide

Anderson, J. O., and associates: Effect on chick growth of amino acid imbalances in diets containing low and adequate levels of niacin and pyridoxine, *J. Nutrition,* **45**:345–360, 1951.
Anonymous: Lime-treated corn, *Nutrition Revs.,* **18**:183–185, 1960.
Birch, Thomas William, Harriette Chick, and Charles James Martin: Experiments with pigs on a pellagra-producing diet, *Biochem. J.,* **31**:2065–2079, 1937.
Fisher, H., H. M. Scott, and B. Connor Johnson: Quantitative aspect of the nicotinic acid-tryptophan interrelationship in the chick, *Brit. J. Nutrition,* **9**:340–349, 1955.

Vitamin B_6

Desikachar, H. S. R., and associates: Effects of vitamin B_6 deficiency on fat metabolism in rats, *Biochem. J.,* **56**:544–546, 1954.
Follis, Richard H., Jr., and Maxwell M. Wintrobe: A comparison of the effects of pyridoxine and pantothenic acid deficiencies on the nervous tissues of swine, *J. Exptl. Med.,* **81**:539–552, 1945.
Ritchie, H. D., et al.: Supplementation of the swine gestation diet with pyridoxine, *J. Nutrition,* **70**:491–496, 1960.

Pantothenic Acid

Krehl, W. A.: Pantothenic acid in nutrition, *Nutrition Revs.,* **11**:225–228, 1953.
Luecke, R. W., W. N. McMillen, and F. Thorp, Jr.: Further studies of pantothenic acid deficiency in weanling pigs, *J. Animal Sci.,* **9**:78–82, 1950.
Sheppard, A. J., and B. Connor Johnson: Pantothenic acid deficiency in the growing calf, *J. Nutrition,* **61**:195–205, 1957.
Ullrey, D. E., et al.: Dietary levels of pantothenic acid and reproductive performance of female swine, *J. Nutrition,* **57**:401–414, 1955.

Folic Acid

Baumann, C. A.: Citrovorum factor: Nutritional aspects, associations with leukemia and anemia, *J. Am. Dietet. Assoc.,* **29**:548–554, 1953.
Cartwright, George E., and associates: Pteroylglutamic acid deficiency in swine; effects of treatment with pteroylglutamic acid, liver extract, and protein, *J. Lab. Clin. Med.,* **33**:397–416, 1948.
Young, R. J., and associates: The chick's requirement for folic acid in the utilization of choline and its precursors betaine and methylamino-ethanol, *J. Nutrition,* **55**:353–362, 1955.

Vitamin B_{12}

Anonymous: Biological life of vitamin B_{12}, *Nutrition Revs.,* **16**:325–326, 1958.
Fox, M. R. Spivey, G. M. Briggs, and L. O. Ortiz: Nutrients affecting vitamin B_{12} requirements in chicks, *J. Nutrition,* **62**:539–549, 1957.

Kon, S. K.: Other factors related to vitamin B_{12}, *Biochem. Soc. Symposia,* **13**:17–35, 1955.

Richardson, L. R., and L. G. Blaylock: Vitamin B_{12} and amino acids as supplements to soybean oil meal and cottonseed meal for growing chicks, *J. Nutrition,* **40**: 169–176, 1950.

Robison, W. L.: Vitamin B-12 supplements for growing and fattening pigs, *Ohio Agr. Expt. Sta. Research Bull.* 729, 1953.

Biotin

Barnes, Richard H., Eva Kwong, and Grace Fiala: Effects of preventing coprography in the rat. IV. Biotin, *J. Nutrition,* **67**:599–610, 1959.

Lardy, Henry A., and Robert Peanasky: Metabolic functions of biotin, *Physiol. Revs.,* **33**:560–565, 1953.

Ascorbic Acid

Anonymous: Biological synthesis of ascorbic acid, *Nutrition Revs.,* **12**:215–217, 1954.

Eaton, H. D., and associates: Blood levels of ascorbic acid and vitamin A during vitamin A depletion and effect of administration of ascorbic acid during terminal vitamin A depletion in the dairy cow, *J. Dairy Sci.,* **35**:607–614, 1952.

Galloway, Nancy M., R. C. Garry, and A. D. Hitchin: Ascorbic acid and epithelial regeneration, *Brit. J. Nutrition,* **2**:228–232, 1948.

King, Charles Glen: Vitamin C, *J. Am. Med. Assoc.,* **142**:563–565, 1950.

Moore, L. A.: Vitamin A, ascorbic acid and spinal fluid pressure relationships in the young bovine, *J. Nutrition,* **31**:229–236, 1946.

Weir, W. C., and associates: The effect of a low carotene winter ration on the blood, milk, and liver concentrations of vitamins A and C of ewes and their lambs, *J. Animal Sci.,* **8**:381–391, 1949.

Miscellaneous and General Papers, "Alleged" Vitamins

Ambrose, Anthony M., and Floyd DeEds: The value of rutin and quercetin in scurvy, *J. Nutrition,* **38**:305–317, 1949.

Anonymous: Lipoic acid in animal nutrition, *Nutrition Revs.,* **15**:109–111, 1957.

Anonymous: Physiological roles of carnitine, *Nutrition Revs.,* **16**:214–215, 1958.

Dam, Richard, A. B. Morrison, and L. C. Norris: Studies of unidentified chick growth factors apparently organic in nature, *J. Nutrition,* **69**:277–282, 1959.

Fisher, H., H. M. Scott, and R. G. Hansen: Further studies on the alfalfa factor and its relation to the liver and whey factors, *J. Nutrition,* **52**:13–24, 1954.

Jacobs, R., and associates: An unidentified chick-growth factor found in litter, *J. Nutrition,* **54**:417–426, 1954.

Kon, S. K., and J. W. G. Porter: The intestinal synthesis of vitamins in the ruminant, in Vitamins and Hormones, Academic Press, Inc., New York, 1954, chap. 12, pp. 53–68.

Schreiber, Manuel, and Conrad Arnold Elvehjem: The influence of flavonoid compounds on the nasal excretion of a red pigment by rats subjected to stress conditions, *J. Nutrition,* **54**:257–270, 1954.

Snell, Esmond E.: Metabolic significance of B-vitamins: a symposium, *Physiol. Revs.,* **33**:509–565, 1953.

Wiesner, B. P., and John Yudkin: An unidentified factor in liver required for reproduction in rats, *Brit. J. Nutrition,* **12**:138–146, 1957.

Chapter 9
Antibiotics, Hormones, and Other Growth-stimulating Substances

The constant effort to produce human foods from animal sources at lower cost to the consumer has spearheaded a continuing search for more suitable combinations of known nutrients and for new chemical substances, with the hope of increasing the efficiency and rate of growth and production. These widespread efforts have led to the present use of antibiotics, hormones, and other chemicals in animal feeds. Thus, while these materials are not nutrients and cannot be considered as dietary essentials, nutritionists must be aware of their effects on animals, since they are widely used in animal diets.

ANTIBIOTICS

The term *antibiotic* means against life, or destructive of life. An antibiotic is a compound synthesized by a living organism which inhibits the growth of another. Realization that antibiotics would stimulate the growth rate of young pigs and chicks fed diets containing only vegetable proteins came largely from the reports in 1949 by Stokstad and associates of the American Cyanimid Co., Cunha and associates at the University of Florida, and McGinnis and associates at Washington State University, although an earlier paper by Moore and associates at Wisconsin had produced evidence that antibiotics improved the growth of chicks. The earliest studies with vitamin B_{12} used crude sources of the vitamin obtained as by-products of fermentations from the production of antibiotics. These residues were shown to have animal protein factor (APF) activity for chicks and pigs fed all vegetable diets (Sec. 8.56). As vitamin B_{12} became available in quantities suitable for farm-animal research, it was shown that fermentation residues gave greater growth responses than the pure vitamin. Stokstad and Jukes[1] demonstrated that the increased response resulted from the chlortetracycline in the fermentation residue. After the early reports that chlortetracycline (aureomycin), would increase the growth rates of chicks and pigs, it was soon found that oxytetracycline (terramycin) and penicillin also stimulated the growth of these animals. Studies at several research stations, as reviewed by Reid and associates,[2] demonstrated that chlortetracycline and oxytetracycline increased the growth rate of calves and lambs but that penicillin was not effective. Bacitracin, streptomycin, and certain others have given less consistent growth stimulation or none at all. The size of the response to antibiotics is highly variable, and sometimes the response disappears entirely for reasons yet unknown.

The great importance of antibiotics in animal feeding as well as in medicine spurred the search for others having different or more specific properties. Of the many that have been discovered more than 20 have been tested in livestock feeds, but not all of them are effective in increasing the growth rate of animals.

9.1. Growth Responses of Animals. There is evidence that certain antibiotics, added to good practical rations, as well as inadequate ones, improve the early growth of chicks, turkey poults, pigs, rats, dogs, lambs, and calves, under most conditions, but not always. There seems to be less response with ducks. The total feed consumed each day is usually increased with antibiotic feeding, and the amount of feed required for a pound of gain is often smaller. The mature body size is not increased. The most commonly reported effect is a more uniform growth response of the animals or birds. Fewer unthrifty, slow-growing individuals occur in the experimental groups, and thus the average rate of gain is increased. There is usually little or no improvement in the performance of the more rapidly growing animals.

In poultry, swine, lambs, and calves produced for meat purposes, the effective antibiotics increase the rate of growth, reduce the feed used to make a unit of gain, decrease the time needed to finish animals for market, and perhaps also lower the death loss of animals during the growing period. Thus, the general use of the effective antibiotics for meat animals increases the return to the producer and lowers the cost of meat products to the consumer.

Heuser[3] has reviewed the research on antibiotics and other feed

[1] E. L. R. Stokstad and T. H. Jukes, Further observations on the "animal protein factor," *Proc. Soc. Exptl. Biol. Med.*, **73**:523–528, 1950.

[2] J. T. Reid, R. G. Warner, and J. K. Loosli, Antibiotics in the nutrition of ruminants, *J. Agr. Food Chem.*, **2**:186–192, 1954.

[3] G. F. Heuser, An evaluation of antibiotics, arsenicals, nitrofurans and surfactants in poultry nutrition, *Proc. Cornell Nutrition Conf.*, 1957, pp. 123–125.

additives for poultry and turkeys. In almost all comparisons young chicks and turkey poults grew faster when antibiotics were added to the feed than on the unsupplemented feeds. The kind of results obtained with swine from feeding antibiotics can be illustrated by the report of Hanson and associates[4] who observed increases in the rate of gain from the addition of 10 g. per ton of feed of chlortetracycline, oxytetracycline, or procaine penicillin when the basal ration contained dry-rendered tankage. There was no significant influence on the amount of feed required to make a unit of gain, in contrast to some of the other studies cited. Withdrawal of the antibiotics when the pigs reached 125 lb. in body weight depressed the rate of gain in comparison with those that received antibiotics until slaughter. In these tests the percentages of moisture, crude protein, and fat in the carcasses were not affected by the antibiotics, but the percentage of ash was significantly decreased.

In other studies with growing-fattening swine, using rations made up of corn, soybean oil meal, alfalfa meal, minerals, and vitamins, antibiotics have decreased the amount of feed per unit of gain along with increasing the average daily gain. At times antibiotic feeding has resulted in increased dressing percentages, thicker back fat, greater fat percentages, and lower carcass grades, such as observed by Wallace and associates.[5] Relatively few carcass analyses have been made to study the question of degree of fatness, but it appears that this is not an important problem from the standpoint of practical swine production if the ingredients of the ration are properly balanced, the fattening period is not too long, and the leaner breeds of pigs are produced.

Studies have shown that baby pigs or those weaned at an early age respond to supplements of oleandomycin, tylosin, spiramycin, and virginiamycin, at least during the early phases of the growth period. The amounts of antibiotics usually incorporated into rations for chicks, poults, and swine are about 5 to 10 g. per ton of feed. Usually 20 to 30 g. or more per ton is used in milk replacers and grain mixtures for dairy calves.

Studies with growing-finishing beef cattle have given more variable results than those with calves. Considering all the evidence, it has been estimated that one can expect about a 4 per cent faster gain on about 3 per cent less feed per unit of gain. This small advantage is enough to favor the use of chlortetracycline and oxytetracycline in commercial feed lots. Responses are more frequently seen when a high "disease level" exists. Feed-lot trials with growing-finishing lambs have given even more variable results than those with cattle, although some favorable results

[4] L. E. Hanson and associates, Growth and carcass characteristics of pigs fed antibiotics for part or all of the growing-fattening period, *J. Animal Sci.*, **14**:30–42, 1955.

[5] H. D. Wallace and associates, The influence of aureomycin on the protein requirement and carcass characteristics of swine, *J. Animal Sci.*, **13**:177–183, 1954.

have been reported. There is yet no established place for antibiotics with this species.

For calves chlortetracycline and oxytetracycline have proved of greatest value. Streptomycin has shown an effect in reducing scours, but little or no growth stimulation occurs. Penicillin generally has failed to give a response and, in some instances, appears to have had a depressing effect upon the rate of gain. In early tests bacitracin alone or in combination with penicillin was not beneficial, but zinc bacitracin, a more stable form, has stimulated growth in later comparisons. Other antibiotics have generally been ineffective for calves. The system of feeding appears to influence the responses. At times there is no increased gain when calves receive liberal amounts of whole milk, whereas on limited milk intakes or milk replacers there is a faster average growth rate and more gain per unit of feed consumed. The responses are greater when the untreated animals exhibit diarrhea or digestive disturbances, and the ability to help reduce the incidence and severity of scours is one of the advantages of antibiotic feeding. This appears to be true for beef and dairy calves alike.

The data available suggest that a large proportion of the improved gain is of muscle and fat rather than of skeleton, although studies at Louisiana report increased skeletal growth in calves. It seems, therefore, that the importance of antibiotics in the nutrition of calves depends on the ultimate disposition of the animals. Control calves given no antibiotics attain the same mature size as those fed antibiotics. Most results agree in showing that, when antibiotics are removed from the rations at 2 to 4 months of age, calves gain more slowly than their controls during a few weeks adjustment period. The use of antibiotics for heifer calves being reared as milking cows may be helpful in preventing scours and decreasing death loss, but the increase in early rate of gain is of no permanent importance, since compensation in growth occurs later and there is no evidence of improvement in mature size, productive ability, or useful life of the animals.

Results differ on the influence of antibiotics for beef cattle. Although growth responses have been reported with suckling beef calves, the problem of administration often makes the procedure impractical. Antibiotic feeding has resulted in only slightly faster weight gains and greater gain per unit of feed with growing or fattening beef cattle. In fattening operations chlortetracycline and oxytetracycline help prevent foot rot, shipping fever complex (respiratory infections), and liver abscesses, or reduce the severity of these diseases when they occur.

Colby and associates at Texas reported that feeding 100 mg. of chlortetracycline daily by capsule to fattening lambs caused feed refusal and weight loss. Later tests gave similar results with penicillin and streptomycin. Various workers have shown that daily intakes of 5 to 20 mg. of chlortetracycline to suckling or fattening lambs have not produced the harmful effects observed with larger intakes. In later experiments, such as that of Bohman, Hunter, and Walker,[6] there has been no significant influence on the amounts of feed consumed, the rates of gain, or the amounts of feed required to produce a unit of gain, but lambs receiving 10 mg. of chlortetracycline per pound of concentrates have gained slightly faster than the controls in some trials. There are about as many studies in which antibiotics have failed to increase the rate of gain of lambs as there are that show favorable results. Attempts to reduce the death loss of newborn lambs and to increase their growth by injecting or implanting antibiotics have been unsuccessful.

9.2. Other Effects of Antibiotics. Antibiotics have been shown to be helpful in controlling certain disease problems. One of the favorable influences of feeding chlortetracycline and oxytetracycline is the reduced incidence and severity of scours in calves and weanling pigs. Especially in calves, scours is an important problem which leads to unthriftiness, secondary infections, and death loss. While antiobiotics greatly reduce the frequency and duration of the problem, they do not prevent all scours, and they cannot be expected to replace sanitary practices and proper nutrition and management.

The use of high levels of antibiotics, 100 to 200 g. per ton of feed, for short periods for poultry flocks having certain chronic infections, such as respiratory diseases, appears to stimulate recovery and bring the birds back into efficient growth or egg production sooner than otherwise possible. The interrelationship between optimum nutrition and resistance to disease is a vast field which is receiving wide attention by workers in nutrition and in veterinary and human medicine. Boyd and associates[7] found that feeding 1000 g. per ton of feed of chlortetracycline and oxytetracycline to broilers and laying hens resulted in storage of antibiotic in the serum, liver, and meat. Adding 0.05 per cent of terephthalic acid doubled the tisue levels and resulted in longer keeping time for cut-up parts of chicken held at 35°F. Low-calcium diets along with high antibiotic levels further increased tissue storage.

Most of the controlled studies by experiment stations show that feeding antibiotics to milking cows does not increase milk yield. There are, however, some tests in which fairly large numbers of cows in commercial dairy herds apparently responded with more than enough extra milk to

[6] Verle R. Bohman, James E. Hunter, and LeGrand Walker, Antibiotics and B vitamins for lambs, *J. Animal Sci.*, **14**:111–117, 1955.

[7] Josephine Boyd, H. H. Weiser, and A. R. Winter, Influence of high level antibiotic rations with terephthalic acid on the antibiotic content and keeping quality of poultry meat, *Poultry Sci.*, **39**:1067–1071, 1960.

pay for the cost of the supplement. The view is presented that in these cases the chlortetracycline helped control foot rot and respiratory infections and that because of improved health the cows produced better. The question remains unsettled how frequently one might expect a favorable response in milk yield from antibiotic feeding. It is clear that low-level feeding (10 mg. per 100 lb. of body weight) is not an effective cure for foot rot, mastitis, or other specific infections. Cases of bloat and off-feed have been reported at the start of antibiotic feeding, but the cows adapt in a few days, and the problems disappear. At this level of intake the antibiotic does not appear in the milk; however, at five to ten times this dosage milk may contain appreciable antibiotic. Infusion of penicillin or other antibiotic into the udder to treat mastitis or intramuscular injections at levels effective in treating infections allow antibiotic transfer to the milk for two to three milkings. Such milk is used in feeding calves, where it is beneficial, rather than sold as human food, since allergic reactions may result in people sensitive to penicillin and such milk is unsuitable for cheese manufacture.

Considerable attention has been given to the question of whether residues will remain in the products when animals fed antibiotics are slaughtered for human food. Antibiotics could not be found in the meat of animals fed at growth-stimulating levels, but it could be detected when fed at ten times higher levels. At 200 p.p.m. in the diet traces were detected in the meat of pigs, and at 1000 p.p.m. most tissues contained detectable amounts. Withdrawal of the antibiotic from the diet for several days before slaughter allowed for clearance of the substance from the tissues. These studies make it seem evident that there is no risk to the user of animal products, especially since antibiotics in meat are destroyed on cooking.

9.3. Influence on Rumen Function and Digestibility. A number of laboratories have studied the rumen bacteria of cattle receiving antibiotics. Most of the results support the view that low levels of intake do not modify the normal development of rumen function in dairy calves and that they effect little or no change in the major types of microorganisms present in the rumen of either calves or older cattle. All reports, however, do not agree with this view. Some workers have found reductions in certain types of bacteria when low intakes of antibiotics were fed. Others have found increases in the total bacterial count of the rumen contents. There is no reliable evidence that the observed minor bacterial changes effected by low levels of antibiotics are either harmful or beneficial to the development of rumen function during the first four or five months of the calf's life.

Bell, Whitehair, and Gallup at Oklahoma reported that feeding 600 mg. of chlortetracycline per head daily caused beef steers to go off feed and develop scours. One-third of this level depressed the digestibility of the crude fiber and the retention of nitrogen. These animals had not previously received antibiotics. Horn, Snapp, and Gall[8] obtained similar depressions of digestibility. Feeding 100 mg. of antibiotic daily depressed the digestibility of protein and crude fiber by yearling Hereford steers. Using calves, research workers at Iowa and Vermont observed no difference in the digestibility of dry matter, protein, crude fiber, or nitrogen-free extract between controls and those fed antibiotics. The age of ruminants may be an important factor in determining the effects of antibiotics on digestion in the rumen. Feeding large amounts to cattle older than a year, or to sheep after six months of age and not previously accustomed to receiving antibiotics in the feed, may cause serious temporary off-feed and diarrhea and will lower the digestibility of the feed.

Chance and associates at Michigan State University removed the total rumen contents of steers at intervals after feeding to study the rate of passage of feed from the rumen and the concentration of various nutrients remaining. Feeding 500 mg. of chlortetracycline daily to two-year old steers receiving a ration of hay and corn grain resulted in a lowering of the concentration of the 10 essential amino acids in the rumen contents. This result was interpreted as indicating an increased rate of digestion of feed protein and passage of the amino acids from the rumen. Lower concentrations of riboflavin and niacin were also observed with antibiotic feeding.

Prescott[9] observed a reduction in the utilization of nonprotein nitrogen from the addition of antibiotics at the rate of 0.5 to 250 μg. per milliliter to rumen liquid using in vitro techniques. A similar lowering of the utilization of certain carbohydrates by rumen bacteria in vitro by added antibiotics has been observed. It appears likely that the levels used were higher than would occur in animals fed usual intakes of antibiotics, but these results suggest the need for animal studies using ruminants to test the utilization of urea, and perhaps other nutrients, when antibiotics are fed.

Antibiotics are helpful in preventing some types of bloat (Sec. 4.18) in ruminants, a condition, often fatal, in which the rumen is overdistended by gas produced by bacterial fermentation. Barrentine and associates[10] reported that feeding penicillin would protect cattle from bloat on ladino clover pastures. Later experience demonstrated that the protective

[8] L. H. Horn, R. R. Snapp, and L. S. Gall, The effect of antibiotics upon the digestibility of feed nutrients by yearling steers, with bacteriological data, *J. Animal Sci.*, **14**:243–248, 1955.

[9] J. M. Prescott, Rumen microorganisms—effects of diet and antibiotics on utilization of non-protein nitrogen, *J. Agr. Food Chem.*, **1**:894–896, 1953.

[10] B. F. Barrentine, C. B. Shawver, and L. W. Williams, Antibiotics for the prevention of bloat in cattle-grazing ladino clover, *J. Animal Sci.*, **15**:440–446, 1955.

action of penicillin disappeared after extended usage. Use of a combination of penicillin, erythromycin, and tylosin greatly extended the effectiveness of antibiotics in preventing bloat in grazing cattle, in studies by Johnson and associates at Iowa. Other antibiotics tested, either singly or in combination, were less effective. While it is thought that microfloral changes explained the bloat prevention, it is not at all clear how the antibiotics cause this effect.

9.4. Mode of Action of Antibiotics. The antibiotics are drugs, not nutrients, and thus their effects upon the nutrition of animals are of necessity secondary. The specific method by which antibiotics exert this influence has not been fully explained, although several theories have been proposed, each of which seems to fit some of the facts but not all of them. It now seems likely that there may be several possible ways in which antibiotics improve the growth responses of young animals. There is evidence both for and against the view that antibiotics "spare" protein, amino acids, and vitamins. A number of experiments have shown that feeding antibiotics permitted equal gains in pigs, chicks, and poults on diets containing 1 to 3 per cent less protein, but balance experiments have often failed to show that there is increased nitrogen retention.

Sauberlich reported with growing rats that antibiotics could replace part of the requirement of lysine, tryptophan, valine, and other essential amino acids. The mechanism of this amino acid sparing action is not known, but the results agree with earlier reports showing that the biological value of the dietary protein influences the response to antibiotics. Greater effects generally have been seen on diets containing protein exclusively from plant sources. It was thought that antibiotics may modify the intestinal bacteria in such a way as to favor synthesis of the essential amino acids in nonruminants. Such a mechanism seems unlikely since it has been shown with pigs and chickens that feeding antibiotics does not enhance the utilization of urea as a partial replacement for dietary protein.

Antibiotics may function by means of a selective action upon the microorganisms of the intestinal tract. This could occur by the control of transmissible agents, either pathogens or nonpathogens, which produce slightly harmful products and which accumulate in quarters where animals or birds are kept year after year, or by favoring the synthesis of nutrients. Support for this view is found in the observation that chicks housed in new quarters do not respond to antibiotics and uniformly make better growth without antibiotics than chicks in buildings used repeatedly.

Growth stimulation would also result if antibiotics favor intestinal bacteria which synthesize nutrients known or unknown, needed for maximum growth rates of young animals, or if they control microorganisms which compete with the host for vitamins, amino acids, or other nutrients or which reduce the availability of any nutrient. Clear evidence has been presented by Barnes and coworkers[11] that feeding penicillin to rats increases the amount of thiamine synthesized in the large intestine. The thiamine was not absorbed, however, and only when *coprophagy* was permitted was an increased growth rate observed in response to antibiotic feeding. Thus, in the rat the thiamine-sparing action of penicillin was abolished when coprophagy was prevented.

Visek and associates[12] have shown that feeding chlortetracycline decreased the amount of C^{14} urea split by the intestines. They proposed that antibiotics alter intestinal bacteria so that less urease is produced, and thus less ammonia is formed wherever body fluids containing urea contact bacterial urease. Ammonia is thought to be one of the toxins whose production is suppressed.

Rather conclusive evidence favoring the "disease level" theory is presented by the studies of Forbes and Park[13] using germfree chicks. On a corn-soybean meal diet chicks hatched and reared in the absence of bacteria and fungi grew 18 to 25 per cent faster than other chicks from the same hatch reared in the animal room. In the initial tests penicillin failed to elicit growth responses in either the germfree chicks or those raised in the animal room, which had not previously been used for chick rearing. When the diet was supplemented with 1 or 2 g. per kilogram of lyophilized intestinal contents from chicks reared in an animal room where growth responses to penicillin were regularly obtained, a growth response to penicillin resulted. In later studies responses to penicillin were always obtained even in the absence of lyophilized intestinal material, but the growth rate was never equal to that of germfree birds. Clearly, therefore, infection of the chicks in the animal room decreased the growth rate, and the decrease was partially overcome by penicillin. Other studies have shown that conventionally reared turkey poults respond to antibiotics but that germfree poults do not respond, although they gain as fast as those fed antibiotics. Furthermore, bacteria isolated from the feces of chlortetracycline-fed calves were more susceptible to *phagocytosis* than bacteria from controls.

It has been observed frequently in practice that animals receiving antibiotics consume more feed. The extra feed is often sufficient to explain fully the faster growth rate and also the fact that these animals make more gain in weight per unit of feed consumed because a higher

[11] R. H. Barnes, E. Kwong, K. Delany, and G. Fiala, The mechanism of the thiamine sparing effect of penicillin in rats, *J. Nutrition*, **71**:149–155, 1960.

[12] W. J. Visek, J. M. Baron, and D. M. Switz, Urea metabolism and intestinal ureolytic activity of rats fed antimicrobial agents, *J. Pharmacol. Exptl. Therap.*, **126**: 359–365, 1960.

[13] M. Forbes and J. T. Park, Growth of germ-free and conventional chicks: effect of diet, dietary penicillin and bacterial environment, *J. Nutrition*, **67**:69–84, 1959.

percentage of the total feed is available for growth. The evidence is not convincing that there is any general increase in the efficiency of feed utilization, since antibiotic-fed animals restricted to the same feed intake as the controls usually have not gained faster. Some studies have reported thinner intestinal walls in animals fed antibiotics, suggesting that more efficient absorption of nutrients may occur, but all workers have not been able to confirm this observation. Furthermore, balance studies with animals have not demonstrated that antibiotics uniformly improve digestion, absorption, or retention of nutrients. Black and Bratzler[14] found little improvement in energy or nitrogen utilization from antibiotics when adequate diets were fed.

HORMONES AND OTHER FEED ADDITIVES

Various drugs, many kinds of chemicals, and countless special fermentation products are being sold for use with farm animals with the claim that they will stimulate growth or in some manner improve the health or performance of the animal. Some of these claims are justified, but others are not supported by scientific evidence. In fact, many chemicals used on farms are clearly toxic if improperly used. The animal husbandman must guard his animals against possible harm from exposure to chemical fertilizers, insect sprays, and similar chemicals which are commonly used. These latter materials cannot be discussed in detail here, but the student is advised to become familiar with their potential dangers so losses can be avoided.

Certain hormones have proved effective as growth stimulators. Other compounds may increase the rate of growth of animals under some conditions. The literature in this field has been comprehensively and critically reviewed by Casida and associates.[15]

9.5. Thyroprotein and Goitrogens. The role of thyroxine in controlling growth and metabolism has led investigators to use thyroid-active materials to stimulate growth of body tissue and wool and secretion of milk by creating a mild hyperthyroidal state. Thyroxine or thyroprotein (iodinated casein) will increase the growth rate of young pigs and calves under some conditions. Results with broilers have been variable. In dairy cows, feeding thyroprotein usually increases milk yields (Sec. 16.3), but there are some important disadvantages to its use. Attempts to increase weaning weights of beef calves, lambs, and pigs have met with

[14] A. Black and J. W. Bratzler, The effects of a vitamin B_{12} supplement, vitamin B_{12} and streptomycin on the metabolism of the rat, *J. Nutrition*, **47**:159–176, 1952.

[15] L. E. Casida and associates, Hormonal relationships and applications in the production of meats, milk and eggs, *Natl. Acad. Sci. Natl. Research Council Publ.* 714, 1959, pp. 53.

only variable success. Thyroprotein has been reported to increase wool growth. In spite of its potential values, thyroprotein is used only to a very limited extent because of the difficulty of regulating the dosage and the uncertain responses obtained.

The goitrogens (Sec. 7.38), which interfere with thyroxine production by the thyroid gland, all depress growth, and they often will increase the rate of fattening. The antithyroid material, thiouracil, increases the fattening rate of pigs. If the dose is too high or if it is fed too long, growth rate and feed efficiency are markedly reduced, and because of these problems little use has been made of this goitrogen in pig feeding. In poultry, especially in combination with diethylstilbestrol, thiouracil improves finish and market quality without depressing growth rate. Goitrogens have been of little value in growing-finishing lambs. Studies at Iowa with growing-finishing beef cattle showed improved performance when methimazole (Tapazole) was fed in combination with stilbestrol, but other stations have found less favorable results. Thyroid-regulating substances seem to have little practical importance in livestock feeding.

9.6. Growth Stimulation from Hormones. Extensive use is being made of synthetic and purified estrogens, androgens, progestogens, and growth hormones to stimulate the growth and fattening of meat-producing animals. Some of these have given important increases in the rate and efficiency of gain or in the quality of the food products that result. There is concern, however, about possible harmful effects of any residues of these materials in the meat. Evidence that traces of estrogenic activity remain in the meat of cockerels implanted with diethylstilbestrol, a practice which had been used for a number of years to improve carcass finish and quality, has led to discontinuation of such implants. There is no general agreement among scientists, however, that the amounts of estrogens found in meat following diethylstilbestrol implants might prove harmful. Many widely used natural foods, including soybeans, contain higher estrogenic activity than found in animal tissues (Sec. 9.7).

Using rat-assay methods, Stob and associates[16] estimated that beef muscle and liver from implanted animals contained not more than 1 μg. of hormone per 100 g. of dried tissue and that lambs and chickens may contain 10 times that level. Davey and associates[17] found no measurable estrogenic activity when the stilbestrol intake was reduced from 5 to 1 mg. per day the last 50 days of the feeding period. Higher doses resulted in significant traces of activity in the body fat of the lambs.

[16] M. Stob and associates, Estrogenic activity of the meat of cattle, sheep and poultry following treatment with synthetic estrogens and progesterone, *J. Animal Sci.*, **13**:138–151, 1954.

[17] R. J. Davey, D. T. Armstrong, and W. Hansel, Studies on the use of hormones in lamb-feeding. II. Tissue assays and physiological effects, *J. Animal Sci.*, **18**:75–84, 1959.

Especially with growing ruminants there is wide use of hormonal preparations to increase performance, but these materials have not increased the growth of pigs, as shown by the work of Thrasher and associates.[18] In cattle and lambs, growth stimulation occurs when the synthetic estrogen, diethylstilbestrol, sometimes called stilbestrol, is implanted, and less feed is required to make a unit of gain. Implants of 24 to 36 mg. for steers increase the rate of gain and decrease the feed required per unit of gain, but lower the carcass grade and reduce somewhat the amount of marbling in cattle. Undesirable side effects were noted in some of the animals given larger implants of 60 to 120 mg., such as mammary development in steers and wethers, pelvic changes in cattle, vaginal and rectal prolapse, difficult urination, and changes in the organs of the urogenital system of lambs.

Burroughs and associates[19] reported that feeding stilbestrol to fattening steers increased the rate of gain and decreased the feed needed to make a unit of gain. These findings have been confirmed by several groups of workers. Feeding 10 mg. of stilbestrol daily resulted in approximately 12 per cent faster gains and 10 per cent less feed to make a unit of gain. It is interesting that the greatest growth stimulation in some trials occurred at the start of the study and seemed to disappear toward the end. The pelvic and mammary changes noted have been less marked than with hormone implantation. Carcass grades of the animals fed hormones appear to be slightly lower than the control steers.

There was no residual hormone in the meat on the basis of the assays used, in contrast to implanted animals.

Studies with fattening lambs have shown that feeding 2 to 5 mg. of stilbestrol daily increased the average daily gain approximately 20 per cent and reduced the feed per unit of gain. Carcass grades in some trials were lower, especially on higher intakes of estrogen.

It has been well established that androgens, such as testosterone and some of its derivatives, stimulate protein anabolism in cattle and some other animals by reducing urinary nitrogen excretion. Females show a greater response to androgens than males, which might be expected since males normally make more rapid and efficient gains than females. Testosterone-implanted swine and cattle have shown no consistent increase in weight gain or feed efficiency. Fattening lambs have responded in some trials but not in others. If suitable dosages and methods of application can be worked out to give uniform responses and if tissue residues are not a problem, testosterone might prove helpful in increas-

[18] G. W. Thrasher and associates, The effect of estrogenic and androgenic compounds upon growth and carcass composition of swine, *J. Animal Sci.*, **18**:399–409, 1959.

[19] W. Burroughs and associates, The effects of trace amounts of diethylstilbestrol in rations of fattening steers, *Science*, **120**:66–67, 1954.

ing protein formation. Problems still exist in the practical applications. In pregnant cattle testosterone crosses the placenta and causes anatomical alterations in female calves more drastic than those seen in freemartins.

Implantations of pellets of dienestrol and estradiol in combination with progesterone have increased the rate of gain of lambs. In some trials implanting dienestrol, hexestrol, or a combination of estradiol and progesterone has produced growth responses in fattening cattle. Feeding dienestrol and hexestrol has also been reported to increase gains of cattle, but there is a question whether they are as effective as diethylstilbestrol.

Optimal amounts of oral dosage or implantation of various hormonal compounds as reported by the National Research Council Committee are summarized in Table 9.1.

TABLE 9.1. HORMONAL COMPOUNDS USED IN ANIMAL PRODUCTION*

Products	Animals	Dosages	Method of use
Diethylstilbestrol	Cattle	10 mg./day	In feed
	Sheep	2 mg./day	
	Cattle	24 to 36 mg.	Subcutaneous
	Poultry	12 to 15 mg.	
Diethylstilbestrol plus testosterone	Cattle	24 mg. plus 120 mg.	Subcutaneous
Testosterone propionate plus estradiol benzoate	Heifers	200 mg. plus 20 mg.	Subcutaneous
Progesterone plus estradiol benzoate	Steers	1.0 g. plus 20 mg.	Subcutaneous
	Lambs	25 mg. plus 2.5 mg.	
Dienestrol diacetate	Poultry	0.002–0.007% of diet	In feed
Thiouracil	Swine and poultry	0.2% of diet	In feed
Iodinated casein (thyroprotein)	Lactating cows	15 g./day	In feed
	Lactating sows	200 mg./kg. diet	

* Modified after *Natl. Acad. Sci. Natl. Research Council Publ.* 714, 1959. Feed-usage laws change from time to time, and the scientist and animal producer must keep informed of the legal problems involved in the use of the various products.

The mechanism by which estrogens induce increases in body weight has not been established. It seems that growth stimulation occurs in ruminants but not in nonruminant animals, although these same compounds exert growth inhibition in rats, and this has been explained as owing to a difference in pituitary-growth hormone. Glandular alteration may be involved as suggested by Clegg and Cole[20] who reported

[20] M. T. Clegg and H. H. Cole, The action of stilbestrol on the growth response in ruminants, *J. Animal Sci.*, 13:108–130, 1954.

that estrogen-implanted animals all had larger pituitary and adrenal glands than controls. The anterior pituitary glands of stilbestrol-treated heifers had about twice the amount of growth hormone as in control animals. These workers also found increased nitrogen retention but no change in the amount digested. Similar results were noted by Whitehair and associates at Oklahoma who also noted increased retention of calcium and phosphorus. The finding of Brooks and associates at the University of Missouri that certain steroids increased nitrogen and cellulose utilization by rumen bacteria using artificial cultural techniques suggests the desirability of metabolism studies with ruminants receiving estrogen treatment.

9.7. Estrogenic Activity of Feeds. One of the hormones concerned in the completion of the estrous cycle and in the maintenance of pregnancy is an estrogen produced by the developing follicles. Following observations that ewes grazing on subterranean clover showed impaired fertility, evidence was obtained that an estrogen present in the grass was responsible. There were morphological changes in the animals indicative of excessive estrogen levels. These findings, reported by Curnow and his associates in Australia,[21] have been confirmed by workers in England and the United States who have shown that subterranean clover and red clover contain genistein and biochanin A, isoflavones having estrogenic activity. A number of other leguminous feeds in the United States have been shown to have activity, as reviewed by Andrews.[22] While serious disturbances in reproductive functions have not been reported on these feeds, it is possible that unrecognized problems exist.

9.8. Other Feed Additives. Arsenic compounds are widely used as an aid in prevention of blackhead in turkeys and coccidiosis in chickens. They are also helpful in stimulating growth of chicks and pigs similar to the antibiotics, but dairy calves have not shown responses. The results are often more favorable under stress conditions or when chicks and pigs are somewhat unthrifty or exposed to a low "disease level." When conditions are ideal, healthy animals may show no growth response and no improvement in feed efficiency, but such conditions are seldom found in practice. Of the organic arsenicals available, arsanilic acid and 3-nitro-4-hydroxyphenylarsonic acid have been most widely studied for growing chicks and pigs. Levels of 0.002 to 0.009 per cent of the complete feed are usually recommended. Arsenic compounds are

[21] D. H. Curnow, T. J. Robinson, and E. J. Underwood, Estrogenic action of extracts of subterranean clover, *Australian J. Exptl. Biol. Med. Sci.*, **26**:171–180, 1948.

[22] F. N. Andrews, Hormonal relationships to nutrition in domestic animals, in Reproductive Physiology and Protein Nutrition, Rutgers University Press, New Brunswick, N.J., 1959, pp. 45–57.

toxic, and feed manufacturers take special care not to exceed the limits set by law. When birds or pigs are removed from the arsenic-containing feeds a few days before slaughter, residues do not occur in the meat.

The addition of *enzymes* to high-barley rations has increased growth rates and feed utilization by poultry in some of the Western states but not in other regions of the United States. Results with other animals have been less favorable. Physiological studies with young pigs and calves suggest that some of the digestive enzymes may be lacking or not produced in adequate amounts for efficient digestion of certain raw plant products during the first 2 or 3 weeks of life. Attempts to correct these apparent inadequacies by adding various enzymes to the feed of young pigs and calves have met with little success. Studies at Iowa with baby pigs gave small growth responses in some trials but not in others. Results in Canada were largely negative. Combs and associates[23] have reviewed these various tests and reported their own findings that diastase, pepsin, or pancreatin did not increase the performance of baby pigs.

While only negative results have been obtained with dairy calves, Burroughs and associates at Iowa reported that growing-fattening cattle gained 7 per cent faster on equal feed intakes when a crude enzyme mixture was added to the feed. Digestibility of the feed was not affected. Less extensive tests at other stations have not confirmed the results, and the true role of added enzymes in livestock feeding remains undefined.

Live yeast cultures are available as an additive for cattle feeds, and they are used to a limited extent. Controlled studies at several experiment stations show they do not increase rate of gain, milk yields, or the efficiency of feed utilization as claimed.

Dried rumen cultures, which are sold with the claim that they stimulate rumen development in calves and improve feed utilization in older ruminants, have given negative results. Earlier studies at the Ohio station had demonstrated that the inoculation of young calves with fresh-cud material resulted in earlier establishment of a mature-type rumen microflora. Later tests have not shown any advantage in growth rate, feed utilization, general health, or appearance from inoculation with either fresh-cud material or dried commercial preparations.

SELECTED LITERATURE

Braude, R., and associates: Antibiotics in nutrition, *Nutrition Abstr. & Revs.*, **23**: 473–496, 1953.

[23] G. E. Combs, W. L. Alsmeyer, H. D. Wallace, and M. Koger, Enzyme supplementation of baby pig rations containing different sources of carbohydrate and protein, *J. Animal Sci.*, **19**:932–937, 1960.

Cole, H. H., and J. M. Boda: Continued progress toward controlling bloat: a review, *J. Dairy Sci.*, **43**:1585–1614, 1960.

Goldberg, Herbert S.: Antibiotics: Their Chemistry and Non-medical Uses, D. Van Nostrand Company, Inc., Princeton, N.J., 650 pp., 1959.

Johnson, R. H., and associates: Sustained prevention of bloat by feeding antibiotics in rotation or in combination, *J. Animal Sci.*, **19**:735–744, 1960.

Jordan, R. M., and H. E. Hanke: Effect of various tranquilizers on growing and fattening lambs, *J. Animal Sci.*, **19**:639–642, 1960.

Lassiter, C. A.: Antibiotics as growth stimulants for dairy cattle: a review, *J. Dairy Sci.*, **38**:1102–1138, 1955.

Perry, T. W., M. T. Mohler, and W. M. Beeson: Effect of feeding different tranquilizers in combination with implanted diethylstilbestrol or oral antibiotic on fattening beef steers, *J. Animal Sci.*, **19**:533–537, 1960.

Rusoff, L. L., and associates: Effect of high-level administration of chlortetracycline at birth on the health and growth of young dairy calves, *J. Dairy Sci.*, **42**:856–862, 1959.

Swinehart, Carl (ed.): A new look at organic arsenicals, *Feed Age*, **10**(5):38–51, 1960.

Part III

The Measurement of Body Needs and Feed Values

Chapter 10
Feeding Experiments. The Determination of Digestibility

Our previous discussion has considered the different nutrients which are required by the animal body and the metabolic changes which they undergo in serving its various functions. A knowledge of the quantitative needs of the body for these nutrients and of the relative value of feeds as sources of them is the basis of scientific feeding, a knowledge which has been gained gradually by means of research and experience over many years. An understanding of the methods by which it has been attained and which are still being employed to augment it is essential for the student of nutrition.

FEEDING EXPERIMENTS

Trial and experience were the means by which the art of feeding animals was originally developed. With the establishment of specific agencies to augment this knowledge, such as the agricultural experiment station, the feeding-trial method naturally was adopted as the means by which current practices could be critically tested and improved with the aid of the underlying sciences. A feeding trial with the species in question still remains the most useful method of obtaining results which have a direct application to feeding practice. But the method has a broader usefulness than this, as is indicated by the fact that feeding experiments with laboratory animals provide fundamental data which find application in human nutrition as well as in the feeding of farm animals. Feeding trials take many forms, a fact which must be appreciated if the results are to be interpreted correctly.

10.1. Comparative Feeding Trials. In its simplest form, a feeding trial is a record of the results produced in terms of growth, milk production, or other function from a given feed or ration. Two or more rations may be compared with each other on this basis. Additional records as to the feed eaten provide a comparison of the relative amounts of the rations required to produce a unit of product, and by the use of cost figures the results may be put on a money basis. The records here obtained tell us nothing as to why one ration proved better than another, unless the poorer one was so unpalatable as to be little consumed or unless it caused absolute harm. As a further step in the interest of more specific information, individual feeds may be compared as a part of rations the other ingredients of which are held constant. Here is an old example showing that fish meal is a better protein supplement for hogs than linseed meal:

	Average daily gain, lb.	Feed required for 100 lb. gain, lb.
Ration 1:		
200 lb. corn		
100 lb. wheat middlings	1.2	390
75 lb. fish meal		
Ration 2:		
200 lb. corn		
100 lb. wheat middlings	0.7	440
75 lb. linseed meal		

This experiment gives us a specific answer as to the comparative over-all effect of these two feeds, but it tells nothing as to why the fish meal was better. Was it the result of the higher percentage of protein in the fish product or a higher biological value of this protein? Was the large amount of calcium supplied by the fish meal in contrast to the very small amount present in the oil meal a factor, or did certain vitamins present in the one but not the other play a role?

It is important to know the specific nutritive quality which makes one feed better than another. For example, if the superiority of the fish-meal ration resulted entirely from the extra calcium supplied, the addition of ground limestone to the linseed-meal ration would provide a cheaper method of getting the same results. The comparison of two feeds with respect to a specific nutrient such as calcium or protein requires that all other nutritive factors be held alike and adequate in the two rations. This can never be achieved absolutely, but feeding trials can be set up in such a way as to give most of the specific information desired, as is illustrated by the modern experiments discussed later.

10.2. Feeding Trials with Laboratory Animals. Today many of the problems of nutrition are being studied with small animals, such as the rat. The processes of growth, reproduction, and lactation can be effectively investigated and the value of various feeds for these various functions determined. The much smaller cost in terms of animals, feed, and labor and the much shorter time involved for a given experiment, in view of the short life cycle of the laboratory animal, are important advantages. The influence of individual variability, a serious disturbing factor in large-animal experimentation, can be reduced to a minimum by the use of animals of similar genetic and nutritional history, by the employment of large numbers, and by close environmental control. Slaughter for chemical and histological examination, a desirable feature of many feeding trials, presents little difficulty with small animals, compared with the economic and other considerations involved in the case of farm animals.

The laboratory animal is thus highly useful for working out many of the fundamental principles of nutrition. The results obtained in feeding trials with the small animals, however, cannot be considered to have direct application to the various species of farm animals, because of the differences in physiology and other considerations. Even here studies with small animals serve as pilot experiments, by means of which much preliminary information can be obtained more quickly and at much less cost than with the large animals and whereby it can be determined what ideas are of sufficient promise to justify the expense involved in giving them a final test with the large animals. The situation is analogous to that of an industry in which processes worked out in the laboratory are first tested on a semicommercial scale before being finally adopted. Of course, there are feeding problems which by their nature are susceptible to solution only by experiments with the farm animals themselves, but the animal industry owes much to experiments with the rat.

10.3. The Purified-diet Method. An important feature of feeding trials which has been developed along with the use of laboratory animals is the employment of purified diets. These diets consist of purified sources of the various nutrients. For example, protein is supplied as casein, carbohydrates as starch and sucrose, fat as lard or some oil, minerals as chemically pure salts, and vitamins as the pure crystalline compounds. Such a diet makes it possible to include or withdraw a given nutrient with a minimum of disturbance of any of the other nutrient relations. The influence of different protein levels can be studied by including varying amounts of casein without any change in the rest of the ration, whereas the addition of the natural source of casein, viz., milk, would introduce many variables because it contains all of the other nutrients as well. Another protein such as zein of corn can be substituted for the casein, and the relative value of the two determined. By similar procedures, the other nutrients can be subjected to specific study.

The extensive use of the purified-diet method has been a development of the last forty-five years, but the idea was conceived more than a century ago at least. As reported in 1816, Magendie fed diets of pure sugar and of pure fat to dogs to ascertain whether or not nitrogen was required in the food. Before the middle of the last century Boussingault,[1] the famous French chemist, carried on nutrition studies with various species, involving the use of diets consisting in part of purified nutrients. As later attempts were made from time to time to use this method, the discouraging result occurred that the more completely the diet consisted of purified nutrients, the less satisfactory was the effect on the animal. It was this discouraging result, however, that led to the conclusion, toward the close of the century, that there were dietary essentials unknown to the chemist and thus led to the later discovery of the vitamins and other previously unappreciated nutritive factors. There followed the intensive application of the purified-diet method by McCollum, by Osborne and Mendel, and by others, as a result of which an increasing knowledge as to essential constituents of a purified diet and new discoveries as to nutritional requirements simultaneously developed.

Thus the purified-diet method became responsible for much of our modern knowledge of nutrition, including the physiology of the vitamins, the establishment of differences in protein quality, and more exact information regarding many of the minerals. Studies of the role of an element needed by the body in small amounts can be effectively carried out only with basal diets which may be freed from it and to which it may be added in known amounts. This is only possible with purified diets, because a diet cannot be prepared from natural foods which will be free from the element in question. The use of purified diets came to be known as the *biological method* for testing foods as to their content of vitamins (Sec. 8.9) and as to the quality of their protein (Sec. 6.8).

The purified-diet method has limitations that should be kept in mind. The ingredients of these diets cannot be considered pure in the absolute

[1] J. B. Boussingault (1802–1877), following a period of service as professor of chemistry at Lyons, France, founded the first agricultural experiment station in 1836 at Pechelbronn. Here his pioneer studies on the nutrition of various species of animals extended over many years and became models for later investigators. Boussingault ranks as one of the foremost agricultural scientists of all time. His two-volume work, Économie rurale, published in 1843 and 1844, and dealing with soils, crops, and fertilizers as well as the nutrition of cattle, horses, hogs, and other animals, is highly worthwhile reading for the modern student.

sense. Starch, for example, cannot be entirely freed from mineral matter without breaking down its structure. The essentiality of some mineral elements, needed only in traces, may remain undiscovered because of the impossibility of eliminating them entirely from the other ingredients of the experimental diet. Some of the recently discovered

FIG. 10.1. This sheep was reared to maturity on a purified diet which it received for 15 months.

vitamins were identified as "impurities" in purified diets earlier assumed to consist only of known nutrients. Some of the constituents, notably protein, in purified diets are altered from their natural state in the process of purification. The kind of pure carbohydrate used affects the significance of the results in the case of certain vitamins because of the effects of various carbohydrates on vitamin synthesis in the alimentary tract.

A completely successful purified diet for a given species cannot be prepared until all of the nutrient requirements of that species are known—which is still apparently not the case for some. The diet must be of a suitable physical nature and sufficiently palatable so that it will be consumed in large enough amounts to support fully the function under study. The method has been developed to its highest degree of usefulness in the case of the rat, both because of the lesser problem involved in preparing purified nutrients on a small scale and also because of the years of experience with this species. The knowledge as to the rat's qualitative and quantitative needs is much greater accordingly, but it may not yet be complete in terms of successive generations. Successful studies are also being made with several other species of laboratory animals. As regards farm animals, the use of purified diets has contributed greatly to the modern knowledge of poultry nutrition. Recent applications of the method are also currently making important contributions to our knowledge of the nutritional needs of pigs, calves, and lambs. Experiments illustrating these applications are reviewed in later chapters which deal with nutritive requirements for various body functions. Some general papers are cited at the end of the present chapter.

10.4. Germfree Techniques. It is evident from previous discussions regarding various vitamins that the contributions of intestinal organisms to the nutrition of the host complicate the interpretation of data on dietary requirements obtained in feeding trials. Thus, the nutrition scientist has a special interest in the techniques which have been developed for obtaining animals which are germfree at birth and for rearing them in an uncontaminated environment thereafter. Germfree means free of contamination by bacteria, yeasts, molds, fungi, protozoa, and parasites in general, that is, free of all other life. The newborn are obtained by Caesarean section and reared in specially designed apparatus by appropriate techniques, involving, of course, sterilized diets. Success has been reported with rats, rabbits, hamsters, mice, chickens, turkeys, and monkeys. Rats, mice, and chickens have been bred through successive generations. Details of the equipment and techniques used, and some of the nutrition studies made, are reported in a series of articles comprising a monograph by Reyniers and coworkers.[2]

10.5. Group Feeding versus Individual Feeding. Feed records are a desirable feature of all feeding trials. Even where the feed cost of the physiological performance is not of primary concern, it is frequently essential from the standpoint of the interpretation of the results to have

[2] James A. Reyniers and coworkers, Germfree vertebrates: present status, *Ann. N.Y. Acad. Sci.*, **78**:1–400, 1959.

some record of the feed consumed. In many feeding experiments, particularly those with farm animals, the animals have been fed as a group. This is the simplest procedure from the standpoint of equipment needed and labor cost, but in many experiments it introduces complications in the interpretation of results. Such complications arise when there is a wide variability in the individual behavior within the lot, as to both production and feed consumption. The difficulty is increased when an animal, owing to accident or other unavoidable cause, has to be removed from the lot. The performance of the individual can be eliminated from consideration, but the food which it ate cannot. Individual feeding eliminates these disadvantages. It makes possible the correlation of individual performance record with the food which the animal ate. It preserves the identity of the individual. Certain species which are fed together in practice may consume somewhat less when fed individually. Thus certain workers stress this "competition in the feed lot" as being of large practical importance in feeding trials with beef cattle, sheep, and hogs. Here several small groups will yield a more sensitive test than a few large ones.

While there are types of feeding experiments in which feed records of the group as a whole are sufficient or in which they may be acceptable in the interest of economy and of the use of larger numbers of animals, individual records are highly desirable in studies where only small differences are to be expected and where quantitative data are of special importance. Individual records are much more useful from the standpoint of statistical treatment (Sec. 10.11). The relative advantages of group and individual feeding are discussed in various papers presented in a symposium before the American Society of Animal Production.[3]

10.6. Controlled versus Ad Libitum Feeding. When the amount of feed consumed is regulated in some way by the experimenter, the feeding is controlled, as distinguished from the ad libitum system in which each animal or group is allowed to eat all it wants. Ad libitum feeding is the most commonly used procedure in farm-animal investigations and gives unbiased results for direct practical application. By keeping records of feed intake, the results can be expressed on an efficiency basis, such as "feed required per 100 lb. gain," as well as in terms of total increase in weight. This system gives unbiased results for direct practical application in terms of the feed, species, and function under study. It is subject to the limitation, however, that with certain feeds and rations differ-

[3] W. E. Carroll, Group feeding as a method of livestock experimentation, *Proc. Am. Soc. Animal Production*, 1930, pp. 34–44; Jay L. Lush, Interpreting the results of group feeding experiments, *Proc. Am. Soc. Animal Production*, 1930, pp. 44–55; E. W. Crampton, Individual feeding for the comparative feeding trial, *Proc. Am. Soc. Animal Production*, 1930, pp. 56–63.

ences in nutritive value may be masked by differences in palatability. Further, the method does not provide the controlled conditions required for certain purposes—for example, the determination of digestibility (Sec. 10.12).

Thus, in many instances there is an advantage in using some system of controlled feeding. Early in their studies of protein quality Osborne and Mendel recognized that ad libitum feeding frequently gave rise to variable results. They raised the fundamental question: "Does one animal grow because it eats more or the other fail because it eats less?" They experimented with various procedures of controlled feeding as a means of eliminating the uncertainties here involved. In one series of studies Osborne and Mendel[4] kept the food intakes alike for each diet under study, in accordance with a prescribed schedule based upon a preliminary experiment. They were thus able to compare the growth made on different diets consumed in the same amount. Recognizing that the more rapidly growing animals might be at a disadvantage under this system in view of their increasing maintenance requirement, they carried out another series in which the food intake was adjusted in accordance with increase in weight. In another experiment Osborne and Mendel[5] allowed ad libitum feeding and selected for comparison the growth records of those animals which had consumed substantially the same amount of food under this system. The discussion presented in these papers clearly shows that a proper assessment of the effect of food consumption as such is a very important matter in any feeding experiment, and the papers are well worth reading by any student who is planning such an experiment. The relative advantages and limitations of controlled and ad libitum feeding are discussed in considerable detail by Lucas.[6] This paper lists many different methods of controlled feeding, ranging from partial to complete control.

10.7. Equalized Paired Feeding. This is a widely used procedure in which the feed intakes are completely controlled. In this method of comparing two rations the animals are most commonly selected by pairs, one animal of a given pair being placed on ration *A* and the other being placed on ration *B* and both animals being given exactly the same amount of food as stated in pounds or some measure of food energy. The latter is accomplished by limiting the intakes of both to that of the

[4] Thomas B. Osborne and Lafayette B. Mendel, A quantitative comparison of casein, lactalbumin, and edestin for growth or maintenance, *J. Biol. Chem.*, **26**:1–23, 1916.

[5] Thomas B. Osborne and Lafayette B. Mendel, The relative value of certain proteins and protein concentrates as supplements to corn gluten, *J. Biol. Chem.*, **29**:69–92, 1917.

[6] H. L. Lucas, Techniques in animal science research, *Proc. Auburn Conf. on Statistics Applied to Research,* Alabama Polytechnic Institute, Auburn, Ala., 1948.

animal consuming the lesser amount. The two animals of the pair are selected to be as nearly alike as possible in size, age, and previous history, but such equalities are not essential from pair to pair. The equalization of food intake is also limited to within the pair. This method is illustrated by the data presented in Table 10.1, obtained in an experiment in which the two rations under comparison were alike with the exception of the phosphorus carrier. Both rations contained the same amount of phosphorus and in the same ratio to calcium. It is noted that for a given pair of rats the food intakes were substantially alike over the experimental period of 35 days. When it is desired to compare three rations at the same time, the animals can be selected in trios. This may involve complications, however, in the equalization of food intake, complications which become increasingly troublesome in comparing more than three rations.

Properly conducted equalized feeding experiments have a distinct advantage over the ad libitum method as regards the adaptability of the results to statistical treatment (Sec. 10.11). Other things being equal, the larger the number of pairs or trios, the greater the reliability of the results. The data given in Table 10.1 include only four of the six pairs

TABLE 10.1. DATA FROM A PAIRED-FEEDING EXPERIMENT IN WHICH DICALCIUM PHOSPHATE (A) AND BONE MEAL (B) WERE COMPARED AS SOURCES OF PHOSPHORUS FOR BONE GROWTH*

	Pair 1		Pair 2		Pair 3		Pair 4	
	A	*B*	*A*	*B*	*A*	*B*	*A*	*B*
Food, g	253.0	253.0	255.0	254.0	252.0	252.0	224.0	228.0
Ash in bone, %	48.44	47.43	51.63	50.64	49.77	48.91	50.81	54.23
Ash in bone, mg	191.0	157.7	190.3	154.7	179.2	166.3	162.3	171.3
Calcium in bone, %	19.81	16.04	18.59	18.20	17.78	17.63	18.20	19.26
Phosphorus in bone, %	9.9	8.5	9.3	9.2	8.9	8.8	9.0	9.6

* From K. V. Rottensten and L. A. Maynard, The assimilation of phosphorus from dicalcium phosphate, C.P., tricalcium phosphate, C.P., bone dicalcium phosphate and cooked bonemeal, *J. Nutrition*, **8**:715–730, 1934.

actually used in the experiment. The statistical analysis of the complete data revealed no certain advantage for one phosphorus carrier over the other.

The method of equalized feeding by pairs commonly referred to simply as paired feeding, has been employed to study a wide variety of problems. A paper by Mitchell and Beadles[7] gives an excellent description of the

[7] H. H. Mitchell and J. R. Beadles, The paired-feeding method in nutrition experiments and its application to the problem of cystine deficiencies in food proteins, *J. Nutrition*, **2**:225–243, 1930.

procedure and its application. The method has the advantage of eliminating the confusing effects which may arise from a variable food intake even when results are compared per unit of feed consumed. The method is subject to the criticism, however, that limiting the food intake may defeat the very object of the experiment, since a frequent effect of a nutritionally deficient ration is to decrease food consumption, with the result that the full effect of the better ration cannot express itself and that the comparison is made at a restricted food intake instead of a normal one. The force of this criticism is dependent upon the nature of the experiment. In practical tests in which palatability and level of food intake are important criteria of the relative value of the rations, equalized feeding would obviously defeat their purpose. One must be careful, however, about drawing conclusions that more fundamental differences exist where some physical factor concerned in palatability may have been solely responsible for the results obtained.

The method is not suitable for finding out *how much* superior one ration is to another for growth, because, as the animal on the superior ration increases in weight over its mate, its maintenance requirement becomes greater than that of its mate. Under these conditions, an equal food intake for both means that the larger animal must be using a larger proportion for maintenance, and less remains for growth promotion. Therefore, an absolute equality of food intake means that the quantities available for the specific function which is being used as the criterion in comparing the two rations are not equal. The faster-growing animal is penalized. Various workers have introduced modifications designed to overcome this limitation and still preserve the principle of controlled feeding. Lactation studies which adjust the feed of each animal on the basis of body weight and production represent a special type of controlled-feeding experiment.

The paired-feeding method is a useful technique but requires judgment in its application and in the interpretation of the results obtained. It would appear to find its largest usefulness in comparisons in which food consumption is not markedly restricted by the conditions imposed and in which the measure is in terms of the specific effect of the nutrient under study, as is illustrated in Table 10.1, instead of the more general measure of increase in weight. Some of the limitations of the method are brought out in the studies by Barnes and coworkers,[8] dealing with methods of measuring protein efficiency. There are many problems concerning which the use in separate experiments of both ad libitum feeding and controlled feeding will give much more information than either procedure alone. If the two give similar results, the validity of the conclusions is greatly enhanced thereby.

[8] Richard H. Barnes and coworkers, Measurement of the growth promoting quality of dietary protein, *Cereal Chem.*, **22**:273–286, 1945.

This discussion of paired feeding illustrates the fact, which holds also for other methods discussed in this chapter, that no single method is suitable for the solution of all types of nutrition problems. The effective investigator must select his method in accordance with his problem, frequently employing more than one method, and finally, he must interpret his results with a full consideration of the advantages and limitations of the method used.

10.8. Slaughter Experiments. In the previously discussed experiment presented in Table 10.1, the relative value of the two mineral supplements was measured in terms of the calcium and phosphorus content of the bones, since the growth of the animals as a whole would not have given definite information as to bone development. Such a procedure, which involves the killing of the animals and the analysis of certain specific tissues or of the body as a whole, is commonly referred to as a slaughter experiment. In many feeding trials, it is desirable to obtain more specific information regarding the effect of a given ration than is furnished by the common measures of weight and size. For example, in studies of the protein requirement for growth or of the comparative value of different protein sources, it is important to know the specific effect in terms of protein tissue formed, since the increase in the body as a whole is due to water, fat, and minerals as well as protein, the relations of which may vary.

The introduction of the slaughter method by Lawes and Gilbert has been referred to. As now used it takes many forms according to the problem under investigation. To study the effect of a given diet on changes in body composition a group of like animals are selected and a part of them are slaughtered and analyzed at the start of the experiment. The others are fed a weighed and analyzed diet for a given period and then slaughtered and analyzed. The difference in their composition from that of the check animals killed at the start reveals the effect of the diet fed. The use of the slaughter method for studying protein and energy requirements is illustrated by the work of Mitchell and Hamilton.[9]

A slaughter experiment requires much more time and labor than is involved in merely weighing or measuring the animals, and in many instances difficult problems are presented in the selection of representative samples of tissues and in their preparation for analysis. For each period of observation, a sufficiently large number of animals must be examined to minimize the rather large individual variability in composition. In general, small laboratory animals are much easier to work with than the larger farm animals. Because of the economic considerations involved, work with the latter must be limited for the most part to those animals

[9] H. H. Mitchell and T. S. Hamilton, Swine type studies. III. The energy and protein requirements of growing swine and the utilization of feed energy in growth, *Illinois Agr. Expt. Sta. Bull.* 323, 1929.

for which a return can be obtained on the carcass after the desired samples for analysis have been taken. As regards farm animals, therefore, the slaughter method has found its greatest application in studying the nutrition of beef cattle, sheep, and swine. Slaughter data may also include various measures of market value, such as dressing percentages and quality of the carcass, and such measures are frequently used in meat-production experiments to study the influence of a given ration upon the quality of the product and upon its selling price.

10.9. Experimental Designs. The statistician refers to those comparative feeding trials which are set up in such a way as to allow statistical analysis as *experimental designs.* This term is applicable to the methods previously described when they are appropriately used. In addition, there are certain specific designs with which the student should be familiar.

One is the *factorial* arrangement of treatments which may be illustrated as follows:

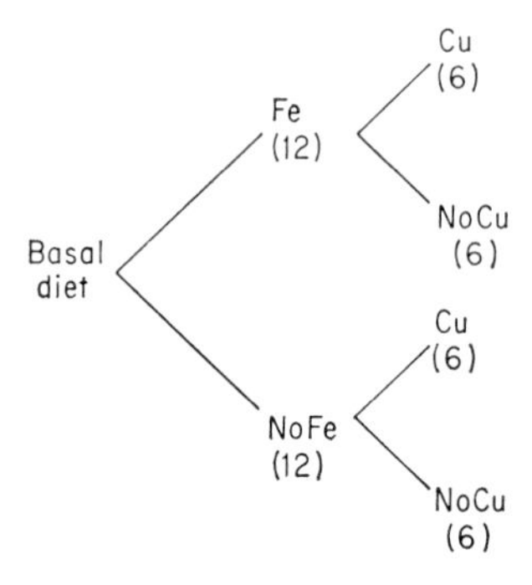

This design provides for testing the effects of iron and/or copper addition to a basal diet, using a total of 24 animals. Twelve are placed on the basal diet with iron, and 12 on the diet without iron. Each group of 12 is in turn subdivided into groups with and without copper. This design provides for a comparison of iron versus no iron, using 12 animals per group, and it also furnishes a comparison with the same number of animals with and without copper. Further, interactions between iron and copper are brought out through statistical treatment, answering the question, for example, as to whether iron supplementation gives a different result in the presence of supplemental copper than in its absence. The factorial design is thus considered to be of high efficiency in terms of information obtained in relation to the number of animals used. The diagram shown represents a very simple experiment of this character. Each of the groups with and without copper might be further broken down, e.g., into groups with and without manganese. More animals could also be used.

There are several methods which involve the feeding of the rations to be compared to the same animal in different periods. Thus, in the *double-reversal system* two rations (X and Y) and two groups of animals (A and B) are used. In period 1, group A receives ration X and group B receives ration Y. At the end of the period the rations are reversed—group A receiving ration Y and group B receiving ration X. One or more additional periods may be included with a shift of the groups at the beginning of each. A related procedure is the *latin square design* illustrated as follows:

		Animals		
		1	2	3
	1	B	A	C
Periods	2	A	C	B
	3	C	B	A

Here A, B, and C represent treatments, such as feeds for a digestibility determination, each feed being fed to each animal in a different period and thus in a different order for each animal. The essential feature of this design is that the number of animals and the number of treatments must be the same. It provides a high precision of measurement with a small number of animals. This general procedure of feeding different rations to the same group of animals in different periods has the advantage of lessening the effects of variability among animals as compared with the method of feeding one group one ration and the other group the other ration throughout the experiment. It has the disadvantage, however, that there are carry-over effects when the same animal is shifted from one ration to another. Lucas[10] has added an extra period to this design to minimize the disadvantage.

10.10. Financial Phases of Feeding Trials. It is obvious that an essential practical consideration in evaluating a ration for farm animals is its cost in terms of the return obtained for the product. Thus, in many feeding trials, records are kept of feed and perhaps of other costs and of the estimated or actual selling price of the product. Profit or loss per animal or per unit of feed thus becomes a measure of the nutritive value of the ration. While it is obvious that the financial phases of feeding operations cannot be neglected, the expression of the results in terms of dollars and cents, unless properly interpreted, may obscure rather than

[10] H. L. Lucas, Extra-period, latin square change-over design, *J. Dairy Sci.*, **40**: 225–239, 1957.

clarify the facts brought out by the experiment. Monetary statements are not experimental results. They are based upon factors which are not under experimental control, the same combination of which may never occur again. The relative prices of feeds and the selling price of the product vary from time to time, in fact from day to day and from place to place, according to market conditions. Clearly the product obtained per unit of feed is a much more stable and useful measure. While financial statements of feeding trials are interesting to the reader, they provide no basic or generalized measure of nutritive value, and relying upon them as a guide for practice may prove disastrous. In contrast, a statement of food consumed and product obtained provides the basic data to which the feeder can apply current prices and thus obtain a much more accurate picture of the probable financial outcome than is given by a statement of the financial results based on prices at the time and under the conditions of the experiment.

10.11. The Use of Statistical Methods in Nutrition Experiments. In a feeding trial certain factors, such as the amounts and quantities of feed, the time and method of feeding, and the general care and management, can be definitely fixed. Certain other factors, inherent in the animals used, cannot be controlled. The object of a well-planned experiment is to reduce these uncontrollable factors to a minimum by giving attention, in the selection of the animals used, to genetic and nutritional history as well as to such factors as age, size, vigor, and the like. Even though this is effectively done, there still remain inherent variables which cause two individuals to respond somewhat differently though treated exactly alike in an experiment. When treated differently, a part, at least, of the difference in response is the result of the inherent variables and not the treatment.

The effect of the inherent variables cannot be measured, but the probability that the observed differences in experimental results could arise from the uncontrollable variables alone can be estimated and taken into account. This is done by a statistical analysis of the data obtained. Such an analysis helps the investigator to decide whether the results from a given comparison reflect a real difference in response to the two treatments or may have occurred simply because of inherent variations in the animals used. As has been indicated in the preceding discussions of experimental designs, statistical methods can be usefully employed in planning experiments in such a way as to make them more likely to give a definite answer to the question under study, particularly by providing results which can be statistically analyzed. Statistical methods have become an essential tool of the investigator in nutrition, and some knowledge of them is helpful to all students in this field as an aid in the evaluation of published research. It is beyond the scope of this book to attempt any presentation of them. Their application to feeding trials is discussed by Lucas.[11] More extensive presentations are to be found in the literature at the close of this chapter.

THE DETERMINATION OF DIGESTIBILITY

It is obviously impracticable to carry out feeding trials with all of the different feeds and combinations which are used in making rations; neither do these trials which measure only the final effect of the feed in terms of the function under study tell us much regarding the intermediate processes involved. There are other measures of nutritive value which give us more definite information as to why a particular result is obtained, and this information is useful both in experimental studies and in feeding practice. Chemical analysis is the starting point for determining the nutritive value of feeds, but the actual value of ingested nutrients is dependent upon the use which the body is able to make of them. The first consideration here is digestibility, since undigested nutrients do not get into the body proper.

Anatomical and physiological differences in the digestive tracts of various species are responsible for large variations among them in their ability to utilize different types of food in their nutrition. These variations are largest in the case of roughages, because of their content of complex polysaccharides. Different species of farm animals do not differ greatly in their ability to digest concentrates such as seeds and their by-products, since most of these feeds are low in crude fiber. Fortunately, for experimental work, digestion in the rat is similar to that in the hog. The ability of the ruminant to handle a large amount of roughage gives it a special place in agriculture in that it can utilize the coarse products of the farm which find little outlet in other directions, whereas the hog competes more or less directly with man or with the demands of industry for most of its food. Because of its capacious digestive tract, the ruminant can consume a ration which it only partially digests and still get enough nutrients for rapid growth or other function, whereas the hog must have a highly digestible ration in order to eat enough to meet its needs for best performance. Thus, for economic reasons, the rations fed to cows, sheep, and even horses are commonly those which are less digestible than those fed to hogs.

10.12. The Determination of Digestibility. A digestion trial involves a record of the nutrients consumed and of the amounts of them voided in the feces. It is essential that the feces collected represent quantitatively the undigested residue of the measured amount of food consumed.

[11] H. L. Lucas, Techniques in animal science research, *Proc. Auburn Conf. on Statistics Applied to Research,* Alabama Polytechnic Institute, Auburn, Ala., 1948.

Various methods are employed for this fecal collection. In the case of Omnivora and Carnivora some indigestible, easily distinguishable substance called a *marker* may be used. The marker is fed just before the beginning of the ingestion of the ration to be tested and again at its close. The feces collection is begun when the first marker appears and is ended with the appearance of the second. A satisfactory marker must be inert physiologically and contain no element under investigation. The less the substance diffuses the better. Carmine is a frequently used marker. Ferric oxide, chromic oxide, and soot have also been employed. No marker can be considered to provide unquestionable accuracy.

In the case of herbivorous animals with their much larger and more complicated digestive tracts, the use of a marker is not a suitable method. For these species and commonly for other farm animals also, the ration to be tested is fed in constant daily amounts for an extended period. After allowing a certain number of days to elapse as a *preliminary* period to free the digestive tract of any indigestible material coming from the feed consumed prior to the start of the constant intakes of the ration under study, the collection of the feces is begun and continued through the *collection* period. The length of the periods required to obtain reliable results depends upon the species, longer periods being necessary in the case of Herbivora, especially ruminants, than of other species. In general, the longer the period of collection, provided the stated amount of food continues to be consumed regularly and completely, the more accurate the results, since the effect of periodic fluctuations is minimized.

10.13. Methods of Collecting Feces. A digestion trial requires the quantitative collection of the feces uncontaminated by urine. While in the old days this was commonly done manually in the case of farm animals, the modern procedures utilize various types of metabolism cages representing modifications of those earlier designed for laboratory animals. An essential feature of these cages is that the animal must have freedom of movement, particularly as regards lying down and getting up. In one type the bottom is a metal grid through which both the feces and urine pass, the feces being caught on a screen underneath. In the types now more commonly used, the animal is confined so that he cannot turn around, and the length of the cage is adjusted to the size of the animal in such a way that the feces fall into a properly placed container. The feed box is attached to the front, so constructed and placed as to prevent scattering.

The construction of such a unit, designed for two steers, is shown in Fig. 10.2 and described in detail by Horn, Ray, and Neumann.[12] The collection boxes are shown detached and a feed box is illustrated sepa-

[12] L. H. Horn, Jr., M. L. Ray, and A. L. Neumann, Digestion and nutrient-balance stalls for steers, *J. Animal Sci.*, **13**:20–24, 1954.

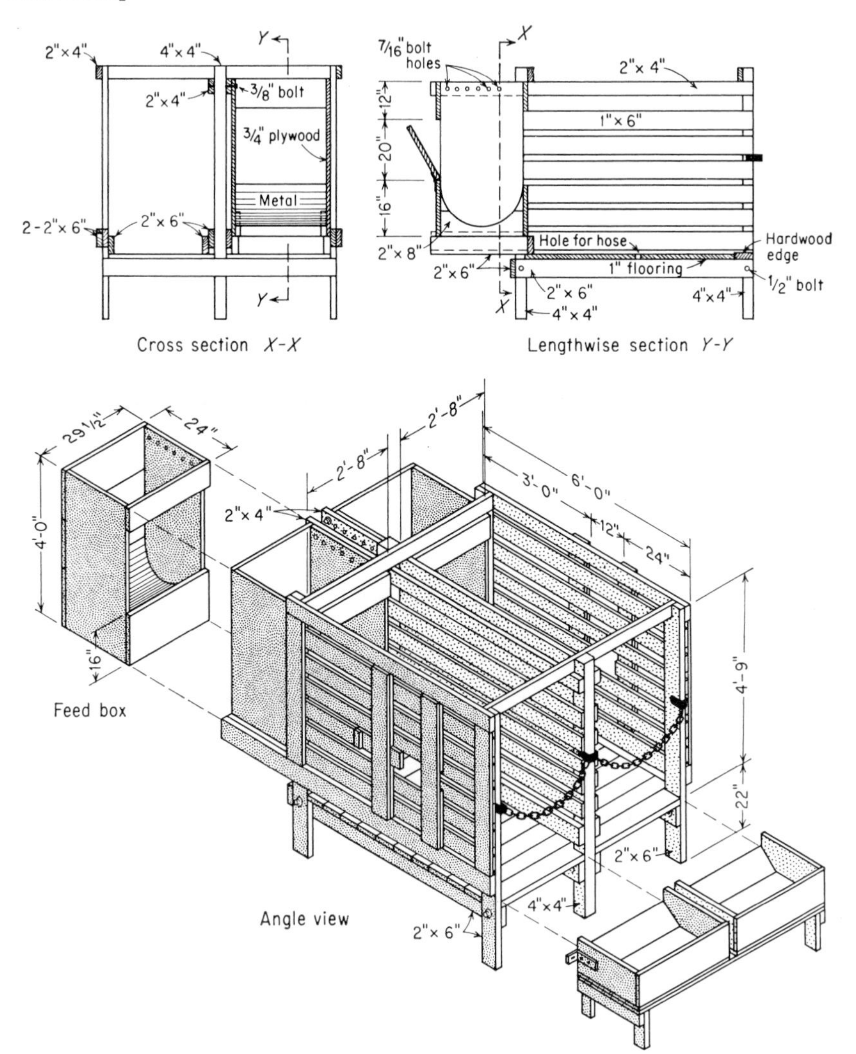

FIG. 10.2. Digestion and metabolism stall. (*Courtesy of A. L. Neumann, University of Illinois.*)

rately to give more of the details of construction. The feed boxes are fastened on runners so that they can be moved backward or forward to regulate the length of the unit in accordance with the size of the animal. A urinal consisting of a rubber funnel is attached to the belly of the steer by a harness and a tube from it leads down through the floor. This permits the quantitative collection of urine also, as is called for in balance studies (Chap. 11).

Obviously the cage described above is suitable only for male animals.

Where digestion and metabolism studies are to be carried out with females, as is the case, for example, with dairy cows, a specially designed urine conduit is attached to the animal. While the difficulties here involved are obvious, experience has shown that quantitative feces and urine separations and collections can be obtained by properly designed and attached conduits. The construction and operation of such a conduit is described in the article by Hobbs, Hansard, and

FIG. 10.3. Harness and bag for collecting feces in a digestion trial. (*Courtesy of D. C. Clanton, University of Nebraska.*)

Barrick,[13] which also gives the details on a metabolism case used for heifers.

Feces collections have also been made with steers and wethers by using a collection bag attached to the animal. This method has advantages for certain purposes, notably for the collection of feces from animals on pasture. A bag and harness used by Clanton and Hemstrom of the Nebraska Agricultural Experiment Station is shown in Fig. 10.3. Equipment which has been successfully used by Reid of Australia for collecting

[13] C. S. Hobbs, Sam L. Hansard, and E. R. Barrick, Simplified methods and equipment used in separation of urine from feces eliminated by heifers and by steers, *J. Animal Sci.*, 9:565–570, 1950.

both feces and urine on pasture to provide the data needed in a balance experiment (Chap. 11) is shown in Fig. 10.4.

The determination of digestibility in poultry requires a special technique, since the feces and urine are voided together, causing a mixing of the urinary and fecal nitrogen. The two forms of nitrogen can be separated by determining the ammonia and uric acid which represent the urinary output. The determination of digestibility is also carried out by the use of an operative technique which involves the formation of an artificial anus.

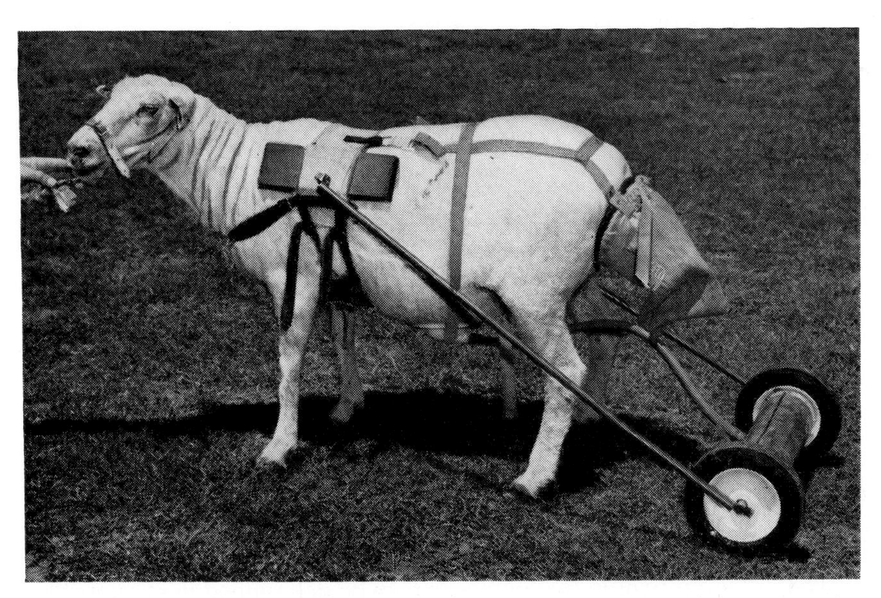

FIG. 10.4. Equipment for collecting excreta of grazing wethers. The roller has the capacity for a 24-hour urine output. (*Courtesy of R. L. Reid, Sheep Biology Laboratory, C.S.I.R.O., Prospect, N.S.W., Australia.*)

10.14. A Digestion Trial. An example of the data obtained in a digestion trial is presented in Table 10.2. In obtaining the data for intake of nutrients, the feed intake was multiplied by figures for its percentage composition as determined by chemical analysis. Similarly, the data for excreted nutrients were calculated, and the digested nutrients obtained by subtraction. The final figures, expressed as percentages, are called *digestion coefficients*. In such a trial, several animals must be used and the results averaged to minimize the factor of individual variability. It has been mentioned (Sec. 6.18) that the coefficient for protein, determined as indicated in Table 10.2, represents *apparent* digestibility because the feces contain metabolic as well as digested nitrogen. Since the digested portion is not determined directly in the case of any of the nutrients, the term *coefficient of apparent digestibility* is frequently used.

It is noted that the mineral nutrients are not considered in Table 10.2. The discussion in Chap. 7 has shown that some of the absorbed minerals are excreted through the gut. There is no method of separating such mineral material from the portion which originally failed of absorption. Since this is true and since the reexcreted portion may be a large as well as a variable part of the whole, it is impossible to arrive at a figure of any value for the digestibility of most of the mineral elements. Data for

TABLE 10.2. DIGESTIBILITY OF DRIED GRASS BY A DAIRY COW*
(Data for a 1-week period)

	Crude protein	Carbohydrates		Ether extract
		Fiber	NFE	
Intake of 44,684 g. dry matter, containing, g.	10,216	8,255	20,823	1,697
Output of 11,609 g. fecal dry matter, containing, g.	2,559	2,158	4,042	783
Digested nutrients, g.	7,657	6,097	16,781	914
Digested nutrients, per cent	75	73.9	80.6	53.9

* These data are taken from J. A. Newlander and C. H. Jones, The digestibility of artificially dried grass, *Vermont Agr. Expt. Sta. Bull.* 348, 1932.

"digestible ash" which are frequently reported in connection with digestion trials have no real significance.

The digestibility of individual feeds may be determined in so far as they provide a satisfactory ration for the period of the test, when fed alone. The digestibility of concentrates by ruminants cannot be determined in this way because they do not furnish sufficient bulk; their coefficients can be obtained only by difference. In this procedure the digestibility of a roughage as a basal ration is first determined, and then the concentrate is added to the roughage for a second test. By a consideration of differences between the figures obtained for the roughage alone and for the combination, coefficients for the digestibility of the concentrate are calculated. Such figures represent the net effect of the addition of the concentrate to the roughage, but they may not be exact for the concentrate because its addition may have influenced the digestibility of the basal ration. The frequent occurrence of impossible coefficients in data thus obtained testifies to this fact.

10.15. The Indicator Method of Determining Digestibility. The conduct of a digestion trial as previously outlined is obviously a laborious and time-consuming procedure. For many years investigators have sought an indirect method of assessing digestibility. Various workers have proposed formulas for calculating digestible organic matter from crude fiber or fiber and protein content, but these formulas have been found to have only limited usefulness for the purpose. An indirect method of comparatively recent development, the accuracy and usefulness of which have become definitely established, involves the use of an "inert reference substance" as an indicator. The ideal specifications for such a substance are that it should be totally indigestible and unabsorbable, have no pharmacological action on the digestive tract, pass through the tract at a uniform rate, be readily determined chemically, and preferably be a natural constituent of the feed under test. By determining the ratio of the concentration of the reference substance to that of a given nutrient in the feed and the same ratio in the feces resulting from the feed, the digestibility of the nutrient can be obtained without measuring either the food intake or feces output. The calculation is made as follows:

$$\text{Digestibility} = 100 - \left(100 \frac{\%\text{ indicator in feed}}{\%\text{ indicator in feces}} \times \frac{\%\text{ nutrient in feces}}{\%\text{ nutrient in feed}}\right)$$

In 1918 Edin, a Swedish scientist, first proposed chromic sesquioxide, Cr_2O_3, as an indigestible substance suitable for use as an indicator, but it did not receive adequate testing until some twenty-five years later. Following the recognition of the indigestibility of lignin and the establishment of methods for its quantitative determination, the use of this compound was proposed as one having the advantage of being a natural feed constituent. Later Reid and coworkers[14] proposed the use of naturally occurring "chromogens" which could be quantitatively determined by light absorption at 406 mμ. During the past few years these three types of indicators have been extensively studied in experiments with ruminants, in which the results have been compared with those obtained by quantitatively measuring feed intake and feces voided. In general there has been close correspondence between the results with the indicator method and the conventional method, with the conclusion that either chromic oxide or lignin or the chromogen technique gives satisfactory results, with little advantage for one over the others. An extensive trial of the three indicator methods compared with the conventional technique has been reported by Kane and coworkers[15] for dairy cattle in which the advantages and limitations of each are discussed.

[14] J. T. Reid and coworkers, A new indicator method for the determination of digestibility and consumption of forage by ruminants, *J. Dairy Sci.*, **33**:60–71, 1950.

[15] E. A. Kane and coworkers, A comparison of various digestion trial techniques with dairy cattle, *J. Dairy Sci.*, **36**:325–333, 1953.

10.16. Indicators in Pasture and Range Studies. The problem of measuring how much feed an animal obtains from pasture or range and of determining the digestibility of this feed is both an important and a difficult one. For estimating consumption on pasture much use has been made of the system devised by Garrigus and Rusk,[16] involving a calculation of the dry matter consumed in a given period from the feces collected during the same period, using a bag as shown in Fig. 10.3. The calculation is based on a previous determination of the digestibility of the dry matter of the feed cut from the pasture in question. The indicator method can be used to shorten this procedure, the calculation being made as follows:

$$\text{Dry-matter consumption (g. per day)} = \frac{(\text{units indicator per g. dry feces}) \times (\text{g. dry matter in feces per day})}{\text{units indicator per g. dry matter of forage}}$$

Digestion trials with pasture and range forage have commonly been carried out by using clippings or manually plucked samples from the area in question. Here, as with dry roughage, the indicator method has been shown to be a useful substitute for the standard procedure. A limitation of the use of clippings or pluckings in estimating the composition and digestibility of the feed obtained from pasture or range lies in the fact that the animal grazes selectively in a way that cannot be duplicated in samplings.

It is possible to determine both the feed intake from pasture and its digestibility by the simultaneous use of two indicators, namely, an external one such as Cr_2O_3 to measure dry-matter intake and a naturally occurring one such as a chromogen to measure digestibility. The procedures are the same as previously described (Sec. 10.15). The reports of Reid and associates[17] and Smith and Reid[18] give further details of the methods. Results to date indicate that this procedure is a very promising one for improving the accuracy of the determination of the nutritive value of the feed actually consumed, as well as being a simplification compared with methods previously used.

10.17. Total Digestible Nutrients. As a general measure of the nutritive value of a feed, digestion coefficients are used to compute its content of total digestible nutrients (TDN). The dried grass used in the diges-

[16] W. P. Garrigus and H. P. Rusk, Some effects of the species and stage of maturity of plants on the forage consumption of grazing steers of various weights, *Illinois Agr. Expt. Sta. Bull.* 454, 1939.

[17] J. T. Reid and associates, A procedure for measuring the digestibility of pasture forage under grazing conditions, *J. Nutrition*, **46**:255–269, 1952.

[18] A. M. Smith and J. T. Reid, Use of chromic oxide as an indicator of fecal output for the purpose of determining the intake of pasture herbage by grazing cows, *J. Dairy Sci.*, **37**:515–524, 1955. See also papers cited.

tion trial presented in Table 10.2 had the following composition: crude protein, 20.11; crude fiber, 16.25; nitrogen-free extract, 40.99; ether extract, 3.34. The digestible nutrients are obtained from these data by multiplying them by the digestion coefficients given in the table, as is shown below. The digestible fat is multipled by the factor 2.25 in

Nutrient	Total nutrients in 100 lb., lb.	Digestion coefficients, per cent	Digestible nutrients, lb.
Crude protein	20.11	75.0	15.08
Crude fiber	16.25	73.9	12.01
Nitrogen-free extract	40.99	80.6	33.03
Ether extract	3.34	53.9 (× 2.25)	4.04
Total digestible nutrients	.....	....	64.16

arriving at the figure 4.04, because it has that much more energy value than the other nutrients, as is explained later (Sec. 11.8). The usefulness of TDN values in evaluating feeds and in formulating ratios is also discussed later (Sec. 12.4).

Digestion trials carried out as previously described have provided data for the calculation of *average digestion coefficients* for the protein, fat, and carbohydrates in the various feeds and thus, in turn, for the calculation of their content of TDN. Such data have been compiled by Morrison[19] and by Schneider.[20] This latter compilation gives separate tables of digestion coefficients for cattle, sheep and goats, and swine.

10.18. Nutritive Ratio. This is the ratio of the digestible protein, expressed as unity, to the sum of digestible carbohydrates and fat, the latter being multiplied by 2.25. The second factor of the ratio is calculated as follows:

$$\frac{(\text{Digestible fat} \times 2.25) + \text{digestible NFE} + \text{digestible fiber}}{\text{Digestible protein}}$$

Based upon the data previously given for dried grass this calculation results in the figure 3.2, and the ratio is therefore 1:3.2. Such a ratio is called a *narrow* one because of the relatively large amount of protein in relation to the other nutrients; where the reverse is true we have a *wide* ratio.

[19] Frank B. Morrison, Feeds and Feeding, 22d ed., Morrison Publishing Co., Ithaca, N.Y., 1956, Appendix Table 1.

[20] Burch Hart Schneider, Feeds of the world—their digestibility and composition, *West Virginia Agr. Exp. Sta.*, 1947.

10.19. Factors Affecting Digestibility. Digestion coefficients are not constants for a given feed or species. They are influenced by several variable factors. Previous discussion (Sec. 4.17) has mentioned various ways in which the breakdown of the higher carbohydrates by rumen bacteria and, in turn, the digestion of other nutrients can be influenced by the nature and relationships of the nutrients fed. It was also mentioned that crude fiber tends to exert a protective influence against the digestibility of all nutrients.

The influence of nutrient relationships in the ration is further illustrated by the results obtained with varying nutritive ratios. As this ratio becomes wider, the digestibility of all nutrients tends to be lower. This is particularly true for protein, and the effect here is readily explainable on the basis of output of metabolic nitrogen, since the protein coefficient determined represents the apparent digestibility (Sec. 6.18). Inasmuch as the metabolic nitrogen is governed by total food intake and thus tends to remain constant although the percentage of protein in the food is lowered, the fecal nitrogen as a whole does not decrease proportionally with the decreased protein intake, even though the residual food nitrogen may. Thus the apparent digestibility of protein is lowered with a wide ratio even though the true value may not be. The lowering of the digestibility of nutrients, other than protein, with a ratio having a wide nutritive ratio is less marked than for protein itself, and published data indicate that it occurs less consistently. In the case of ruminants, however, the addition of protein or of nitrogen compounds utilized by bacteria to a ration having a wide ratio definitely increases the breakdown of the higher carbohydrates, and this in turn makes other nutrients more digestible.

Variations, according to feed sources, in the digestion coefficient for ether extract reflect its variable nature. While in seeds and their by-products this extract consists almost entirely of readily digestible esters of fatty acids, the extract of roughages contains a high proportion of nonsaponifiable constituents as well as nonlipid substances (Sec. 5.17).

Digestibility may be limited by a lack of time for complete digestive action on less easily digestible substances or by a lack of complete absorption. Such an effect is heightened by a rapid passage of the food through the tract. On the other hand, food may move so slowly through the intestines as to be excessively subject to wasteful fermentations. Lack of time for digestion or absorption may explain why, as the level of food intake increases above a certain value, the digestibility of all nutrients tends to decrease. Average digestion coefficients determined at or near maintenance are frequently found not to hold at the level of food intake required for liberal production. The early studies of Eckles[21] showing

[21] C. H. Eckles, Nutrients required for milk production, *Missouri Agr. Expt. Sta. Research Bull.* 7, 1913.

digestibility in the dairy cow to be lower at full feed than at maintenance have been confirmed by later workers.

It is recognized that the digestibility of a mixture is not necessarily the average of the values for its constituents determined separately or indirectly. Each feed may exert an influence on the digestibility of the others. Although it is impossible to determine the specific factors involved in this *associative digestibility*, the previous discussion of the influence of crude-fiber content and of nutritive ratio makes it easy to understand that marked variations from computed averages may occur.

10.20. Influence of Feed Preparation on Digestibility. Grinding grain usually does not increase digestibility in those animals which masticate their feed thoroughly, but seeds which escape mastification may remain largely undigested in passing through the tract. Sheep masticate their feed so effectively that there is no advantage in grinding grain for them, except in the case of very small and hard seeds. Cattle chew their grain less thoroughly and thus digest it somewhat better when it is ground. Grinding helps for very young animals before their teeth are developed and for old animals that have poor teeth. Digestibility in growing swine is only slightly increased by grinding, but the effect is more marked in older animals.

Differing from the case with grains, roughage is chewed by all animals sufficiently to break it up so that the digestive juices can penetrate it. For a given intake, there is no advantage in grinding or chopping hays which are of sufficiently good quality and palatability to be completely consumed without it. Several studies with ground and pelleted hays have shown, however, that, because of their more rapid passage through the tract, total consumption is increased. This has an advantage for fattening cattle and lambs more than offsetting any decrease in digestibility which may occur. Grinding to increase the consumption of low-grade roughage, and particularly the less nutritious portion, is disadvantageous for high production. Blaxter and coworkers,[22] in a study of digestibility-trial techniques with sheep, have reported data regarding the effects of feeding long and pelleted hay on appetite, rate of passage through the tract, and digestibility.

Cooking feeds does not help digestibility in mature farm animals except in the case of a few feeds for swine and poultry. The newborn calf develops the ability to digest uncooked starch rather rapidly. A coefficient of digestibility of 90 per cent at four weeks of age has been reported. None of the various processes of fermenting, "predigesting," and malting which have been exploited as methods for getting more

[22] K. L. Blaxter, N. McC. Graham, and F. W. Wainmax, Some observations on the digestibility of food by sheep and on related problems, *Brit. J. Nutrition,* **10:** 69–91, 1956.

nutrient value from roughages and other fibrous feeds have been found to have any advantage when subjected to critical tests.

A special case in which feed preparation influences animal metabolism and performance is represented by the changes in the concentrations of acetic and propionic acid produced in the rumen and the consequent lowering of milk-fat percentage, which results from the feeding of ground roughage and certain concentrates, as mentioned in Sec. 4.21. Shaw and coworkers[23] have reported that such a ration increased weight gain and feed efficiency in calves.

10.21. The Significance of Digestion-trial Data. The previous discussion has indicated that a variety of factors influence the nature of the results obtained in a digestion trial. This fact must be borne in mind in interpreting the data and applying them to practice. The most significant data for practical application are obtained where the ration is fed at the level required for satisfactory production. This means both an adequate total intake and also an adequate protein content. A sufficient supply of other nutrients is also desirable because a deficiency of some of them may affect digestion processes even though there is no evident effect on production over the short period of the trial. These various considerations can be met in the case of mixed rations, but not in the case of many individual feeds. The alternative in the latter case is to employ the indirect method, which, however, brings in other possible errors as has been discussed.

Digestion data measure the disappearance of the nutrient in passing through the tract in absorption. In the case of ruminants particularly, coefficients for the higher carbohydrates are always too high as a measure of absorbed nutrients because of the gaseous losses. There are some gaseous losses from nitrogen-free extract also. A crude-fiber coefficient is subject to further question because a part of the undigested residues of this feed component may be sufficiently broken down to appear in the nitrogen-free extract of the feces instead of in the crude-fiber portion. In the case of the usual rations for Herbivora, fat-digestion coefficients are subject to rather large errors owing to various causes attributable principally to the ether-extract method. These errors are not of large significance, however, in terms of the digestibility of the ration as a whole because the ether-extract fraction represents such a small part of the total.

Despite these various limitations, digestion coefficients remain distinctly useful. A consideration of the limitations serves to emphasize the importance of proper planning of digestion trials and of the matters

[23] J. C. Shaw and coworkers, Relation of diet to rumen volatile fatty acids, digestibility, efficiency of gain and degree of unsaturation of body fat, *J. Nutrition,* **71**:203–208, 1960.

that should be borne in mind in interpreting the results. Much helpful information along these lines is to be found in the publication by Mitchell.[24] This publication also contains a discussion of the relation between chemical composition and digestibility and considers the usefulness of formulas for calculating digestibility from crude-fiber and protein content. Other studies dealing with this question are cited in the list of papers that follows.

SELECTED LITERATURE

Anderson, Gerald C., and Albert G. Hogan: Adequacy of synthetic diets for growth and reproduction of swine, *J. Animal Sci.,* **9**:163–169, 1950.

Anthony, W. B., and J. T. Reid: Methoxyl as an indicator of the nutritive value of forage, *J. Dairy Sci.,* **41**:1715–1722, 1958.

Balch, C. C., S. Bartlett, and V. W. Johnson: Apparatus for the separate collection of feces and urine from cows, *J. Agr. Sci.,* **41**:98–101, 1951.

Carpenter, K. J.: The concept of an "appetite quotient" for the interpretation of ad libitum feeding experiments, *J. Nutrition,* **51**:435–440, 1953.

Crampton, Earle W., and associates: The apparent digestibility of essentially similar diets by rats, guinea pigs, sheep, swine and by human subjects, *J. Nutrition,* **43**: 541–550, 1951.

———: Design for comparative feeding trials in Techniques and Procedures in Animal Production Research, American Society of Animal Production, 1960, pp. 122–135.

Harris, Lorin E., C. Wayne Cook, and L. A. Stoddart: Range nutrition techniques, *J. Animal Sci.,* **11**:181–190, 1952.

Irwin, H. M., and associates: The role of plant pigments in digestion trial studies, *J. Animal Sci.,* **12**:541–551, 1953.

Loosli, J. K.: Feeding laboratory animals, *Ann. N.Y. Acad. Sci.,* **46**:45–75, 1945.

Lucas, H. L.: Critical features of a good dairy feeding experiment, *J. Dairy Sci.,* **43**:193–212, 1960.

Mitchell, H. H., and Jessie R. Beadles: The determination of the protein requirement of the rat for maximum growth under conditions of restricted consumption of food, *J. Nutrition,* **47**:133–145, 1952.

Putnam, P. A., J. K. Loosli, and R. G. Warner: Excretion of chromium oxide by dairy cows, *J. Dairy Sci.,* **41**:1723–1729, 1958.

Schneider, Burch H., and Henry L. Lucas: The magnitude of certain sources of variability in digestibility data, *J. Animal Sci.,* **9**:504–512, 1950.

Yoshida, M., and H. Morimoto: Reliability of the chromic oxide indicator method for the determination of digestibility with growing chicks, *J. Nutrition,* **61**:31–38, 1957.

[24] H. H. Mitchell, The evaluation of feeds on the basis of digestible and metabolizable nutrients, *J. Animal Sci.,* **1**:159–173, 1942.

Chapter 11
Nutritional Balances

The physiologists of four centuries ago, though they knew nothing about respiration, recognized that there must be some other loss from the body besides those in the feces and urine. They referred to this loss as the *insensible perspiration*, by which they meant the invisible exhalations which are known today as carbon dioxide and water. Sanctorius, a professor in the Medical School at Padua, who died in 1616, spent much of his life trying to measure this insensible loss by weighing himself, his food, and his excreta. An old print shows Sanctorius eating while seated in a chair balanced on a steelyard. He weighed himself before eating, added a weight corresponding to the amount of food he proposed to eat, and stopped eating when his chair dipped.

In making these various measurements, Sanctorius performed what may be termed the first balance experiment. Such an experiment, as we know it today, involves a quantitative accounting for the intake of a given nutrient in the food and for its outgo in the excreta, providing data for determining whether there is a gain or loss of this nutrient by the body. Such an experiment constitutes another method of measuring nutritive value and the state of nutrition of the body. It gives specific information comparable to that of a slaughter experiment, previously described, and has the obvious advantage that it can be carried out with the living animal. Balance measures are commonly divided into two classes: those which deal with substances that can be weighed or measured, the *balance of matter;* and those which include heat losses, the *balance of energy*. A distinction between matter and energy is untenable according to modern physics, but it remains useful for the present discussion.

THE BALANCE OF MATTER

Boussingault[1] carried out the first real balance experiment in 1839. He measured the carbon, hydrogen, oxygen, nitrogen, and ash in the food of a dairy cow receiving a ration that maintained her weight, and the outgo of these nutrients in the feces, urine, and milk. He recognized that he had not accounted for gaseous forms of the elements, and he used his data to estimate the atmospheric oxygen that was required by the cow. Later he made similar studies with a horse and other species. In our nutrition studies of today frequent use is made of the nitrogen balance, of various mineral balances and, to a lesser extent, of the carbon balance.

11.1. The Nitrogen Balance. A determination of the nitrogen in the food and excreta under controlled conditions provides a quantitative measure of the protein metabolism and specifically shows whether the body is gaining or losing protein. This is illustrated by the data in the following table, obtained with a steer receiving 8 lb. of clover hay daily:

Average daily nitrogen	Income, g.	Outgo, g.
In hay	71.4	
In feces	....	28.4
In urine	....	58.5
Lost from body	15.5	
Total	86.9	86.9

It is noted that the daily nitrogen intake was 15.5 g. less than the total outgo from the body and that the animal was thus in *negative nitrogen balance.* It was losing 96.9 g. (15.5 × 6.25) of protein from its body daily, representing the amount by which the intake of protein fell short of meeting the needs of the animal for maintenance. Had the nitrogen intake equaled the outgo, the animal would have been in *nitrogen equilibrium,* the normal picture in the mature animal which is receiving an intake of protein adequate for its needs. An excess of intake over outgo would have represented a *positive nitrogen balance,* involving a storage of protein in the body such as occurs in growth. Such a protein balance shows an increase in actual protein tissue, thus representing a more exact measure of growth than increase in weight which may result in a varying degree from fattening.

[1] J. B. Boussingault, Analyses comparées des aliments consommés et des produits rendus par une vache laitière; recherches entreprises dans le but d'examiner si les animaux herbivores empruntent de l'azote à l'atmosphère, *Ann. chim. et phys.*, (2)**71**:113–127, 1839.

The preceding example represents the simplest form of a nitrogen-balance experiment. The use of a ration consisting of several feeds may or may not require a record of the nitrogen intake from each, depending upon the feeding system and the objective sought. In a study of the protein metabolism in lactation, the nitrogen output in the milk must be accounted for. A determination of a nitrogen balance in a lactating cow shows whether the protein intake is adequate for the milk being produced or whether the milk protein is secreted in part at the expense of the body tissues of the animal. There are slight nitrogen losses in skin excretions and shed hair, amounting to around 1.9 g. per day for the steer as determined in brushings, which are customarily disregarded in nitrogen-balance studies. Although not applicable to species without sweat glands, Mitchell and Hamilton[2] have reported data suggesting that human subjects may lose significant amounts of nitrogen in perspiration in hot, humid environments and at hard work.

A nitrogen-balance experiment is carried out similarly to a digestion trial with the additional provision for the collection and analysis of the urine and of any nitrogenous product such as milk. For the determination of the balance, feces and urine can be collected together, and this is sometimes done, since it is the simpler procedure and eliminates separate analyses. In most experiments, however, it is desirable to know what part of the outgo is indigestible matter and what part represents a loss in metabolism, and for this purpose the collections must be made separately using a metabolism cage as described (Sec. 10.13). The nitrogen-balance method is used to determine the protein requirements for various body functions, to study the quality or biological value of the protein supplied by different feeds and rations, and for other purposes. These various uses are described later (Sec. 14.17), and reference is made to papers which give detailed procedures.

11.2. Mineral Balances. The balance of any mineral element can be obtained in the same way as is done for nitrogen, since the same paths of outgo are involved. In fact, balance studies of nitrogen and of several mineral elements are frequently carried out together in the same experiment. The most frequently determined mineral balances are those for calcium and phosphorus. They provide an accurate measure of bone development during growth and of the adequacy of calcium and phosphorus nutrition for various body functions such as maintenance, pregnancy, and lactation. Their use is described later (Sec. 14.34).

11.3. The Measurement of Gaseous Exchange. In utilizing the balance method to determine the gain or loss of fat in the body and to study the value of any nutrient or ration for the production of energy, it is

[2] H. H. Mitchell and T. S. Hamilton, The dermal excretion under controlled environmental conditions of nitrogen and minerals in human subjects, with particular reference to calcium and iron, *J. Biol. Chem.*, **178**:345–361, 1949.

necessary to ascertain the intake and outgo of carbon. Since this element is eliminated in part in gaseous form, an accounting for such losses becomes essential. The amount of carbon lost through the lungs in respiration is obtained by a measurement of gaseous exchange, involving a determination of the oxygen consumed as well as the carbon dioxide eliminated. This measurement is an important feature also of the determination of the energy metabolism of the body, since the production of energy is an oxidative process which involves the intake of oxygen and the output of carbon dioxide and water. It is to Lavoisier that we owe the discovery of the true significance of respiration[3] as an oxidation comparable to combustion outside the body.

The determination of gaseous exchange can be carried out either by placing the subject in a chamber, the atmosphere of which can be controlled and measured, or by the use of a facepiece which provides for the analysis of the inspired and expired air. The use of the chamber makes possible an accounting for the water lost as perspiration and for the intestinal gases produced (Sec. 4.17), as well as the pulmonary exchange. These gaseous losses resulting from fermentations are of sufficient magnitude in Herbivora, especially ruminants, to require that they be determined or calculated in arriving at a carbon or energy balance. The various devices which are used in either of these methods are referred to as *respiration apparatus.* The earliest forms consisted of closed chambers in which the subject was placed and in which the change in the composition of the air was determined. The limitation of this procedure, which failed to provide for any renewal of the air or removal of waste products during the course of the experiment, is obvious. Two types of apparatus were later devised to remedy this defect: the *closed-circuit type* designed by Regnault and Reiset and the *open-circuit type* developed by Pettenkofer.

The closed-circuit type derived its name from the fact that the same air is continuously circulated, with provision for the removal of the waste products and the addition of oxygen. This apparatus is illustrated diagrammatically in Fig. 11.1. It is noted that the carbon dioxide and water are removed from the outgoing current by absorbents. Their output is determined by recording the increase in weight of the absorbing vessels. The oxygen of the circulating air is renewed through a meter by means of which the volume added is recorded. The residual air at the close of the experiment is analyzed to take account of any changes in composition from that at the start. In this apparatus, the intestinal carbon dioxide is absorbed along with that from the lungs. The other intestinal gases, chiefly methane, can be determined in the residual air. Methane is determined by drawing the air sample over platinized kaolin or a similar substance at red heat. The methane is thus oxidized and determined

[3] See footnote, p. 3.

from the carbon dioxide produced. Methane and other oxidizable gases present are thus referred to as combustible gases, a term which has special significance in connection with the energy balance (Sec. 11.12). Regnault and Reiset used their apparatus for studies with sheep, calves, hogs, and poultry. The same principle is employed in the apparatus designed for man by Atwater and Benedict,[4] but the larger the animal, the greater the difficulty and cost of constructing an airtight unit in which the temperature and humidity are well defined.

The open-circuit type differs from the one just described in that the circulating air is drawn from the atmosphere, and the outgoing air or a measured fraction of it is passed through the absorbents. When it is

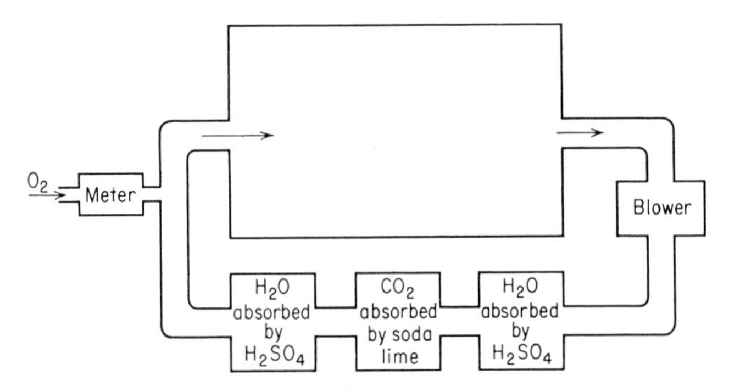

FIG. 11.1. Closed-circuit respiration apparatus.

desired to account for the intestinal gases other than carbon dioxide, provision for their determination in the outgoing air as well as in the residual air of the chamber must be made. The Pettenkofer apparatus, originally designed for studies with men, was adapted for use with farm animals by later German workers, a development with which the names of Henneberg and Stohmann, Kühn, and later Kellner are especially associated.

In either the closed- or open-circuit type the chamber can be replaced by a facepiece or some other device for determining the pulmonary exchange only. Zuntz modified the Pettenkofer apparatus for use with

[4] Wilbur Olin Atwater (1844–1907) served for thirty-four years as professor of chemistry at Wesleyan University, Middletown, Conn. The first agricultural experiment station in the United States was established at Middletown under his direction in 1875. It was later moved to New Haven. Atwater also served as the first chief of the Office of Experiment Stations of the U.S. Department of Agriculture. In 1892, with the assistance of E. B. Rosa, professor of physics at Wesleyan, Atwater began the construction of the first human-respiration calorimeter which he later employed in his pioneer studies of heat production in man, of energy requirements for various body functions, and of the nutritive value of foods. In this work Francis Gano Benedict early became associated. Upon Atwater's death, the calorimetric studies were continued at Boston in the Nutrition Laboratory of the Carnegie Institute of Washington, where for forty years Benedict and his associates carried on outstanding studies of the energy metabolism in man and in various species of animals.

the horse by eliminating the chamber and collecting the expired air by a tracheal canulae, thus providing a portable device which was widely used by early German workers. Flatt and associates[5] describe equipment, designed for studying energy metabolism in grazing animals, which combines a tracheal canulae installation and a lightweight portable gas meter with a continuous portable aliquoting device, as shown in Fig. 11.2. It is noted that the cow is also equipped with a bag for collecting feces and urine.

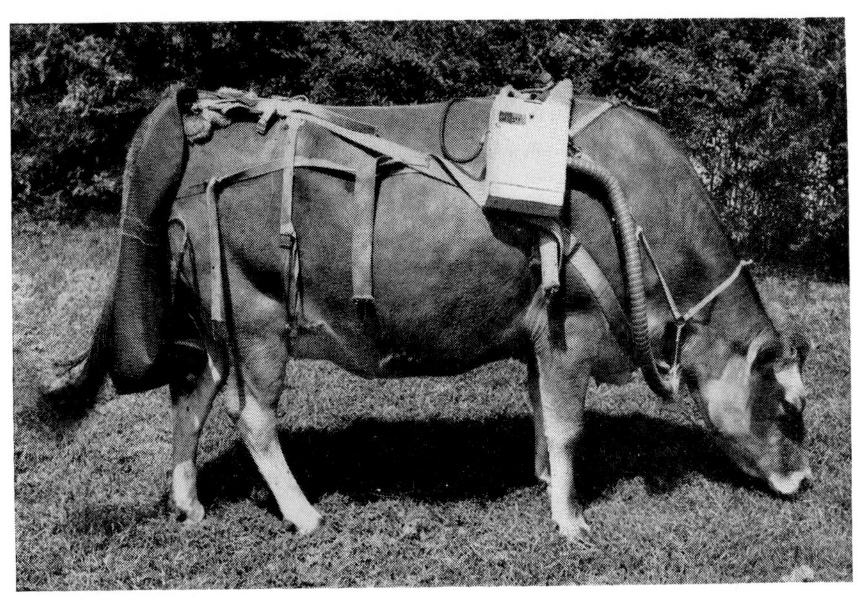

FIG. 11.2. Cow with tracheal canula and equipment for collecting respiratory gases, feces, and urine while grazing. (*Courtesy of W. P. Flatt, U.S. Department of Agriculture.*)

Several workers have devised face masks for farm animals. The problem is to obtain an airtight fit which does not unduly disturb the animal. Fig. 11.3 shows the portable closed-circuit equipment used by Brody, including the spirometer for measuring the oxygen consumption and the tube of soda lime through which the expired air passes for absorption of carbon dioxide. Larger equipment, which provides for measurements over longer periods and for obtaining the respiratory quotient (RQ) as well as the oxygen consumption is described by Blaxter and Howells.[6]

[5] W. P. Flatt and associates, A proposed method for indirect calorimetry for energy metabolism studies with large animals under field conditions. Proc. I. Symposium on energy metabolism, Copenhagen, *European Assoc. for Animal Production Publ.* 8, 1958, pp. 101–109.

[6] K. L. Blaxter and A. Howells, The nutrition of the Ayrshire calf. II. A spirometer for the determination of respiratory exchange in the calf, *Brit. J. Nutrition,* **5**:25–29, 1951.

FIG. 11.3. Apparatus for measuring pulmonary exchange. (*Courtesy of S. Brody, Missouri Agricultural Experiment Station.*)

11.4. Respiratory Quotient. The relation between the oxygen consumed and the carbon dioxide given off in respiration is expressed as the respiratory quotient (RQ), computed as follows:

$$\frac{\text{Volume of } CO_2 \text{ produced}}{\text{Volume of } O_2 \text{ consumed}} = RQ$$

The numerical value of this quotient is dependent upon the chemical nature of the substance being oxidized within the body. The burning of a molecule of glucose, the form in which carbohydrates are catabolized, takes place according to the following equation:

$$C_6H_{12}O_6 + 6O_2 \longrightarrow 6CO_2 + 6H_2O + \text{heat}$$

Since the carbohydrate molecule contains hydrogen and oxygen in the proportion to form water, oxygen from the outside is required only for the oxidation of the carbon. One molecule of carbon dioxide is formed for each molecule of oxygen consumed, and therefore the RQ is 1.0. The fat molecule, on the other hand, does not contain nearly enough oxygen to take care of the hydrogen present, and thus a part of the oxygen used in burning fats appears as water. More oxygen is consumed, therefore, than is represented by the carbon dioxide given off, and the RQ becomes less than 1.0. For most body and food fats, it is approximately 0.7. Such is the case for triolein, for example, as shown by the following equation for its complete oxidation:

$$C_3H_5(OOCC_{17}H_{33})_3 + 80O_2 \longrightarrow 57CO_2 + 52H_2O + \text{heat}$$

For protein the basis for computing the RQ is less certain because the mode of its utilization in the body varies, because it is incompletely oxidized in catabolism, and because different ones vary in composition. The average figure commonly given for the RQ of protein is 0.8.

The magnitude of the RQ gives an approximate idea of the kind of nutrient which is being burned in the body. The closer the quotient approaches unity, the larger is the proportion of carbohydrates being used, while values lying close to 0.7 indicate that fat predominates as the body fuel. The meaning of an intermediate value is less clear, since the quotient for protein lies in between those for carbohydrate and fat, and since a determined quotient may represent the result of the burning of variable proportions of all three. Respiratory quotients larger than unity are sometimes obtained, and they are explainable either on the basis that carbon dioxide is temporarily being given off more rapidly than it is being produced or on the basis that carbohydrate is being converted into a fat in the body. The synthesis of oxygen-poor fats from the relatively oxygen-rich carbohydrates involves a liberation of carbon dioxide. Wierzuchowski and Ling[7] report quotients of 1.4 and higher in rapidly fattening hogs, and they cite a quotient of similar magnitude obtained by Benedict for the goose. On the other hand, RQ's below 0.7 have been observed in fasting, particularly in hibernating animals, and they may be the result of the conversion of fat into carbohydrate.

11.5. The Nitrogen-Carbon Balance. When carried out in conjunction with the nitrogen balance which measures changes in protein content, a carbon balance provides the additional data needed to obtain the gain or loss of fat. In thus measuring the changes in protein and fat content, an approximately complete picture of the influence of food upon the organic composition of the body is obtainable, since its carbohydrate content is so small. Determinations are made of the carbon and nitrogen in the food, feces, and excreta and of the carbon in the gaseous output. Recognizing the limitations of his determinations of digestibility as measures of feed value, Henneberg, prior to 1870, turned his attention to the nitrogen-carbon balance in farm animals, taking his cue from the work of Voit and associates with man. Later a respiration chamber for large animals was built at the Möckern Experiment Station under the direction of Gustav Kühn, and studies were undertaken which were carried out for the most part by Kühn's successor, O. Kellner.[8]

[7] M. Wierzuchowski and S. M. Ling, On fat production in a young hog, *J. Biol. Chem.*, **64**:697–707, 1925.

[8] Oscar Kellner (1851–1911), following short periods of service in the agricultural experiment stations at Proskau and Hohenheim and an extended period as professor of agricultural chemistry at the University of Tokyo, became director of the experiment station at Möckern in 1893. Here he served until his death. His many accurately conducted respiration studies with farm animals made a large contribution to the fundamental knowledge of nutritional physiology and found practical application in his feeding standards. Kellner's textbook, Die Ernährung der landwirtschaftliche Nutztiere, the first edition of which was published in 1905, contains an extensive account of his respiration studies and describes his feeding standards.

As an example of a nitrogen-carbon balance, the data from one of Kellner's experiments are presented in a condensed form in Table 11.1. It is noted that from the nitrogen balance the amount of carbon gained as protein is calculated and that this value subtracted from the total carbon gained gives a figure which represents that gained as fat, from which the amount of fat can be computed. The computation is based upon the fact that the carbon content of the body exists almost entirely as protein and fat. It disregards the small amount of glycogen which

TABLE 11.1. EXAMPLE OF A NITROGEN-CARBON BALANCE*

Item	Nitrogen		Carbon	
	Intake, g.	Outgo, g.	Intake, g.	Outgo, g.
Feed	390.55	......	5668.2	
Feces	......	105.69	......	1456.9
Urine	......	263.76	......	283.3
Gases	......	......	......	3247.9
Gain to body	......	21.10	......	680.1
Total	390.55	390.55	5668.2	5668.2

NOTE: Based upon a content of 52.54† per cent carbon and 16.67† per cent nitrogen in fat-free, ash-free flesh and of 76.5 per cent carbon in fat, the following calculations gave the protein and fat gained:

21.1 g. nitrogen gain divided by 0.1667 equaled 126.6 g. *protein gain.*
126.6 g. protein times 0.5254 equaled 66.5 g. carbon in protein.
680.1 g. carbon gain minus 66.5 equaled 613.6 g. carbon gained as fat.
613.6 divided by 0.765 equaled 802.1 g. *fat gain.*

* Data from O. Kellner and A. Kohler, Untersuchungen über den Stoff- und Energieumsatz des erwachsenen Rindes der Erhaltungs- und Produktionsfütter, *Landw. Vers. Sta.*, **53**:1–16, 1900.

† Figures used by later workers are slightly different.

is normally present, since it is considered that any changes in this constituent are so small as to be of very minor importance under normal feeding conditions. This is less true when the diet is such as to cause a loss, rather than a storage, of fat. For experiments over an extended period, disregarding the glycogen is of no concern, but in experiments of only a few hours' duration, a considerable error may be introduced. The glycogen changes can be estimated by including determinations of hydrogen and oxygen in the balance data, a procedure which makes the experiment much more difficult and laborious. The most important use of the carbon- and nitrogen-balance method today is in connection with indirect calorimetry (Sec. 11.14).

11.6. Kellner's Starch Values. Using the nitrogen-carbon-balance method, Kellner added pure carbohydrate, protein, and fat to a basal-maintenance ration and thus determined the relative amounts of these pure digestible nutrients required to produce a unit of body fat. When he tested feeding stuffs instead of pure nutrients, he found that the fat-producing power was less than calculated from their content of digestible nutrients and that the discrepancy was larger with those feeds high in fiber. He concluded, therefore, that some of the calculated fat-producing power was lost as a result of the "work of digestion" which increased with fiber content. Having determined the actual fat-producing power of a number of typical feeds, he worked out factors for estimating the loss which he ascribed to the work of digestion for feeds of varying fiber content. He thus obtained a basis for computing fat-producing power for a given feed from its content of digestible nutrients. He did not express this fat-producing power of the feed directly but rather in terms of the number of kilograms of starch that would be required to produce the same amount of fat as 100 kg. of the feed. Hence his values were called *starch equivalents,* or *starch values.* For example, the starch value of corn (maize) meal, 81.5 kg., was the amount of starch which would produce as much fat as 100 kg. of the meal. Expressed in pounds, the starch value of corn meal is thus 81.5 per 100 lb. of feed. In the appendix of his book, Kellner published such values for approximately 300 feeds, a few of which are listed below:

Oats	59.7
Wheat	71.3
Linseed oil meal	71.8
Wheat bran	45.0
Timothy hay	29.1
Oat straw	17.0

Kellner's starch values became the basis of his feeding standard, and his system is still used, with various modifications, for evaluating feeds and computing rations for animals in many European countries. The system, as used in Great Britain, is described in the bulletin by Woodman.[9]

THE BALANCE OF ENERGY

The largest purpose which food serves is the production of energy for body processes. Since all the organic nutrients can serve this purpose, energy value provides a common basis for expressing their nutritive value. The fact that all these nutrients, notably protein, may have specific and unique functions as well does not alter their common usefulness as sources of energy. This holds whether they are used for

[9] H. E. Woodman, Rations for livestock, *Ministry Agr. and Fisheries (Engl.) Bull.* 48, 13th ed., 1954.

the purpose immediately upon absorption or are built into body tissue; for the glycogen and fat of the body constitute reserves which can be used as needed, and when these supplies are exhausted, the protein of structural tissues can be broken down to serve as energy. Thus a measure of the gain or loss of energy provides a useful measure of the state of nutrition of the body and of the relative value of various foods. It takes into account a further loss not measurable by the balances previously discussed, viz., the loss of heat.

11.7. Units of Energy Value. Mention has been made (Sec. 3.7) that the energy which can serve the body is the free energy (ΔF), as distinguished from the heat energy (ΔH). Thus as a means of arriving at the useful energy of a food, we would like to measure its free energy. Since this is impossible and since all forms of energy are convertible into heat, it has been found convenient to express the energy changes of body processes in terms of heat units (calories). In this connection it is important to realize that it is not heat itself which the body uses. The body is not a heat engine (Sec. 17.2). The *small calorie* is defined as the amount of heat required to raise 1 g. of water 1°C. The *large Calorie,* written with a capital C to distinguish it from the small calorie, is the amount required to raise 1 kg. of water 1°C. This unit, which is the one used in expressing the energy value of foods, is also called the *kilocalorie* (kcal.) The latter term[10] is the one used in this text, instead of Calorie. A *Therm* is 1000 kcal. and is used as a matter of convenience when large values are involved. The term megacalorie (megacal. or mcal.) is also in use to designate 1000 kcal. One kilocalorie equals approximately 4 British thermal units (B.t.u.). This unit is the amount of heat required to raise 1 lb. of water 1°F.

11.8. Gross Energy, or Heat of Combustion. When a substance is completely burned to its ultimate oxidation products, viz., carbon dioxide, water, and other gases, the heat given off is considered as its gross energy, or heat of combustion. This measure is the starting point in determining the energy value of foods. The determination is carried out in a calorimeter, of which there are various types.

The *bomb calorimeter* consists essentially of a bomb in which the food is burned, enclosed in an insulated jacket containing water which surrounds the bomb and which thus provides the means of measuring the heat produced. The construction of the Parr oxygen calorimeter is illustrated in Fig. 11.4. In *A*, the bomb is shown in cross section. A weighed amount of substance to be tested is placed in the cup *a* of the bomb, and the fuse wire *b* connecting the two terminals is put in place.

[10] This usage, which has necessitated changes from the original in certain tables reproduced in the text, is in the interest of clarity in situations where the rules of capitalization call for a capital C whether or not a kilocalorie is meant.

The cover is screwed on and the bomb charged with 25 to 30 atmospheres of oxygen. The bomb is then placed in the calorimeter jacket as shown in *B*, surrounded by a known volume of water. The stirrer is started, and when the temperature becomes constant, the charge is ignited electrically and readings are taken on the thermometer to ascertain the maximum rise. This value multiplied by the sum of thermal capacity of the metal parts and the mass of water gives the number of calories

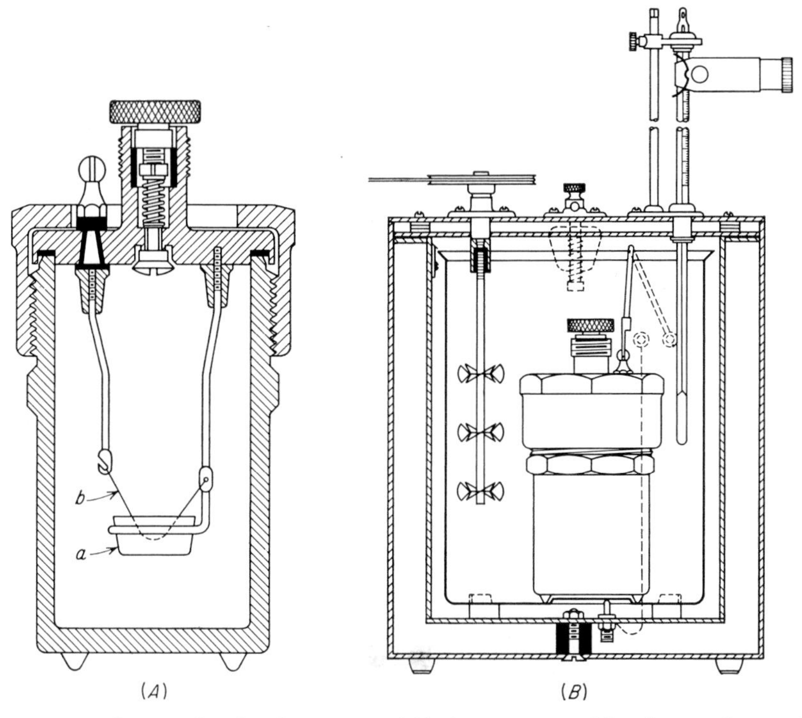

FIG. 11.4. The Parr bomb calorimeter. (*A*) Cross section of bomb; *a* is the cup in the bomb, and *b* is the fuse wire. (*B*) Cross section of calorimeter with bomb in place. (*Reproduced by permission of the Parr Instrument Company, Moline, Ill.*)

produced by the burning of the sample. Various corrections are required for radiation, for the fuse wire, for acids produced, and other factors in arriving at the final figure for the calorific value of the food. The radiation corrections are eliminated in the *adiabatic type* of bomb calorimeter.

The gross energy values of some pure nutrients and feeding stuffs are given in Table 11.2.

It is noted that among the pure nutrients the fats have approximately twice the energy value of the carbohydrates and that the proteins occupy an intermediate position. These differences are governed by elementary composition, especially the relative amount of oxygen contained in the molecule, since heat is produced only from the oxidation which results from the union with oxygen from without (Sec. 11.4). In the case of carbohydrates, there is enough oxygen present in the molecule to take care of all the hydrogen present, and thus heat arises only from the oxidation of the carbon. In the case of fat, however, there is relatively much less oxygen present and relatively more atoms requiring oxygen from without, and the combustion involves the oxidation of hydrogen as well as carbon. The burning of 1 g. of hydrogen produces over four times as much heat as is the case for carbon. These facts explain the much greater gross energy values for the fats compared with the carbohydrates. The heat produced in the burning of protein comes from the oxidation of both carbon and hydrogen, but the nitrogen present gives rise to no heat at all because it is set free as such in its gaseous form. No oxidation of it has taken place, and thus no heat is produced.

TABLE 11.2. GROSS ENERGY VALUES, OR HEATS OF COMBUSTION
(Dry-matter basis)

Pure nutrients	*Kcal. per g.*	*Feeding stuffs*	*Kcal. per g.*
Glucose	3.76	Corn meal	4.43
Sucrose	3.96	Oats	4.68
Starch	4.23	Soybeans	5.52
Butterfat	9.21	Wheat bran	4.54
Lard	9.48	Linseed oil meal	5.12
Seed fat	9.33	Timothy hay	4.51
Casein	5.86	Clover hay	4.47
Elastin	5.96	Corn stover	4.33
Gliadin	5.74	Oat straw	4.43

These differences in elementary composition also explain the differences which occur among members of the three classes of nutrients. In both starch and glucose, for example, the hydrogen is taken care of by the oxygen in the molecule, but there is relatively more carbon in 1 g. of starch than in 1 g. of glucose, and thus starch has the higher energy value accordingly. The following values were derived by Atwater and Bryant as the heats of combustion of the three classes of nutrients as they occur in foods making up the average United States mixed diet (Sec. 11.10). These figures provide a basis for computing the gross energy

Carbohydrates	4.15 kcal. per gram
Fats	9.40 kcal. per gram
Protein	5.65 kcal. per gram

SOURCE: W. O. Atwater and A. P. Bryant, The availability and fuel value of food materials, *Storrs Agr. Expt. Sta. Ann. Rept.*, 1899, pp. 73–110.

values from chemical composition. They also serve to explain the differences in gross energy among various feedstuffs exemplified in Table 11.2. Fat content is of special importance because of its high heat of combustion. The difference between the values for the soybean, an oil-bearing seed, and for the cereal grains, which contain only about one-fifth as much fat, is illustrative of this.

11.9. Metabolizable Energy. Not all of the gross energy as determined in the bomb calorimeter is useful to the body. By determining the heat of combustion of the feces and subtracting this value from the gross energy of the feed one obtains the *digestible energy.* There is a further loss in digestion which is of practical significance in the case of ruminants, viz., the combustible gases, primarily methane, which are produced in the breakdown of carbohydrates by microorganisms. While these gases are readily burned, giving rise to heat which is included in gross energy, their energy is not useful to the body. A further portion of the gross energy escapes unused because, in the case of protein, the complete oxidation which gives rise to this energy value does not take place in the body. Whereas the end products of protein oxidation in the calorimeter are carbon dioxide, water, and nitrogen, catabolism in the body results in urea and other incompletely oxidized nitrogenous end products which are excreted in the urine.

A determination of the heats of combustion of the feces and urine and a measurement or calculation of the calorific value of any combustible gases produced in the digestive tract furnish data as to the part of the ingested gross energy which is unavailable to the body. The sum of these losses subtracted from the gross energy gives what is called *metabolizable energy*—the portion of the total which is actually capable of transformation within the body. There are small amounts of energy which escape as perspiration, epidermal scales, and shed hair. If accounted for, they should be subtracted in arriving at metabolizable energy, but they are so small that no significant error is ordinarily involved in neglecting them.

An illustration of the data involved in the determination of metabolizable energy is given in Table 11.3, comprising figures obtained with sheep by Hamilton, Mitchell, and Kammlade. It is noted that by far the largest part of the losses is that which occurs in the feces as a result of lack of digestion. This illustrates the fact that metabolizable energy takes account of the same losses, for the most part, as does digestible energy. It does represent a more accurate measure, since further losses are accounted for. The much larger fecal loss for the straw is the primary factor causing its lower metabolizable energy, corresponding to its lower digestibility. The straw has a smaller urinary loss than does the hay because of its lower content of protein, the nutrient which is less completely oxidized in metabolism than in the bomb. The urine data in this table contain the corrections called for to arrive at exact metabolizable energy values when the subject is losing or gaining body protein, using the correction factors suggested by Rubner. These factors call for the subtraction of 7.45 kcal. for each gram of nitrogen lost from the body (represented by a negative N balance) and the addition of 7.45 kcal. for each gram of nitrogen stored (represented by a positive N balance).

The determination of the metabolizable energy of a feed for a nonruminant requires no accounting for methane and, thus, is similar to a nitrogen- or mineral-balance experiment. The measurement of the

TABLE 11.3. METABOLIZABLE ENERGY OF FEEDS FOR SHEEP*

Feed	Dry matter eaten per day per head, kg.	Energy per kilogram of dry matter, Therms				
		Intake in food	Losses			Metabolizable
			Feces	Urine	Methane	
Soybean hay.....	0.795	4.333	2.033	0.196	0.208	1.896
Soybean straw...	0.674	4.345	2.676	0.042	0.229	1.398

* Data from T. S. Hamilton, H. H. Mitchell, and W. G. Kammlade, The digestibility and metabolizable energy of soybean products for sheep, *Illinois Agr. Expt. Sta. Bull.* 303, 1928.

methane production, however, called for in the case of cattle and sheep, requires an airtight chamber for housing the animal (Sec. 11.15). This makes the determination a complicated and expensive one in terms of both equipment and operation. For this reason most of the metabolizable-energy values reported in the literature have involved the calculation of methane production rather than its actual measurement. The data presented in Table 11.3 were calculated on the basis that 4.5 g. of methane is produced per 100 g. of digested carbohydrate—a relationship proposed by Armsby from experiments with the respiration calorimeter (Sec. 11.12).

Several studies have been made of the data of metabolism experiments in which the combustible gases were actually determined to develop formulas for the calculation of these methane losses from the total dry matter or from the digested nutrients of the ration. Swift and coworkers[11] have developed a formula for sheep and compared it with the one

[11] R. W. Swift and coworkers, The effect of dietary fat on utilization of the energy and protein of rations by sheep, *J. Animal Sci.*, 7:475–485, 1948.

earlier developed at the Pennsylvania Institute of Animal Nutrition for cattle. The two formulas are as follows:

$$\text{(sheep) } E = 2.41X + 9.80$$
$$\text{(cattle) } E = 4.012X + 17.68$$

where E = methane in grams and X = digested carbohydrate in hundreds of grams. Methane contains 13.34 kcal. per gram.

A comprehensive study of the European data for cattle has been made by Axelsson.[12] Formulas are presented for calculating methane energy from dry matter, digested carbohydrates or digested crude fiber. The formulas proposed for making the calculation from digested carbohydrates are as follows:

$$Y_2 = 984X_2 - 64.2X_2^2 - 213$$

or

$$Y_2 = 1083X_2^{0.638}$$

where Y_2 = methane energy in kilocalories and X_2 = digested carbohydrates in kilograms. These formulas are considered useful for obtaining approximate values but not for critical research purposes. The energy lost as methane with most of the usual rations of ruminants is approximately 5 to 8 per cent of the gross intake. The determination of the metabolizable energy of feeds for chicks is illustrated by the study of Hill and Anderson,[13] in which the chromium oxide indicator method was used to avoid the need for quantitative measurements of feed intake and excretion.

11.10. Physiological Fuel Values. These are calorific values for nutrients as originally set forth by Atwater for use in human nutrition to calculate the portion of the gross energy which is available for transformation in the body, a calculation which resulted in figures having a similar significance as metabolizable energy. Account was taken of losses in digestion on the basis of the following average figures for digestibility of a mixed diet: carbohydrates, 98 per cent; fats, 95 per cent; protein, 92 per cent. The figures for gross energy were multiplied by these coefficients, and in the case of protein a subtraction of 1.25 kcal. per grain was made for the energy lost in the urine. This factor was obtained by studies with men eating mixed diets. It varies somewhat with the make-up of the diet. By these calculations the average physiological fuel values became:

Carbohydrates	$4.15 \times 98\%$	= 4 kcal. per g.
Fats	$9.4 \times 95\%$	= 9 kcal. per g.
Protein	$(5.65 - 1.25) \times 92\%$	= 4 kcal. per g.

[12] Joel Axelsson, The amount of produced methane energy in the European metabolic experiments with adult cattle, *Ann. Roy. Agr. Coll. Sweden,* **16**:405–419, 1949.

[13] F. W. Hill and D. L. Anderson, Comparison of the metabolizable energy and productive energy determinations for chicks, *J. Nutrition,* **64**:587–603, 1958.

These values are not applicable to feeds and rations of farm animals because the digestibility figures on which they are based are too high. The factor 1.25 kcal. is too low to estimate the urine loss in the case of Herbivora because of the relatively large amount of hippuric acid excreted. The average physiological fuel values have limitations, for use with certain human foods and diets, which can be overcome by making use of Atwater's basic data, as is done in the U.S. Department of Agriculture publication[14] on food composition.

11.11. Heat Loss. In addition to the losses which are subtracted in obtaining metabolizable energy, the energy balance must take account of a further loss, viz., that energy escaping in the form of heat. In every cell of a living organism, chemical reactions are constantly occurring as an essential accompaniment and manifestation of life processes. Most of these reactions are oxidative in nature and produce heat. There results a continual outgo of heat from the body in amounts which represent a considerable fraction of the total income of chemical energy. The heat that is eliminated from the body may constitute 25 to 40 per cent or even more of the gross calorie intake. It is therefore of large importance in nutrition from the standpoint both of the economy of food utilization and of body-temperature relations.

In all warm-blooded animals the maintenance of a constant body temperature is a factor affecting heat production and heat outgo. Since the temperature of the body is normally above its environment, the heat constantly being produced serves in the maintenance of this temperature. The environmental temperature and the amount of heat being produced within the body are the factors which determine the extent to which this heat must be conserved. The amount which is allowed to escape from the body is subject to control which is referred to as *physical regulation*. This control is brought about by an adjustment of the blood flow to the skin and by the perspiration mechanism. If the conditions call for the dissipation of body heat, the blood flow to the surface is increased as a result of a dilation of the capillaries, which facilitates the escape of heat by radiation, and the pores are opened, which allows for a loss of heat through evaporation. These processes are reversed when there is need for the conservation of body heat.

The effects of a low environmental temperature may be combated also by *chemical regulation*, involving the increased oxidation of body substance and resulting in an increased heat production. Shivering is an involuntary form of muscular activity, the function of which appears to be to increase heat production when physical regulation proves insufficient. The environmental temperature at which physical regulation

[14] Bernice K. Watt and Annabelle L. Merrill, Composition of foods—raw, processed, prepared, *U.S. Dept. Agr. Handbook* 8, 1950.

proves insufficient to maintain body temperature, and the point, therefore, at which chemical regulation must come into play, is called the *critical temperature.* As determined for the quiet-fasting condition, the following values have been reported: rat, 28°C.; mouse 29 to 30°C.; chick, 17°C.; guinea pig, 32 to 33°C.; rabbit, 27 to 28°C.; hog, 21°C. These values are modified by humidity and other factors. Removing the hair coat, as in shearing, raises them, and so does exposure to wind. Increasing fatness tends to lower the critical temperature of the individual by increasing the insulating layer under the skin.

As the environmental temperature is raised above the critical, physical regulation operates without any increase in metabolism until this regulation becomes insufficient to cool the body. At this point a supernormal body temperature ensues, referred to as the *hyperthermal rise.* This in turn results in an increased metabolism. The range of temperature between the critical and the point of hyperthermal rise is referred to as the *range of thermal neutrality,* and it is in this range that basal metabolism studies are made (Sec. 13.1).

By using the same principle that is employed in measuring the heat produced by burning a feed in a bomb calorimeter, the heat loss resulting from body oxidation processes may be measured by enclosing the animal in a specially constructed chamber called an *animal calorimeter.* Such an apparatus for use with pigs is described by Deighton.[15]

11.12. Respiration Calorimeter. The direct measurement of heat loss can also be carried out in a respiration calorimeter which combines the features of a respiration chamber and a calorimeter. Such an apparatus makes possible an accounting for the income of feed, water, and oxygen and the outgo of the solid, liquid, and gaseous excreta and of the heat eliminated. In the lactating animal, milk outgo can also be accounted for. Shortly after Atwater and his associates perfected their respiration calorimeter for use with man, Armsby[16] built a similar one for experiments with cows at Pennsylvania State College, introducing certain modifications required for use with animals. This calorimeter is still in active

[15] Thomas Deighton, A new calorimeter for use with young farm animals, *J. Agr. Sci.,* **16**:376–382, 1926.

[16] Henry Prentiss Armsby (1853–1921), following periods of service at the New Jersey, Connecticut, and Wisconsin Experiment Stations, became director of the newly established Pennsylvania Experiment Station at State College in 1887. In 1907 the Institute of Animal Nutrition was established at this institution with Armsby as director, and here he served until his death, winning lasting fame for himself and his institute. During his postgraduate study at Leipzig, he became interested in the respiration experiments being carried out by Kühn and others at Möckern, and this resulted in his construction of a respiration calorimeter for farm animals and in the inauguration of his studies of heat production in cattle. These epoch-making studies, which led to the development of the net-energy system of evaluating feeds, are frequently referred to in this book.

service. The following brief description of it is taken from a bulletin by Braman.[17]

A horizontal cross section of the respiration calorimeter is shown in Fig. 11.5. The three walls, with the air spaces in between, provide the special construction which prevents the chamber from gaining or losing heat. This is accomplished by maintaining the temperature in the air spaces the same as in the chamber by means of water pipes for cooling and resistance coils for heating, both of which are located in the air spaces. The necessity for heating or cooling is determined by a large

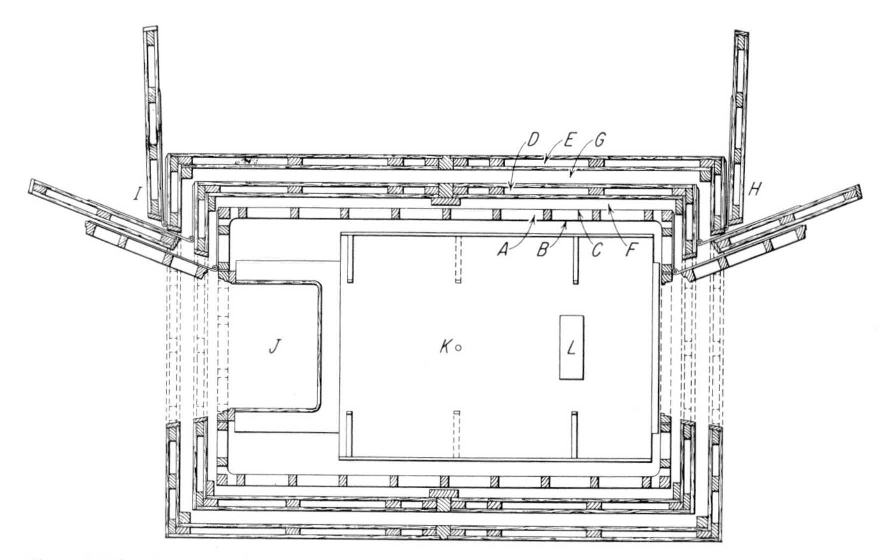

FIG. 11.5. Horizontal cross section of the Armsby respiration calorimeter. *A*, double metal wall. *B*, inner wall of copper. *C*, outer wall of zinc. *D* and *E*, double wooden walls. *F* and *G*, air spaces. *H*, entrance doors. *I*, feedbox doors. *J*, feedbox, *K*, opening for urine tube. *L*, opening for feces hopper. (*Courtesy of E. B. Forbes, Institute of Animal Nutrition.*)

number of thermocouples in the walls of the inner metal chamber and of the wooden chamber next outside. This control is so delicate that changes as small as 0.01°C. can be detected and immediately corrected.

The heat lost by the animal is removed as fast as eliminated by cold water flowing through a series of pipes suspended from the ceiling of the chamber. The heat thus removed is translated into calories by recording the difference in temperature between the ingoing and outflowing water and the water volume. This heat plus the latent heat of vaporization of moisture condensed on the heat-absorbing apparatus or carried out in the air current gives the heat loss.

[17] Winfred W. Braman, The respiration calorimeter, *Pennsylvania Agr. Expt. Sta. Bull.* 302, 1933.

A steady flow of air is drawn in and out of the chamber by a special pump, and its volume is measured by passing it through a meter. The entrance flue is equipped with both heating and cooling facilities to keep the temperature of the incoming air identical with that of the outgoing, thus avoiding the error which would otherwise be introduced in the measurement of the heat lost. A continuous sample is drawn from the incoming air for the determination of water and carbon dioxide by absorption and of any methane by combustion. Continuous samples are taken from the outgoing air for the same determinations, and there is also provision for analyzing this air for oxygen. These measurements, together with analyses of the chamber air at the beginning and end of the period, provide the data for gaseous exchange.

It is noted in the diagram that there are openings for the discharge of urine and feces. The one for urine is for use with a steer equipped with a harness holding a tube leading to a urine receptacle under the floor. Similarly, there is special equipment for guiding the feces through L into a container underneath. These features provide for the quantitative collection of the excreta. In addition to the arrangement for feeding as indicated by the feedbox, there is also provision for watering. There are many other features, such as devices for recording the movement of the animal and for accounting for the proportion of the time spent standing and lying down. For further details of the construction and operation, the student is referred to the descriptive bulletin.

A test in the respiration calorimeter is normally preceded by a considerable preliminary period during which the animal receives the same feed intake as that during the test. A digestion trial is commonly carried out during the preliminary period. Of course, the digestion trial, as well as feeding during the test itself, is omitted when fasting metabolism is being studied. An accounting is made for insensible losses from the animal by weighing it at the beginning and end and by taking into account the weights of food, water, and excreta. It is evident that the conduct of a test in the respiration calorimeter requires a high degree of skill. The accuracy of the apparatus itself is amazing. The heat and gaseous products of combustion which are obtained by burning a known amount of alcohol in a special lamp in the chamber are generally found to be within less than 1 per cent of the theoretical values.

An illustration of the data obtained in an experiment carried out in a respiration calorimeter is given in Table 11.4. It is noted that an accounting for all energy losses left a balance of 608 kcal. as the net gain to the animal from the feed ingested. The striking feature of these data is the large loss of energy as heat, representing approximately 40 per cent of the total intake. The importance of giving attention to heat losses in measuring the usefulness of feeds is thus indicated.

TABLE 11.4. DAILY ENERGY BALANCE OF A STEER*

Items	Income, kcal.	Outgo, kcal.
6,988 g. timothy hay	27,727	
400 g. linseed meal	1,811	
16,619 g. feces	......	14,243
4,357 g. urine	......	1,210
37 g. brushings	......	88
142 g. methane	......	1,896
Heat	......	11,493
Gain by body	......	608
Total	29,538	29,538

* Data from Henry Prentiss Armsby and J. August Fries, The available energy of timothy hay, *U.S. Dept. Agr. Bur. Animal Ind. Bull.* 51, 1903.

11.13. Net-energy Values. In connection with his studies with the respiration calorimeter, Armsby developed his net-energy system of evaluating feeds founded upon a concept not basically different from that underlying Kellner's starch value (Sec. 11.6). While not agreeing that it was literally "work of digestion" in its entirety, Armsby recognized that the assimilation of a feed resulted in an energy cost to the organism in addition to those losses accounted for in arriving at metabolizable energy and that this energy cost could be measured as the heat lost from the body. He therefore measured the heat resulting from the ingestion of a feed at a given level of intake, increased the intake, and, by a second measurement, obtained by difference the *heat increment* (Sec. 11.6) corresponding to the amount by which the level of food intake was increased. He then subtracted the heat increment, expressed in terms of a given unit of intake, from the metabolizable energy of the same intake to obtain the net-energy value. In the case of concentrates, it was necessary to add them to a basal roughage ration in measuring their net-energy value with steers. Some of Armsby's values and the data on which they were based are given in Table 11.5.

Since the direct determination of net-energy values was necessarily slow and expensive, Armsby and Fries developed, from respiration calorimeter experiments, factors for computing metabolizable energy values from digestible organic matter. Given the metabolizable energy for a feed, they subtracted the value for its heat increment either directly determined or estimated from the value for a similar feed. In this way they prepared a table of net-energy values for the common feeds. Later studies by Forbes and Kriss[18] resulted in improved methods of computing

[18] E. B. Forbes and Max Kriss, Revised net-energy values of feeding stuffs for cattle, *J. Agr. Research*, **31**:1083–1099, 1925.

these values from Armsby's data and in the publication of a table of revised values.

It is evident that both Kellner and Armsby arrived at essentially the same measure of feed values, the former by calculating the productive value as measured by the gain in fat shown by the carbon-nitrogen balance, the latter by directly accounting for all losses and thus arriving at a value which represented energy gained. In fact, Kellner stated his gains in fat in calories, and he computed the percentage of metabolizable energy thus stored, but he expressed the energy value of his feeds in terms of matter instead of calories, because he felt that starch values

TABLE 11.5. NET-ENERGY VALUES OF FEEDS FOR RUMINANTS*
(Therms per 100 lb. of dry matter)

Feeds	Gross energy	Losses in excreta	Metabolizable energy	Heat increment	Net energy
Timothy hay	204.94	120.84	84.10	35.47	48.63
Red clover hay	202.40	111.63	90.77	44.13	46.64
Corn stover	196.50	107.96	88.54	48.31	40.23
Corn meal	201.49	50.58	150.91	58.33	92.58
Hominy feed	213.60	53.84	159.76	61.92	97.84
Wheat bran	205.57	91.67	113.90	53.39	60.51
Wheat straw	201.58	138.89	62.69	52.62	11.07

* Data from Henry Prentiss Armsby and J. August Fries, Net energy values for ruminants, *Pennsylvania Agr. Expt. Sta. Bull.* 142, 1916.

would be more readily understood in practice. Armsby regarded Kellner's figures as real net-energy values, and he made use of them in preparing his own table.

11.14. Indirect Calorimetry. The measurement of heat loss as just described is referred to as *direct calorimetry* in contrast to *indirect calorimetry*, which is based on a calculation of the heat production responsible for the loss measured directly. Such a calculation is possible if the complete chemical metabolism is known, since every chemical process is related to a definite transformation of energy. Fortunately, it is not necessary to know all the chemical changes, but only the initial and final states, because the sum of all transformations of chemical energy results in a heat production which is independent of any variations in the intermediary processes (law of Hess). The heat loss can thus be computed either from the data of a nitrogen and carbon balance or from the data of gaseous exchange.

The procedure of the first method, most applicable to animals receiving feed, may be illustrated from the work of Armsby. He used the data of nitrogen-carbon balances to compute the heat loss in order to compare the values thus obtained with those actually observed in the calorimeter. For example, data obtained in connection with the energy balance listed in Table 11.4 showed gains of nitrogen and carbon which corresponded to gains of 66.6 g. of protein and 15.2 g. of fat. On the basis that the energy value of each gram of protein stored is 5.7 kcal. and of each gram of fat, 9.5 kcal., he calculated that the total energy thus gained was 524 kcal. The metabolizable energy was calculated from the data in the table by subtracting all outgo except heat from the total income, giving a figure of 12,101 kcal. Subtracting the figure for energy gained as protein and fat, 524 kcal., from the metabolizable energy left a balance of 11,577 kcal., which represented the energy lost as heat, as thus determined by indirect calorimetry. These calculations both illustrate the method of computing the heat loss from the nitrogen-carbon balance and indicate the accuracy of the method, since the value thus obtained by indirect calorimetry closely approximates the directly determined value of 11,493 kcal. as given in Table 11.4.

Instead of obtaining the changes in protein and fat in the body as described in the preceding paragraph, these changes can be directly determined by the slaughter method. This involves the slaughter of a check group at the start and of an experimental group at the end (Sec. 10.8). By analysis of the carcasses of the two groups for fat and protein and by calculation of the gross calories thus represented, the energy gained as a result of the ration or feed under test can be determined. This method was devised by Fraps of Texas over twenty years ago to arrive at what he referred to as *productive energy* values of chicken feeds. An improved procedure is detailed by Hill and Anderson.[19] In the case of large animals for which the slaughter technique is impracticable, it has been suggested that body composition might be estimated by the procedure described in Sec. 2.5. Lofgreen and Otagaki[20] have reported a trial of this general procedure, using equations for estimating the water and fat content of the dressed carcass of steers.

The measurement of respiratory exchange, using a face mask and appropriate other equipment, provides another method of indirect calorimetry. The heat production can be computed from oxygen consumption by the use of the average heat equivalent of a liter of the gas. The heat production may be more accurately calculated from the determination of both the oxygen consumption and carbon dioxide output, which thus gives the RQ and thereby makes possible the use of an exact

[19] Hill and Anderson, *loc. cit.*

[20] G. P. Lofgreen and K. K. Otagaki, The net energy value of blackstrap molasses for fattening steers by a comparative slaughter technique, *J. Animal Sci.,* 19:392–403, 1960.

value at the heat equivalent for the oxygen consumed. Knowing the RQ, the proportion of fat and carbohydrate being burned, and thus the energy being produced per liter of oxygen consumed at that RQ, can be computed. This calculation has been made for all respiratory quotients between 0.7 and 1.0, and the values are available in a table compiled by Zuntz and Schumberg. For illustrative purposes a few of the values are presented in Table 11.6. Intermediate values are omitted. It is noted

TABLE 11.6. ENERGY VALUES OF OXYGEN AND CARBON DIOXIDE AT DIFFERENT RESPIRATORY QUOTIENTS
(Zuntz and Schumberg)

RQ	Kcal. per liter O_2	Kcal. per liter CO_2	Kcal. per gram CO_2
0.70	4.686	6.694	3.408
0.75	4.739	6.319	3.217
0.80	4.801	6.001	3.055
0.85	4.863	5.721	2.919
0.90	4.924	5.471	2.785
0.95	4.985	5.247	2.671
1.00	5.047	5.047	2.569

that increasing respiratory quotients correspond with increasing oxygen consumption and decreasing carbon dioxide output. As an example of the use of the values, if the data of a respiration experiment show that 70 liters of oxygen were consumed and that the RQ was 0.9, multiplying this number of liters by 4.924, the calorific equivalent given in the table for a liter of oxygen at this RQ, gives 344.7 kcal. as the heat production. This is the procedure commonly used in the case of man. Today it is being increasingly employed for farm animals using equipment referred to in Sec. 11.3.

11.15. Respiration Chamber for Farm Animals. The demonstration of the usefulness of indirect methods of calorimetry stimulated the construction of airtight chambers for farm animals, similar to the respiration calorimeter with the absence of the calorimetric feature. Some thirty years ago chambers large enough for studies with cattle were constructed in this country by Ritzman and Benedict at New Hampshire, Mitchell and associates at Illinois, and Kleiber and associates at California. Provision was made for the measurement of gaseous exchange and thus for the calculation of heat production, over periods of several hours or even days. Facilities for the measurement of feed intake, urine and fecal losses, and methane production provided for the determination of metabolizable energy. These respiration chambers were found to produce highly reliable data, and their use has resulted in large contributions to our knowledge of energy metabolism and the energy value of feeds.

A much more modern chamber has recently been constructed at the U.S. Department of Agriculture research center at Beltsville, Maryland, and is described by Flatt and associates.[21] Actually, there are six open-circuit chambers in the unit, constructed from transparent acrylic plastic, making it possible for the animals to see each other and the operator to observe the animals much more closely. A rear view of one of these chambers is shown in Fig. 11.6, including the ventilating and recording

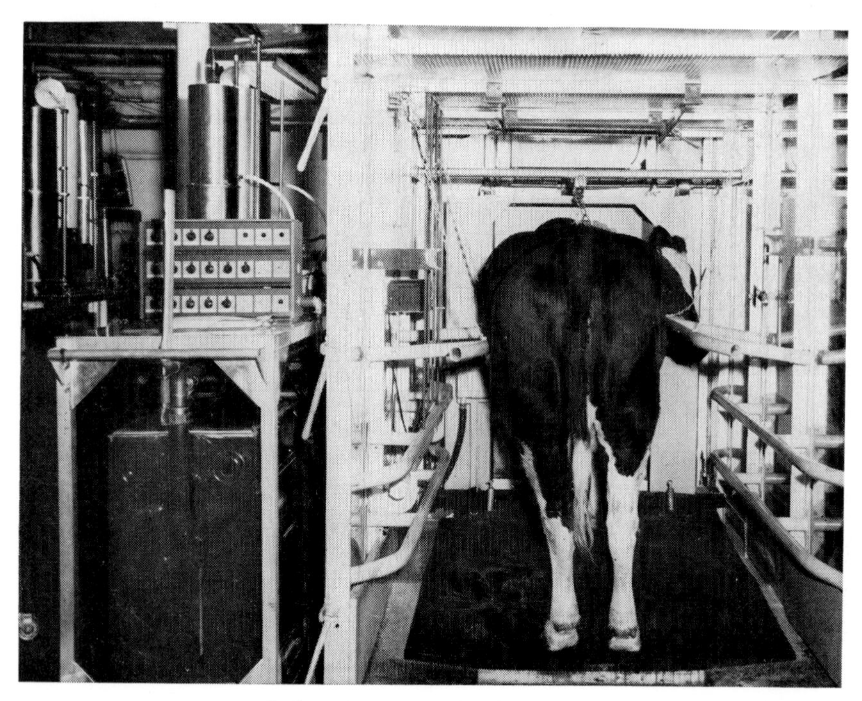

FIG. 11.6. Rear view of the respiration chamber, unit for indirect calorimetry, U.S. Research Center, Beltsville, Md. (*Courtesy of W. P. Flatt, U.S. Department of Agriculture.*)

device. The special features of this unit include many automatic measuring and recording devices, IBM equipment for recording and processing data, and others, which all contribute to the accuracy of the data obtained as well as result in large savings of time and labor. The chambers are adjustable for animals of different size.

11.16. Heat Increment, Its Cause and Variability. The concept of net energy focuses attention on an important aspect of nutrition which

[21] W. P. Flatt and associates, A description of the energy metabolism laboratory at the U.S. Department of Agriculture, Agricultural Research Center in Beltsville, Maryland. Proc. I. Symposium on energy metabolism, Copenhagen, *European Assoc. Animal Production Publ.* 8, 1958.

DuBois[22] has referred to as "the neglected field of heat loss." This loss reflects the wastage of food energy in the course of its metabolism which has been previously referred to as heat increment. The increase in heat production following the ingestion of food or a specific nutrient is commonly referred to as specific dynamic effect or action (SDA). Heat increment results in a significant loss of the ingested energy, the extent of which is influenced by various factors. Its consideration is of special importance in the feeding of farm animals because of its bearing on the efficiency of production.

In the case of ruminants an important variable in the loss as heat increment is the varying nature of the microbial process in the rumen. The heat produced from the fermentation process itself has been found to range from 1.5 to 11 per cent of the gross energy of mixed rations. Another variable factor arises from the differing proportions in which the volatile fatty acids are produced and the different heat losses resulting from their metabolism. In comprehensive studies by indirect calorimetry with fattening sheep Armstrong and Blaxter[23] obtained the following heat increments: acetic acid, 67.1; propionic acid, 43.7; butyric acid, 38.1, expressed as kilocalories per 100 kcal. acid metabolized. Evidence that the lower heat loss from propionic than from acetic may have practical significance is indicated by the finding of Elliot and Loosli[24] that the efficiency with which digestible energy is converted to fat-corrected milk was highly correlated with the relative proportion of propionic acid in the rumen VFA. In all species the loss of energy as heat increment is largely the result of the metabolic processes which the absorbed nutrients undergo in serving the body, processes which have been discussed in the chapters dealing with carbohydrates, lipids, and protein. The specific stages at which losses occur and their extent are only partially known. Much more needs to be learned about the thermodynamics of intermediary metabolism.

Many data have been obtained on the SDA resulting from the ingestion of pure, readily absorbable nutrients. The summation of such values for the individual nutrients in a feed does not necessarily represent the heat increment of the feed itself and, further, the heat increment of a ration is not necessarily the sum of the values of its feed components, as shown by the studies of Forbes and Swift.[25] The relative proportion

[22] Eugene F. DuBois, The neglected field of heat loss, *Nutrition Revs.*, **1**:385, 1943.

[23] D. G. Armstrong and K. L. Blaxter, The utilization of acetic, propionic and butyric acids by fattening sheep, *Brit. J. Nutrition*, **11**:413–425, 1957.

[24] J. M. Elliot and J. K. Loosli, Relationship of milk production efficiency to the relative proportions of the rumen volatile fatty acids, *J. Dairy Sci.*, **42**:843–848, 1959.

[25] E. B. Forbes and R. W. Swift, Associate dynamic effects of protein, carbohydrate and fat, *J. Nutrition*, **27**:453–468, 1944.

in which the various nutrients are present in a ration influences the percentage of the gross or metabolizable calories that are lost as heat increment. For example, as previously referred to (Sec. 5.30), the substitution of fat for carbohydrates in a diet can result in a more economical use of the energy fed because of the lesser amount dissipated as heat. Deficiencies of phosphorus, riboflavin, and certain other minerals and vitamins tend to increase the heat increment of a ration. In fact, there is evidence that, other factors being equal, if the ration is unbalanced with respect to any nutrient in terms of physiological needs, the wastage of heat tends to be greater accordingly. The percentage of total protein in the ration has a definite effect on heat losses. In experiments with rats, it has been found that, as the protein level in equicaloric diets is increased from 4 to 18 per cent or even higher, there is a progressive decrease in heat elimination. Similar results have been reported for chickens. These decreased heat losses with increasing protein level had the practical effect of increasing the net-energy value.

The heat increment per unit of food increases with the level of intake. The percentage of the gross energy which is lost as heat differs according to the body function for which it is being used. For example, the workers at the Pennsylvania Institute of Animal Nutrition found that 1 Therm of metabolizable energy is equivalent to 0.693 Therm of milk energy but only 0.575 Therm as deposited fat. Growth is also a more efficient process energetically than fattening, and maintenance involves less heat loss than either of these two processes. There are also species differences in efficiency, notably between ruminants and nonruminants. Studies by Zuntz showed that high-grade concentrates had a much higher net-energy value for fattening pigs than for fattening cattle. Thus the former operation was found more efficient in terms of feed intake because of a lesser wastage as heat. The same is true for broiler production.

These variations in heat increment, resulting from various factors, explain why the same intakes of total digestible nutrients or metabolizable energy can produce different results in terms of animal performance in different feeding operations. Just how a given combination of foods may affect the heat loss cannot be predicted. These variations also have an important bearing on the practical usefulness of the net-energy system as a measure of food energy, as is discussed later (Sec. 12.8).

11.17. Usefulness of Energy and Balance Studies. In these days when so much emphasis is being placed upon the more alluring studies of vitamins and minerals, it should not be forgotten that energy metabolism is concerned in every body function and that its study is making equally important, though less spectacular, contributions to our knowledge of the physiology of animal nutrition. First of all, the ration must supply an adequate amount of useful energy, and thus, a knowledge of energy needs and energy utilization is essential to profitable production. Energy studies are concerned with the determination of relative food values; with the influence of various environmental factors, methods of feeding, and combinations of nutrients upon food utilization; and with the efficiency of various animals as converters of food energy. The methods and results of energy studies in these various fields will become evident in later discussions.

The balance method provides exact information as to metabolic processes and as to the effect of a specific nutrient or ration which cannot be obtained by the more general measures of weight and size, and such studies can be made repeatedly without sacrificing the animal as is required by the slaughter method. It is necessarily an expensive and laborious procedure which must be limited to a few animals and for short periods. The animals must be kept in confinement and subjected to other unnatural conditions.

SELECTED LITERATURE

Armstrong, R. G., et al: The utilization of the energy of two mixtures of steam-volatile fatty acids by fattening sheep, *Brit. J. Nutrition,* **12**:177–188, 1958.

Atwater, W. O.: Methods and results of investigations on the chemistry and economy of food, *U.S. Dept. Agr. Office Expt. Stations Bull.* 21, 1895.

Black, Alex, K. H. Maddy, and R. W. Swift: The influence of low levels of protein on heat production, *J. Nutrition,* **42**:415–422, 1950.

Brouwer, E.: On simple formulae for calculating the heat expenditure and the quantities of carbohydrate and fat metabolized in ruminants, from data on gaseous exchange and urine-N. Proc. I. Symposium on energy metabolism, Copenhagen, *European Assoc. for Animal Production Publ.* **8**, 1958, pp. 182–192.

Crampton, E. W., Florence A. Farmer, and R. K. Shaw: An improved method for determining bomb calorimeter values, *J. Animal Sci.,* **13**:658–659, 1954.

De Vuyst, A., et al.: Comparaison entre les valeurs energétiques brutes mesurées et calculées dans les aliments, *Agricultura,* **8**:3–20, 1960.

Duncan, Dorothy L.: The interpretation of studies of calcium and phosphorus balances in ruminants, *Nutrition Abstr. & Revs.,* **28**:695–715, 1958.

Kriss, Max: A comparison of direct and indirect calorimetry in investigations with cattle, *J. Agr. Research,* **30**:393–406, 1925.

Marston, Hedley R.: Energy transactions in the sheep. I. The basal heat production and heat increment, *Australian J. Sci. Research,* **1**:93–129, 1948.

Rhoad, Albert O.: The influence of environmental temperature on the respiratory rhythm of dairy cattle in the tropics, *J. Agr. Sci.,* **26**:36–44, 1936.

Swift, Raymond W., and Cyrus E. French: Energy Metabolism and Nutrition, The Scarecrow Press, Washington, D.C., 1954.

Chapter 12
Feeding Standards. Measures of Food Energy

Feeding standards are tables showing the amounts of food and nutrients which should be provided in the rations of different species for different purposes, such as growth, fattening, and lactation. They serve as guides in feeding practice. They also provide essential data for setting up many types of nutrition experiments, such as those which require a basal ration adequate in all nutrients except the one under study.

12.1. Early History of Feeding Standards. In 1810, many years before the nature of the organic nutrients in foods was appreciated, Thaer developed his "hay values" as measures of relative nutritive value. His basic hay value consisted of the sum of the ingredients extractable with water, alcohol, dilute acid, and dilute alkali. Similar determinations made on other feeds were referred to this basic value as the standard. Following the recognition of protein, fat, and carbohydrate as the essential organic nutrients, Grouven made use of analyses for these nutrients to formulate in 1859 the first feeding standard for farm animals.

In 1864 Wolff devised a standard based on digestible nutrients which was derived from results of various feeding trials. His standards were republished annually without fundamental change until modified by Lehmann in 1897. In 1914 an important advance in the accuracy of the standard for dairy cows was made, as a result of many years' study by Haecker[1] of the University of Minnesota, showing that the nutritive requirements varied not only with the quantity of milk produced but also with its quality, especially its fat content. In the following words Haecker set forth a principle which should be recognized in all studies of nutritive requirements.

[1] T. L. Haecker, Investigations in milk-production, *Minnesota Agr. Expt. Sta. Bull.* 140, 1914.

In order to determine the actual net nutrients required to produce a given animal product, the composition of the product should be known, as well as the composition and the available nutrients in food which is to be fed for its production, so that the nutrients in the ration might be provided in the proportions needed by the animal. Before a builder bids on a contract, he determines the quantity needed of each of the materials that are to appear in the structure. Without such specifications he would not know how much of each of the different materials would have to be provided.

Since the time of Haecker several different standards, based upon digestible nutrients, have been proposed for farm animals by various American workers. Such is the basis of the Morrison standard long widely used. Kellner in 1907 and Armsby in 1915, followed by others in this country and in Europe, set forth standards based on digestible true protein and the net-energy system. The features of these various standards, which dealt only with protein and energy needs, have been excellently set forth by Kriss.[2]

12.2. National Research Council Nutrient Requirements. As the knowledge developed regarding minerals and vitamins, recommendations regarding their quantitative requirements for various body functions were made by the investigators concerned. In 1942 the Committee on Animal Nutrition of the National Research Council (N.R.C.) undertook the task of setting forth, for farm animals, a statement of quantitative needs for all the recognized nutrients. Subcommittees of experts for each class of stock were accordingly set up to review the literature. Beginning in 1944 there was thus published the Recommended Nutrient Allowances for Farm Animals, comprising separate reports for poultry, swine, dairy cattle, beef cattle, sheep, and horses. The term "allowance" was used, following the lead of the N.R.C. Food and Nutrition Board, which first adopted it for use in human dietary standards. These allowances were, in general, set higher than average determined requirements to provide a margin of safety. In 1953, the Committee on Animal Nutrition decided not to include such margins in future recommendations but to set forth intakes considered adequate for normal growth, health, and production, based on the average needs of groups of animals to achieve these results. Accordingly, it was agreed that future reports would be designated as "nutrient requirements," instead of "recommended nutrient allowances." Revised reports for swine, dairy cattle, beef cattle, sheep, poultry, and new ones for dogs, rabbits, foxes, and minks have been issued on this basis. It is believed that these N.R.C. reports, representing in each case the pooled judgment of a group of experts in the field of the species in question, should be considered the

[2] Max Kriss, A comparison of feeding standards for dairy cows, with especial reference to energy requirements: editorial review, *J. Nutrition,* **4**:141–161, 1931.

most authoritative statements of the nutritional needs of farm animals, at least for feeding practice in the United States. Thus, where specific data on these needs are set forth in this text, they are those in the N.R.C. reports,[3] except as important new data have become available since their publication. In applying them, the difference in concept between allowances and requirements, as discussed above, should be recognized.

12.3. Usefulness and Limitations of Feeding Standards. The N.R.C. reports comprise feeding standards for total food needs and for all nutrients for which quantitative data are available. They are designed to be the best general guides for practice but should be considered subject to modification in special instances. In practical feeding operations it is frequently desirable to take economic factors into account. Thus, modifications may be called for in the interest of obtaining the rate of gain or level of milk production that seems the most economical in terms of current feed costs and the market price of the product. No standard can be a complete guide to feeding because other factors such as palatability and the physical nature of the ration must also be taken into account. The significance of these various considerations in using feeding-standard data in planning experiments and interpreting the results depends upon the nature and objective of the investigation.

MEASURES OF FOOD ENERGY

The expression food energy is used to denote the value of food for its largest function, viz., to furnish energy for body processes and to form the nonnitrogenous, organic matter of tissues and secretions, functions in which all organic nutrients can take part. First of all, a feeding standard must provide the amount of food needed to furnish this energy for the species and function in question. In the cases of poultry and swine, feeding standards commonly express this requirement merely in terms of pounds of feed, although other measures have been proposed. For other classes of stock, where digestion and certain metabolic losses are much larger, some measure of food energy which takes account of these losses is generally used. Total digestible nutrients, digestible energy, starch values, metabolizable energy, physiological fuel values, and net energy, the determinations of which were discussed in the two preceding chapters,

[3] Committee on Animal Nutrition. I. Nutrient requirements of poultry, *Natl. Acad. Sci. Natl. Research Council Publ.* 827, 1960; II. Nutrient requirements of swine, *ibid.* 648, 1959; III. Nutrient requirements of dairy cattle, *ibid.* 464, 1958; IV. Nutrient requirements of beef cattle, *ibid.* 579, 1958; V. Nutrient requirements of sheep, *ibid.* 504, 1957; VI. Recommended nutrient allowances for horses, *ibid.*, 1949; VII. Nutrient requirements for foxes and minks, *ibid.* 296, 1953; VIII. Nutrient requirements for dogs, *ibid.* 300, 1953; IX. Nutrient requirements for rabbits, *ibid.* 331, 1954.

are all different measures of food energy. In addition to their use in setting forth energy needs in feeding standards, they are employed as a yardstick for measuring the over-all value of feeds and in equalizing the food-energy intakes in feeds and rations being compared with respect to their contributions of specific nutrients. For these experimental purposes the measurements are frequently used in studies with poultry and swine as well as with Herbivora. Their use is based on the fact that a measure which recognizes one or more of the losses in metabolism is more valuable than a mere statement of pounds of feed or its nutrient or gross-energy content.

Since these measures differ as regards the actual feeding value represented, it is desirable to understand clearly the exact significance of each and to know something of their advantages and limitations in practice.

12.4. Total Digestible Nutrients. Previous discussion has indicated that, in order to arrive at the actual useful portion of a ration, we must deduct losses in the feces, urine, combustible gases, and heat elimination. It is obvious that the determination of digestibility is only one step in this direction and thus that digestible nutrients must not be considered as the final measure of useful energy because they are subject to several losses in the course of metabolism. The fecal loss, however, is a large one, exceeding the sum of all the others in many cases. It is a loss which may vary widely among feeds which are alike as regards content of gross energy or total nutrients. Thus it is evident that the determination of digestibility is a highly useful measure, not only because it eliminates an important loss, but also because, by the elimination of a highly variable loss, it places the feeds upon a much more nearly comparable basis as regards their actual physiological value.

Of all the measures of food energy, digestible nutrients are the easiest to determine. This largely accounts for the fact that digestion coefficients are available for all of the common feeds. This is an important consideration from the standpoint of their usefulness in practice. Published average digestion coefficients make possible the calculation of the digestible nutrients of a given supply of a feed from its specific nutrient content as determined by analysis, rather than relying on figures calculated from average analyses. This is frequently very important in experimental work as well as in the compounding of mixed feeds or rations on a large scale. Some of the factors that affect the general applicability of average coefficients of digestibility values calculated from them have been discussed (Sec. 10.19). They are not constants but are affected by the plane of nutrition, the make-up of the ration, and other factors.

The limitation of total digestible nutrients (TDN) as a measure of food energy is that it does not take account of the other important losses, such as the combustible gases in the case of Herbivora and, most important, the heat loss. These losses are relatively larger for roughages than for concentrates, and thus a pound of TDN in roughage has considerably less value for productive purposes than a pound in concentrates. This fact was shown experimentally by Wolff as early as 1888, but the recognition of the extent of the difference and of its practical importance has come primarily from modern experiments, such as the one by Smith and coworkers.[4] In a statistical study, Moore and associates[5] report the following approximate relationships between TDN and net energy:

1 lb. TDN in corn $\approx$ 1 Therm net energy
1 lb. TDN in better hays $\approx$ 0.75 Therm net energy
1 lb. TDN in poor roughage $\approx$ 0.5 Therm net energy

Thus, as the roughage component of the ration, especially low-grade roughage, is substituted for grain, the productive value drops when the substitution is made on a TDN basis. This fact is of importance, both in practical feeding and also in experiments where shifts in the relative amounts of roughages and concentrates fed or in the quality of the roughage are involved. The recognition of this limitation of the TDN measure constitutes an important reason why active consideration is being given at the present time to other measures which account for additional losses.

The term total digestible nutrients implies that digestion losses only are taken account of in its calculation, but this is not strictly the case. In early feeding standards, digestible protein, fat, and carbohydrates were added together to give "total digestible substances." Later when the current practice (Sec. 10.17) of multiplying fat by 2.25 was introduced, a change apparently not generally understood resulted. The practice with respect to fat apparently originated from a consideration of the physiological fuel values of Atwater (Sec. 11.10) or similar values of Rubner, which give fats two and one-quarter times the energy value of either carbohydrates or protein. It seems to have been overlooked, however, that the value for protein here involved was one from which the portion of the digested energy lost in the urine had been substracted. Thus it would be more exact, in arriving at a value assumed to take account of digestion losses only, to base the relationship on the gross fuel values (Sec. 11.8). This would involve multiplying the protein by 1.36 ($5.65 \div 4.15$) as well as the fat by 2.25, assuming the use of carbohydrates as a base. The substitution of such a calculation would be in

[4] V. R. Smith, I. R. Jones, and J. R. Haag, Alfalfa with and without concentrates for milk production, *J. Dairy Sci.*, **28**:343–354, 1945.

[5] L. A. Moore, H. M. Irvin, and J. C. Shaw, Relationship between T.D.N. and energy value of feeds, *J. Dairy Sci.*, **36**:93–97, 1953.

the interest of scientific accuracy if it is intended to take digestion losses only into account, as the term TDN implies. The inconsistency here involved, however, does not interfere with the usefulness of TDN values, as now calculated, for practical and most experimental purposes, because they are the ones on which the requirements as set forth in feeding standards are commonly based.

12.5. Food Energy Expressed in Heat Units. With the exception of TDN all the measures of food energy are expressed in kilocalories or Therms. The relationship of these measures to each other is shown by the following chart.

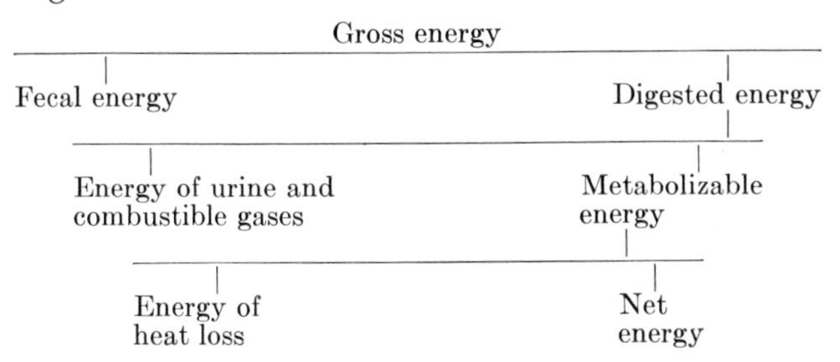

The methods by which the various losses are accounted for have been described in the previous chapter.

12.6. Digested Energy. Digested-energy measurement takes account of digestion losses only, which is not the case for TDN as customarily calculated (Sec. 12.4). Either it can be determined by measuring the gross calories in feed and feces, or it can be calculated from the digested nutrients by the use of the gross calorie factors: protein, 5.65; carbohydrates, 4.1; fat, 9.4. Since these factors were designed to apply to the average human diet (Sec. 11.8), their use with animal feeds and rations cannot be expected to give as reliable data as are obtained in direct measurements. Data for digested energy (DE) can also be obtained by calculation from TDN values using the factor 2000 kcal. per pound TDN, as is being done in the reports on nutrient requirements by the N.R.C. Committee on Animal Nutrition. This is an average figure based on studies, primarily with swine data, by Crampton and associates,[6] and with cattle and sheep data by Swift.[7] The basic data were obtained from experiments in which both DE and TDN were measured. As is to be expected, the data of these investigators show that the value 2000 is somewhat variable according to species and type of ration, but this variation is small, indicating the reliability of the average figure. In the older literature a lower figure of 1814 has been used, arrived at by a

[6] E. W. Crampton, L. E. Lloyd, and V. G. Mackay, The calorie value of TDN, *J. Animal Sci.*, **16**:541–545, 1957.

[7] R. W. Swift, The caloric value of TDN, *J. Animal Sci.*, **16**:753–756, 1957.

calculation which failed to recognize that TDN as customarily computed does not represent digestion losses only (Sec. 12.4.)

There are relatively few experimentally determined DE values of feeds, but they can be calculated from TDN values by the use of the appropriate factors. Such calculated values are given in tables in the N.R.C. publications on nutrient requirements. These publications also set forth requirements on the basis of DE as well as TDN. Thus rations can be computed on the basis of either measure of food energy.

12.7. Metabolizable Energy. In taking account of all the losses in the urine and combustible gases as well as those in the feces, metabolizable energy represents a step beyond digested nutrients or digested energy, as a measure of nutritive value. It falls short of being the final measure in that a portion of it is lost as heat not useful to the body, but it is clearly a better measure than one that considers digestion losses only. Its determination involves additional steps beyond a digestion trial. The urine must be collected, and its gross energy value determined. More important, the determination of the losses in combustible gases calls for the use of an expensive and complicated apparatus, a respiration chamber, and involves much labor as well as technical skill accordingly. By reason of these limitations, actually determined values are available for only a few feeds.

There are many published figures for metabolizable energy that have been calculated from digestible nutrients using factors developed from experiments in which both TDN and metabolizable energy have been determined. A perusal of the variable data here involved makes it very questionable whether the metabolizable energy values thus calculated have sufficient reliability to make them more significant measures of useful energy than the TDN values on which they are based. On the other hand, the determination of the urine losses plus the calculation of the gaseous losses (Sec. 11.9) seems much more promising.

The additional losses accounted for in a metabolizable-energy determination are much smaller than those eliminated in arriving at digested energy, being of the order of approximately 5 to 10 per cent or the gross intake. They are greater, however, for roughages than for concentrates, primarily because of larger urine losses, and thus taking them into account helps overcome the criticism that TDN overvalues roughages for productive purposes. Clearly, metabolizable energy is a better measure of useful energy than is the digestion measure alone, but whether it is sufficiently better for practical purposes to justify the establishment of feed and requirement data on this basis remains to be determined by further research. In this connection its value compared with net energy (Sec. 12.8) also needs consideration.

A special case where metabolizable energy provides a much better measure than does TDN has been reported by Cook and coworkers.[8] Certain species of forage were found to have high gross energy and high TDN values due to essential oils, but low metabolizable energy values because the oils, though absorbed, were not metabolizable, and thus there was a large energy loss in the urine.

Physiological fuel values (Sec. 11.10) are measures of metabolizable energy for man, since no gaseous losses are involved and since the urine loss is accounted for by a reliable calculation. They have been inappropriately used for other species where the specific conditions of digestion and metabolism on which they are based do not hold.

12.8. Net Energy. The net-energy system, which originated with Kellner's studies of the fat-producing power of feeds (Sec. 11.6) and with Armsby's respiration-calorimeter experiments (Sec. 11.12), conceives of the measurement of that portion of the feed which is completely useful to the body. By taking account of all losses in metabolism, net energy, according to this concept, is that portion of the ingested energy which actually appears as a product, viz., milk, meat, work. Theoretically, 1 Therm of feed energy corresponds to 1 Therm actually produced. On this basis it certainly represents a more nearly exact measure than any of the others, which fail to account for one or more of the losses always involved. The distinguishing feature of the net-energy system is an accounting for the loss as heat increment of that portion of the metabolizable energy which fails of conversion into body substance or product. A large loss is here involved, as is indicated by the data in Table 11.5 showing that approximately 15 to 30 per cent of the gross energy appears as heat in the case of ruminants. The data in this table also show that this represents a loss of 35 to 50 per cent or more of the metabolizable energy, indicating that the latter is a very incomplete measure of energy actually utilized. The percentage of heat thus lost is greater for roughages than for concentrates, the most important reason why the TDN measure overvalues roughages for productive purposes (Sec. 12.4).

Net-energy values are not suitable measures of the usefulness of a ration for maintaining an animal in a cold climate. This is the case because the values are based on data obtained with animals in a sufficiently warm environment so that the heat increment resulting from the consumption of food is of no benefit. In a cold environment, represented by many winter feeding conditions, the heat produced from a maintenance ration does serve a useful purpose in keeping the body temperature up to normal, a requirement which would otherwise call for chemical regulation through tissue breakdown (Sec. 11.11). Under these condi-

[8] C. Wayne Cook, L. A. Stoddart, and Lorin E. Harris, Determining the digestibility and metabolizable energy of winter range plants by sheep, *J. Animal Sci.,* 11:578–590, 1952.

tions, therefore, the food has a higher useful energy value than represented by the net-energy measure. For example, all of the energy recorded as heat increment for wheat straw in Table 11.5 might prove useful in a cold environment, and thus, for maintenance under such conditions, its feed value would be represented by its metabolizable-energy figure, which is nearly five times its value for productive purposes (net energy).

In theory net-energy values are far superior as measures of productive energy to the others previously discussed because all losses are taken into account. Their usefulness, however, is subject to the limitation that the heat increment per unit of food intake varies according to the balance of the nutrients in the ration, the level of intake, the productive function, the species and other factors, as discussed in Sec. 11.16. Thus, while no measure can be considered a constant, net energy becomes, by its very exactness for specified conditions, the more difficult to apply as a workable measure under the variable conditions of practice. The recognition of the many factors influencing the net-energy values of individual feeds caused many authorities working in the field in this country to consider that the data provided a very unreliable basis for arriving at the productive values of rations representing different combinations of feeds and fed at different levels and for different purposes. Further, it was recognized that the actual determination of net-energy values, as carried out by either direct or indirect calorimetry, was so expensive and difficult as to be impractical for any long list of feeds. Thus, interest in the Armsby net-energy feeding standard declined. There has been a revival of interest, however, in indirect calorimetry, reflected in the development of modified procedures which involve savings in both time and labor. Quite evidently the net-energy system is coming in for a restudy in this country in view of the continued recognition of its scientific superiority. The system is widely used in Europe, involving various modifications of Kellner's starch-equivalent procedure.

Various proposals have been made for estimating appropriate values from a consideration of data obtained in feeding trials. These proposals are based on the general principle of setting forth the "replacement value" of a given feed in a balanced ration for the species and function in question, fed at a level resulting in full production. This basis, at least in theory, eliminates the variable effects of balance of ration and level of intake on heat production. In some of these proposals heat increment has also been taken into consideration.

The *Scandinavian feed-unit system*, usually associated with the name of Hansson, is based on the results of practical group-feeding experiments, with 1 kg. of barley as the standard unit. It is expressed in accordance with the net-energy concept by computations making use of Kellner's starch values. As so computed for cattle, one food unit is equivalent to 1.65 Therms net energy for fattening or 2.1 Therms milk energy.

Fraps[9] utilized data from published experiments and the results of his own feeding trials with sheep, chickens, and rats to arrive at the *productive energy* of feeds. In 1937 Morrison presented a method of estimating net-energy values from feeding trials using corn as the base. In his book[10] he has published *estimated net-energy* values for long list of feeds based largely on the analysis of the results of feeding experiments and a consideration of the previously published production values of Fraps, the starch equivalents of Kellner, and the net-energy values of Armsby. His feeding standard sets forth net-energy requirements for production for various classes of stock. There are other proposals. Kleiber and coworkers[11] critically reviewed several of these proposals and compared them with TDN, metabolizable energy, and with Armsby's system. They also report studies with the Scandinavian group-trial method, concluding that this is the most reliable method of measuring replacement equivalents.

None of the measures discussed in this section has found any wide use in the United States. Space cannot be taken to give further details regarding their bases or to discuss their advantages and limitations. Additional papers dealing with them are cited at the end of this chapter.

12.9. Food Energy—A Field for Further Study. The foregoing discussion has indicated that our present bases for measuring and expressing the energy value of feeds and rations are subject to various limitations and uncertainties. While no measure of useful food energy can be exact in its general application because of the many variables involved, the field is clearly an important one for further research. In view of the limitations of the TDN measure in terms of net feeding value, further studies of the measures which take account of more of the losses are clearly desirable. The superiority of a given method of evaluating energy cannot be established, however, merely from theoretical considerations or by emphasizing the limitations of other measures. Research must definitely show its greater usefulness for general application, both in experimental comparisons and in feeding practice. Such research is greatly needed, and the time and labor involved can be fully justified in view of the importance of arriving at a more useful measure of the largest function of feeds and rations. For use in a feeding standard, any measure arrived at must be accompanied by data for requirements set forth

[9] G. S. Fraps, Composition and productive energy of poultry feeds and rations, *Texas Agr. Expt. Sta. Bull.* 678, 1946.

[10] Frank B. Morrison, Feeds and Feeding, 22d ed., Morrison Publishing Company, Ithaca, N.Y., 1956, pp. 1070–1081.

[11] Max Kleiber, W. M. Regan, and S. W. Mead, Measuring food values for dairy cows, *Hilgardia,* **16**:511–556, 1945.

on the same basis. Blaxter[12] has made a comprehensive review of the various systems for evaluating energy value and of the physiological factors involved.

SELECTED LITERATURE

Irvin, H. M., and associates: Net energy vs. T.D.N. in evaluating the efficacy of an all-alfalfa hay ration for milk production, *J. Animal Sci.,* **10**:947–960, 1951.

Kleiber, Max: Dietary deficiencies and energy metabolism, *Nutrition Abstr. & Revs.,* **15**:207–222, 1945.

Kriss, Max: Evaluation of feeds on the basis of net available nutrients, *J. Animal Sci.,* **2**:63–79, 1943.

Leroy, André M.: Utilization de l'energie des aliments par les animaux, *Annales de Zootechnie,* **4**:337–372, 1954.

Mitchell, H. H.: The evaluation of feeds on the basis of digestible and metabolizable nutrients, *J. Animal Sci.,* **1**:159–173, 1942.

Morrison, F. B.: Determining net energy values by means of feeding experiments, *Proc. Am. Soc. Animal Production,* 1937, pp. 12–20.

Swift, R. W.: The nutritive evaluation of forages, *Pennsylvania Agr. Expt. Sta. Bull.* 615, 1957.

Walker, D. M., and W. R. Hepburn: The nutritive value of roughages for sheep. I. The relationship between the gross digestible energy and the chemical composition of hays, *J. Agr. Sci.,* **45**:298–310, 1955.

[12] K. L. Blaxter, The nutritive value of feeds as sources of energy, *J. Dairy Sci.,* **39**:1396–1424, 1956.

Part IV

Nutritive Requirements for Body Processes and Productive Functions

Chapter 13
The Fasting Catabolism. Maintenance

Whether an animal is being fed for growth, fattening, milk secretion, or other productive function, a substantial part of its food is used for supporting body processes which must go on whether or not any new tissue or product is being formed. This demand for food is referred to as the maintenance requirement, since it comprises the amount needed to keep intact the tissues of an animal which is not growing, working, or yielding any product. If this need is not met, tissue breakdown occurs, which is commonly revealed by a loss in weight and which leads to various undesirable consequences. For a considerable part of the human population, the maintenance requirement comprises the principal need for food. While this is much less true for farm animals because they are always fed for productive purposes, maintenance is an important "overhead" of the livestock business. The income is governed by the ability of the animal to consume and utilize feed in addition to its maintenance requirement. Thus the knowledge of this requirement, which the student must have in order to understand the principles underlying nutrition, has a direct practical interest. The starting point of this knowledge is the fasting catabolism.

THE FASTING CATABOLISM

The animal receiving no food, doing no external work, and yielding no product is nevertheless carrying on a variety of internal processes which are essential to life. These processes include respiration, circulation, maintenance of muscular tonus, manufacture of internal secretions, and several others. In the absence of food, the nutrients required to support these activities must come from the breakdown of body tissue itself. This destruction of body tissue is referred to as the fasting catabolism, and it can be measured in terms of the waste products eliminated through the various paths of excretion. Most of the breakdown which occurs is in response to the demand of the fasting organism for energy for its vital processes.

13.1. Energy Catabolism of Fasting. The energy consumed in the fasting animal appears as heat and thus can be measured in the respiration calorimeter, or it can be obtained by one of the methods of indirect calorimetry. Its measurement provides a useful basis of reference for other phases of energy metabolism. In order that the fasting catabolism may be measured at its minimum value, it is necessary that all influences tending to increase heat production above the minimum expenditure compatible with the maintenance of life be eliminated in so far as possible. Such a minimum value is called *basal metabolism*, or *basal metabolic rate*. It has its most exact meaning in the case of man, because it is with this species that the conditions which are essential for a true minimum value can most nearly be attained. The conditions for its measurement in man are commonly specified as follows:

1. Good nutritive condition
2. Environmental temperature of approximately 25°C.
3. Relaxation on bed prior to and during measurement
4. Postabsorptive state

A good nutritive condition implies that the previous diet of the subject has been adequate, especially as regards energy and protein. A poor state of nutrition tends to decrease the heat production during fasting. The temperature of 25°C. is specified as one which is above the critical, assuring that no tissue breakdown is occurring to keep up the temperature of the body, and as one below the point of hyperthermal rise where the onset of febrile conditions increases heat production. Both of these first two conditions are entirely realizable in the case of animals. The minimum muscular activity assured by the third condition, however, is obviously much less subject to control, particularly in farm animals. In addition to various miscellaneous movements, the animal may be expected to spend a variable portion of the experimental period standing and lying down. The magnitude of the influence of voluntary muscular activity is illustrated by the observations that, with the exception of the horse, the basal metabolism of different species and individuals is 10 to 15 per cent greater when they are standing than while they are lying down. In making the measurements, therefore, the heat production is calculated separately for the periods of standing and lying and then computed to a standard day of 12 hr. of each. The horse, an exception because of the structure of its ligaments, seems to rest as comfortably standing as lying, without any increased energy expenditure.

The fourth condition implies a state of fasting in which a long enough time has elapsed since the ingestion of food to make certain that the heat increment due to its digestion and assimilation has been dissipated. Such a condition is readily obtainable in animals with simple stomachs, but not in the case of the ruminant. In this species the anatomy and physiology of the digestive tract result in a prolonged retention of food in the rumen and a correspondingly slow passage through the tract and into the blood stream. The achievement of a truly postabsorptive state cannot be obtained except after such a prolonged period of fasting as may result in other disturbing factors which alter the normal catabolic processes. Thus the measurement of basal metabolism in the ruminant cannot have the exact significance that it does in man.

In the ruminant a minimum value for the methane excretion is one criterion of the establishment of the postabsorptive state. Another criterion of the attainment of a basal condition is a respiratory quotient which indicates that little or no carbohydrate is being burned, a condition that is generally reached after two or three days of fast. On the latter basis the heat eliminated in the next experimental period following the attainment of a metabolism which is characterized by the nonprotein, respiratory quotient of fat (0.707) is frequently referred to as the basal metabolism. Some workers determine what is called a *standard metabolism*, which is a value obtained under specified conditions as to time after the last feeding. It is preferable from a strict point of view to refer to any value determined on a ruminant as a measure of the fasting catabolism rather than of the basal metabolism. The conditions under which such a value is obtained should be accurately defined. The term *resting metabolism* has been used to denote the heat eliminated when an animal is lying at rest, though not strictly in a thermo-neutral environment or in the postabsorptive state. It is important that the significance of these various terms should not be confused.

Determinations of fasting catabolism for a given species provide a basis for studying the factors which affect this function and for comparing the metabolism in different species. They also provide a base line for measuring the effect of any superimposed factor such as muscular work, digestion, and other body activities.

13.2. Units of Reference in Fasting Catabolism. Heat production is obviously related to body size. In making use of determined values it is necessary to have some unit of reference. Rubner developed the concept, commonly referred to as the *surface-area law*, that the heat given off by all warm-blooded animals is directly proportional to their body surface and that, expressed on this basis, heat production is a constant for all species. Thus it became customary to express fasting catabolism in terms of surface rather than of weight, for example, as calories per square meter per hour. In view of the difficulties and uncertainties involved in measuring surface area, formulas were devised for computing it from weight, recognizing that surface was proportional to some fractional power of weight. Thus most of the values were really based on weight, though expressed in relation to surface.

It is now recognized that the surface-area theory rests primarily on an empirical basis and that it does not have so general an application as previously thought. While the concept has been and still remains very useful, it is agreed that the various methods of measuring or estimating surface area give such variable results that a statement of heat elimination per unit of surface has a very limited meaning except in terms of the specific method used in obtaining the surface measure. The body surface is not a constant but varies with the position of the body. The fact that the skin is elastic causes its measurement to vary with conditions, whether measured on the live animal or after its removal.

It has now become the practice among investigators of the energy metabolism of animals to use a fractional or decimal power of weight, instead of surface area, as the unit of reference. On the basis of an analysis of a very large number of basal-metabolism data of mature animals of different species, ranging in weight from 0.02 to 4000 kg. (mice to elephants), Brody[1] suggested the power 0.73. He later eliminated the second decimal, as giving a false idea of the precision involved, and thus adopted the power 0.7. The student is referred to his text[1] for the details of these studies. This general field has also been extensively studied and reviewed by Kleiber,[2] who feels that $W^{3/4}$ provides a better-fitting formula for relating basal metabolism to body size than does $W^{0.7}$. Both are in use. The ¾ power has the practical advantage of being readily calculated by the use of a slide rule or by arithmetic, while the other requires the use of logarithms. The basal metabolism per day for adult homeotherms may be represented by the general formula:

$$\text{Basal metabolism (kcal.)} = 70W^{0.75}$$

where W = weight in kilograms. The coefficient 70 represents an average value for the kilocalories of basal heat produced per unit of metabolic size in experiments with groups of adult mammals. For a 500-kg. cow the value would thus become 7399 kcal. per day, and for a 50-kg. sheep, 1316 kcal. These data show that heat production per

[1] Samuel Brody, Bioenergetics and Growth, Reinhold Publishing Corporation, New York, 1945, chap. 13. The author (1890–1956) was professor of dairy husbandry at the University of Missouri, where for thirty-five years he conducted pioneer research in the field of energy metabolism with special reference to the energetic efficiency of growth, milk and egg production, and muscular work. The book here cited summarizes much of his work, which is referred to frequently in the present text.

[2] Max Kleiber, Body size and metabolic rate, *Physiol. Revs.*, **27**:511–541, 1947.

kilogram is greater in the smaller animal, reflecting its relatively larger surface area and more active body mass. It should be emphasized that the constant relationship discussed above refers to mature animals. The same constancy is not found for animals of different species and size during growth, for various reasons.

The unit of reference for metabolic size, $W^{0.7}$ or $W^{3/4}$, is useful as a base value for calculating energy requirement for various purposes and for measuring feed efficiency, as is illustrated in later discussions. In such use it should be kept in mind that the unit is an average value subject to variability according to individuals and species. Brody notes, for example, that in the data which he analyzed, the power of weight found for mature birds of different species ranged from 0.62 to 0.70; for dogs of different size, the average was 0.6, and for rabbits, 0.82.

13.3. Lability of Fasting Metabolism. While a properly determined value for basal metabolism is conceived as being a constant, it must be recognized that this is not true in the absolute sense. Differences in the degree of muscle tonus may exist in animals which appear entirely relaxed. The minimum influence of this tonus becomes evident during sleep. Basal metabolism is lowered by undernutrition but increased by emotional stimuli. It decreases with age. Certain internal secretions, notably that of the thyroid gland, augment heat production by increasing the heart rate, the respiration, and probably, by affecting body oxidations in other ways. Thus variations in the activity of the thyroid influence basal metabolism accordingly. Any marked abnormality of this gland is recognized as pathological, and an altered basal metabolism is expected. The fact that this and certain other pathological conditions are accompanied by characteristic changes in the metabolic rate make the determination of the basal metabolism an important diagnostic agent in the case of various diseases in man. The lowering of basal metabolism which results from castration is due presumably to alterations in the endocrine relationships. This lowered basal-energy requirement is reflected in the cheaper feed costs of gains in castrated farm animals.

Some rather large deviations in the fasting catabolism of ruminants, not adequately explainable by the recognized factors of variability, have been noted. In the case of sheep on pasture in Australia, marked variations according to the season of the year have been reported for values obtained after 48 hr. of fast. Perhaps a true seasonal factor was involved, or perhaps differences in previous feeding were not eliminated by the short period of fast. Benedict and Ritzman,[3] however, have reported from studies with dairy cows that the fasting metabolism may vary for a given animal as much as 30 to 80 per cent within a period of two months, without any marked change in body weight.

[3] F. G. Benedict and E. G. Ritzman, Lability of the basal metabolism of the dairy cow, *Proc. Natl. Acad. Sci.*, **21**:304–308, 1935.

Their studies were made under conditions which closely approximate the basal condition. These investigators mention the observation of less marked variations in sheep and horses. Large variations in the fasting catabolism may be exceptional rather than usual, but an important field for further study is here presented, because the possibility of extensive variations obviously must limit the general application of determined values.

13.4. Endogenous-nitrogen Metabolism. There is a minimum essential nitrogen catabolism incident to the maintenance of the vital processes of the body, even as is the case for energy. This catabolism is measured as the minimum urinary excretion on a nitrogen-free, energy-adequate diet and called endogenous nitrogen (Sec. 6.22). Upon the inauguration of a nitrogen-free diet the urinary nitrogen decreases gradually. After the attainment of a postabsorptive state as regards protein, there remains "deposit protein" (Sec. 6.21) to be eliminated, at least in part, before the minimum endogenous value is reached. Thus the higher the level of previous nutrition, the larger the reserve of protein and the longer the time to reach the minimum level. It may be reached in a week with a rat previously on a low-protein diet, whereas on a high-protein diet four weeks or longer may be required. The minimum endogenous nitrogen is the maximum reduction of nitrogen waste of which the body is capable. It may represent a balance between destruction and synthesis—the net catabolism.

In order to arrive at a true value for endogenous nitrogen, it is essential that the animal be receiving a diet adequate in energy, because otherwise the output of urinary nitrogen may include some from body protein which has been broken down to furnish energy and thus be in excess of the value representative of the minimum essential nitrogen catabolism. Muscular activity has no appreciable influence on endogenous nitrogen so long as the energy intake is sufficient to cover it, for such activity has little, if any, influence on protein catabolism (Sec. 17.1).

While the measurement of the minimum endogenous-nitrogen metabolism is simple in theory, it is difficult in practice to obtain reliable and significant values, particularly with certain species. Not only is a variable and, frequently, a long time required to arrive at what may, by reason of its constancy, be considered a minimum value; but it is difficult, if not impossible, to get most animals to eat a sufficient amount of a nitrogen-free diet for any extended period. Any marked failure of adequate consumption destroys the significance of the results.

13.5. Relation of Endogenous Nitrogen to Energy Catabolism. Like basal metabolism, endogenous-nitrogen metabolism is a function of body size. Since this is true and since both represent the minimum catabolism essential to life, one would expect a relationship between them.

That a relationship actually exists was first proved by Terroine and Sorg-Matter.[4] Their studies, which included mice, rats, pigeons, chicks, rabbits, and pigs, resulted in the conclusion that the *law of constant relationship of minimum nitrogen and energy output* holds for all warm-blooded animals irrespective of body weight or age. The values actually reported ranged from 2.3 to 2.9 mg. of nitrogen per kilocalorie. Brody and coworkers[5] confirmed this relationship in showing that endogenous nitrogen is related to the same power of body weight in adult animals as is the basal metabolic rate. He suggested the following formula for calculating the endogenous nitrogen (EN) output per day:

$$\mathrm{EN} = 146W^{0.72}$$

where EN is expressed in milligrams and W is weight in kilograms.

In most of his studies, Terroine included the metabolic fecal nitrogen on his nitrogen-free diets as a part of the endogenous whole. While this fecal loss is of body origin, its level is related to food intake and not to basal metabolism (Sec. 6.17), and thus the ratio may be more appropriately calculated on the basis of the urinary nitrogen only, considering that the latter is more truly representative of the same vital processes which are responsible for the energy catabolism. Using this basis, Smuts,[6] in studies with mice, rats, guinea pigs, rabbits, and pigs, confirmed the work of Terroine on the approximate constancy of the ratio among different species. As was to be expected, since the metabolic fecal nitrogen was excluded, his results gave a lower ratio than those of Terroine, viz., around 2 mg. of nitrogen per basal kilocalorie. This ratio, as shown particularly by other studies, must be considered somewhat variable according to species and age.

A study of these various experiments is convincing that a *relationship* between the energy and nitrogen catabolism of fasting exists for the mature animal. The variability of the data reported, however, suggests that further studies are needed to *determine the degree* to which the ratio may be considered constant, particularly for all individuals and species. It seems likely that much of this variation may reflect the special difficulties involved in determining true values for endogenous nitrogen (Sec. 13.4). Additional studies with these points particularly in mind

[4] E. F. Terroine and Helène Sorg-Matter, Loi quantitative de la dépense azotée minima des homéothermes: validité intraspécifique, *Arch. intern. physiol.*, **29**:121–132, 1927.

[5] Samuel Brody, Robert C. Procter, and Ural S. Ashworth, Growth and development. XXXIV. Basal metabolism, endogenous nitrogen, creatinine and neutral sulphur excretions as functions of body weight, *Missouri Agr. Expt. Sta. Research Bull.* 220, 1934.

[6] D. B. Smuts, The relation between the basal metabolism and the endogenous nitrogen metabolism, with particular reference to the estimation of the maintenance requirement of protein, *J. Nutrition,* **9**:403–433, 1935.

seem called for to check further the validity and general applicability of the widely accepted ratio of 2 mg. of nitrogen per kilocalorie. The usefulness of such a ratio, if reliable, is based on the fact that it enables one to calculate endogenous nitrogen from the more easily determined basal-energy value. The nitrogen value is in turn used in arriving at protein requirements by methods discussed later.

13.6. Mineral Catabolism in Fasting. From the discussion in Chap. 7 of the functions of mineral elements, it is evident that an active mineral metabolism continues during fasting. Differing from organic constituents of the body, however, catabolized minerals may be reutilized instead of being excreted. For example, although the red cells of the blood are constantly being destroyed, the catabolized iron is available for the resynthesis of hemoglobin.

There is, nevertheless, a constant excretion of mineral elements during fasting, as is evident from the study reported by Benedict.[7] He measured the urinary excretion of certain minerals by a man during a fast of 31 days. The outputs gradually decreased during the early days and then reached values which tended to become constant. The figures obtained for the last day's output, expressed in grams, were as follows: chlorine, 0.13; phosphorus, 0.58; sulfur, 0.49; calcium, 0.138; magnesium, 0.052; potassium, 0.606; sodium, 0.053. The relatively large excretions of phosphorus and especially of sulfur doubtless were due in part to the breakdown of protein containing these elements as reflected by the endogenous-nitrogen catabolism. This fact suggests that the data cannot be considered to indicate the catabolism of mineral fasting alone. Had there been an adequate intake of energy and protein, certainly less sulfur- and phosphorus-containing protein would have been broken down. The large output of potassium in contrast to the low excretions of sodium, calcium, and chlorine is less readily explainable. These data from Benedict do not measure the total excretion of all the minerals considered, since the feces are an important path of outgo for some of them.

MAINTENANCE REQUIREMENTS

The term requirement implies an exactness which it does not have, as frequently employed, and which it cannot have when used in feeding standards for practice. Strictly speaking, it is the minimum amount of a given nutrient needed to promote a given body function to the optimum in a ration adequate in all other respects; i.e., a perfectly balanced ration. Such a minimum value will not be the same for any two individuals, and thus, for this reason alone, any determined individual

[7] Francis G. Benedict, A study of prolonged fasting, *Carnegie Inst. Wash. Pub.* 203, pp. 247–291, 1915.

value or any average of such values must be increased as a practical recommendation in order that the optimum performance of all may be assured. The intakes which are just sufficient to be fully adequate in a closely controlled experiment may fail to do so under less favorable conditions in practice.

The term *minimum requirement* as employed in this text denotes an experimental average minimum value, a figure that is not suitable, however, as a practical recommendation. Despite this limitation, its determination is highly useful because it provides a base line for studying the influence of factors which increase it in practice and thus for arriving at safe and yet economical recommendations as guides for feeding operations. Such recommendations are expressed by the National Research Council requirements as was previously explained (Sec. 12.2). They are used in this text accordingly in future discussions. Frequent citation is also made of the Morrison feeding standards[8] in referring to recommendations for practice. When the term requirement is used without qualification, it has a general and thus indefinite meaning. This usage cannot be avoided easily because of the variable ways in which the term is employed in the literature on which the following discussions are based. Specific terms, such as minimum requirement and others, are introduced, however, where needed to clarify the meaning. In all cases the figure given refers to a day's need.

13.7. The Maintenance Need for Food Energy. The energy requirement for maintenance is the minimum amount needed to keep the animal in energy equilibrium, i.e., to prevent any loss from its tissues. Thus an intake sufficient to offset the loss represented by the fasting catabolism would be the requirement under the conditions specified for measuring the latter. Expressed as net energy, it would be represented by the fasting catabolism itself, but expressed as any other measure of food energy, it would obviously be larger, since no other measure represents energy which is completely utilizable for the prevention of tissue breakdown. For example, in translating the fasting catabolism into metabolizable energy, it is necessary to choose a value for the latter which includes the fasting value plus the heat increment resulting from the food ingested.

13.8. Basal Metabolism as a Measure of Energy Maintenance. Under conditions of practice, however, an intake of food energy sufficient to balance the fasting catabolism is not an adequate maintenance value because the animal is never so restricted in its activity as represented by the standard, confined conditions which are specified for the determination of the basal value. At the present time there are no adequate ex-

[8] Frank B. Morrison, Feeds and Feeding, 22d ed., Morrison Publishing Company, Ithaca, N.Y., 1956.

perimental data for deciding what this activity factor should be. Clearly, it must vary for different animals and conditions, and any value selected for general use needs to be high enough to cover the extreme cases in order to arrive at a maintenance figure which would be adequate under all conditions of practice. The same principle applies, however, to the formulation of any generalized feeding standard. Mitchell and coworkers[9] increased the basal-metabolism values determined on chickens of different ages by 50 per cent to obtain their minimum requirements in terms of net energy, on the basis that the added 50 per cent should cover the activity increment. He has used a figure of 45 per cent for dairy heifers.

When the maintenance need is expressed as metabolizable or digestible energy, other losses must be accounted for. Brody and coworkers[10] have published a set of maintenance values calculated from basal-metabolism data and expressed in terms of total digestible nutrients. They use a general formula similar to the one listed in Sec. 13.2 to calculate basal metabolism from body weight. From a consideration of data of feeding trials, they decided that maintenance needs would be satisfied by providing an intake of TDN equal to twice the basal metabolism. Hereby provision was made for both the activity factor and the losses undergone by digested nutrients in metabolism. Thus they multiplied the basal metabolism values for different weights by 2 to obtain the maintenance requirements as digested energy. On this basis the requirement may be expressed:

$$\text{DE} = 2 \times 70W^{3/4} \qquad \text{or} \qquad \text{DE} = 140W^{3/4}$$

Brody and coworkers used the factor 1814 kcal, per pound for translating DE into TDN, a factor now recognized as being too low (Sec. 12.6). Using the higher factor of 2000 would have lowered the TDN values published in their table accordingly. On the basis that the calories expended in basal metabolism represent approximately 75 per cent of the total metabolizable energy needed for an idle adult human, the Canadian Council on Nutrition[11] uses the following formula to calculate the maintenance need:

$$\text{kcal.} = 93W^{0.75}$$

where W = weight in kilograms.

[9] H. H. Mitchell, L. E. Card, and T. S. Hamilton, The minimum nutritive requirements of single comb white leghorn chickens, *Proc. 4th World Poultry Cong., Sec. B, Nutrition and Rearing, Paper* 49, pp. 323–328, 1930.

[10] Brody, Procter, and Ashworth, *loc. cit.*

[11] Canadian Council on Nutrition, A dietary standard for Canada approved by the Canadian Council on Nutrition, Ottawa, Dec. 7, 1948, *Can. Bull. Nutrition,* vol. 2, no. 1, 1950.

These examples illustrate how basal-metabolism data can be used to arrive at the maintenance requirement. The general procedure is theoretically sound. Because of the lability of the fasting catabolism and the uncertainty as to the expenditure which should be allowed for activity, however, values so obtained need to be checked in practical feeding trials to test their reliability as bases for maintenance allowances. The calculation of the need for maintenance by starting with the basal expenditure and adding increments for the other expenditures involved is an example of the *factorial method* of arriving at a nutritional requirement.

13.9. Determination of Maintenance Needs from Feeding Trials. The maintenance values of feeding standards now in common use have been arrived at by feeding trials. In its simplest form this method involves the determination of the amount of food required to hold adult animals at constant weight. The inclusion of a digestion trial in the course of the experimental period allows the expression of the requirement in terms of TDN, or the latter may be calculated from the average coefficients. It is also possible, of course, to calculate the results to metabolizable energy. In such an experiment, in which live weight is the sole criterion, the importance of accurate and representative data for this measure is clear. If the experiment is successful in maintaining the weight substantially constant over an extended period, a fairly accurate measure of the maintenance requirement is obtainable and a measure which is directly applicable to the conditions of practice. Allowances can be made for changes in live weight by estimating the food equivalent of the losses or gains and correcting the observed intakes accordingly. The figures proposed for this purpose by Knott and associates[12] are as follows:

$$\text{Pounds gained} \times 3.53 = \text{TDN required for gain}$$
$$\text{Pounds lost} \times 2.73 = \text{TDN equivalent to loss}$$

Such corrections can be only approximate at best because of a lack of knowledge of the kind of tissue gained or lost. As an extreme example, the change in weight might be due entirely to water, which, of course, would have no food equivalent at all. It is clear that the larger the corrections which have to be applied, the less significant become the results.

The preceding considerations indicate the basis of a more general criticism of the live-weight method, viz., that constancy of weight does not necessarily imply the maintenance of the integrity of the body tissues or a constancy of energy content. In the case of a young animal, for example, in spite of a constant weight, an increase in protein and minerals

[12] J. C. Knott, R. E. Hodgson, and E. V. Ellington, Methods of measuring pasture yields with dairy cattle, *Washington Agr. Expt. Sta. Bull.* 295, 1934.

may take place, representing a growth the energy for which is furnished in part by a catabolism of body fat. This uncertain feature of the feeding-trial method can be eliminated by including a slaughter test, as is illustrated by the work of Mitchell and coworkers[13] with lambs. In this experiment a check group was slaughtered at the start, and the experimental group was slaughtered at the close of the period during which the food intake for maintenance was determined. A comparison of the slaughter data for the two lots showed that the experimental lot actually gained in energy, and a corresponding deduction was accordingly made in the observed food intakes in arriving at the maintenance requirement. The experiment included a digestion and metabolism trial which enabled the expression of the results both as TDN and as metabolizable energy. This method has also been used in studies with swine.

A very comprehensive study of the requirements of sheep and cattle has been reported by Garrett and coworkers.[14] Feeding trials were conducted in which check groups were slaughtered at the beginning and end, providing data for calculating energy changes as well as weight changes. Digestion trials were also included. By the inclusion of different groups, requirement data both for maintenance and for different rates of growth were obtained. The over-all data enabled the authors to express the requirements in terms of TDN, DE, ME, and NE. Thus, they give the following expressions for arriving at the estimated daily energy requirements in terms of the different measures of food energy:

$$\begin{aligned} \text{TDN} &= 0.036W^{3/4} \\ \text{DE} &= 76W^{3/4} \\ \text{ME} &= 62W^{3/4} \\ \text{NE} &= 32W^{3/4} \end{aligned}$$

It is noted that according to these formulas the ME and NE requirements are approximately 80 per cent and 45 per cent, respectively, of the DE requirement.

From feeding trials with beef calves, using pairs of identical twins, Winchester[15] has proposed the following formula for arriving at the maintenance requirement in pounds TDN from the weight of the animal in pounds:

$$\text{TDN} = 0.0553W^{2/3}$$

[13] H. H. Mitchell, W. G. Kammlade, and T. S. Hamilton, A technical study of the maintenance and fattening of lambs and their utilization of a ration of alfalfa hay and corn, *Illinois Agr. Expt. Sta. Bull.* 314, 1928.

[14] W. N. Garrett, J. H. Meyer, and G. P. Lofgreen, The comparative energy requirements of sheep and cattle for maintenance and gain, *J. Animal Sci.,* **18**:528–547, 1959.

[15] C. F. Winchester, Energy requirements for maintenance and growth, *U.S. Dept. Agr. Tech. Bull.* 1071, 1953.

This formula results in somewhat lower values than those arrived at by the previously mentioned one of Garrett and coworkers.

13.10. The Determination of Energy Equilibrium. The use of a respiration apparatus, or respiration calorimeter, makes possible the measurement of the effectiveness of a given ration for the maintenance of tissue integrity without slaughter of the animals. This procedure was early used by Kellner, Armsby, and others as a basis for obtaining the minimum requirement. It involves the determination of the energy balance with a ration which is just adequate to maintain weight. It cannot be expected that any such ration will result in exact energy equilibrium, but the procedures furnish specific data as to any tissue gains or losses, and the feed-energy intake, whether expressed as digestible, metabolizable, or net, can be corrected accordingly to arrive at the exact maintenance requirement. Kriss[16] has cited findings of the Institute of Animal Nutrition that the average heat production of the seven cows in energy equilibrium on a normal mixed ration was 8.487 Therms of metabolizable energy per 1000 lb. live weight. The nitrogen-carbon balance method of indirect calorimetry has also been used to determine the maintenance requirement.

The energy-equilibrium method of determining the maintenance requirement is recognized in the Report of the Conference on Energy Metabolism[17] in the following words:

> The standard *physiologic* maintenance requirement of an animal for net energy is that quantity necessary for the maintenance of energy equilibrium under ideal conditions, computed to a day of 12 hours standing and 12 hours lying. The standard conditions of environment are as in the respiration calorimeter or chamber, with the air temperature neither below the critical nor above the point of hyperthermal rise. The *economic* maintenance requirement must include an additional quota of energy sufficient to cover the energy expenditure in muscular activity under the particular conditions prevailing.

Forbes and Kriss recognized the need for this additional quota in connection with their standard for dairy cows when stating that their values determined in the respiration calorimeter would presumably need revision upward to be applicable in practice.

13.11. Values for Maintenance Needs. Some maintenance values obtained for different species by the various procedures previously discussed are given in Table 13.1. Those listed for Garrett and coworkers (GML) were calculated using their general formulas given in Sec. 13.9.

[16] Max Kriss, A comparison of feeding standards for dairy cows, with especial reference to energy requirements, *J. Nutrition*, **4**:141–161, 1931.

[17] Report of the Conference on Energy Metabolism, held at State College, Pa., June 14–15, 1935, under the auspices of the National Research Council, Committee on Animal Nutrition, Washington, D.C.

Even when expressed in the same units these values are not strictly comparable because some of them are minimum requirements while others are designed to be allowances for practice, as is evident from a consideration of the methods used. They serve, however, to indicate the relative magnitude of the requirements as expressed in different ways and as arrived at by different procedures. It is noted that the values

TABLE 13.1. SOME MAINTENANCE VALUES OBTAINED BY VARIOUS METHODS

Method	Species	Body weight, lb.	Total digestible nutrients, lb.	Metabolizable energy, Therms	Net energy, Therms
Fasting	All	1000	6.75 (B)		
metabolism	Horse	1000			4.08 (ZH)
	Pullet	4			0.141 (MCH)
Energy	Dairy cow	1000	5.51 (FK)	8.487 (FK)	5.5 (C)
balance	Steer	1000			6.0 (A)
	Sheep	100		1.32 (A)	0.72 (A)
	Horse	1000		11.9 to 13.1 (ZH)	
Live weight..	Dairy cow	1000	6.48 (H)		
	Dairy cow	1000	5.97 (FK)		
	Dairy cow	1000	7.925 (Ha)		
	Sheep	100		1.37 (A)	0.79 (A)
	Beef calf	800	4.8 (W)		
Live weight	Beef cow	1000		12.92 (TMH)	
and		1000	6.4 (GML)	11.02 (GML)	6.23 (GML)
slaughter	Sheep	100		1.64 (MKH)	
		100	1.12 (GML)	1.96 (GML)	1.11 (GML)
	Pig	100		1.86 (MH)	

The letters given in parentheses refer to the investigators as follows: A, Armsby; B, Brody; C, Cochrane, Fries, and Braman; FK, Forbes and Kriss; GML, Garrett, Meyer, and Lofgreen; H, Hills; Ha, Haecker; MCH, Mitchell, Card, and Hamilton; MH, Mitchell and Hamilton; MKH, Mitchell, Kammlade, and Hamilton; TMH, Trowbridge, Moulton, and Haigh; W, Winchester; ZH, Zuntz and Hagemann. Their publications have been previously cited or are to be found at the end of the chapter.

are given in terms of specific body weights. The original publications list a series of corresponding values for various weights or indicate how they may be obtained.

Current feeding standards for maintenance of dairy cattle, beef cattle, and sheep are based on a figure of 7 to 8 lb. TDN per 1000 lb. body weight. Requirements for other weights are calculated on the basis that the requirement is proportional to $W^{0.75}$. The N.R.C. standard calls for 7 lb. for a 1000-lb. dairy cow. The Morrison standard provides a range of 7 to 7.9 lb. It also lists a net-energy figure of 5.6 to 6.3 Therms. Most of these various figures are higher than corresponding ones in Table 13.1. They recognize that recommendations for practice should be more liberal than a value obtained under closely controlled experimental conditions, especially to allow for a greater activity expenditure. Of course, how much activity should be chargeable to maintenance is debatable. Grazing represents an extreme example. Reid and coworkers[18] found that the energy expenditure by dairy cows caused by grazing resulted in a "maintenance" requirement which was 40 per cent higher than when the cows were fed in the barn. The importance of the activity expenditure, however, is illustrated by the fact that cattle and sheep expend some 10 per cent more energy when standing than when lying down.

It is recognized that the energy expended in certain types of activity is directly proportional to body weight, as shown by Erickson and coworkers[19] for the energy cost of moving the body. Thus, though the basal metabolism represents by far the principal expenditure chargeable to maintenance, there are those who feel that the power of body weight used in calculating the maintenance requirement should be higher than 0.75 which applies to basal metabolism. Axelsson,[20] from studies of the data from European experiments on maintenance requirements, has developed a formula which is based on $W^{0.8}$ for calculating the energy needed for the maintenance of cattle. It has been previously stated that there is no adequate basis for deciding between 0.75 and the figure of 0.7 in so far as the basal expenditure is involved. Similarly there would not appear to be any adequate evidence at present for choosing a figure higher than 0.75 for use in this country. This conclusion is contrary, however, to the results of a statistical study with dairy cows by Gaines[21] indicating that *working maintenance, i.e.*, maintenance under practical conditions, is more nearly directly proportional to weight than to the 0.7 power thereof.

In connection with this discussion it should be borne in mind that feeding standards serve only as guides to be modified by the feeder in accordance with the condition of his animals and the results desired.

[18] J. T. Reid, A. M. Smith, and M. J. Anderson, Difference in the requirements for maintenance of dairy cattle between pasture and barn feeding conditions, *Proc. Cornell Nutrition Conf.*, 1958, pp. 88–94.

[19] L. E. Erickson and coworkers, The energy cost of horizontal and grade walking on the motor-driven treadmill, *Am. J. Physiol.*, **145**:391–401, 1945.

[20] Joel Axelsson and Sture Eriksson, Energy requirements for maintenance of domestic animals, *Ann. Roy. Agri. Coll. Sweden*, **20**:51–70, 1953.

[21] W. L. Gaines, Working maintenance as a function of live weight in dairy cows, and its bearing on an energy-size index of lactation, *J. Dairy Sci.*, **20**:583–598, 1937.

Attempts to express them to a high degree of refinement do not seem worthwhile.

13.12. The Protein Requirement for Maintenance. The discussion in Chap. 6 has shown that the need of the body for nitrogenous food, which we commonly refer to as a protein requirement, is actually a need for the building stones of protein, viz., the amino acids. It was also brought out in that chapter that the figures for the protein content of foods are conventional values, calculated from nitrogen content, and thus that they include both proteins and other nitrogenous compounds calculated to a protein basis. Despite these limitations, we express the nitrogen phase of nutrition on a protein basis because it is simpler to do so and because our knowledge is insufficient for a more exact expression. No serious disadvantage is here involved providing the limitations are kept in mind.

A separate figure for a maintenance allowance is commonly utilized in feeding standards only in the case of the dairy cow. The protein need of the horse is essentially a maintenance requirement, however, because work does not involve the catabolism of protein. Maintenance values for all species are useful, nevertheless, as a base line for arriving at the over-all need during production. A stated requirement assumes that the ration is adequate in energy content so that protein need be utilized only for its specific purpose.

13.13. Functions of Protein in Maintenance. The absorbed protein required for maintenance needs must make good the endogenous urinary losses and the metabolic fecal losses incident to the digestion of the ration in question and also provide for "adult growth." While the urinary losses are considered to be reasonably constant per unit of body size ($W^{0.7}$), the fecal losses are variable according to the make-up of the maintenance ration and the species (Sec. 6.17). Studies have shown that in man the fecal loss is approximately one-fourth or one-fifth as much as the urinary endogenous output. In adult ruminants on a high-roughage ration the metabolic fecal output may exceed the endogenous.

The term *adult growth* refers to the growth and renewal of hair, nails, feathers, and other epidermal tissues, a process which continues throughout life, even though the protein intake is inadequate for the maintenance of the body as a whole. As an extreme example, Mitchell and associates found that sheep fed an inadequate diet for 200 days were continuously in negative nitrogen and energy balance; yet there was appreciable growth of wool, and its content of protein was normal. This wool growth represented an increase of 0.014 lb. of protein per day in the fleece per 100 lb. live weight, an approximately normal rate, at the expense of the breakdown of other protein tissues of the body. In general the amount of protein required for adult growth is very small compared to the over-all need. In the case of the adult rat, however, the need for the continuing hair growth is a substantial one. The same is true for feather replacement in moulting hens.

Theoretically, the minimum requirement for absorbed protein might be met by supplying the amounts needed for the above-mentioned functions. Actually, a substantially larger amount is needed in practice. The minimum endogenous nitrogen represents the output of an animal in a depleted state in so far as protein nutrition is concerned. An appropriate maintenance intake should also cover the needs for maintaining a protein reserve (Sec. 6.21). The absorbed intake must be large enough to cover a variable wastage in metabolism. Where the protein requirement is expressed on a total-intake basis, it must be increased to cover losses in digestion.

13.14. Biological Value and Protein Requirement. The wastage of absorbed protein in metabolism results from the fact, as discussed in Chap. 6, that body need is for specific amino acids which make up the protein or other nitrogenous tissues or compounds to be formed. The process is most efficient when all the essential amino acids are supplied at the site of synthesis in the proportions which correspond exactly to the amino acid make-up of the product to be formed. In general the amino acid mixture absorbed and carried to the tissues differs, as regards the proportions of amino acids at least, from those required for tissue synthesis. The kinds of amino acids needed for a given synthesis are taken up from the available mixture in the proportions required, and the "leftovers" are wasted in so far as protein nutrition is concerned. This loss is a very substantial one where the mixture absorbed is relatively very deficient in any one essential amino acid. The ability of a given source of protein to supply amino acids in the relative amounts needed to form the nitrogenous tissues and compounds required for body functions is referred to as its *biological value.* For a given source the value differs according to function. For example, the relative amounts of the amino acids required differ somewhat for milk production compared with egg production because these two products contain the essential amino acids in different proportions. All of this means that in stating protein requirements biological value must be taken into account.

Studies with rats and man have clearly shown that various protein sources differ in their biological value for maintenance, and this is undoubtedly true for farm animals. Few studies have been made with them, however, because, with the exception of the dairy cow, feeding standards set forth data for the combined requirement of maintenance and growth or other productive functions. Since farm animals are nearly always being fed for productive purposes, the biological values for the combined functions of maintenance and production are the ones of practical importance. For this reason the discussion of how biological values are obtained for various feeds and how they are used in formulating rations is taken up in the chapter on growth. In this later discussion methods for determining biological value for maintenance are also described. In the discussion of methods of arriving at protein requirements, which is now taken up, consideration is given to the bearing of biological value on the results obtained.

13.15. Estimation of Protein Requirement from Endogenous Nitrogen. Several workers have proposed formulas for estimating the protein requirement from the endogenous-nitrogen output, either measured directly or calculated from basal metabolism (Sec. 13.5). This procedure is illustrated by the method proposed by Smuts.[22] Using the general equation (Sec. 13.2) for the relation of basal metabolism to body weight and considering that 2 mg. of nitrogen or 12.5 mg. of protein is required per kilocalorie of basal heat, he proposed the following formula for calculating the protein requirement:

$$P = 0.88M^{0.734}$$

where P = the day's protein requirement expressed in grams and M = the body weight in kilograms. Such a value obviously refers to protein actually utilized in the replacement of endogenous nitrogen and must, therefore, be increased, especially to allow for wastage in metabolism. Smuts suggested, therefore, that the value calculated from the formula should be doubled to arrive at a minimum requirement in terms of digestible protein. Thus, for a 1000-lb. animal he proposed a figure of 0.35 lb., a value that is only about 60 per cent of the present recommended requirements for a 1000-lb. cow.

In a later publication Smuts and Marais[23] report that the following formula is more applicable to the pig:

$$P = 0.81M^{0.734}$$

From studies with sheep, du Toit and Smuts[24] proposed the following formula for the species:

$$P = 0.74M^{0.734}$$

These formulas recognized the principle that the protein requirement for maintenance is proportional to metabolic size even as is true for the

[22] Smuts, *loc. cit.*

[23] D. B. Smuts and J. S. C. Marais, The endogenous nitrogen metabolism of young sheep, with reference to the estimation of the maintenance requirement of sheep, *Onderstepoort J. Vet. Sci. Animal Ind.*, **13**:219–255, 1939.

[24] B. A. duToit and D. B. Smuts, The endogenous nitrogen metabolism of pigs with special reference to the maintenance protein requirement, *Onderstepoort, J. Vet. Sci. Animal Ind.*, **16**:169–179, 1941.

energy requirement, a principle that is now generally followed in feeding standards. They provide a simple method for arriving at base values for animals of any size, which obviously must be greatly increased to provide recommendations for practice. The increases must take into account metabolic and food nitrogen losses in the feces and the biological value of the absorbed protein to arrive at a minimum intake figure. A further increase is called for because the base value determined, endogenous-nitrogen output, is a minimum value measured when the animal is in a depleted state of protein nutrition. A maintenance requirement for practice should be large enough to maintain a protein reserve (Sec. 6.21).

The Canadian Council on Nutrition[25] used the relationship proposed by Brody for developing the following formula for computing the human protein requirement from body weight:

$$\text{Protein, g.} = \frac{1.4 \times 2 \times 6.25 \times 146 W_{\text{kg.}}^{0.75}}{1000 \times 92} = 2.78 W_{\text{kg.}}^{0.75}$$

In the numerator the factor 1.4 covers the fecal metabolic loss which is considered to be 40 per cent of the endogenous loss, the factor 2 provides for an assumed 50 per cent biological value, and the factor 6.25 converts nitrogen to protein. In the denominator the factor 1000 converts milligrams into grams, and the factor 92 is an average figure for the coefficient of digestibility of protein. This formula is another example of the factorial method of arriving at a nutrient requirement.

Differing from the situation with respect to energy needs, activity does not require consideration in calculating a protein requirement from the basic nitrogen excretion because activity does not significantly increase protein metabolism. While it is agreed that endogenous nitrogen provides the basic value for arriving at the maintenance need for protein, the uncertainties as to the constancy and general applicability of such a value, as previously discussed, suggest that any figure so arrived at should be tested in practice before being accepted as a recommended requirement.

13.16. Nitrogen-balance Data as a Measure of Protein Maintenance. The minimum protein intake in a ration otherwise complete which will keep a previously well-nourished animal in nitrogen equilibrium is a reliable measure of the requirement for the protein mixture in question. It is important that the animal be in a good state of protein nutrition at the start and that the minimum intake necessary to maintain nitrogen equilibrium in such an animal be determined. The latter is important because the animal cannot store protein appreciably and an unnecessarily high intake tends to result in equilibrium also, giving a false picture of the maintenance need. On the other hand, if the animal is in a protein-

[25] Canadian Council on Nutrition, *loc. cit.*

depleted state, equilibrium may be established by intake levels which fall short of maintaining the needed protein reserves. The minimum level of intake which will maintain there reserves represents the true requirement, in contrast to the smaller amount which may result in equilibrium in a depleted body. For example, Wang and coworkers[26] found that the minimum nitrogen intake required to cause equilibrium in a partially depleted dog did not prevent certain liver changes and loss of appetite. Thus, the maintenance of nitrogen balance does not always guarantee protein adequacy.

Around the turn of the century many German workers conducted nitrogen-balance studies with steers and dry cows. Armsby[27] summarized these various studies along with ones of his own and thus arrived at his recommendation of 0.6 lb. digestible crude protein or 0.5 lb. digestible true protein per 1000 lb. live weight for the maintenance of cattle. Nitrogen-balance data provided the basis for the protein intakes for maintenance which were specified by Armsby for computing rations for farm animals. It is interesting to note that, at this early date, he recognized that not all proteins were of equal value. Nitrogen-balance data have also provided the basis for arriving at the N.R.C. protein allowance for human maintenance.

A balance experiment is a short-term measure carried out under closely controlled conditions, and thus the question always arises as to how accurately the results apply to practice over the long term. Further, a given experiment measures the amount of protein needed for the specific feeds used. Other feeds or mixtures may have a lower biological value, and thus a higher level of protein intake is required to cause nitrogen equilibrium. For these reasons recommendations for practice are customarily set higher than the values obtained in the balance experiment.

13.17. Determination of Protein Maintenance from Feeding Trials. The protein requirements which are used in most of the feeding standards at the present time are based upon the results of feeding trials, representing intakes, in rations considered otherwise satisfactory, which were found adequate for keeping the animals in good condition without loss of weight. Scientifically, the maintenance of weight and condition is no certain measure of the integrity of the nitrogenous tissue or of the minimum requirement for this purpose, but the rations which prove satisfactory for such maintenance over extended periods are considered to supply an amount of protein which is at least adequate. It is evident that the inclusion of slaughter data in feeding trials provides for a more

[26] C. F. Wang, A. Lapi, and D. M. Hegsted, The minimum protein requirements or adult dogs, *J. Lab. Clin. Med.*, 33:462–479, 1948.

[27] Henry Prentiss Armsby, The Nutrition of Farm Animals, The Macmillan Company, New York, 1917, pp. 326–327.

accurate measure of protein requirement than do observations on weight and condition alone.

Since protein maintenance allowances for farm animals find their principal use in practice for dairy cows, most of the feeding trials designed to determine them have been carried out with this species. While some of the investigators have suggested higher values, the most extensive study of all, by Hills,[28] resulted in the conclusion that the Armsby figure of 0.6 lb. digestible protein per 1000 lb. weight provides a sufficient intake. Morrison has adopted this figure as the minimum allowance in his standard. It is also the figure proposed in the recommended nutrient requirements of the N.R.C. In these requirements the ¾ power of weight is used in calculating the value per 1000 lb. to other weights.

While it is reasonable to believe that the efficiency of utilization of absorbed amino acids for maintenance purposes in cattle and sheep depends upon their qualitative and quantitative distribution in the mixture, as is the case for nonruminants, the biological value of the mixture as fed is of minor importance. This is true because, as discussed in Sec. 6.15, rations of poor protein quality as fed are improved through the intervention of microorganisms in the rumen. Essential amino acids which are deficient in the feed are supplied by bacterial synthesis. The absorbed acids are a mixture of those coming from the feed and from microorganisms, and there is evidence that this mixture does not vary markedly in biological value no matter what combination of feeds are used in commonly fed rations. Thus, the recommendation of 0.6 lb. of protein per 1000 lb. body weight would seem to have general application for cattle and sheep.

13.18. Does the Protein Requirement for Maintenance Remain Constant during Production? The Folin theory (Sec. 6.22) postulates a constant endogenous catabolism of nitrogen independent of the total protein catabolism, and the theory implies that there is a constant requirement to meet this loss, irrespective of the protein metabolism which may be taking place for the support of other body functions. It is considered that the feeding of protein to meet the needs of such a function as growth does not alter the amount required for maintenance where the latter alone is involved. Many do not agree with this concept, basing their objection on the view that the maintenance requirement in part is for certain amino acids only and that on a nitrogen-free diet the catabolism of body nitrogen compounds to furnish the acids needed results in "leftovers" which are wasted. It is argued that during protein ingestion, on the other hand, this wastage is decreased.

[28] J. L. Hills et al., The protein requirements of dairy cows, *Vermont Agr. Expt. Sta. Bull.* 225, 1922; J. L. Hills, The maintenance requirements of dairy cattle, *ibid.*, 226, 1922.

The questions here involved are of minor importance from the standpoint of feeding practice. It may be agreed that amino acids which are unsuitable or unneeded for a given productive function may serve in maintenance and thus lessen the specific intake for this purpose, but whether the gain here should be subtracted from the maintenance requirement or from the production requirement is a matter of bookkeeping.

13.19. Mineral and Vitamin Needs for Maintenance. The discussion in Chap. 7 has shown that many of the mineral elements undergo a very active metabolism in connection with various processes which are essential for the normal functioning of the body in maintenance. Differing from the energy and protein metabolism, however, they are not necessarily used up and excreted in the process. It has been mentioned that the iron released from the constant breakdown of red cells is reutilized for hemoglobin synthesis. Chlorine which is secreted in the gastric juice to provide for digestion can be reabsorbed from the digestive tract and reutilized. There are other examples.

Nevertheless, for reasons only partially understood, there are regular and substantial losses of certain minerals from the body of a mature animal, as described for the fasting condition in Sec. 13.6. The maintenance of an appropriate electrolyte balance in the blood and other tissues is an important factor governing mineral conservation and excretion. The amount of a given mineral required to keep the body store intact during maintenance is readily determined by a balance experiment. This is the technique which has been used to provide the data for the mineral allowances for human adults. Few similar studies have been made with farm animals because they are fed primarily for productive purposes, and mineral-maintenance data do not have the same usefulness as a base line for arriving at production requirements as is the case for energy and protein. The report by Gallup and Briggs[29] illustrates how the balance technique can be used to arrive at the intake of a mineral required to maintain the body's supply. In this study it was found that approximately 2 g. of phosphorus per 100 lb. body weight was sufficient to maintain lambs in phosphorus equilibrium. In the discussions in the following chapters of the requirements of the various minerals by animals in production, mention will be made of the separate maintenance needs where this information is pertinent.

On the basis of our knowledge of the specific functions performed by the various vitamins, their importance during maintenance as well as for productive purposes is clear. In the case of farm animals, however, no separate consideration of their needs for maintenance is of value, and thus their quantitative requirements are discussed in the chapters to follow.

[29] Willis D. Gallup and H. M. Briggs, The minimum phosphorus requirement of lambs for phosphorous equilibrium, *J. Animal Sci.*, **9**:426–430, 1950.

SELECTED LITERATURE

Blaxter, K. L., and W. A. Wood: The nutrition of the young Ayrshire calf. I. The endogenous nitrogen and basal energy metabolism of the calf, *Brit. J. Nutrition,* **5**:11–25, 1951.

Cochrane, Donald C., J. August Fries, and Winfred W. Braman: The maintenance requirement of dry cows, *J. Agr. Research,* **31**:1055–1082, 1925.

Lofgreen, G. P., and Max Kleiber: The metabolic fecal nitrogen excretion of the young calf and the true digestibility of casein, *J. Nutrition,* **49**:183–190, 1953.

Mitchell, H. H.: Adult growth in man and its nutrient requirements, *Arch. Biochem.,* **21**:335–342, 1949.

———, W. G. Kammlade, and T. S. Hamilton: Relative energy value of alfalfa, clover, and timothy hay for the maintenance of sheep, *Illinois Agr. Expt. Sta. Bull.* 317, 1928.

Trowbridge, P. F., C. R. Moulton, and L. D. Haigh: The maintenance requirement of cattle as influenced by condition, plane of nutrition, age, season, time on maintenance, type, and size of animal, *Missouri Agr. Expt. Sta. Research Bull.* 18, 1915.

Chapter 14
Growth

Growth is such a universal phenomenon that it commonly incites little curiosity in the layman; but when the physiologist faces the question "What is growth?" he is overwhelmed by its complexities. The fertilization of a single cell starts a multiplication and a differentiation which becomes highly varied in kind and rate in the differentiated cells yet remain coordinated and culminate in the adult. There is no complete explanation as to why the process starts, how it is coordinated during its course, or why it stops at the definite point which characterizes adult development. As expressed by Rubner:[1]

> Throughout the animate kingdom, from the simplest microorganisms to the most complexly organized beings, that inexhaustible power of growth which ever since the genesis of the first protoplasm in the infinite past has created the structure of the fossil remains of former ages as well as our own existence —this capacity to grow, has remained as the most remarkable phenomenon of nature, the supreme riddle of life.

Despite the complexities involved, physiological studies have produced a large body of information regarding the major processes of growth, and some knowledge of these facts is obviously essential for an understanding of the nutritive requirements involved and as to how they can be met.

THE PHYSIOLOGY OF GROWTH

14.1. The Nature of Growth. Clearly, a process as complex as growth cannot be simply defined. It is much more than an increase in size. Schloss[2] defines growth as a "correlated increase in the mass of the body

[1] Rubner, Max, Das Problem der Lebensdauer und seine Beziehung zum Wachstum, R. Oldenbourg, Munich, 1908, p. 81. Translation given in Lafayette B. Mendel, Abnormalities of growth, *Am. J. Med. Sci.*, **153**:1–20, 1917.

[2] Ernst Schloss, Pathologie des Wachstums, S. Karger, Berlin, 1911, p. 4.

in definite intervals of time, in a way characteristic of the species." This brief statement is excellent because it has very broad implications. It implies that, subject to individual variability, there is a characteristic rate of growth for each species and a characteristic adult size and development. It is considered that the maximum size and development are fixed by heredity. Nutrition is an essential factor determining whether this maximum will be reached, and an optimum nutritional regime is one which enables the organism to take full advantage of its heredity. According to the basic concept, however, the maximum development fixed by heredity cannot be exceeded through nutrition or by any other means, in the normal organism. The definition by Schloss also implies that in the growth of the organism as a whole there must be a complete and coordinated growth of all its parts. This simply stated characteristic involves a multitude of interrelated processes which are very imperfectly understood at the present time.

Optimum growth should result in an adult organism capable of optimum performance through its normal life. This is an extension to the life span as a whole of the previous statement that an optimum development is one which enables the organism to take full advantage of its heredity. Here again we are ignorant of many of the factors concerned, but it is evident that optimum growth in this sense includes much more than the rate of increase of weight and size.

True growth involves an increase in the structural tissues such as muscle and bone and also in the organs. It should be distinguished from the increase that results from fat deposition in the reserve tissues. Thus growth is characterized primarily by an increase in protein, mineral matter, and water. From the nutritional standpoint, it involves in addition a large intake of energy-producing nutrients to support the growth processes, and an adequate supply of the various vitamins concerned is also required. A minute amount of lipid material goes into the structure of each cell, but this does not represent a specific dietary requirement with the exception of the essential fatty acids (Sec. 5.28), in view of the synthesis of lipids from carbohydrate.

14.2. The Cell, the Unit of Growth. Growth takes place both by means of an increase in the number of cells, *hyperplasia*, and also through an increase in their size, *hypertrophy*. In early embryonic life both processes occur in the case of all cells. In the adult three types of cells are differentiated: the *permanent* cells, such as those in the nerves, which ceased to divide early in prenatal life and whose number has remained fixed thereafter; the *stable* cells, including those of most organs, which continued to divide for a variable but major part of the growth period but which have become fixed in the adult; the *labile* cells, composing the epithelial and epidermal tissues, which continue to divide throughout life, the process in the adult being limited to the replacement of cells worn out. All of these three types of cells undergo hypertrophy during growth, and some of them may increase in size thereafter in accordance with special physiological demands. For example, the increased muscular development which can be brought about through exercise involves a hypertrophy. The cells of the adult kidney can undergo enlargement if an increased burden is placed on this organ. It seems probable that the ability of the cells of the adult organism to hypertrophy becomes less with age.

14.3. The Course of Growth of the Body as a Whole. Conception is the starting point of growth. The discussion in the present chapter deals with postnatal growth, since it is more convenient to discuss intrauterine growth as reproduction (Chap. 15), but it should be remembered that the character of the latter has important bearings on the course of growth after birth. The evident vigor of the newborn, their content of certain nutrient reserves, and other qualities are influenced by the intrauterine nutrition. This fact is reflected in the recognized desirability of considering the diet of the mother and other factors affecting intrauterine development when selecting animals for many types of growth experiments. The percentage of the total growth period which is spent *in utero* differs in different species, and this also has a bearing on the nutritional and other factors concerned in postnatal development. The longer the portion of the total period spent *in utero*, the more advanced are the young at birth. The rat is born with its eyes closed, has no hair, does not gain the use of its legs for a considerable period, and must be nourished for a relatively long period solely by its mother's milk. In contrast, the guinea pig has a full coat of hair, its eyes are open at birth, and within a few hours it is running around nibbling leafy material. The calf, lamb, and foal resemble the guinea pig as regards their stage of development at birth, while the pig and the human baby are more like the rat.

In the various species the time that is normally spent in growth bears a rather definite relation to the length of life. The data in Table 14.1, calculated by Brody and associates, give the age, in months from conception, at which definite percentages of the mature weight are achieved in the different species. While such data must be considered only approximate, they present a useful picture for comparative purposes. A more recent analysis of the data on the comparative chronological age and stage of growth of various species is presented by Asdell.[3] The rate of growth is not constant, nor does its entire course follow any simple

[3] Sydney A. Asdell, Comparative chronological age in man and other mammals, *J. Gerontology*, **1**:224–226, 1946.

mathematical expression. There are periods of acceleration and of retardation. In the human, for example, the curve of growth is characterized by a decreasing rate during childhood, an acceleration during adolescence, and a decreasing rate thereafter.

14.4. The Growth of Parts. The growth of the body as a whole is a resultant of the simultaneous growth of its parts for which the individual rates are widely variable. The skeleton increases as a percentage of the total body weight for a short period after birth and then decreases on this relative basis. This means that skeletal development tends to precede muscle growth. The musculature increases as a percentage of body weight during growth, provided there is no marked fat deposition.

TABLE 14.1. EQUIVALENCE OF GROWTH AGE*
(In months)

Species	Percentage of mature weight				
	10%	30%	50%	80%	98%
Holstein cow	10.6	16.0	23.4	43.3	93.2
Duroc-Jersey sow	5.9	10.1	15.7	31.0	67.3
Suffolk ewe	5.3	6.7	8.6	13.7	26.5
Guinea pig, male	2.8	3.9	5.3	9.3	18.9
White rat, male	2.1	2.8	3.6	5.9	11.7
White mouse, male	1.1	1.3	1.8	2.8	5.6

* Data from Samuel Brody, Chester D. Sparrow, and Hudson H. Kibler, Time relations of growth. II. The equivalence of age in mammals estimated on the basis of their growth constants, *J. Gen. Physiol.*, **9**:285–308, 1925.

There is always some deposition of fat which becomes greater as maturity approaches. The head of the human baby is 25 per cent of its body size at birth, but only 7 to 8 per cent at maturity. These different growth rates for the various parts of the body explain the changes in conformation which take place as growth proceeds. Based upon his extensive studies, Hammond[4] has prepared the diagram shown in Fig. 14.1, illustrating how changes in body form and composition in hogs are brought about by differences in the time and rate of growth of different parts and tissues. Markedly different rates are exhibited by certain organs. The brain reaches adult size early in the growth period. The thymus increases to puberty and then decreases. The suprarenals actually lose weight for a time after birth, but this loss is balanced by an accelerated development toward the end of the growth period.

[4] John Hammond, Pigs for pork and pigs for bacon, *J. Roy. Agr. Soc.*, **93**:1–15, 1932.

Callow[5] has published the results of a very exhaustive study of the changes in the percentages of the various tissues of the body during the growth and fattening of cattle, sheep, and pigs, including data on chemical composition. Data on the composition of 132 dairy animals, ranging from a 135-day old fetus to a 12-year-old cow, including extensive data on calcium and phosphorus content, are to be found in a bulletin by Ellenberger, Newlander, and Jones.[6]

14.5. Measures of Growth. The growth of the body as a whole is most commonly measured as an increase in weight. Size measures, such

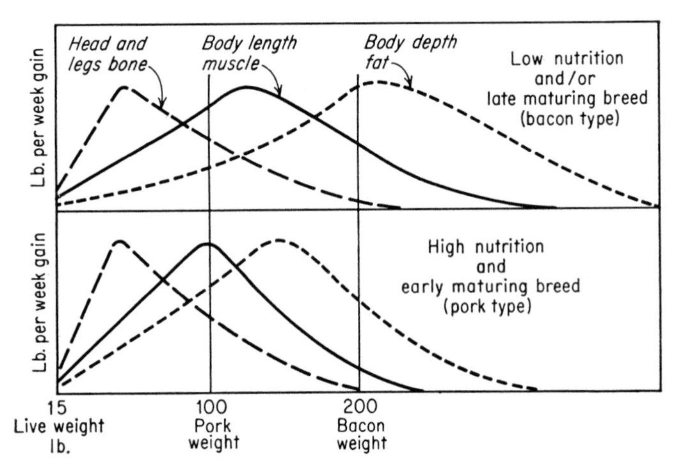

FIG. 14.1. Rates of growth of parts. The curves portray the rates of growth for the parts considered. It is noted in both charts that the rate of growth for the head and legs reaches its maximum earlier than the rate for body length and that the maximum for the latter is followed in turn by that for body depth. These three curves are considered to represent, respectively, bone growth, muscle growth, and fat deposition. All these processes occur earlier where the plane of nutrition is higher and earlier in the lard type of hog than in the bacon type. (*Courtesy of John Hammond, University of Cambridge.*)

as height, and various other body dimensions are also frequently employed. A combination of both weight and size measures is much more useful than either alone. An animal may increase in weight through the deposition of fat without any increase in the structural tissues and organs which characterize growth. An animal which is receiving insufficient protein and energy to permit of growth of its muscles and organs may still show an increase in size due to skeletal growth.

[5] E. H. Callow, Comparative studies of meat. II. The changes in the carcass during growth and fattening and their relation to the chemical composition of the fatty and muscular tissue, *J. Agr. Sci.*, **38**:174–199, 1948.

[6] H. B. Ellenberger, J. A. Newlander, and C. H. Jones, Composition of the bodies of dairy cattle, *Vermont Agr. Expt. Sta. Bull.* 558, 1950.

The increase in mass of the body as a whole may be expressed absolutely, as in grams per day, or it may be expressed as a percentage of the mass at the start. The absolute measure is the one most commonly employed in growth experiments, but the relative measure, which records the percentage increase, gives a more useful picture in many instances. The latter measure is plotted on semilogarithmic coordinate paper as is shown in Fig. 14.2. These curves illustrate the usefulness of the measure in comparing the growth rates of species of widely different size. Clearly the absolute increases in weight would be useless for such comparison.

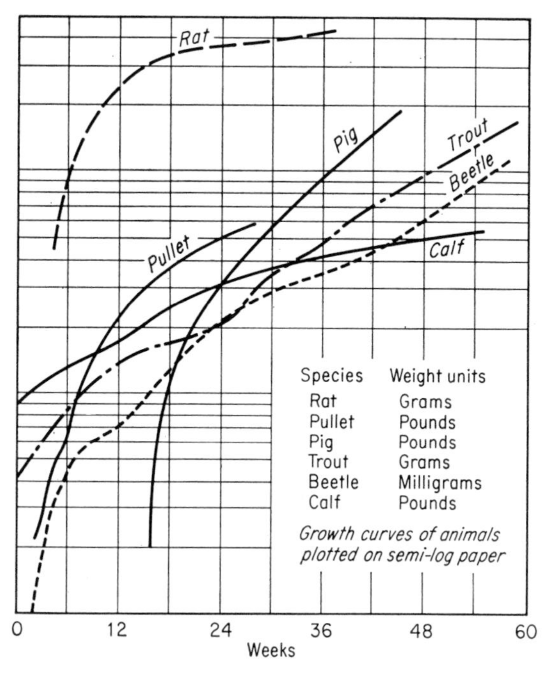

FIG. 14.2. Growth of various species plotted on semilogarithmic coordinates. (*Courtesy of C. M. McCay, Cornell University.*)

Increases in weight and size are highly useful measures of growth, but they are obviously incomplete. They do not show the nature of the tissue formed, nor are they suitable measures of coordinated development. The amounts of the true growth tissue, viz., protein and the skeletal minerals, can be obtained by a balance experiment or by the slaughter procedure. The latter must be employed to record the growth of organs and other parts which provide measures of coordinated growth.

14.6. "Normal Growth." In nutrition studies much use is made of "normal" growth data as illustrated by height-weight tables for children and by curves for increase in weight and size for farm animals. Such data are useful for comparative purposes, but their limitations must be realized. They are *averages* of the increases found for a group of individuals for which the nutritive and other factors were considered to be adequate to produce a satisfactory adult. Since the time that some of the growth data which are still used as criteria of normal growth were obtained, modern discoveries have resulted in more rapid rates of growth for various species. Some present-day investigators continue to regard their growth results as "normal" or "above normal" by comparing them with the earlier data which no longer reflect the rates that can be achieved by taking full advantage of the more recent discoveries in nutrition (Sec. 14.9). At the same time it should be recognized that increase in weight and size may be an inadequate measure of the coordinated growth which means an optimum development (Sec. 14.1). The word "normal" is much too loosely used in referring both to the state of nutrition and health and in describing growth and productive performance.

14.7. Internal Secretions and Growth. The striking abnormalities of growth which result when certain organs of internal secretion fail to function normally bear witness to the vital role of these secretions in controlling and coordinating the growth processes and furnish a further illustration of their complexity. In view of the influence that the thyroid secretion has upon metabolic rate one would expect this secretion to affect the character of growth. Such is the case. An overactive gland speeds up metabolism and steps up the requirements of all nutrients, increasing the growth rate in some species. Feeding dried thyroid gland or active iodinated proteins stimulates the secretion of milk and butterfat (Sec. 16.3). Thyroidectomy, on the other hand, stunts growth of the body as a whole and causes a relative overgrowth of certain parts. Thyroidectomy has been advocated as a means of increasing fat deposition in hogs. Feeding of the drug thiouracil, a goitrogen (Sec. 7.38), slows down or completely inhibits thyroid activity, thus promoting fattening and also feed efficiency, especially toward the end of the fattening period. A secretion from the anterior lobe of the pituitary gland determines the extent of growth. Its overproduction results in *gigantism*. There is an excessive skeletal growth which produces a giant in stature but a weakling physically because other growth processes do not keep pace. When the pituitary gland is underactive, the individual is small and infantile in appearance. In beef cattle and sheep it has been shown that implantation of pellets containing the synthetic estrogen, diethylstilbestrol, and particularly feeding the hormone, increases the rate of growth and reduces the feed required per unit of gain, as discussed in Sec. 9.6. Other internal secretions also play roles in growth, and there are definite interrelations in the functions of certain of the endocrine glands in the coordinating of the processes which combine to produce normal development, physical and mental.

14.8. Retardation of Growth. The severe retardation or arrest of growth which results from a failure of glandular secretions is fortunately comparatively rare. Much more common are the lesser retardations which are caused by undernutrition, either in calories or in some specific essential nutrient. The nature and extent of the effect on growth are dependent upon the character and severity of the deficiency and upon the period involved. A deficiency of energy, for example, will immediately check growth in mass, while a lack of calcium may not, since its primary effect is upon bone structure rather than its size. A deficiency of certain other nutrients, such as phosphorus or vitamin B, exerts an indirect influence on increase in size by decreasing appetite, as well as causing direct physiological effects.

The influence of varying degrees of undernutrition on the growth process has been the object of much study. One of the pioneer studies was that of Waters,[7] in which steers were placed on a ration which permitted no gain in weight, and the resulting changes in conformation were observed. Though the weight remained stationary, growth was not entirely inhibited, for the steers increased in length and height; but they became exceedingly thin because of a depletion of their fat reserves. Many experiments with laboratory animals, notably those by Osborne and Mendel,[8] have shown that, following a period of retardation, growth in weight can be resumed at a more rapid rate than normally exhibited at any time during life. There is no adequate explanation of this. In stunting, cells may be depleted yet remain in outline, capable of being filled in later without complete rebuilding. The rapid increase in weight which follows retardation may be to a considerable extent a replacement of lost fat, and this process may take place more rapidly than true growth. The actual suppression of growth may be less than the weight measures indicate. Cellular development may proceed in important ways and yet not be reflected in any increase in weight.

The major interest in the effects of growth retardation lies in the question of its influence on ultimate body development and productive life. Does any prolonged or severe retardation permanently harm any tissues or functions? The view is commonly expressed that any marked retardation is definitely undesirable. This may be true, but experiments have shown that underfeeding may prolong the growth period without affecting the ultimate size. The previously mentioned severe treatment to which steers were subjected by Waters did not result in any perma-

[7] H. J. Waters, The capacity of animals to grow under adverse conditions, *Proc. Soc. Promotion Agr. Sci.*, 1908, pp. 71–96; How an animal grows: the influence of nutrition on the size and form of animals, *Kansas State Board Agr. Rept.* 113, pp. 59–85, 1910.

[8] Thomas B. Osborne and Lafayette B. Mendel, The resumption of growth after long continued failure to grow, *J. Biol. Chem.*, **23**:439–454, 1915.

nent stunting, according to later reports from the Missouri Experiment Station where the study was carried out. U.S. Department of Agriculture workers[9] have reported two studies with identical twins. One animal of each pair was liberally fed for rapid growth, the other receiving a maintenance ration or a lesser allowance. Some of the restricted animals received such a ration from 6 to 12 months of age, others for shorter periods beginning at an earlier age. The rations were designed to supply adequate amounts of the essential nutrients. The only effect of the underfeeding was to prolong the over-all growth period. The restricted animals attained the same final weights as the controls, without loss of meat quality. At the Fifth International Congress on Nutrition, Breirem and associates[10] reviewed various experiments, mostly with cattle, on the effects of undernutrition on growth rate and ultimate body size. They drew the general conclusion that, while restrictions in energy intake have a retarding effect on growth, by growing more rapidly during following periods of liberal feeding the animals are capable of recovering and may eventually reach the same size as animals well fed from birth. It was noted, however, that severe and prolonged undernutrition at an early age may result in permanent stunting.

An example of recovery from extreme underfeeding was reported by McCay and associates.[11] Rats held undersized by calorie restriction beyond the average life span for the species were able to resume growth on ad libitum feeding. This growth was reflected in organ development as well as in weight, but those severely retarded animals never reached full body size. McCance[12] has reported a study in which, by restriction of the total food intake, young cockerels were maintained with little or no gain for 6 months and weanling pigs for 1 to 2 years. Data are given on the appearance and behavior of the undernourished animals and on various post-mortem findings. Some of the retarded animals were given unlimited food after the periods of undernutrition, which resulted in rapid rate of growth and the disappearance of various physical symptoms. From the standpoint of animal-husbandry practice, the question of the desirability or undesirability of energy restriction during growth involves considerations which differ depending on whether the

[9] C. F. Winchester and P. E. Howe, Relative effects of continuous and interrupted growth on beef steers, *U.S. Dept. Agr. Tech. Bull.* 1108, 1955; C. F. Winchester and N. R. Ellis, Delayed growth in beef cattle, *ibid.* 1159, 1957.

[10] Knut Breirem, Asmund Ekern, and Thor Homb, Relation of nutrition of the young animal to subsequent fertility and lactation. III. *Federation Proc.*, **20**:275–283, 1961.

[11] C. M. McCay, Mary F. Crowell, and L. A. Maynard, The effect of retarded growth upon the length of life span and upon the ultimate body size, *J. Nutrition,* **10**:63–79, 1935.

[12] R. A. McCance, Severe undernutrition in growing and adult animals. I. Production and general effects, *Brit. J. Nutrition,* **14**:59–73, 1960.

animals are being fed for meat production or for later breeding and lactation performance, as shown by the discussions which follow.

14.9. Accelerated Growth Performance. It is evident that nutrition discoveries during the past fifty years have resulted in an accelerated rate of growth. A study of the inbred rat colony of the Connecticut Agricultural Experiment Station during three periods from 1910 to 1935, the era of large advances in nutrition, revealed a gradual increase in growth rate and markedly larger body size at maturity. Similar data have been reported for man. There are convincing data from selected groups in this country and elsewhere that a physical evolution is occurring whereby children are growing to be taller and heavier than their parents. Better and more abundant food is listed as one of the causes.

Today's methods of feeding result in a more than 50 per cent greater weight in broilers at 12 weeks than was obtained twenty-five years ago. Similarly, modern methods are resulting in more rapid gains in swine and cattle. It should be recognized that improvements in breeding and management, as well as in feeding practices, have been concerned in these developments. In considering these data showing increased rates of gain in weight, it is important to bear in mind that growth proper is represented by increases in protein and in skeletal development and that in this sense gains resulting from increased fat deposition do not constitute an acceleration of growth rate. The value of an increased rate of fattening during the growth of meat animals depends upon the market for the product.

These various examples of improved rates of growth do not necessarily mean that the development fixed by heredity is actually being exceeded. Rather, they may mean that we are merely learning how to take fuller advantages of the hereditary capacity to grow and that the attainment of the maximum possible development lies in the future.

14.10. Effect of Growth Rate on Feed Efficiency and Carcass Quality. From the standpoint of animal production we are particularly interested in the influence of the growth rate on feed economy and on the final product. Following his initial study previously mentioned, Waters planned an extensive series of experiments dealing with the effect of nutritional plane and of age on the efficiency of food utilization and on body development and composition. These experiments were carried out at the Missouri Agricultural Experiment Station, and the results have been reported in a classical series of papers.[13] The data clearly show that the higher planes of nutrition proved more efficient from the standpoint of energy recovery and the production of edible meat. The papers contain a wealth of data on carcass composition as influenced by

[13] C. R. Moulton, P. F. Trowbridge, and L. D. Haigh, Studies in animal nutrition. III. Changes in chemical composition on different planes of nutrition, *Missouri Agr. Expt. Sta. Research Bull.* 55, 1922; and earlier papers here cited.

different levels of nutrition. The large body of data presented was analyzed and evaluated by Watson[14] as a basis for determining wartime food policies in England. His analysis brings out clearly the increased physiological efficiency resulting from high nutritional planes of intake. Guilbert and coworkers[15] have published an important study demonstrating the superior results obtained through continuous growth in steers, brought about by supplementing the range feed during the dry season, as compared with the interrupted growth which otherwise resulted. Today's improvements over former years in the rates of growth obtained in farm animals (Sec. 14.9) also result in marked savings in feed consumed per pound gain.

TABLE 14.2. VARIATION IN PERCENTAGE COMPOSITION OF CARCASS AS INFLUENCED BY PLANE OF NUTRITION*

Plane of nutrition	Live weight, lb.	Percentage composition of carcass†		
		Bone	Muscle	Fat
High-high	200	11	40	38
Low-low	200	12	49	27
High-low	200	11	45	33
Low-high	200	10	36	44

* Data from C. P. McMeekan, Growth and development in the pig with particular reference to carcass quality, *J. Agr. Sci.*, **30**:276–343, 387–436, 511–569, 1940; **31**:1–49, 1941.

† Data obtained by dissection.

The outstanding studies by McMeekan of New Zealand, carried out under the direction of Hammond at the University of Cambridge, have demonstrated how the plane of nutrition can be adjusted in relation to the growth rate of the different parts, as illustrated in Fig. 14.1, to influence the composition of the carcass at market weight. One group of animals designated "high-high" was kept on a high plane of nutrition through a slaughter weight of 200 lb. at 180 days. Another group, "low-low," was fed on a low plane to the same weight, 300 days being required. The third group, "high-low," first were fed at a high and then a low plane of nutrition, reaching 200 lb. at 240 days. The fourth group, "low-high," received the reverse treatment. The results in terms of carcass composition are shown in Table 14.2.

The high-low system produced the best bacon type, as a result of the

[14] D. M. S. Watson, Beef cattle in peace and war, *Empire J. Exptl. Agr.*, **11**:191–228, 1943.

[15] H. R. Guilbert and coworkers, The importance of continuous growth in beef cattle, *California Agr. Expt. Sta. Bull.* 688, 1944.

heavy feeding during the period of maximum bone and muscle formation and the limited feeding when fat deposition normally predominates. The reverse feeding system produced a hog with the characteristics of the early maturing, lard type. The low-low group had too large a portion of bone, poor development of loin and hindquarter, and too little fat. These papers contain a tremendous store of unique and valuable data on the growth of individual bones, muscle, and other tissues, as influenced by dietary regimes.

Crampton and associates[16] have shown that restricting the feed intake of market hogs or "diluting" highly digestible rations with fibrous feeds, during the finishing period, improves the carcass for bacon by reducing fat deposition and increasing the actual size of the muscle area. As expected, there was a decreased rate of gain and an increase in the length of the feeding period accordingly.

Fevrier[17] has published a very extensive review (141 citations) of experiments carried out in many countries dealing with the influence of nutrition on body composition and carcass quality of the pig.

14.11. Rate of Growth and Productive Life. Clearly, the recent studies in nutrition have resulted in practices that have markedly increased the growth rate as measured by weight and size. It has been the general belief that this is a desirable development in terms of the life span as a whole, but there are experiments which challenge this belief. The studies by McCay and associates[18] clearly showed that rats whose growth is severely retarded in early life, by calorie restriction only, have a longer life span than those which grow rapidly under ad libitum feeding. Their later studies showed that retarded animals were much less subject to chronic disease. They also found that, with animals which had grown normally on ad libitum diets until middle age, calorie restriction thereafter resulted in a longer life. McCay's studies on the effects of retardation during growth and thereafter have been confirmed and extended by Berg and by Berg and Simms,[19] who found that less drastic restrictions up to 800 days of age resulted in much leaner animals with somewhat less skeletal size, but improved health, female fertility, and longevity, and delayed the onset of degenerative disease.

[16] E. W. Crampton, G. C. Ashton, and L. E. Lloyd, The effect of restricting feed intake of market hogs during the finishing period on the quality of the bacon carcass, *J. Animal Sci.*, **13**:321–326, 1954; Improvement of bacon carcass quality by the introduction of fibrous feeds into the hog finishing ration, *ibid.*, **13**:327–331, 1954.

[17] R. Fevrier, Influence de l'alimentation sur l'importance des reserves graisse du porc, *Ann. nutrition et aliment.*, **13**:A65–A110, 1959.

[18] McCay, Crowell, and Maynard, *loc. cit.*

[19] Benjamin N. Berg, Nutrition and longevity in the rat. I. Food intake in relation to size, health and fertility, *J. Nutrition,* **71**:242–254, 1960; Benjamin N. Berg and Henry S. Simms, Nutrition and longevity in the rat. II. Longevity and onset of disease with different levels of food intake, *ibid.*, **71**:255–262, 1960.

During the past twenty years several comprehensive experiments have been conducted with dairy cattle on the effects of different levels of nutrition during growth on lactation performance and breeding efficiency, some of them covering the productive life of the animals. Breirem and associates[20] have reviewed the published results. Their summary states that energy intakes 20 to 30 per cent below current feeding standards during growth, though decreasing the growth rate, have no detrimental effects on lactation ability and that, though the milk yield may be somewhat lower during the first lactation, yields in later lactations are at least as high as obtained with animals reared on energy levels called for by the standards. It was noted that energy levels during growth in excess of the standards seem to depress lactation performance and impair fertility and longevity. Since 1948 an experiment has been in progress at Cornell University in which dairy calves were fed from birth to first calving at three different levels of TDN intake, viz., 65, 100, and 140 per cent of the Morrison standard. Thereafter, all were fed alike in accordance with production. The results support the conclusions of Breirem and associates, previously mentioned.

These experiments serve to emphasize the fact that growth should be looked at primarily as a preparation for life. In man we are interested in a healthy, productive life in which the infirmities of old age are postponed as long as possible. In breeding stock and in animals kept for milk and egg production, lifetime performance is the final measure of the success achieved in rearing these animals. The possibility must be considered to exist, particularly since there may be nutritional factors still unknown, that, from the standpoint of productive life, there are limitations in a system of rearing which relies upon a rapid increase in weight and size as the primary measure of success. However much one may doubt this possibility, it cannot be said with certainty that all the factors for growth are optimum until their influence on lifetime performance has been studied as thoroughly as their effects during the growth period itself.

ENERGY REQUIREMENTS FOR GROWTH

Previous discussions have shown that the rate and character of the body increase vary with age, as well as with species. It is evident, therefore, that a feeding standard for growth must be different for each species and must consist of a series of values corresponding to the different ages and body weights representing the growth period. Such a detailed presentation for all species is beyond the scope of a text dealing with the principles of nutrition. Rather, the physiological bases of the requirements will be considered, typical procedures for arriving at

[20] Breirem, Ekern, and Homb, *loc. cit.*

specific values will be outlined, and reference will be made to sources of detailed information for the different species which have been studied.

The total requirement for a given nutrient during growth must include the amount needed for maintenance as well as the amount required for the new tissue formed. The values given in feeding standards represent these combined requirements. Of the various nutrient needs for growth, the requirement for energy is by far the largest and primarily governs the total food allowance. It is therefore advantageous to discuss this requirement first.

14.12. Factors Governing the Energy Requirement for Growth. The maintenance component of the total energy requirement during growth increases regularly with body size, but the additional demand for the growth itself varies with the rate and with the composition of the tissue formed. Per unit of body weight, the amount of energy represented by the growth tissue formed decreases with age, reflecting the declining rate of body increase measured on a percentage basis (Sec. 14.5). But the amount of energy stored per unit of body increase becomes larger with age because of its lower water and higher fat content. While the true growth tissue contains only a trace of fat, a certain amount of fat deposition is an inevitable accompaniment of growth, and in practice a considerable amount of fattening is an integral part of growing animals for meat. Since fat contains much more energy than does protein, it is evident that the energy requirement per unit of body gain increases in accordance with its fat content. In fact, if the fattening is very rapid, the normal trend of decrease in energy stored per unit of body weight may not occur. In feeding standards for meat animals, no separate statement is made of the requirements for growth proper and for the fattening which concurrently takes place, but a distinction may be made according to the amount of fattening desired.

Except under conditions where very rapid fattening is sought, the maintenance component of the total growth requirement always markedly exceeds the portion required for the formation of new tissue. Thus the faster the growth rate, the lower the total requirement per amount of gain tends to be, but this tendency may be partially counterbalanced by the decreasing efficiency of food utilization as the intake is increased.

Since balanced rations (Sec. 11.16) involve less wastage as heat loss, they have the practical effect of decreasing the total feed required per unit of gain. The economy of balancing the hog ration with respect to protein has been shown by Ellis and Hankins[21] in studies involving

[21] N. R. Ellis and O. G. Hankins, The influence of the protein content of the ration on the growth and fattening of hogs fed at a moderately restricted level, *Proc. Am. Soc. Animal Production*, 1935, pp. 107–111.

three levels of protein intake. The higher the level, the more economical were the gains in terms of total feed required. The differences were most marked during the early part of the growth period. Similar data have been obtained with chickens.

14.13. Energy Requirements by the Factorial Method. The net-energy requirement for growth may be considered to be the sum of the energy of the tissue formed plus the basal metabolism, increased by an activity factor (Sec. 13.8). Mitchell, of the University of Illinois, has applied this general procedure to various species of farm animals. By special permission his unpublished data for Holstein heifers are reproduced in Table 14.3. The footnotes at the bottom of the table explain how the various values are obtained. The nutritional needs at any period during growth are determined by the rate of gain expected and the average body weight during the period in question. Body-weight data provide the basis for arriving at the energy required for basal metabolism and activity. Pounds to be gained plus data from slaughter experiments on the composition of such gains furnish the figures for computing the calories required for the growth desired. The sum of the calories thus obtained for basal metabolism, activity, and growth tissue formed is the estimated net-energy requirement, which can in turn be translated into metabolizable energy or TDN by applying factors such as those listed in the footnote to the table. The data show that at all stages of growth the major energy need is to cover the maintenance demands (basal metabolism and activity) of the body already formed. It is also noted that the requirement for growth reaches a maximum during the middle of the growth period and then falls off rapidly. It should be understood that the data here presented apply only to the species and growth rate on which they are based. They serve to illustrate how the factorial method can be used to arrive at requirements for a given weight and rate of growth.

Several assumptions are necessarily involved in the factorial method. The results require testing in feeding trials before being adopted in practice. The method does provide data, not obtainable in any other way, which are useful for various experimental purposes, as well as for consideration along with feeding-trial data in arriving at recommendations for practice.

14.14. Energy Requirements Obtained from Feeding Trials. The data contained in the currently used feeding standards for farm animals are based primarily on the results of feeding trials. In the more critically conducted trials different groups of animals have been fed throughout the growth period at different levels of energy intake to ascertain the level that would produce normal growth and development without being unnecessarily high. A feeding trial enables the statement of the require-

TABLE 14.3 THE ENERGY REQUIREMENTS OF GROWING HEIFERS DETERMINED BY THE FACTORIAL METHOD[1]

Body weight, lb.	Age,[2] mo.	Daily gains[3]		Energy requirements				
		lb.	g.	Basal metabolism,[4] kcal.	Activity,[5] kcal.	Growth,[6] kcal.	Total metabolizable energy,[7] kcal.	Total digestible nutrients,[8] lb.
109	0	1.039	471					
150	1.30	1.063	482	2150	968	444	5258	3.25
200	2.85	1.092	495	2686	1209	584	6620	4.10
300	5.99	1.644	746	3563	1603	1434	9927	6.14
400	8.14	1.467	665	4241	1908	1390	11,264	6.97
500	10.57	1.290	585	4783	2152	1140	11,961	7.40
600	13.35	1.140	517	5235	2356	996	12,654	7.83
800	20.56	0.761	345	5976	2689	706	13,694	8.47
1000	32.36	0.403	183	6639	2988	395	14,539	9.00
1200	70.35	0.0547	25	7303	3286	64	15,347	9.50

[1] Calculated by H. H. Mitchell from Vermont Agricultural Experiment Station data.

[2] Growth data for Holstein heifers are taken from *Vermont Bull.* 558, 1950. The growth equation describing the data is $W_{\text{lb.}} = 1231 - 1278e^{-0.05288t}$ from 6 months to 50 months of age, t being the age from birth in months. The growth from birth to 6 months of age is well described by the quadratic equation

$$W_{\text{lb.}} = 109 + 31.17t + 0.2778t^2$$

The point of inflection in the growth curve is approximated at 6 months of age.

[3] Obtained by differentiation of the growth curves: $\frac{dw}{dt} = 2.2569e^{-0.05288t}$, expressed in pounds per day. For the first 6 months of age: $\frac{dw}{dt} = 1.039 + 0.5556t$.

[4] Brody's equation for Holstein heifers (*Missouri Agr. Expt. Sta. Research Bull.* 166):

$$\frac{Q}{m} = 28e^{-0.0045m} + 11$$

in which Q = basal calories per day, m = body weight in kilograms.

[5] From a comparison of the net energy intake, estimated from the intake of TDN required for maintenance of body weight and the estimated basal metabolism of dairy cows kept under herd conditions (see *Missouri Agr. Expt. Sta. Research Bull.* 222), it was shown that the activity of the dairy cow expressed in calories required averages about 45 per cent of her basal expenditure of energy. Application of this percentage to calves of all ages implies a greater activity of the younger calf, because activity expenditures vary with body weight and the ratio of surface area to body weight increases the smaller the animal.

[6] Computed from the chemical composition of body-weight gains for the respective ages, as determined by analysis of growth data for "organic-matter-not-fat" and "fat," as reported in the Vermont bulletin.

[7] Assuming the availability of metabolizable energy in a well-balanced mixed ration is 69.5 per cent for maintenance (basal + activity) and 57.5 per cent for body gain (see Forbes et al., *J. Agr. Research,* **33**:483–492, 1926).

[8] Assuming that there are 1616 kcal. of metabolizable energy per pound of total digestible nutrients in a good mixed ration for cattle (see *Proc. Am. Soc. Animal Production,* 1931, pp. 113–120).

ment in terms of specific feeds or in terms of any desired measure of the energy required, by the inclusion of appropriate procedures. Most commonly the data obtained with farm animals are expressed as TDN, either by including digestion trials or by the use of average coefficients of digestibility.

The feeding-trial method of determining the energy requirements for growth is illustrated by the studies of Eckles and Gullickson with Holstein and Jersey cattle, based upon data for 50 animals divided among three levels of energy feeding. The intakes of those which were considered to have made a normal growth, as measured by weight, were then averaged to provide the data selected to represent the requirements. These estimated requirements are given in Table 14.4.

TABLE 14.4. TOTAL DIGESTIBLE NUTRIENTS REQUIRED BY GROWING DAIRY CATTLE

Body weight, lb.	*Total digestible nutrients, lb.*	*Body weight, lb.*	*Total digestible nutrients, lb.*
100	2.32	450	6.77
150	3.36	500	7.06
200	4.23	550	7.34
250	4.96	600	7.65
300	5.55	650	7.96
350	6.03	700	8.26
400	6.44	750	8.56

SOURCE: C. H. Eckles and T. W. Gullickson, Nutrient requirements for normal growth of dairy cattle, *J. Agr. Research*, **42**:603–616, 1931.

The recommended energy intakes for growth that are found in the feeding standards for various species have been arrived at primarily from feeding-trial data obtained in experiments similar to the one cited above. The data presented in Table 14.3 and Table 14.4 are in close agreement with each other over the period for which a comparison is possible. The requirements for growing dairy cattle proposed by the N.R.C. are also very similar up to 600 lb. weight. Thereafter they are more generous, presumably because they provide for more fattening than occurred in the animals on which the other two sets of values were based.

From data obtained in growth studies with beef calves, Winchester[22] developed the following equation for the combined maintenance and growth requirement:

$$f = 0.0553W^{2/3}(1 + 0.805g)$$

where f = TDN, W = body weight, and g = daily gain, all expressed in pounds. The expression $0.0553W^{2/3}$ represents the maintenance require-

[22] C. F. Winchester, Energy requirements of beef calves for maintenance and growth, *U.S. Dept. Agr. Tech. Bull.* 1071, 1953.

ment, and the expression in parentheses gives the growth requirement at the specific rate of gain expected or desired. A table of values calculated from this formula is given, setting forth maintenance requirements at different body weights and the combined maintenance and growth requirements for daily gains at rates of ½ to 2 lb.

From data obtained in the previously described (Sec. 13.9) growth and slaughter experiment, Garrett and associates developed the formulas shown in Table 14.5.

TABLE 14.5. EQUATIONS TO ESTIMATE THE ENERGY REQUIREMENTS OF SHEEP AND CATTLE FOR MAINTENANCE AND WEIGHT GAIN*

Sheep	*Cattle*
TDN† = $0.036W^{3/4}(1 + 2.3g)$	TDN = $0.036W^{3/4}(1 + 0.57g)$
DE = $76W^{3/4}(1 + 2.4g)$	DE = $76W^{3/4}(1 + 0.58g)$
ME = $62W^{3/4}(1 + 2.5g)$	ME = $62W^{3/4}(1 + 0.60g)$
NE = $35W^{3/4}(1 + 1.8g)$	NE = $35W^{3/4}(1 + 0.45g)$

* Table reproduced from Garrett, Meyer, and Lofgreen, The comparative energy requirements of sheep and cattle for maintenance and gain, *J. Animal Sci.*, **18**:528–547, 1959.

† TDN, W, and g are in pounds; DE, ME, and NE, in kcal.

The N.R.C. energy requirements for the growth of swine, dairy cattle, beef cattle, and sheep are set forth in Appendix Tables I, III, IV, and V, respectively, expressed as both TDN and DE. The Morrison standards include recommendations in terms of TDN and NE.

THE PROTEIN REQUIREMENTS FOR GROWTH

Aside from water, the body increase during growth consists very largely of protein. The theoretical minimum protein requirement is the amount actually stored in the body. But this is far below the actual requirement because of the wastage in digestion and metabolism. The loss in digestion can be taken account of by stating the requirement in terms of digestible protein, and data on digestibility are available for all of the common feeds. The wastage in metabolism is much less readily assessed. It is governed primarily by the efficiency with which the digested protein supplies the amino acids required for the construction of body tissue.

14.15. Amino Acid Requirements. The discussion in Chap. 6 listed the amino acids which have been found essential for the growth of rats, pigs, and chickens and described how this information was obtained. Many data have been secured on the quantitative requirements of these acids, and this continues to be a very active field of study. The general procedure has been to feed a diet designed to be adequate except in the amino acid to be tested and to add varying levels of it to different groups

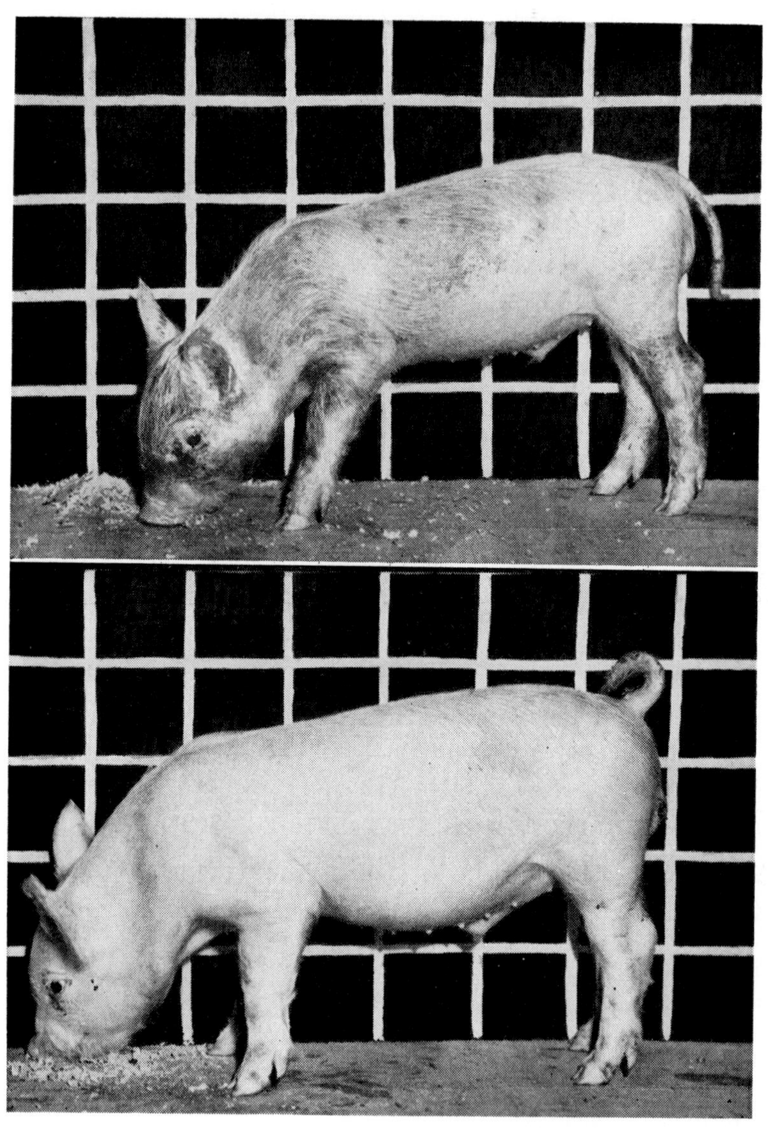

FIG. 14.3. Leucine deficiency. The top pig received a diet deficient in leucine; the bottom pig received the same diet with added leucine. (*Cornell University.*)

to arrive at the level which is sufficient to result in satisfactory growth. Weight increase has been the usual criterion, but in some experiments the nitrogen-balance measure has also been employed. The procedure is illustrated by the studies of Brinegar and coworkers[23] on the isoleucine

[23] M. J. Brinegar and coworkers. The isoleucine requirement for the growth of swine, *J. Nutrition,* **42**:619–624, 1950.

requirement of pigs and by Grau and Peterson[24] in the case of chicks. Such studies measure the combined requirement for maintenance and growth.

Data on amino acid requirements for growth are presented in Table 14.6, based on the N.R.C. reports in the case of chicks, poults, and pigs and on the work of Rose for rats. The table serves to indicate the order of the requirements among the different species. The values are expressed in terms of the utilizable form of each acid, usually the L form. The mixture of amino acids provided by the data in the table must be supplemented by nonspecific nitrogenous sources of the nonessential acids (Sec. 6.10). The data apply to the period of rapid growth and to the protein levels listed and assume an energy intake adequate for rapid growth. While lesser amounts of the acids are required for slower rates of growth, the proportionate needs do not change. This reflects the fact that whether protein formation is rapid or slow, it requires amino acids in the proportions represented by the protein to be formed. This means that an appropriate amino acid balance in the ration is important for efficient and optimum protein nutrition. This

TABLE 14.6. ESSENTIAL AMINO ACID REQUIREMENT FOR OPTIMUM GROWTH OF CHICKENS, TURKEYS, SWINE, AND RATS
(Per cent of diet)

Amino acid	Starting chicks	Starting poults	Pigs, 27 to 70 lb.	Weanling rats
Dietary protein	20.0	28.0	16.0 to 18.0	20.0
Arginine	1.2	1.6	0.20	0.2
Glycine	1.0	1.0	None	None
Histidine	0.3	?	0.20	0.4
Isoleucine	0.6	0.84	0.60	0.5
Leucine	1.4	?	0.60	0.9
Lysine	1.0	1.5	0.65	1.0
Methionine*	0.45	0.52	0.60	0.6
Phenylalanine†	0.7	?	0.50	0.9
Threonine	0.6	?	0.40	0.5
Tryptophan	0.2	0.26	0.20	0.2
Valine	0.8	?	0.40	0.7

* Cystine will replace methionine for chicks as long as the ration contains 0.45 per cent methionine. It can replace one-half the methionine requirement listed for pigs and one-fourth that listed for the rat.

† Tyrosine will replace phenylalanine for chicks as long as the ration contains not less than 0.7 per cent phenylalanine. It can replace 30 per cent of the phenylalanine listed for pigs and one-half that listed for the rat.

[24] C. R. Grau and D. W. Peterson, The isoleucine, leucine and valine requirements of chicks, *J. Nutrition,* **32**:181–186, 1946.

balance can be upset by relative excesses of one or more of the acids, as well as by deficiencies. At a very slow rate of growth, compared with a maximum rate, one would expect some differences in the proportions of acids called for, because here maintenance needs dominate, and they are somewhat different from those for growth, as previously discussed.

Another method of estimating amino acid requirements is the determination of the amino acid composition of the species in question. Williams and coworkers[25] have done this for the essential amino acids for pigs, chicks, and rats at various stages of growth. The data show comparability within each species at different stages of growth and also close correlation among species. The requirements thus indicated are in reasonable agreement, for the most part, with those determined by growth experiments on which the data in Table 14.6 are based.

The data on amino acid requirements of pigs and chickens are being used in conjunction with those available on feed composition (Sec. 6.13) to help formulate rations for more efficient and economical protein nutrition. Almquist[26] and Grau[27] have shown how the data available for chicks and poultry feed ingredients can be utilized to evaluate the protein quality of various feeds and combinations and to combine them in efficient rations accordingly. They provide a basis, in both experiments and practice, for putting together combinations of feeds, the amino acid make-up of which will supplement each other (Sec. 14.23). Of course, the selection of a ration which contains amino acids in the optimum quantities and proportions as fed may be rendered less efficient by differential losses in digestion (Sec. 6.16).

The proportionate amino acid requirements can be most readily visualized by taking one of them as unity, thus providing a useful "pattern" for comparative purposes. Such a pattern is shown for pigs in Table 14.7, constructed from the data in Table 14.6. Here arginine, histidine, and tryptophan, which have an identical requirement on a percentage basis (Table 14.6), are taken as unity, and thus all values in that table are multiplied by 5 to arrive at the data in Table 14.7. The calculated values for methionine and phenylalanine are, of course, subject to partial replacement as indicated in the footnotes to Table 14.6. Such a proportionality pattern is useful for comparison with a similar pattern which may be constructed for a given feed to show the extent to which the proportions of the amino acids in the feed correspond with body

[25] Harold H. Williams and coworkers, Estimation of growth requirements for amino acids, by assay of the carcass, *J. Biol. Chem.*, **208**:277–286, 1954.

[26] H. J. Almquist, Effective use of proteins in the nutrition of the chick, *Trans. Am. Assoc. Cereal Chemists*, **3**:158–168, 1945.

[27] C. R. Grau, Amino acid problems of poultry nutrition, *Proc. Cornell Nutrition Conf.*, 1948, pp. 7–14.

needs. Proportionality patterns for the requirements for different species and functions also provide a useful basis for comparative purposes.

One cannot at present visualize a protein feeding standard for practice expressed solely in terms of amino acids. But it seems clear that a knowledge of amino acid requirements and their distribution in feeds can be used to select more efficient and economical protein mixtures. In some instances, as commercial supplies become more available and cheaper, the addition of one or more specific amino acids may become the most economical way of providing an efficient mixture with available feeds. It seems evident that with the usual feed supplies attention will need to be given to only a few amino acids which may be deficient in terms of body needs—rather than to even all the essential ones. In the case of chicks, arginine, lysine, tryptophan, and the sulfur-containing amino acids appear to be the only ones which thus need attention.

TABLE 14.7. PROPORTIONALITY PATTERN OF AMINO ACID REQUIREMENTS FOR PIGS

Amino acid	Requirement	Amino acid	Requirement
Arginine	1.0	Methionine	3.0
Histidine	1.0	Phenylalanine	2.5
Isoleucine	3.0	Threonine	2.0
Leucine	3.0	Tryptophan	1.0
Lysine	3.25	Valine	2.0

Amino acid research is a very rapidly moving field, and up-to-date information on both basic facts and their applications to practice must come from the current literature, not from textbooks.

The discussion in this section has dealt with pigs and chickens. There is little point in trying to obtain data on the amino acid requirements of ruminants in terms of their feed supply, because, as previously discussed, the activities of microorganisms in the rumen make the amino acid mixture as fed of minor importance. There is need, however, for investigations as to how combined studies of rations and rumen processes can provide information for the most efficient protein metabolism of the animals, a metabolism that rests on an amino acid basis even as it does in pigs and chickens.

14.16. The Determination of Biological Value. The term biological value of protein denotes the measure of protein quality which is obtained in an animal study in which the percentage of the intake which is actually utilized is determined. The measure is sometimes expressed as the percentage of the total intake that is stored. Here losses in digestion as well as in metabolism are taken into account. The biological value, properly speaking, takes account of metabolic losses only and thus should be computed on the basis of the digested protein. This procedure measures the efficiency of the absorbed protein in supplying the amino acids needed for the synthesis of body protein, thus arriving at a figure for biological value which constitutes the more exact and preferred usage of the term. The calculation is made most simply as follows:

$$\frac{\text{N intake} - (\text{fecal N} + \text{urinary N})}{\text{N intake} - \text{fecal N}} \times 100 = \text{biological value}$$

It is evident that the data for such a calculation can be obtained from a nitrogen-balance experiment. The level of protein fed must be high enough so that marked growth will actually result as indicated by the positive balance; yet it must not be in excess of the amount needed to cause maximum growth, because an intake above this would be catabolized and excreted and thus give a biological value lower than the true one. There must be a sufficient intake of nonnitrogenous food so that the protein will not be needed as a source of energy. Other nutrients must be supplied adequately also.

14.17. The Thomas-Mitchell Method. The formula previously given measures the biological value of protein for growth purposes only. A more useful measure is one that takes account of maintenance as well. This can be accomplished by considering the metabolic and endogenous losses separately from the total fecal and urinary excretions. A method for this purpose was originated in 1909 by Karl Thomas[28] of Leipzig, who first used the term biological value. In so doing he had amino acid make-up in mind. It is interesting to note that Thomas developed this concept and a method for its measurement prior to the work of Osborne and Mendel which inaugurated the modern studies of protein quality. The Thomas method was modified by Mitchell,[29] and this modified procedure continues to be widely used. The method is best explained by a consideration of the formula which Mitchell uses in calculating the value obtained:

$$\frac{\text{N intake} - (\text{fecal N} - \text{metabolic N}) - (\text{urinary N} - \text{endogenous N})}{\text{N intake} - (\text{fecal N} - \text{metabolic N})} \times 100$$

The feature of this formula, distinguishing it from the previous one, is its recognition of the fact that endogenous and metabolic nitrogen represent fractions which have actually been utilized by the body even though they appear as excretions. Thus, in the numerator, the fecal loss subtracted from the total intake is limited to the part actually undigested, and the urinary loss is reduced by its endogenous fraction before being subtracted. The numerator, therefore, represents the total nitrogen utilized, including the part used in maintenance as well as that built into growth tissue.

[28] Karl Thomas, Über die biologische Wertigkeit der stickstoff Substanzen in vershiedenen Nährungsmittel, *Arch. Anat. u. Physiol., Physiol. Abt.*, 1909, pp. 219–302.

[29] H. H. Mitchell, A method of determining the biological value of protein, *J. Biol. Chem.*, **58**:873–903, 1924; H. H. Mitchell, Wise Burroughs, and Jessie R. Beadles, The significance and accuracy of biological values of proteins computed from nitrogen metabolism data, *J. Nutrition*, **11**:257–274, 1936.

Since in the denominator, also, the metabolic nitrogen is subtracted from the total fecal output, the biological value computed is the percentage of the actually digested nitrogen that is utilized. In excluding the metabolic and endogenous nitrogen from the losses, the Thomas-Mitchell method provides a measure of the efficiency of the absorbed protein for the combined functions of growth and maintenance.

The values for metabolic and endogenous nitrogen cannot be determined while the protein is under study but must be calculated from values obtained in separate periods when the animals are receiving a nitrogen-free diet. A frequent difficulty here, particularly with certain species, is that some individuals will not eat enough of the nitrogen-free diet to supply their energy needs, and thus true endogenous nitrogen values are not obtained. To obviate this difficulty a small amount of protein, such as egg or milk, which is considered to be utilized to an approximately complete degree in both digestion and metabolism, can be included in the ration. Some workers, instead of using the nitrogen-free-diet procedure, have arrived at the metabolic fecal nitrogen by the Titus extrapolation method (Sec. 6.17) and calculated the endogenous nitrogen from basal metabolism (Sec. 13.5). Others have used average values which have been reported for metabolic fecal nitrogen per unit of dry matter consumed and for endogenous nitrogen per unit of metabolic body size.

The data presented in Table 14.8, taken from a publication by Mitchell, illustrate the nature of the results obtained by the Thomas-Mitchell procedure. These figures reveal the wide differences which exist in the efficiency of various proteins, as measured by the rat, and they illustrate the extensiveness of the role that biological value can play in governing the amount of dietary protein required. The values given in Table 14.8 were determined by introducing the food in question into the basal diet in such amounts as would provide a protein level lying between 8 and 10 per cent. In addition to avoiding too high levels, it is desirable to hold to approximately the same level where the data obtained with different foods are to be compared. Since the over-all usefulness of a given source of protein depends on its digestibility as well as on the biological value of the absorbed fraction, the *net protein value* is frequently expressed as the product obtained by multiplying the biological value by the coefficient of digestibility for the source of protein in question. Hence, for milk:

$$85 \times 0.97 \text{ (digestibility coefficient)} = 82 \text{ (net protein value)}$$

Armstrong and Mitchell[30] have compiled data from the literature giving the biological values of various feeds for growing swine which show a variability similar to that revealed in Table 14.8 for rats.

[30] David G. Armstrong and H. H. Mitchell, Protein nutrition and the utilization of dietary protein at different levels of intake by growing swine, *J. Animal Sci.*, **14:** 49–68, 1955.

The *nitrogen-balance index* is a measure of biological value similar to those measures obtained by the Thomas-Mitchell method in that it takes account of the same data on intake and outgo of nitrogen. It takes advantage of the fact found to hold for different species that a linear relationship exists between nitrogen intake and nitrogen balance in the region of negative and low-positive balance, and thus it is applicable to studies of biological value for maintenance and some growth. It measures the rate of change of nitrogen balance with respect to absorbed nitrogen; the higher the rate, the greater the efficiency of retention, and thus the higher the biological value. For a detailed explanation of the method and how it is carried out, the student is referred to the article by Allison,[31] which also reviews other methods of measuring the nutritive value of proteins.

TABLE 14.8. BIOLOGICAL VALUE OF THE PROTEINS OF HUMAN FOODS*

Food	*Biological value of protein*	*Food*	*Biological value of protein*
Whole egg	94	Whole wheat	67
Milk	85	Potato	67
Egg white	83	Rolled oats	65
Beef liver	77	Whole corn	60
Beef heart	74	Wheat flour	52
Beef round	69	Navy beans (cooked)	38

* Data from H. H. Mitchell, The protein values of foods in nutrition, *J. Home Econ.*, **19**:122–131, 1927.

14.18. Protein Efficiency as Measured by Feeding Trials. As an alternative to the nitrogen-balance methods, another procedure for measuring protein quality is based on the method originally developed by Osborne, Mendel, and Ferry,[32] involving a feeding trial in which protein sources are compared in terms of gain in body weight per gram of protein or nitrogen fed. This procedure is frequently referred to as the determination of the "protein efficiency ratio" or "growth-promoting value." As carried out with rats to compare specific proteins or protein sources, a nitrogen-free, otherwise adequate basal diet is used in which the protein sources to be compared are included for different groups of young animals, and records are kept of growth and feed consumption. The results thus obtained are illustrated in Table 14.9, representing data taken from a study by Jones and Divine with rats in which the comparisons were

[31] James B. Allison, Biological evaluation of proteins, *Physiol. Revs.*, **35**:664–700, 1955.

[32] Thomas B. Osborne, Lafayette B. Mendel, and Edna L. Ferry, A method of expressing numerically the growth-promoting value of proteins, *J. Biol. Chem.*, **37**: 223–229, 1919.

made at a protein level of 9.1 per cent. Examination of the data for gain per gram of protein shows that the protein of patent flour is of low quality compared with that of the other sources and that skim milk has the highest value. The superiority of whole-wheat flour over the highly milled product is indicated, though the cereal flour fell below the oil-seed flours in value.

A limitation of measuring protein efficiency in terms of body gain is that the protein content of this gain may be variable. Thus some investigators have included slaughter data, where laboratory animals were involved, as a check on the results. From comparative studies which have been made, it appears that the possible errors here concerned

TABLE 14.9. COMPARATIVE GROWTH-PROMOTING VALUE OF PROTEINS*

Source of protein	Average food consumed, g.	Average weight gained, g.	Average gain per gram of protein consumed, g.
Patent flour	278	19	0.75
Whole-wheat flour	342	36	1.15
Peanut flour	419	75	1.95
Cottonseed flour	455	85	2.05
Soybean flour	408	87	2.35
Skim-milk powder	560	141	2.78

* Data from D. Breese Jones and J. P. Divine, The protein nutritional value of soybean, peanut and cottonseed flours and their value as supplements to wheat flour, *J. Nutrition*, **28**:41–49, 1944.

are not likely to be of large importance in a well-planned and well-conducted experiment.

The animals used in the experiment illustrated by the data in Table 14.9 were fed ad libitum. Various systems of controlled feeding have also been employed. In Sec. 10.6 reference was made to Osborne and Mendel's critical studies of ad libitum versus various systems of controlled feeding as techniques of measuring protein efficiency in terms of body gain. In a later publication they revealed the limitations of making the comparison at a single protein-intake level because different proteins differed as to the level at which they showed their maximum efficiency. Mitchell[33] has critically reviewed the advantages and limitations of various feeding-trial procedures for determining protein efficiency, and Barnes and coworkers[34] have reported a comparative study with rats of

[33] H. H. Mitchell, Biological methods of measuring the protein values of feeds, *J. Animal Sci.*, **2**:263–277, 1943; Determination of the nutritive value of the proteins of food products, *Ind. Eng. Chem. Anal. Ed.*, **16**:696–700, 1944.

[34] Richard H. Barnes and coworkers, The measurement of the growth promoting quality of dietary protein, *Cereal Chem.*, **22**:273–286, 1945.

various methods. The viewpoints expressed in these two papers are largely in agreement though differing somewhat in emphasis. While Mitchell believed that ad libitum feeding has no place as an exact measure of protein efficiency, Barnes and coworkers have shown that there are pitfalls in paired feeding also. These papers should be read by students of protein nutrition as a basis for critically evaluating experimental work in this field, as well as for planning any studies of their own.

14.19. The "Rat Repletion" Method. In this method developed in Cannon's laboratory at the University of Chicago, the relative ability of various protein sources to restore weight in protein-depleted adult rats is measured. The animals are fed an otherwise adequate basal ration practically devoid of protein until there is a weight loss of 25 to 30 per cent, involving also a large drop in the concentration of serum proteins. These animals are then used to test the value and efficiency of the protein sources in question for causing weight recovery. The details of the method and its application for evaluating protein quality are illustrated by the study of Frost and Sandy.[35] While adult animals are used, the method measures the values of a protein for the restoration of protein tissue, and thus much more than maintenance is involved, at least quantitatively. The rat repletion method is also used to study the relative value of amino acids and various protein sources for the regeneration of plasma protein and erythrocytes. The method has been found applicable to the study of protein requirements for the growth of baby pigs.

14.20. Estimation of Protein Quality from Amino Acid Composition. A comparison of the quantitative distribution of the essential amino acids in a feed (Table 6.3) with the relative amounts needed by the body per unit of feed provides a method of estimating protein quality. As a composite measure of the quality of a given protein, Mitchell and Block devised a chemical rating, or score, from amino acid composition data based on the essential amino acid in greatest deficit in the protein compared with egg protein as a reference, chosen because of its top biological value. In general, there was a close correspondence between these ratios and determined biological values for growth. Later, Oser devised a similar measure based on the contribution the protein makes to all essential amino acids rather than to the one in greatest deficit. He named this measure the *essential amino acid index* (EAAI). These indices were found in general to be highly correlated with biological values. Oser[36] has described the bases of these indices and discussed their usefulness

[35] Douglass V. Frost and Harry R. Sandy, Assay of dry proteins by rat repletion method: nutritive value and amino acid composition of six reference proteins, *J. Nutrition,* 39:427–439, 1949.

[36] Bernard L. Oser, An integrated essential amino acid index for predicting the biological value of proteins, in Anthony A. Albanese (ed.), Protein and Amino Acid Nutrition, Academic Press, Inc., New York, 1959, chap. 10.

and limitations in an article which also refers to the work of Block and Mitchell. Oser points out that EAAI is useful as a tool in predicting biological value in that it permits estimates to be made for combinations of proteins or for proteins supplemented with amino acids. He notes, however, that the method is predicated on the assumption that the amino acids determined in the feed are actually available to the animal and that factors which impair the rate or degree of digestion and absorption, and thus this availability, limit the usefulness of the method for the protein sources in question. Proteins injured by heat represent a case in point.

14.21. Comparative Usefulness of Various Measures of Protein Quality. It is clear from the previous discussions that none of the methods described is free from limitations. Each has its usefulness, however, if properly carried out. The advantages and limitations of the various methods and their modifications can best be appreciated by reading the discussions of them both by Mitchell[37] and by Barnes and Bosshardt.[38] In a review of the data on the nitrogen-balance procedure compared with those measured as the "protein efficiency ratio" in feeding trials Block and Mitchell[39] found the correlation of the results obtained by the two methods to be fairly close. Using a modification of the Oser method, Armstrong and Mitchell[40] found that values calculated for various feeds corresponded rather closely in most cases with those determined with pigs by the Thomas-Mitchell procedure.

There is no single procedure for determining protein efficiency or biological value which is best for all purposes. One method may provide more reliable and specific basic scientific information yet be less suitable than another for the solution of animal feeding problems in practice. The critical investigator can find, however, a method useful for his purpose which will yield reliable results if they are properly interpreted. Various methods of estimating protein quality have been compared by Rippon.[41]

14.22. Comparative Protein Quality of Various Foods. On the basis of the studies with rats and the much fewer ones which have been made with pigs and chicks, certain generalizations have been made regarding the comparative biological value of individual foods and combinations. Animal products as a class are superior to foods of plant origin. Eggs

[37] See all preceding studies by this author on this subject cited in this chapter.

[38] Richard H. Barnes and David K. Bosshardt, The evaluation of protein quality in the normal animal, *Ann. N.Y. Acad. Sci.*, **47**:273–296, 1946.

[39] R. J. Block and H. H. Mitchell, The correlation of the amino acid composition of the proteins with their nutritive value, *Nutrition Abstr. & Revs.*, **16**:249–278, 1946.

[40] Armstrong and Mitchell, *op. cit.*, p. 63.

[41] W. P. Rippon, A comparison of several methods for calculating the nutritive value of proteins, *Brit. J. Nutrition*, **13**:243–260, 1959.

stand at the top, followed closely by milk. Muscle meats, including fish, and glandular organs rank somewhat lower but above most proteins of plant origin. Most of the oil-bearing seeds and their meals have higher values than the cereal seeds. The latter do not show marked differences from one to another. Milling, which removes the germ and bran, results in a lowering of the value for the resulting flours. Thus, whole wheat ranks above white flour, and the milling by-products commonly used for animal feeds above both. The lower rankings of the various feeds, compared with eggs and milk, are due to specific amino acid deficiencies. The principal deficiency in cereals and in cottonseed and linseed meals is lysine. Soybean meal and peanut meal are deficient in the sulfur-containing amino acids. A deficiency of these acids also exists in casein. with a resulting markedly lower protein quality than that shown by milk proteins as a whole. Most of these lower-ranking products mentioned have lesser deficiencies of one acid or more besides the one mentioned.

The above generalizations, based primarily on growth studies, cover the field very incompletely, and they are subject to variations according to species and function being supported (Sec. 14.25). Many of the studies on which they are based were made with the food products as a whole and not with their proteins alone. It is now recognized that the presence of vitamins, unknown and thus not taken into account at the time the studies were made, contributed to the superior results in some cases. We can still speak with confidence regarding the nutritional superiority of certain protein foods, but we are less sure than formerly that the superiority is due to protein biological value alone. The comparatively recent discoveries regarding vitamin B_{12} are a case in point (Sec. 8.56).

14.23. The Supplementary Relations among Proteins. While data on the protein quality of individual proteins and foods provide important basic information, their usefulness in evaluating the combinations which occur in rations in practice is limited by the fact that, when two protein sources are combined, the resulting value is not necessarily the mean of the individual values. The explanation here is that certain proteins mutually supplement each other so that the resulting amino acid mixture has a biological value superior to that of either protein when fed alone, each liberally supplying one or more amino acids in which the other is deficient. This is strikingly illustrated by the studies of Mitchell and Kick[42] with corn and tankage, long known to represent an effective combination for the growth of swine. Using eight growing pigs the average biological values were corn, 54; tankage, 42; the combination (2:1), 61.

[42] H. H. Mitchell and C. H. Kick, The supplementary relation between the proteins of corn and of tankage determined by metabolism experiments on swine, *J. Agr. Reseach,* **35**:857–864, 1927.

Though an animal product, tankage consists of tissues which by themselves furnish a very inefficient amino acid mixture, but it supplies certain amino acids in which corn is deficient, and the latter performs a similar service for tankage.

The different protein efficiencies which result when corn is combined with other feeds are illustrated by the data shown below taken from an extensive experiment by Hart and Steenbock with growing pigs.

Ration	Percentage of total nitrogen retained	Percentage of absorbed nitrogen retained
Corn and alfalfa	31.7	47.3
Corn and tankage	40.3	56.7
Corn and milk	61.7	71.4

SOURCE: E. B. Hart and H. Steenbock, Maintenance and production value of some protein mixtures, *J. Biol. Chem.*, **38**:267–285, 1919.

These data also show the differences in values obtained by two methods of calculating the efficiency. The percentage retention is always larger when computed on the basis of the absorbed nitrogen than on the basis of the total fed because of the loss in digestion. The lower the digestibility of the ration, the greater the difference between the values calculated by the two methods. Hegsted and coworkers[43] showed that replacing one-third of the protein in an all vegetable diet by meat protein resulted in a 10 to 15 per cent increase in the biological value of the diet for rats, dogs, and man. In the case of the chick, blood meal, a feed very deficient in isoleucine but rich in lysine, combines with gluten meal, which has a surplus of isoleucine but a deficiency of lysine, to provide a mixture having a growth-promoting value greatly exceeding that of either feed alone.

The experiments just cited also illustrate the fact that the most useful data for biological value are those obtained with specific combinations used in practice, since single feeds seldom provide the entire ration. Combinations of vegetable and animal products generally provide effective mixtures, and when seeds are supplemented with 10 to 15 per cent of one of the better animal products, the combination is nearly as good as the animal source alone. In general, seeds and their products do not supplement each other, but a combination of soybeans or peanuts with cereal seeds is an exception. Wheat-germ and wheat-bran protein sup-

[43] D. M. Hegsted and coworkers, A comparison of the nutritive value of the proteins in mixed diets for dogs, rats and human beings, *J. Lab. Clin. Med.*, **32**:403–409, 1947.

plements the protein of white flour, explaining the superior growth-promoting value of whole compared to patent flour shown in Table 14.9.

The previous discussion of supplementary relationships does not apply to ruminants because the biological value of a feed or ration for these species depends in large measure on the nature and extent of the microbial action in the rumen (Sec. 6.15). On the basis that, in ruminants, most of the feed nitrogen is converted into bacterial protein and that this protein has a biological value around 60, it has been concluded that all protein sources are utilized approximately alike and that the figure of 60 is applicable as a measure of the protein quality of rations however made up. There are various experiments with sheep, however, mostly with isolated proteins, showing marked deviations from the general figure, particularly on the high side. These experiments have been reviewed by Ellis and coworkers[44] in an article which also reports their own studies. Using isolated proteins, they obtained values which ranged from 54 for gelatin to 83 for blood fibrin. These differences, and others cited by the authors, reflect differences both in the nature of the protein fed and in the resulting microbial action in the rumen. An important variable concerned is the extent to which ammonia is produced, as discussed by Head.[45] Whether the various differences in biological value for ruminants which have been noted experimentally may have an important practical application is a matter for further study.

14.24. Effect of Heat on Protein Quality. The heating which occurs in many commercial processes and also in home cooking can injure protein quality unless carefully controlled. For example, the following data on a menhaden fish meal subjected to high temperature in "flame drying" and on a steam-dried product were obtained in the authors' laboratory in 1932. In the field of human foods it was early shown that

	Digestibility, per cent	Biological value
Flame-dried fish meal.......	62	71
Steam-dried fish meal.......	73	77

the toasting of bread and the high heating of other cereal products resulted in an impairment of protein value. Milk protein can also be injured by overheating in the manufacture of evaporated and dried milks.

[44] W. C. Ellis and coworkers, Nitrogen utilization by lambs fed purified rations containing urea, gelatin, casein, blood fibrin and soybean protein, *J. Nutrition,* **60:** 413–425, 1956.

[45] M. J. Head, Protein utilization by the dairy cow, *Proc. Nutrition Soc.,* **18:**108–112, 1959.

The high heat developed in the expeller process in removing the oil as completely as possible from oil-bearing seeds has also been found to cause injury. This has been shown to be true in the case of cottonseed meal, sunflower seed meal, and others. The protein of any feed which is heat-treated in processing or drying can be injured unless the treatment is controlled. Both the temperature and the duration are involved.

Many studies have sought the specific cause of the injury. Certain amino acids, notably lysine, arginine, tryptophan, and histidine, are specifically involved. They are more slowly and less completely liberated in digestion. There may be some actual destruction of the amino acids, but the blocking of amino groups in such a way as to affect hydrolysis unfavorably and the combination of the acids with other chemical groups or compounds to form enzyme-resistant linkages appear to be more important causes. Much stress has been laid on the combination of the acids with reducing sugars, as occurs in the "browning reaction." Some workers have stressed the importance of the delayed digestion and absorption in lowering biological value because of the time factor in protein synthesis (Sec. 6.20). Whatever may be the cause, data are available to guide feed and food manufacturers for processing their products in such a way as to avoid injury to protein quality. This is an important matter in both human and animal nutrition.

Heat also has a beneficial effect on protein quality in the case of certain legume seeds, notably soybeans and peanuts. When they are fed raw to rats, swine, and chickens, they have a rather low biological value which is markedly improved by appropriate heat treatment. Various legume seeds and nuts contain an antienzyme which is a trypsin inhibitor. Unless destroyed by heat, the presence of this antienzyme results in a decrease in the rate and in the completeness of the liberation of amino acids in digestion. Liener[46] has shown with rats that raw soybeans contain a toxic protein, *soyin,* which is partially responsible for their poor nutritive value. Appropriate heating inactivates this substance as well as the antienzymes. Producers of soybean meal have learned how to apply sufficient heat to bring about the needed inactivation without causing the harmful effects discussed earlier in this section. There are several reports indicating that the causes of the inferior values of raw soybeans are not completely understood. One puzzling fact is that, despite the inferiority of these beans for chicks, hens utilize both the raw and the heated forms equally well for egg production, according to Fisher and associates.[47]

[46] Irvin E. Liener, Soyin: a toxic protein from the soybean, *J. Nutrition,* **49**:527–539, 1953.

[47] Hans Fisher, Dewey Johnson, Jr., and S. Ferdo, The utilization of raw soybean meals for egg production in the chicken, *J. Nutrition,* **61**:611–621, 1957.

14.25. Biological Values for Different Species and Functions. Most of the data for biological value or protein efficiency have been obtained with rats. Several studies have been made with pigs and chickens, and a few with sheep and cattle. The question as to the extent to which the values obtained with one species apply to another is an important one from the standpoint of their general usefulness, particularly in view of the special suitability of the rat for determining these values. There are several experiments, such as those of Schneider[48] with fish meals, indicating that the values obtained with rats tend to hold for pigs also, though this is not true for all feeds. Hegsted and coworkers[49] have compared the nutritive value of the protein in mixed diets for dogs, rats, and man. While certain differences were noted, the striking feature of the results as a whole is the similarity of the biological values for the species studied. Other workers have concluded that the utilization of dietary protein in rats, pigs, and dogs is essentially similar. This similarity is explainable on the basis of the similar amino acid make-up of the tissues formed in growth, as illustrated by the data of Williams and coworkers[50] in the case of rats and pigs.

Chickens present a special case because, differing from the mammals studied, they require a dietary source of glycine. Thus, a diet could be devised, from purified nutrients at least, which would have a high biological value for the growth of mammals and yet not even maintain a chick. A relatively higher requirement for arginine also seems to be characteristic of the chick. Casein has a lower biological value for chick than for rat growth because glycine and arginine are limiting. No requirement for histidine for maintenance in man has been demonstrated, differing from findings with rats and chicks. These various differences have been discussed in Sec. 6.9.

There are certain differences in the relative amounts of the various essential amino acids required in accordance with the function being served. This fact is illustrated for growing and mature rats in Table 14.10. These data are taken with the permission of H. H. Mitchell, from a report by Mitchell and Beadles[51] which cites the sources of data not obtained by the authors. The authors explain that wheat gluten has a much lower value for rat growth than for maintenance because of its deficiency in lysine, the requirement for which seems to be much less prominent for maintenance than for growth. Both casein and peanut flour are deficient in sulfur-containing amino acids, but their biological values indicate

[48] Burch H. Schneider, Nitrogen-balance studies with various fish meals, *J. Agr. Research*, **44**:723–732, 1932.

[49] Hegsted and coworkers, *loc. cit.*

[50] Williams and coworkers, *loc. cit.*

[51] H. H. Mitchell and Jessie R. Beadles, Biological values of six partially purified proteins for the adult albino rat, *J. Nutrition*, **40**:25–40, 1950.

more intensive requirements for them for maintenance than for growth, explainable by the large need for these acids for hair growth, which is a prominent feature of protein maintenance in rats. A comparison of the data for mature rats with those for mature humans indicates that certain species differences exist. Apparently the previous explanation that wheat gluten has a relatively high efficiency for the adult rat because the lysine need is low does not hold in the case of man.

TABLE 14.10. THE BIOLOGICAL VALUE OF PROTEINS FOR GROWING RATS, MATURE RATS, AND ADULT MEN

Protein	Growing rats	Mature rats	Mature humans
Egg albumin	97	94	91
Beef muscle	76	69	67
Wheat gluten	40	65	42
Casein	69	51	56
Peanut flour	54	46	56

14.26. Factors Governing Protein Needs. As commonly stated in feeding standards, the protein requirement for growth includes the amount needed for maintenance as well. The maintenance component increases with body size, but the demand per unit of new tissue formed decreases with age and body size because of the decreasing protein content of this tissue. While the total daily requirement increases with age and size, at least during early growth, it decreases per unit of weight and in relation to the energy requirement. For example, according to the N.R.C. data, a 25-lb. pig requires 17 per cent of protein in its feed, whereas a 100-lb. pig requires only 13 per cent. Standards for children, expressed as grams per kilogram of body weight, decrease from 3.5 g. during the first year to 1 g. near maturity. This relative change in the protein requirement with age means that its experimental determination should be made at different stages of the growth period. An average requirement obtained for the period as a whole would be inadequate for early growth. A figure obtained for early growth would be adequate for the entire period but wasteful during the latter part.

In view of the factor of biological value, it is evident that there can be no fixed minimum requirement except in terms of specific food sources. The fact that biological value tends to decrease with level of intake has the effect of increasing the requirement per unit of tissue gained as the growth rate is increased. The previously discussed evidence (Sec. 11.16) that, within rather wide limits, the wastage of energy in metabolism is decreased as the level of protein is raised suggested that the most efficient level of intake may be higher than the amount needed for its specific function as protein. All of these considerations suggest higher allowances in practice than certain minimum values which have been determined for specific combinations.

14.27. Factorial Method of Estimating Protein Requirement. The protein requirement for growth can be estimated factorially as a sum of the amount needed for maintenance plus that in the growth tissue formed, with an allowance for losses in metabolism. The net amount needed for maintenance is considered to be the endogenous nitrogen, which may be determined directly as endogenous nitrogen or calculated from the basal energy metabolism (Sec. 13.8). The amount required for the tissue formed is estimated from slaughter data. The procedure in thus arriving at the net protein need is similar to that shown for the net energy requirement (Sec. 14.13). This net protein figure is then increased to cover estimated average losses in metabolism in arriving at a figure for absorbed protein. The procedure is illustrated in the publication of Blaxter and Mitchell,[52] which shows the basis of the calculations and the resulting estimated requirements for fattening lambs and dairy heifers. The procedure has the advantage of arriving at figures which reflect the changing needs at the various stages of the growth period in terms of animal size, rate of gain expected, and composition of the gain. In view of the assumptions involved in the various calculations, the data obtained cannot be considered, by themselves, to be reliable recommendations for practice. They are very useful, however, for consideration along with the results of more direct methods in arriving at such recommendations. They have been considered in setting up many of the N.R.C. requirements for farm animals.

14.28. Protein Requirements as Measured by Nitrogen Balance. The nitrogen-balance method provides an exact measure of the actual requirements in terms of a specific ration by determining the minimum intake which will provide maximum retention. The animals must be making the expected rate of growth during the study. The measurement should be made at a minimum of two or three times during the growth period to obtain data representing amounts which are adequate early but not wasteful later. Recommendations for practice must be set higher than the average data thus obtained to cover the needs of all individuals and to allow for the probability that the protein of some rations fed in practice will be of lower biological value than the one tested.

Mitchell and Hamilton[53] have made a brief report of an extensive ex-

[52] Kenneth L. Blaxter and H. H. Mitchell, The factorization of the protein requirements of ruminants and of the protein value of feeds, with particular reference to the significance of the metabolic fecal nitrogen, *J. Animal Sci.*, 7:351–372, 1948.

[53] H. H. Mitchell and T. S. Hamilton, The balancing of rations with respect to protein, *Proc. Am. Soc. Animal Production*, 1935, pp. 241–252.

periment with pigs, carried out by the paired-feeding technique, in which the nitrogen retained was used as a measure of the protein requirement. On this basis a ration containing 15 per cent of protein proved superior to those containing lower levels for pigs weighing from 130 to 186 lb. as well as for younger pigs. A ration supplying 18 per cent of protein caused a larger retention than one furnishing 15 per cent for pigs weighing from 42 to 70 lb. but not for those weighing 140 lb. or more. Digestibility data were obtained as were also growth records which checked the nitrogen-balance results. It was concluded that pigs weighing from 40 to 100 lb. require a ration containing more than 17 per cent of total protein, corresponding to 15.4 per cent of the digestible nutrient, but that, for higher weights, a total figure of 15 per cent, corresponding to 12 per cent digestible protein is sufficient. A more recent example of the nitrogen-balance method is in the report by Lassiter and coworkers.[54] They used protein levels ranging from 10 to 22 per cent to determine the minimum level which would give maximum nitrogen retention in 50- and 150-lb. pigs.

14.29. Protein Requirement from Feeding Trials. In the feeding-trial method of measuring the protein requirement different levels are fed to find the minimum one which will give a maximum rate of growth. The inclusion of slaughter tests to show the nature of the increase made provides valuable additional data which are obtainable in the case of meat animals. The studies with chicks by Norris and Heuser,[55] in which rations containing different percentages of protein were prepared by varying the amount of meat scrap included, illustrate the feeding-trial method. Levels varying from approximately 13 to 21 per cent were compared. The requirement was found to be higher than 18.58 per cent for the first 8 weeks, whereas a level of 15 to 16 per cent was adequate thereafter. The birds were fed ad libitum, and the highest level of protein intake gave the largest gain per gram of feed during the first 8 weeks, as well as the greatest total gain. The gain per gram of protein decreased with the level of intake as was to be expected. The use of equalized feeding by pairs in arriving at the protein requirement is illustrated by the study of Becker and associates[56] with pigs.

Lofgreen and associates[57] have combined growth and nitrogen-balance studies in an investigation of the protein needs of dairy calves, in which

[54] J. W. Lassiter and coworkers, Protein levels for pigs as studied by nitrogen balance, *J. Animal Sci.*, **15**:392–399, 1956.

[55] L. C. Norris and G. F. Heuser, The relation of the protein requirement of chicks to the rate of growth. I. The quantity of protein required by chicks during early growth, *Poultry Sci.*, **9**:378–392, 1930.

[56] D. E. Becker and coworkers, Levels of protein in practical rations for the pig, *J. Animal Sci.*, **13**:611–621, 1954.

[57] G. P. Lofgreen, J. K. Loosli, and L. A. Maynard, Comparative study of the conventional protein allowances and theoretical requirements, *J. Animal Sci.*, **10**:171–183, 1951.

they compared the results with those obtained by the factorial method. According to their data, the factorial method as carried out by Blaxter and Mitchell[58] underestimates the needs of heifers during the latter part of the growth period.

While feeding trials have shown, as is to be expected from the nature of the tissue formed, that the protein needs decrease relative to energy needs as growth proceeds, few critical studies have been made of the differential quantitative requirements at different stages. Most of the experiments, especially those with cattle and sheep, have compared different percentages of the total ration or different intakes per unit of live weight for the growth period as a whole. Whatever level is selected as adequate on one of these bases, it automatically results in an increasing daily intake as weight and total feed consumption increases. Thus feeding standards based on feeding-trial data specify large increases with age and size during the growth period, in marked contrast to the calculation by the factorial method. Further studies, such as those reported by Lofgreen and associates, are needed to clear up the discrepancies here involved.

In any experiment set up to study the protein requirement, provision cannot be made for keeping the biological value constant. Varying amounts of different sources of protein must be used, except where the purified-diet method is employed, and even in the latter case, the values will vary with the level tested. This is not a serious limitation from the standpoint of arriving at reliable figures for practice, provided the feeds are properly selected. In the experiments previously cited, the shifts in the combinations of the ingredients were those which would normally be made in good feeding practice where a change in protein intake is desired. In the case of the studies with the pigs and chickens, the rations providing the minimum protein which gave the best results contained protein mixtures known to have good biological values for the species. The requirements suggested by these results should apply to the rations recommended to represent good feeding practice. They might prove inadequate for less efficient combinations.

14.30. Methods of Stating the Protein Requirement. In the previously cited studies, the protein needs have been expressed in different ways. The relationship between the figures expressed by the different methods is illustrated by the N.R.C. requirements for swine. Expressed as daily needs, the figures begin at 0.34 lb. of protein for the 25-lb. pig and rise to 0.96 lb. for the 200-lb. animal, showing the increased need as growth proceeds. Expressed as the requirement per pound of air-dry feed, the figures drop from 0.17 to 0.12 lb. over the growth period, reflecting the fact that the protein need decreases relative to total food required

[58] Blaxter and Mitchell, *loc. cit.*

with advancing growth. Thus, as a percentage of the total feed, the requirements drop from 17 to 12 over the growth period. The requirements for chickens are expressed similarly, being 20 per cent for the first 8 weeks and 16 per cent thereafter. This method is not suitable for Herbivora because of the large differences in digestibility of the various feeds and rations. For dairy cattle, sheep, and horses the requirements are expressed as digestible protein per day for the different weights during growth and also as per cent digestible protein in the air-dry feed, along with corresponding allowances of total digestible nutrients. Since the total food intake for growth is governed primarily by the energy needs, stating the protein needs in relation to the energy intake has certain advantages. The nutritive ratio provides a means of doing this where digestibility data are available. A similar relationship is provided in dietary standards for man by the statement that the intake of protein calories should be 10 to 15 per cent of the total calories, using the factors employed in calculating physiological fuel values (Sec. 11.10). Having specified the relation between energy and protein for a given age and selected the ration accordingly, the only intake figure needed is for the total food intake which will supply the energy needs.

14.31. Wool Production. Since the wool fiber is practically pure protein, a substantial amount of food protein is required for its production. Thus the protein requirements for sheep are somewhat higher than for cattle at the same stage of maturity. There are two aspects of wool growth which distinguish it from the growth of muscle. In the first place, despite a negative nitrogen and energy balance, wool growth continues at the expense of the breakdown of other protein tissues (Sec. 13.13). Secondly, wool protein has an amino acid distribution quite different from that found in muscle, calling physiologically for a different pattern for its formation. Of special note, wool protein contains, on a percentage basis, over 10 times as much cystine as does muscle protein, a difference which is only partially balanced by the higher content of methionine in muscle.

Several early studies were made to ascertain whether the feeding of cystine or sulfur as a supplement to the usual rations would improve wool production, with generally negative results. These results are explainable on the basis that microorganisms in the rumen can utilize inorganic sulfur and nonspecific sources of nitrogen to form these essential amino acids. In the studies by Thomas and coworkers[59] in which a ration lacking in the sulfur-containing amino acids and inorganic sulfur as well prevented the synthesis of these amino acids in the rumen of lambs, wool growth was interfered with also. In rats the addition of

[59] W. E. Thomas and coworkers, The utilization of inorganic sulfates and urea nitrogen by lambs, *J. Nutrition*, **43**:515–523, 1951.

methionine to a diet deficient in the sulfur-containing amino acids produces more hair and hair richer in cystine.

CALCIUM, PHOSPHORUS, AND VITAMIN D

The general functions of the mineral elements and vitamins required by the body have been discussed in Chaps. 7 and 8. As a result of many studies, fairly reliable data for several species are available on their quantitative requirements for growth of those which particularly need attention to ensure that the ration selected will contain an adequate supply. The calcium, phosphorus, and vitamin D needs for growth have been extensively studied in farm animals, not only because of their individual importance but also because of their interrelations in metabolism. They are best discussed together.

Vitamin D is essential for the growth of all species of higher animals in so far as studied, but there are marked species differences as regards quantitative needs. There are also species differences with respect to the requirements for calcium and phosphorus, depending upon the rate of growth and other factors. In every case the interrelations between the three nutrients are such that a minimum requirement for a given one cannot be specified except in terms of rather definite amounts of the other two also. Failure to recognize this fact in many of the experiments designed to determine requirements limits the usefulness of the data obtained. Since the intakes in diets consisting of natural feeds cannot, at best, be adjusted exactly to the optimum relations which make possible a minimum requirement, recommendations in practice must specify more liberal allowances accordingly.

By far the principal needs for calcium, phosphorus, and vitamin D during growth are for the formation of the skeleton, and thus they may be termed the bone-forming nutrients. Phosphorus plays an important role also in the growth of the soft tissues, as is evident from its occurrence in important amounts elsewhere in the body than in the bones (Sec. 7.7). In addition, this element exerts an indirect effect on growth because of its relation to appetite. To a lesser extent this is true also for calcium and vitamin D.

14.32. Measures of Skeletal Growth. The development of the skeleton cannot be measured by increase in weight, nor can its adequacy be determined by dimensional measures of the body or even of the bones themselves. Size of bone is governed largely by inheritance, and a large bone may be a very weak one if the nutrition has not been adequate. Severe nutritive deficiencies during growth manifest themselves in misshapen bones as in severe rickets, but mild deficiencies may have serious consequences without any evident early symptoms. There may be later deformities or fractures or a breakdown of the teeth, as a result of prolonged periods of mild deficiency. Even though these evident symptoms never occur, the bone development may still be inadequate, particularly as regards its content of calcium and phosphorus reserves which are normally called upon during reproduction and especially during lactation (Sec. 16.29).

The real measure of the adequacy of skeletal development is the density and strength of the bones formed as conditioned by their content of calcium and phosphorus and their histological structure. Thus the requirements for the bone-forming nutrients can be determined by slaughter

FIG. 14.4. Phosphorus deficiency. The pig on the left received a phosphorus deficient ration. Note the weak and crooked leg bones, in contrast to the condition of the pig on the right which received the same ration adequate in available phosphorus. (*Courtesy of M. P. Plumlee and W. M. Beeson, Purdue University.*)

experiments in which representative bones are analyzed for calcium and phosphorus or studied histologically. The measurement of density and hardness and the determination of breaking strength are useful supplementary measures. Since the ash of bone consists almost entirely of calcium and phosphorus and since this remains true no matter what the quality of the bones, the determination of the ash is more commonly used as the measure of the adequacy of bone nutrition than the more time-consuming analyses for calcium and phosphorus. Radioactive calcium and phosphorus have been found highly useful in studying bone development by an autoradiographic technique illustrated by the report of Tomlin and coworkers.[60]

[60] D. H. Tomlin and coworkers, Autoradiographic study of growth and calcium metabolism in the long bones of the rat, *Brit. J. Nutrition,* 7:235–252, 1953.

The progress of bone development can be followed quantitatively in the living animal by calcium and phosphorus balances. The blood serum levels of the elements and of alkaline phosphatase and X-ray photographs are useful supplementary measures. The application of the radiographic technique to the living animal is illustrated by the studies of Benzie and coworkers[61] with lambs.

14.33. Optimum Bone Development. In the discussion of bone growth in Chap. 7, it was pointed out that calcium and phosphorus are deposited in the bone as reserve material as well as constituents of the structural portion itself. Presumably the building of the latter has first call on the bone-forming nutrients, but where the intakes are large enough, deposition in the trabeculae doubtless occurs also. In the case of animals grown for slaughter, the state of the reserves would seem to be of minor importance, but other considerations enter for those being reared for breeding and milk production.

In an interesting study of skeletal development in the rat, Outhouse and Mendel[62] found that an increased rate of body growth, caused by a diet richer in various nutritive factors including calcium, was accompanied by an increased rate of calcification compared with that in the slower-growing animals. When the latter reached the same mature body weight, however, there were no differences between the two groups as regards the ash content of the bones. Thus it is suggested that, if bone development keeps pace with body growth, the end result is satisfactory, even though the rate of calcification is not at its maximum. Such is not the case if the calcification lags markedly behind body growth. Sherman and Booher[63] reported that, as diets containing increasing levels of calcium are employed, not only is maturity reached earlier, but an increased storage of calcium per unit of body weight also results. They concluded that the diet which causes the maximum rate of retention should be considered optimum until the normal store at maturity, including reserves, is attained. There are special reasons for believing that this is true in the case of animals which are to become milking cows, and in fact for all breeding females, because of the desirability of providing them with liberal reserves before they are subjected to gestation and lactation. This must be accomplished by a ration which will cause a rapid rate of calcification throughout the growth period, or else the time of breeding must be delayed accordingly.

[61] D. Benzie and coworkers, Studies of the skeleton of the sheep. IV. The effects of interactions of dietary supplements of calcium, phosphorus, cod-liver oil, and energy, as starch, on the skeleton of growing blackface wethers, *J. Agr. Sci.*, **54**: 202–221, 1960.

[62] Julia Outhouse and Lafayette B. Mendel, The rate of growth. I. Its influence on the skeletal development of the albino rat, *J. Exptl. Zool.*, **64**:257–285, 1933.

[63] H. C. Sherman and L. E. Booher, The calcium content of the body in relation to that of the food, *J. Biol. Chem.*, **93**:93–103, 1931.

While, within rather wide limits, increasing the bone-building nutrients in the ration results in an increased storage in the bones, the percentage retention falls off markedly at the higher intake levels. This suggests that as the limit of the capacity for the deposition of reserves is approached, the process becomes increasingly less efficient. If a maximum rate of calcification is considered to be optimum, a high intake in proportion to the amount stored must be supplied. There is no present reason to believe that calcification can be overdone during growth, except by massive doses of vitamin D, nor is there evidence that excretory or other

FIG. 14.5. Severe rickets produced on a ration lacking in vitamin D. Note humped back, enlarged joints, and buckling of front legs. (*Courtesy of S. I. Bechdel, Pennsylvania State University.*)

functions are unduly burdened by the ingestion of amounts of calcium and phosphorus which are large compared to the amounts stored. Duckworth and Hill[64] have presented an excellent review of the knowledge regarding the storage and mobilization of calcium, phosphorus, and other minerals in bone.

14.34. Calcium and Phosphorus Requirements Measured by Balance Studies.[65] Balance determinations at different levels of intake ascertain the minimum level which will provide maximum retention. For a study

[64] J. Duckworth and R. Hill, The storage of elements in the skeleton, *Nutrition Abstr. & Revs.*, **23**:1–17, 1953.

[65] H. C. Sherman and Edith Hawley, Calcium and phosphorus metabolism in childhood, *J. Biol. Chem.*, **53**:375–399, 1922.

of one of the minerals, the ration must have an adequate supply of the other and vitamin D must be provided. This method is the most reliable one which can be employed with living animals and thus has found its largest use in human nutrition studies. An example of the use of the procedure for studying the phosphorus requirements of dairy heifers is provided by the experiment of Archibald and Bennett. Some of their data representing summarized values for the trials noted are presented in Table 14.11.

TABLE 14.11. PHOSPHORUS BALANCES WITH DAIRY HEIFERS*

Ration and period	Daily P intake per 100 lb. live weight, g.	Daily P retained per 100 lb. live weight, g.	Percentage of intake retained
High-phosphorus ration:			
As calves, 16 trials	3.25	1.01	31.08
As yearlings, 21 trials	2.49	0.61	24.50
As 2-year-olds, 5 trials	2.49	0.37	14.86
Average (weighted)	2.78	0.73	26.26
Low-phosphorus ration:			
As calves, 17 trials	1.80	0.73	40.56
As yearlings, 13 trials	1.68	0.54	32.14
As 2-year-olds, 5 trials	1.18	0.32	27.12
Average (weighted)	1.67	0.60	35.93

* Data from J. G. Archibald and E. Bennett, The phosphorus requirements of dairy heifers, *J. Agr. Research*, **51**:83–96, 1935.

It is noted that the amounts of phosphorus retained were larger for the high-phosphorus ration for each group. The difference is nearly 40 per cent for the calves, a large figure which was shown statistically to be clearly significant. It is thus demonstrated that calves under one year of age require considerably more than 1.8 g. of phosphorus daily per 100 lb. live weight. Whether the intake should be as high as 3.25 g. or even higher cannot be stated without further comparisons. While not statistically significant, the differences shown by the amounts retained as yearlings and two-year-olds suggest that the intakes on the low-phosphorus ration were inadequate for maximum retention for these ages also. The data for percentage retained reveal the expected lower efficiency of utilization which occurs with higher intakes even though the total retention is greater. In the one case where the intakes were identical (high-phosphorus group, yearlings and two-year-olds) the declining rate of retention with age is revealed.

14.35. Blood Data as Measures of Calcium and Phosphorus Needs. Inadequate bone nutrition is reflected in a lowering of the serum inorganic phosphorus and sometimes of calcium. The blood picture varies according to the specific deficiency concerned and also according to the species. A rapid rate of body growth which is accompanied by normal levels of calcium and phosphorus in the blood is highly indicative of adequate skeletal development, and these measures are frequently employed to determine the actual requirements for the minerals.

Huffman and associates[66] have used this procedure for studying the phosphorus requirements of dairy cows, resulting in the following conclusions as regards growth requirements. A ration containing 0.2 per cent of phosphorus caused a lowering of the blood phosphorus of calves, which persisted up to eighteen months of age. Intakes of 5.7 to 9.9 g. of phosphorus per day were inadequate where the calcium-phosphorus ratio was 4:1 or wider. An intake of 10.3 g. daily sufficed from three to six months of age. From eighteen months to first calving 10 to 12 g. daily were adequate. Similar studies by these Michigan workers have led to the conclusion that an intake of 6 to 12 g. of calcium daily from birth to two years of age is sufficient for the growth of calves. Beeson and associates[67] compared different levels of phosphorus intake for fattening lambs in terms of growth, efficiency of feed utilization, and blood-phosphorus level. They concluded that the need should be set at 2.40 g. per 100 lb. of live weight and that the ration, on a dry basis, should contain 0.17 per cent or more of the element.

Serum alkaline phosphatase activity, which rises when bone development is inadequate, is a useful supplementary blood measure.

14.36. Calcium and Phosphorus Requirements from Growth and Bone Data. Aubel, Hughes, and Lienhardt compared rations containing various levels of phosphorus for pigs receiving ample D, using growth, blood, and bone analyses and breaking strength as measures. The data obtained for bone composition are illustrated by the following figures from one period of their first experiment, expressed in per cent:

Constituent	Lot I	Lot II	Lot III
Calcium in feed	0.77	0.78	0.77
Phosphorus in feed	0.18	0.33	0.59
Ash in femur and humerus	48.14	57.35	59.64
Calcium in femur and humerus	18.35	21.93	22.70
Phosphorus in femur and humerus	8.69	10.58	10.82

SOURCE: C. E. Aubel, J. S. Hughes, and H. F. Lienhardt, Phosphorus requirements in the rations of growing pigs, *Kansas Agr. Expt. Sta. Tech. Bull.* 41, 1936.

[66] C. F. Huffman and associates, Phosphorus requirements of dairy cattle when alfalfa furnishes the principal source of protein, *Michigan Agr. Expt. Sta. Tech. Bull.* 134, 1933.

[67] W. M. Beeson and associates, The phosphorus requirement for fattening lambs, *J. Animal Sci.,* 3:63–70, 1944.

It is noted that the calcium was held constant in all lots at a level which was certainly adequate while the phosphorus was varied. Such a scheme unavoidably involves a variation in the ratio between the two elements. The ratio of 4.4:1 existing for the ration fed Lot I may have been in part responsible for the poorer bone development, but the ample amount of vitamin D supplied in each ration would tend to overcome any such effect. The data for ash, calcium, and phosphorus clearly reveal the superiority of the intermediate level over the lower one. While the data for the highest level are still better, the differences are small. For the experiment as a whole, the bone analyses and other measures employed failed to show significant differences in favor of the highest

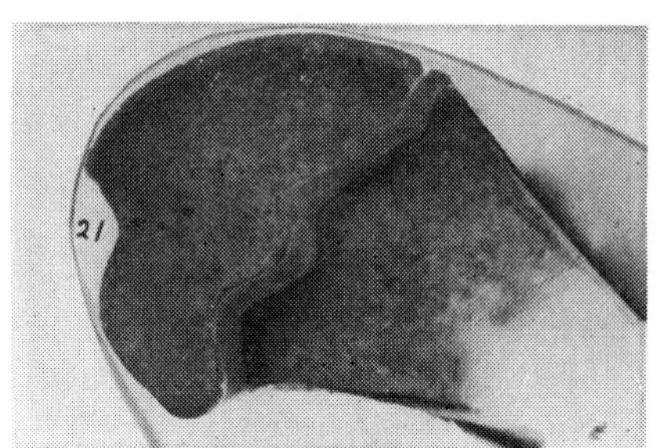

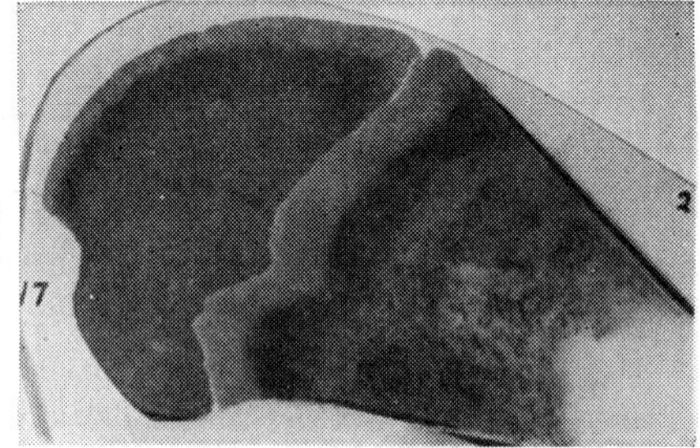

FIG. 14.6. Autoradiograms of calf femurs. The bone on the left is from a phosphorus-deficient calf. The bone on the right is from a calf fed adequate phosphorus. Note the difference in growth of new bone at the epiphyseal plate. (*Courtesy of S. E. Smith, Cornell University.*)

phosphorus level. Aubel, Hughes, and Peterson[68] have reported a similarly conducted study of the calcium requirement of pigs. They found that a level of 0.25 per cent in the ration was insufficient but that a level of 0.41 per cent was definitely adequate.

The larger the number of measures used in a given study, the better the basis for arriving at requirements. Here the experiments of Wise and coworkers[69] are of special interest because they measured growth, feed efficiency, serum inorganic phosphorus and phosphatase activity, bone ash, and bone growth by autoradiography. The last measure is illustrated in Fig. 14.6. The combined measures lead to the conclusion that the minimum phosphorus requirement for calves 12 to 18 weeks of age and weighing 200 to 275 lb. is 0.22 per cent, a figure which should be increased to 0.30 per cent in practice in view of variations in animals and feedstuffs.

[68] C. E. Aubel, J. S. Hughes, and W. J. Peterson, Calcium requirements of growing pigs, *J. Agr. Research,* **62**:531–542, 1941.

[69] M. B. Wise, S. E. Smith, and L. L. Barnes, The phosphorus requirements of calves, *J. Animal Sci.,* **17**:89–99, 1958.

14.37. Estimation of Calcium and Phosphorus Requirements by the Factorial Method. Using a procedure similar to that detailed for energy (Sec. 14.13), Mitchell has estimated the calcium and phosphorus requirements on the basis of calculated maintenance values, storage during growth as shown by carcass analyses, and percentage retention data. The detailed procedures are set forth in a publication of the N.R.C.[70] The data are reproduced with minor changes in a later publication.[71] This method of arriving at the requirements is the only one which provides data for the different ages and weight throughout the growth period. The calculations are necessarily based on several assumptions. By contrast, the methods previously described provide actually determined values for specific periods during growth with only a limited basis for translating them into values at other periods. The data obtained by the factorial method specify relatively higher intakes early and relatively lower ones toward the end of the growth period than are suggested by the limited experimentally determined requirements.

14.38. Calcium and Phosphorus Requirements for Practice. As is indicated by all studies of body composition, skeletal development is at a maximum early in the growth period. The requirements of both calcium and phosphorus decrease with age per unit of body weight and also per unit of dry-matter intake, but the extent of this decrease varies for the different species. The calcium requirements exceed those for phosphorus at the start, but differences become much less or nil as maturity is approached.

Requirements for practice should provide for maximum skeletal development in the species in question during the period of most rapid bone growth. Lesser intakes will suffice later. The N.R.C. nutrient requirements set forth the amounts needed at the various stages of growth, either as grams per day or as percentages of the air-dry feed, or both. These recommendations are presented in condensed form in Appendix Tables I to V. Requirements expressed as percentage of the feed intake or as grams per day can be calculated into the other measure by taking into consideration the intake of the air-dry feed for different weights. It is noted that, per pound of air-dry feed, the requirements range from 1 to 0.15 per cent in the case of calcium and from 0.6 to 0.15 per cent for phosphorus, depending upon the species and the stage of growth. The data also show that for each species the requirements are smaller toward the end of the growth period than at the start. In practice it is not feasible to follow exactly recommendations which change several times. If one chooses a single figure, it should not be

[70] H. H. Mitchell and F. J. McClure, Mineral nutrition of farm animals, *Natl. Research Council (U.S.) Bull.* 99, 1937.

[71] H. H. Mitchell, The mineral requirements of farm animals, *J. Animal Sci.*, **6**: 356–377, 1947.

the average for the period as a whole but should be high enough to meet the needs when the maximum rate of bone growth normally occurs, even though this would be a waste later.

14.39. The Requirements for Vitamin D. The growth requirements for this vitamin are measured by bone studies involving periodic X rays in the living animal or slaughter and bone analysis and measurement or both. Blood phosphorus, calcium, and phosphatase are useful supplementary measures. The full metabolic requirements can be determined only where the sunlight factor is excluded. In translating the results into practice, however, the actual dietary requirements become very low or nil for animals sufficiently exposed to sunlight.

Bechdel and associates[72] have reported a comprehensive study with dairy calves which well illustrates the experimental procedure required. Using a basal ration adequate in other nutrients but selected to be as low as possible in vitamin D, different groups of calves received different levels of the vitamin, as irradiated yeast or cod-liver-oil concentrate, after the first month until they were six months of age or older. From birth they were kept out of direct sunlight (first experiment) or in the dark (second experiment). The observations included growth rate, physical condition, periodic X rays and blood studies, and chemical analysis and line-test studies of the bones on slaughter. On the basis of their results the investigators concluded that the minimum requirement of the vitamin is approximately 300 U.S.P. units per day per 100 lb. live weight. Since the experimental calves grew slowly, it remains uncertain whether this level is adequate for rapid growth. The N.R.C. requirement, expressed as I.U. per pound of air-dry feed, ranges from 170 at birth down to 100 at 200 lb. body weight. Data are not available for higher weights. On the above basis, the recommendation for pigs is 90 I.U. from 25 to 50 lb. weight and 60 I.U. thereafter. For chickens, the figure is 90 I.C.U.; but for turkey poults, it is set much higher, 400 I.C.U.

14.40. Meeting the Requirements for Bone-forming Nutrients in Practice. Nursing young never suffer from a deficiency of calcium or phosphorus, and neither does the dairy calf reared on a liberal supply of skim milk. Herbivorous animals will receive ample calcium if their roughage is one-half or more legume hay, but where grass hay is the sole roughage and particularly where it is not consumed liberally, a calcium supplement should be included unless the hay is known to contain 0.5 per cent or more of this element. No concentrate mixture is rich in calcium, but a liberally fed mixture which contains 25 per cent or more of some phosphorus-rich feed, such as wheat bran or one of the oil meals, will take care of the needs for the latter element unless the roughage

[72] S. I. Bechdel and associates, The vitamin D requirement of dairy calves, *Pennsylvania Agr. Expt. Sta. Bull.* 364, 1938.

is unusually low in it. Roughage alone will not suffice. Under some conditions of practice, it is more economical to make up the deficiency in the roughage and cereal-grain ration by adding a mineral source rather than a high-phosphorus concentrate, as has been shown by the experiments of Maynard and associates.[73]

Whether or not herbivorous animals on pasture will receive enough bone-forming minerals depends upon the nature of the soil and the resulting calcium and phosphorus content of the forage. In the absence of specific information in these respects, giving the grazing animals access to dicalcium phosphate or bone meal is a desirable procedure. These various provisions for ensuring adequate minerals in the rations of Herbivora require more attention in the case of calves than in the case of lambs and colts because of the lower requirements of the latter. For a given species, the provisions demand less attention with advancing age because of the decreasing requirements.

If pigs are being fed corn or other cereal grain with the additional protein required furnished as tankage or fish meal, they will receive sufficient calcium and phosphorus. Where a vegetable-protein concentrate is used instead, additional calcium is required, and it can be supplied as a mineral supplement. Where a milk by-product is the protein concentrate, it must be liberally fed to meet the calcium requirements.

Animals which are outdoors in summer will always receive plenty of vitamin D, but in winter the sunlight is an uncertain source in the northern latitudes even though the weather allows the animals to be outside much of the time, because of the generally less sunlight and its lower efficiency (Sec. 8.17). Whole milk cannot be relied upon to supply the vitamin D requirements of the calf, and skim milk is certainly deficient. It takes only a small amount of sunlight to be effective, however. Johnson and Palmer[74] report, for example, that rickets was cured in pigs exposed to January sunshine in Minnesota for an average of 45 min. per pig per day for two weeks.

A real problem occurs with the dairy calf during the early weeks of life, the time when bone formation is normally most rapid, because the calf is usually kept inside and is eating little or no roughage. A vitamin D supplement is called for at this time. Later, with good roughage, it is not needed. As little as 1 lb. a day of good-quality sun-cured legume hay will supply the needs of the young calf. Similarly, 5 to 10 per cent of such hay in the ration of growing pigs will take care of their needs when sunlight is not available.

[73] E. J. Maynard, J. E. Greaves, and H. H. Smith, Phosphorus supplements improve sugar-beet by-product rations for cattle, *Utah Agr. Expt. Sta. Bull.* 265, 1936.

[74] D. W. Johnson and L. S. Palmer, Meeting the vitamin D requirements of pigs with alfalfa hay and winter sunshine, *J. Agr. Research*, **63**:639–648, 1941.

In general, it is preferable feeding practice to supply the mineral and vitamin needs of farm animals, in so far as possible, by an appropriate selection of the natural feeds rather than by resorting to special supplements.

OTHER MINERALS

14.41. Iron. The requirement of iron is measured as the amount needed to maintain a normal hemoglobin level and to provide an appropriate positive balance accordingly. Few such studies have been made with farm animals. Matrone and coworkers[75] have reported that the minimum requirement for maintaining the hemoglobin level in young, growing dairy calves is approximately 30 mg. per day. Based on weight gain, hemoglobin concentration, and other blood measures, Ullrey and coworkers[76] have reported that 125 p.p.m. of iron in the diet is adequate for the baby pig. The N.R.C. requirement for starting chickens is 9 mg. per pound of feed. Studies have not yet been made with lambs. There has been no clear-cut evidence of area deficiencies in grazing animals to stimulate requirement studies, as has been the case with copper and cobalt. In general, the iron requirements of farm animals are liberaliy supplied by their usual rations. Pigs get an additional supply from the soil.

A special case of iron deficiency is that represented by the anemia which frequently occurs in suckling pigs. Owing to the labored breathing which is always characteristic of severe cases, this trouble was known as *thumps* long before it was discovered to be due to a lack of sufficient iron for blood formation. The trouble is most frequent in litters farrowed in late fall or early spring and kept inside without access to soil or forage. Anemic pigs are listless and flabby, their skin becomes wrinkled, and their coats have an unhealthy appearance. As the disease progresses, the skin and mucous membranes become pale and the animals become thin and weak. In advanced stages, the breathing is labored and the pigs may have a swollen appearance, especially around the head and shoulders. This anemia can be prevented or cured in its early stages by drenching the sucklings with a saturated solution of ferrous sulfate or other soluble iron salt. The weekly dosage is ⅓ teaspoonful for pigs under one week of age up to 1 teaspoonful at four weeks. A simpler and entirely effective procedure consists of the injection of iron. An injection of 100 mg. of iron dextran at three days of age followed by 50 mg. at twenty-one days will maintain normal hemoglobin levels.

This nutritional anemia in pigs and the recognized deficiency of iron

[75] Gennard Matrone and coworkers, A study of iron and copper requirements of dairy calves, *J. Dairy Sci.*, **40**:1437–1447, 1957.

[76] D. E. Ullrey and coworkers, The requirement of the baby pig for orally administered iron, *J. Nutrition*, **70**:117–192, 1960.

in the milk of all species have led to the suggestion that all mammals should have supplements of this mineral during the suckling period. Such is not the case. While this anemia has been produced experimentally in calves and lambs, it does not occur in practice because these species begin to supplement their milk diet with other foods relatively earlier than does the pig. The store of iron with which they are born suffices until their needs are met adequately by grain and hay.

14.42. Salt and Iodine. While it is recognized as desirable to add salt to the rations of all farm animals, only limited information is available on the specific requirements for the growth of different species. Some discussion of this mineral and its constituent elements is given in Chap. 7. Growth and balance studies to determine salt requirements have been carried out with pigs and chickens, as is illustrated by the report of Meyer and associates[77] for swine. They concluded that the requirements are 53 to 64 mg. of sodium daily per kilogram of body weight, amounts which would be provided by 0.3 per cent of salt in the dry matter of the ration. The N.R.C. requirements call for 0.5 per cent in the air-dry rations of both pigs and chickens. It is commonly recommended that lambs and calves have free access to salt.

The practice of allowing salt ad libitum to farm stock undoubtedly results in an intake in excess of requirements. There is no harm in this ordinarily, but certain species may be injured by overeating when salt is offered ad libitum after a long period of deprivation. Since salt increases the palatability of rations, an intake in excess of the minimum physiological requirements is desirable from this standpoint. When it is fed free choice, the nature of the ration is a large factor governing the intake, and this may be in part a response to a variation in physiological need according to the mineral and other relations in the ration fed.

The N.R.C. requirement of *iodine* for swine is tentatively set at 0.09 mg. per pound air-dry feed. For chicks a requirement of 0.5 mg. per pound of feed is specified for the first 8 weeks and 0.2 mg. thereafter. These levels for the chick are higher than those found adequate for goiter prevention in other species. One reason for this high recommendation is to provide insurance against the goitrogenic effect of soybean meal (Sec. 7.38), which is commonly used as a feed ingredient. While the growth needs for calves and lambs have not been established, it is clear that they do not exceed the amounts found adequate to prevent goiter troubles in reproduction (Secs. 7.38, 15.12) in areas where these troubles otherwise occur. Harm can result from excessive intakes of iodine, as has been shown for lambs by Malan and associates.[78]

[77] J. H. Meyer and associates, Sodium chloride and potassium requirements of growing pigs, *J. Animal Sci.*, **9**:300–306, 1950.

[78] A. I. Malan, P. J. du Toit, and J. W. Groenewald, Studies in mineral metabolism. XXXIII. Iodine in the nutrition of sheep, *Onderstepoort J. Vet. Sci.*, **5**:189–200, 1935.

The data available on the requirements for magnesium, potassium, copper, cobalt, zinc, and manganese have been discussed in Chap. 7.

VITAMINS

As regards the fat-soluble vitamins, the growth requirements for vitamin D have been previously discussed (Sec. 14.39). The present knowledge of growth needs and feed supplies of vitamins E and K has been

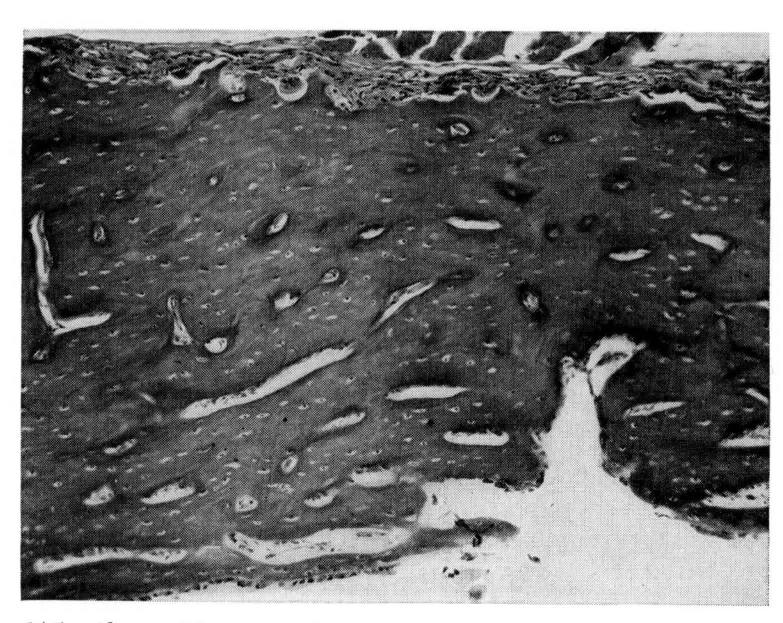

FIG. 14.7. Abnormal bone growth in vitamin A deficiency. The figure shows the parietal bone of a mink (decalcified, H & E, × 110). Near the striated muscles on the external side (top) are several multinucleated osteoclasts located in Howship's lacunae or flattened along the bone. The internal side (bottom) is lined by a single layer of mononucleated osteoblasts. This is the reverse of normal growth of the skull and explains the overcrowding of the cranium in vitamin A deficiency. (*Courtesy of L. Krook, Cornell University.*)

covered in Chap. 8. Vitamin A requires further consideration, however, in the present chapter.

14.43. Vitamin A. All higher animals, in so far as they have been studied, require vitamin A for growth, and there is a considerable amount of information on their quantitative requirements. In addition to the failure of growth there are various other characteristic deficiency symptoms which differ somewhat with the species (Sec. 8.3). The need of vitamin A by calves was first shown by Jones, Eckles, and Palmer in 1926. Later studies have added greatly to the knowledge of the specific physiological effects and of the requirements. While the early studies by Guilbert and Hart[79] showed that 1.5 mg. of carotene per 100 lb. body weight was sufficient to prevent night blindness in calves, this was considered a minimum requirement. Later studies by the same investigators indicated that the needs of sheep, swine, and horses were similar per unit of body weight. It was also shown by these California workers, as well as by others, that much higher than the minimum intakes were needed to ensure maximum growth, storage, and normal reproduction. The N.R.C. requirements for various species are shown in Appendix Tables I to V. It is noted that the requirements per pound of air-dry feed are of the order of 1 to 3 mg. of carotene, according to the species.

A comparison of the preceding requirement for Herbivora with the data for the carotene content of roughages in Table 8.1 makes it clear that their needs can readily be met even from hay of rather poor quality if readily consumed. As little as ½ lb. of bright green, leafy legume hay will supply the requirement for a 300-lb. calf. Nursing lambs and calves will get plenty from milk if their mothers are being properly fed. The dairy calf that is transferred soon after birth to skim milk or a special concentrate mixture ("calf starter") presents a special problem. The newborn calf has only a small store of the vitamin at birth. Here it is greatly benefited by receiving the colostrum, which is especially rich in the vitamin unless the cow has been on a ration low in it for a considerable time. It seems probable that calves which are transferred from whole milk soon after birth and are slow in starting to eat hay or receive hay of poor quality would be benefited by supplementary vitamin A during these early weeks of life. It has been claimed that such supplementary feeding will markedly lower the incidence of scours, but the evidence here is not clear. Experiments have shown that feeding large amounts of the vitamin will by no means eliminate this trouble or cure cases which have developed.

Concentrate mixtures supply very little vitamin A, with the exception that yellow corn can provide a substantial amount if its activity has not been depleted in storage. The needs of pigs can be met readily, however, by including 5 to 10 per cent of green, leafy alfalfa hay, a provision which will take care of vitamin D needs also if the hay has been sun-cured. Fresh, leafy forage crops supply the vitamin A activity in abundance.

14.44. Vitamin B Group. The information presented in Chap. 8 has indicated that experiments have failed to show any dietary need by cattle and sheep for the B group of vitamins after the rumen commences

[79] H. R. Guilbert and G. H. Hart, Minimum vitamin A requirements with particular reference to cattle, *J. Nutrition,* **10**:409–427, 1935.

FIG. 14.8. Riboflavin deficiency. Top pig received no riboflavin; bottom pig received an adequate supply. (*Pictures furnished by R. W. Luecke, Michigan Agricultural Experiment Station.*)

to function. The recognition of the need for various of these factors by swine and poultry was followed by many studies to establish the quantitative requirements for normal growth. The common procedure in these studies has been to feed a basal diet lacking in the vitamin under study but otherwise adequate and to add increasing levels of the vitamin to different groups. In this way the amount resulting in optimum growth without any appearance of characteristic deficiency symptoms was established. The commercial availability of synthetic sources of the vitamins has been largely responsible for the development in this field. On the basis of the studies made, quantitative requirements have been established for all the B vitamins which appear to be of practical importance in swine and poultry feeding. The N.R.C. requirements are presented in Appendix Tables I and II. It is noted that, with the exception of choline, the requirements per pound of feed call for only a few milligrams or fractions thereof, depending upon the vitamin.

The establishment of these quantitative requirements does not mean that appropriate amounts of the vitamins as such should be added to rations. The feed sources of them have been discussed in Chap. 8. For the most part body needs are easily met by properly selected rations of common feeds. Thiamine deficiency is not encountered in either pigs or chickens in practice because their customary rations contain large proportions of whole grains and milling by-products rich in the vitamin. Chicks require special supplements of riboflavin during the early weeks, but this does not appear to be the case for pig rations. The need for nicotinamide as such is modified by the tryptophan content of the diet (Sec. 8.37). There appears to be no need for special sources of niacin in either poultry or hog rations which contain protein in the amount and quality recommended. There is no evidence at present that special supplements to otherwise good diets are needed in the case of any of the other B-factors with the exception of B_{12}. Rations lacking in animal protein need a special source of this vitamin. Such a source is provided by the B_{12} feed supplements now in common use. The feed sources of the various factors which are essential for growth have been discussed in detail in Chap. 8.

14.45. Vitamin Supplements for Newborn Dairy Calves. Previous discussions (Chap. 8) have shown that newborn ruminants have a dietary need for certain B-vitamins which are later provided by rumen synthesis. For this reason and because of possible health benefits from extra-liberal intakes early in life, it has been proposed by some authorities, and particularly by those who have vitamin products to sell, that dairy calves should receive supplementary B-vitamins, as well as A and D, from birth. Most experiments have failed to find any value in such a practice. Various studies in this field are reviewed by Erb and associates[80] in a report of their own experiments, with 347 calves, which failed to reveal any benefits from massive doses of nicotinic acid and vitamins A and D.

SELECTED LITERATURE

Almquist, H. J.: Proportional requirements of amino acids, *Arch. Biochem. and Biophys.*, **48**:482–483, 1954.

Clausen, Hjalmar, and Jorgen Ludwigsen: Quantity and quality of final products other than milk: nonruminants (pigs), *Federation Proc.* **20**, Pt. III, 275–283, 1961.

Converse, Henry T.: Calcium requirements of dairy cattle, *U.S. Dept. Agr. Tech. Bull.* 1090, 1954.

Germann II, A. F. O., E. T. Mertz, and W. M. Beeson: Evaluation of the L-lysine requirements of the weanling pig, *J. Animal Sci.*, **17**:52–61, 1958.

Hammond, John, and A. B. Appleton: Growth and Development of Mutton Qualities in Sheep, Oliver and Boyd, Ltd., Edinburgh and London, 1932.

Hogan, A. G.: Retarded growth and mature size of beef steers, *Missouri Agr. Expt. Sta. Research Bull.* 123, 1929.

Jacobson, W. C., H. T. Converse, and L. A. Moore: Effects of vitamin A and carotene intake on depletion time of young dairy calves, *J. Dairy Sci.*, **32**:418–428, 1949.

Joubert, D. M.: The influence of winter nutritional depressions on the growth, reproduction, and production of cattle, *J. Agr. Sci.*, **44**:5–66, 1954.

McCay, C. M., and associates: Retarded growth, life span, ultimate body size and age changes in the albino rat after feeding diets restricted in calories, *J. Nutrition*, **18**:1–13, 1939.

Palmer, Leroy S., and associates: Genetic differences in the biochemistry and physiology influencing food utilization in growing rats, *Minnesota Agr. Expt. Sta. Bull.* 176, 1946.

Pálsson, H., and Juan B. Vergés: Effect of the plane of nutrition on growth and the development of carcass quality in lambs. Part I. The effects of high and low planes of nutrition at different ages, *J. Agr. Sci.*, **42**:2–91, 1952.

——— and ———: Effects of the plane of nutrition on growth and the development of carcass quality in lambs. II. Effects on lambs of 30 lb. carcass weight, *J. Agr. Sci.*, **42**:93–149, 1952.

Winters, L. M., C. F. Sierk, and J. N. Cummings: The effect of plane of nutrition on the economy of production and carcass quality of swine, *J. Animal Sci.*, **8**: 132–140, 1949.

[80] R. E. Erb and associates, Observations on efficiency of vitamin supplements for new-born calves, *J. Animal Sci.*, **8**:425–431, 1949.

Chapter 15
Reproduction

While it has long been appreciated that regular and normal reproduction is the essential basis of a successful animal industry, including commercial milk production, it is only within comparatively recent years that the various aspects of this primary physiological function have received detailed study. With the recognition of infectious abortion as a major cause of reproductive troubles, concentration on the disease aspects was a natural development, with the result that other phases were in part neglected. It is now appreciated, however, that the reproductive function is conditioned by a long series of distinct but interrelated physiological events in which the body as a whole, as well as the sex organs, is concerned and that important, though less obvious, causes of failure reside in abnormalities which are not the result of infectious disease. The economic importance of these less obvious causes has been stressed by Marshall and Hammond[1] as follows:

> Low fertility and sterility of a temporary nature, because of their prevalence, are the cause of much greater loss to the breeding industry than infertility of a more permanent kind which occurs less frequently, although the latter, because of its striking effects, generally attracts most attention.

It is self-evident that nutrition must play at least a general role in the development and functioning of the organs of reproduction, but its significance is much larger than this. It is apparent also that, although there are no substances needed by the reproductive organs which are not needed by the tissues, the metabolic pathways followed by some of the nutrients provided by the blood stream differ from those which have been identified in other organs. To understand these functions some knowledge of the physiology of reproduction is required. This discus-

[1] F. H. A. Marshall and John Hammond, Fertility and animal breeding, 6th ed., *Ministry Agr. Engl. Fish. Bull.* 39, 1945.

sion which immediately follows deals with mammalian reproduction and its nutritive requirements. At the close of this chapter the avian process is very briefly considered from the standpoint of the nutritive needs for egg production.

PHYSIOLOGY OF REPRODUCTION

The sexual organs reach their full development and become functional at an age which varies with the species, the breed, and the nutrition of the individual. The development of these organs is a rather gradual process controlled by secretions from the pituitary, the gland which also secretes a substance controlling body growth (Sec. 14.7). Apparently the gland cannot provide both secretions at a maximum at the same time, and thus the development of the sex organs proceeds more rapidly as the rate of growth declines. These organs become functional before body growth is completed. If their ability to function is immediately utilized, there may be an unfavorable effect on body development because of an undue diversion of the secretions of the pituitary from body growth to sexual activity. The lactation which follows premature breeding may cause the arrest of growth in the female. If the male is subjected to heavy service too early, his growth and vigor are likewise impaired. Herein lies an explanation of the deleterious effects on growth and development which may occur in practice from premature breeding.

15.1. Spermatozoa Production. Sexual maturity in the male is characterized by the full development of the testicles and the production of viable sperm which become motile when mixed with the secretions of certain accessory organs. Malnutrition can cause sperm production to cease entirely, as is discussed later for specific nutrients. Much more commonly it lessens the volume of the sperm produced and their viability and motility, with a resulting failure of conception, even though the female is highly fertile.

15.2. Ovulation and Fertilization. In the female the functional development of the ovary is followed by a recurring cycle of events, an early stage of which is characterized by the onset of heat, or estrus. The ovary contains a large number of minute eggs, each enclosed in a *Graafian* follicle. As the animal comes in heat, one or more of these follicles enlarge, the egg is matured and liberated and then passes down the *Fallopian* tubes, or oviducts, to the uterus. It is during this passage that fertilization usually occurs provided the animal has been served during the heat period. With the shedding of the egg, the cavity of the Graafian follicle becomes filled with the *corpus luteum*, or yellow body. While this yellow body is present, no more follicles are ripened and thus no more eggs are matured. If fertilization has occurred, the corpus luteum normally persists during the ensuing pregnancy, and thus no new fertilization can take place until its termination. If pregnancy does not occur, the corpus luteum usually degenerates after a brief period, allowing a new follicle to mature as the start of a new cycle. The ovarian changes of the estrus period are accompanied by cyclic changes in the epithelial lining of the vagina. A study of these changes in the rat and guinea pig by the *vaginal-smear* technique[2] has proved useful as an indicator of the regularity of estrus and of the ovarian processes involved, as influenced by various nutritional and other factors. Less well-defined cyclic, vaginal changes have been noted also in the cow, sow, and ewe.

15.3. Hormonal Control. Each of the events which comprise the estrus cycle is under hormonal control. Three hormones arising from the anterior pituitary gland, namely, the *follicle stimulator* (FSH), *luteinizer* (LH), and *prolactin*, control the activity of the gonads. FSH is responsible for spermatogenesis in the male as well as the development of the Graafian follicle in the female. The changes in the follicle which result in ovulation and the formation of the corpus luteum are caused by the action of LH. This hormone also causes the secretion of testosterone by the testes. Prolactin is responsible for the secretion of other hormones by the corpus luteum, as is discussed later. These pitutiary hormones are protein in nature.

Various hormones secreted by the gonads also play essential roles. *Estradiol*, produced by the Graafian follicle, promotes the growth of the vaginal epithelium and maintains the uterine mucosa. In large quantities it suppresses the activity of FSH, thus exerting a reciprocal control over ovulation. The corpus luteum produces *progesterone*, which promotes the development of the glandular system of the uterus and is required for the implantation of the embryo and the continuance of pregnancy. Progesterone, along with hormones from the placenta, suppresses the secretion of FHS so that no new follicles are formed during pregnancy. The corpus luteum also produces *relaxin* at the end of pregnancy, which acts to enlarge the channel through which the fetus is expelled. The testes secrete *testosterone*, which causes the functional development of the male sex organs. Estradiol and progesterone are steroids, closely related chemically to those produced by the adrenal cortex.

The foregoing, very incomplete discussion of the roles of hormones in reproduction serves, at least, to indicate that the physiology involved is of an intricate nature and that various reciprocal hormonal actions are concerned at different stages of the cycle. Some of the hormones here discussed also play roles in mammary development and function (Sec.

[2] Charles R. Stockard and George N. Papanicolaou, The existence of a typical oestrous cycle in the guinea-pig—with a study of its histological and physiological changes, *Am. J. Anat.*, **22**:225–265, 1917.

16.2). Many of the effects of nutrition on the reproductive process are mediated through the endocrine system. Meites[3] has reviewed the various experiments, mostly with laboratory animals, which support this conclusion.

15.4. Fetal Growth. The fertilized egg is nourished for a short time by secretions from glands of the uterus, and during this time it develops the placenta by which it becomes attached to the uterine walls. Following this implantation, it receives its nourishment from the maternal blood through its placenta and umbilical cord. The blood vessels are among the first permanent structures in the embryo, providing for the circulation of nutrients and the removal of waste products through interchange with the maternal blood. This interchange, including the oxygenation of the fetal blood, occurs in capillaries in the placenta. While the fetus receives most of its nutrients preformed, it certainly carries on some synthetic functions in connection with its growth.

Expressed arithmetically, the growth of the fetus takes place at an increasing rate throughout the gestation period. More than half of the period elapses before the weight of the fetus equals that of its membranes, whereas, at term, the placenta make up only about 20 per cent of the total weight of the products of conception. Most of the growth takes place in the last third of the gestation period, as is illustrated by the curves in Fig. 15.1 taken from the studies of Mitchell and associates[4] with swine. These workers slaughtered pregnant gilts in groups of one to three at weekly intervals from the fifth to the sixteenth week of gestation and determined the nutrients stored in the fetus and the placenta. The data were corrected to a standard litter of eight and treated mathematically to provide curves showing the increase in nutrient storage over the gestation period.

It is evident from Fig. 15.1 that approximately half of the protein and more than half of the energy storage occurs in the last quarter of pregnancy. Additional data showed that even larger proportions of the calcium and phosphorus are stored toward the end of the period. In accordance with the general picture in growing organisms, the percentage of water in the fetus decreases with age. On a dry-matter basis, protein makes up about two-thirds of the products of conception, a figure which shows little change over the gestation period. Neither do the percentages of fat or iron change markedly, but the calcium and phosphorus contents make up an increasing percentage with age. It is therefore clear that the quantitative demands for nutritive material are small in early pregnancy

[3] Joseph Meites, Relation of nutrition to endocrine reproductive functions, *Iowa State Coll. J. Sci.*, **28**:19–44, 1953.

[4] H. H. Mitchell, W. E. Carroll, T. S. Hamilton, and G. E. Hunt, Food requirements of pregnancy in swine, *Illinois Agr. Expt. Sta. Bull.* 375, 1931.

and that they progressively increase to become several times as large toward the close of the period.

In multiparous animals, the larger the number of fetuses the smaller the individuals tend to be, owing to crowding, and there is frequently a marked difference in size among the individuals of a litter. In animals which may give birth to one or more young, multiple births do not produce so large individuals as do single births.

For each species there is a certain duration of pregnancy which is recognized as normal. Its termination is associated with the degeneration of the corpus luteum and is probably under the influence of both

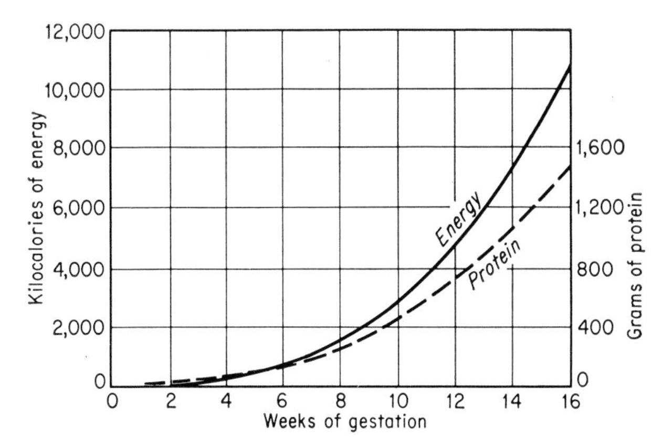

FIG. 15.1. Gross energy and protein in products of conception at different stages of gestation—sow. (*Mitchell, Carroll, Hamilton, and Hunt.*)

nervous and endocrine factors. The delivery of young is followed by the expulsion of the placenta, or afterbirth.

NUTRITIVE REQUIREMENTS

Nutritional factors play vital roles in the various physiological events which occur in the attainment of sexual maturity and in the course of the reproductive process. As is detailed later in the discussions of the requirements for the various nutrients, specific deficiencies can result in injury and even complete failure at specific stages in the reproductive process. More commonly, however, the troubles that occur in practice apparently result from multiple deficiencies which reflect general undernutrition caused by rations inadequate in amount as well as in quality.

15.5. Importance of Plane of Nutrition. Undernutrition delays puberty in both the male and the female, and, if severe, it may cause retrogressive changes in the sex organs after they are fully developed. It is a well-recognized fact that half-starved animals are relatively infertile. If the severely undernourished animal becomes pregnant, the drain on her body by the developing young may result in permanent damage. The death of the fetus *in utero* or the birth of a weak animal, perhaps prematurely, may also occur. In the male, undernutrition decreases the number and vigor of the sperms and may cause cessation of spermatogenesis.

Casida[5] has reviewed various experiments with farm animals on the effects of undernutrition. In his summary he concludes that the restriction of food intake during the growing period delays the occurrence of puberty in both sexes of cattle and sheep and reduces the production of eggs immediately after puberty in swine and sheep and of sperm in cattle, sheep, and swine. He notes that potential fertility in the three species was not greatly affected, however. There is little evidence on how a moderate restriction of the feed supply specifically causes these results. In some cases at least, the levels of the hormones are probably lowered, and they may operate at a lower efficiency.

The practical importance of adequate nutrition during gestation has been demonstrated with various species. For example, the bad effects of general undernutrition are illustrated by the excellent experiment with ewes by Thomson and Thomson.[6] They reported studies of a high versus a low plane of nutrition during the latter half of pregnancy and during lactation on reproduction and lactation performance. The high plane provided a ration excellent in amount and quality. The low plane supplied little more than half the calories and nutrients supplied by the high plane. The low plane produced small, weak lambs, most of which died at birth or soon after—in contrast to vigorous lambs and few deaths on the high plane. The milk yield on the high plane was approximately 20 gal. in a 13-week lactation period compared with 11 gal. on the low plane.

Overfeeding during the growth period may also be disadvantageous. Studies with dairy cattle have indicated that feeding 40 to 50 per cent more TDN than called for by feeding standards, while hastening the onset of puberty, tends to result in breeding troubles later and a shorter productive life accordingly. With gilts, Casida has reported that what is gained by increased ovulation rate on full feeding may be lost by increased embryo mortality.

A condition of extreme fatness appears to be deleterious to reproduc-

[5] L. E. Casida, Effect of feed level on some reproductive phenomena of cattle, sheep, and swine, in Reproductive Physiology and Protein Nutrition, Rutgers University Press, New Brunswick, N. J., 1959, pp. 35–44.

[6] A. M. Thomson and W. Thomson, Lambing in relation to the diet of the pregnant ewe, *Brit. J. Nutrition,* **2**:290–305, 1948; Effect of diet on milk yield of the ewe and growth of her lamb, *ibid.,* **7**:263–274, 1953.

tion. The ovaries may become so infiltrated with fat as to hinder the development of the follicles, with a consequent irregularity or cessation of estrus which results in delay or failure in breeding. There may be also such an excessive amount of fat in the reproductive tract that, even if the egg is matured and fertilized, it may fail to reach the uterus and become implanted properly. Extreme fatness has also been noted to interfere with the production of fertile sperms in the male and lessens his desire to mate. In attributing reproductive failure to extreme fatness, it must be recognized that in some instances the condition may be merely an accompaniment of some specific deficiency or other cause.

While the nutritive intake is qualitatively of equal importance in both sexes, obviously the quantitative requirements are vastly greater for the female. Thus most of the following discussion deals with the needs of the mother. Her nutrition must have the double object of producing normal offspring and of protecting her own tissues, for on an inadequate ration the mother sacrifices her bones and other tissues to nourish her fetus.

As is indicated by the curves in Fig. 15.1, the last quarter of the gestation period is the time of critical importance. It has been clearly proved that a system of feeding which takes full account of the increased needs at this time is much more effective than one which supplies the same amount of feed over the period as a whole but at the same intake level throughout. The beneficial effects of meeting fully the current needs toward the end of the period are reflected not only in more vigorous young but also in a higher potential level of milk secretion by the mother. It is during the last part of the period of gestation that the formation of secretory cells in the udder is most active (Sec. 16.1). Inadequate nutrition at this time limits this process and thus lessens the milk-secreting capacity that is developed.

15.6. Energy Requirements. While the effects of general undernutrition previously mentioned are undoubtedly the result of more than one deficiency, it is evident that the energy supply is an important factor. Experiments with rats have shown that a deficiency of energy alone results in a delay in the opening of the vagina, a prolongation of the period between this event and the first estrus, and an irregularity or cessation of the estrus cycle. The studies by Asdell and Crowell[7] showing these effects included observations on sexually mature rats which were held at constant weight far below normal size by energy restriction. Under these conditions, the cycles were highly irregular. When the animals were given an increment of energy sufficient to cause some growth, regular cycles occurred until the animals reached a weight where

[7] S. A. Asdell and Mary F. Crowell, The effect of retarded growth upon the sexual development of rats, *J. Nutrition*, **10**:13–24, 1935.

growth ceased because the total energy intake was needed for maintenance. Here sexual activity ceased also. Thus it was shown that neither growth nor sexual activity takes precedence over the other.

The energy requirement for reproduction consists of the energy stored in the new tissue formed plus the energy expended in the process. The tissues formed include the fetus and its membranes, the enlargement of the uterus, and the mammary development (Sec. 16.1). The energy content of these tissues at different stages provides the basic figures for estimating the nutritive requirements over the gestation period. Mitchell

TABLE 15.1 COMPUTED DAILY RATE OF INCREASE IN WEIGHT AND ENERGY CONTENT AND COMPUTED DAILY DEPOSITION OF NUTRIENTS IN THE UTERI OF PREGNANT GILTS*

Week of gestation	Total weight, g.	Gross energy, kcal.	Crude protein, g.	Ash, g.	Calcium, g.	Phosphorus, g.	Iron, mg.
1	27	1.6	0.54	0.028	0.0001	0.0011	0.28
2	49	5.9	1.5	0.126	0.0018	0.0074	0.71
3	71	12.5	2.7	0.30	0.0081	0.022	1.24
4	91	21.0	4.2	0.57	0.024	0.048	1.84
5	111	32.0	5.9	0.93	0.055	0.087	2.50
6	131	45.0	7.7	1.38	0.109	0.142	3.2
7	150	59.0	9.6	1.93	0.194	0.215	4.0
8	169	76.0	11.8	2.6	0.32	0.31	4.8
9	187	94.0	14.0	3.3	0.50	0.42	5.6
10	205	115.0	16.0	4.3	0.74	0.56	6.5
11	224	137.0	19.0	5.2	1.05	0.72	7.4
12	242	160.0	21.0	6.2	1.46	0.91	8.3
13	259	186.0	24.0	7.4	1.97	1.13	9.2
14	277	213.0	27.0	8.7	2.60	1.38	10.2
15	294	242.0	30.0	10.1	3.37	1.67	11.2
16	312	272.0	33.0	11.7	4.29	1.98	12.3

* Data from H. H. Mitchell, W. E. Carroll, T. S. Hamilton, and G. E. Hunt, Food requirements of pregnancy in swine, *Illinois Agr. Expt. Sta. Bull.* 375, 1931.

and associates in their studies, previously cited, with swine computed the daily increase in energy and other nutrients in the products of conception. These data are reproduced in Table 15.1. It is noted that the energy storage is very small during the early weeks. While 272 kcal. are stored daily during the last week, computation shows that the average daily deposition for the period as a whole is only 104 kcal. No data are available for estimating the energy stored in the mammary growth, but except in a first pregnancy, it should not exceed 10 per cent of that in the uterine products. On this basis a daily intake of 115 kcal. could be considered as the net-energy requirement for reproduction in a sow producing a litter of eight pigs. That these calculations are only approximations is clear, but the final value obtained is useful for comparison with the estimated net-energy requirement for maintenance.

The gilts studied by Mitchell weighed around 200 lb. Armsby gives the net-energy requirement for maintenance of a pig of this weight as 1.99 Therms. Even on the basis of this figure, which is probably too low, the average daily need for reproduction itself adds only 6 per cent to the maintenance requirement and less than 15 per cent during the last week of gestation when the demand is greatest. Approximately the same relations should hold for the requirements in terms of digestible nutrients. The preceding calculations are useful to show that even for the sow, in which multiple birth involves a relatively higher reproductive performance than for other farm mammals, the additional energy needs above maintenance are very small until the last part of the gestation period. The data are not particularly useful, however, for arriving at allowances for practice because of other factors involved. Animals are usually bred before they have reached their full growth, and thus allowances during gestation must take account of growth needs as well. Mature animals frequently begin their gestation in rather poor flesh because of the previous lactation and need additional feed accordingly. Thus, in practice, most pregnant animals must be given a sufficient energy allowance to enable them to gain some weight during the period as a whole, with special attention given to the last quarter when the specific needs are substantial. The aim should be to have the animals in good flesh at parturition without being too fat.

15.7. Protein Requirement. Controlled studies with rats have shown that a low-protein diet causes a cessation of estrus and that, if fertilization occurs, fetal resorptions or the birth of premature, dead, or weak offspring results. These findings are illustrated by the study of Nelson and Evans.[8] Other work by these authors has indicated that in the absence of dietary protein the reproductive failure is due to a lack of ovarian hormones. In the male rat a lack of protein results in limited testes growth and sperm formation and even in the absence of testosterone secretion, as a result of a reduction in the level of circulating pituitary gonadotropic hormones, according to the review by Leathem.[9] Studies with other species also indicate reproductive failures when the protein nutrition is inadequate, although the evidence is less specific than for the

[8] Marjorie M. Nelson and Herbert M. Evans, Relation of dietary protein levels to reproduction in the rat, *J. Nutrition,* **51**:71–84, 1953.

[9] James H. Leathem, Male reproductive system and protein nutrition, in Reproductive Physiology and Protein Nutrition, Rutgers University Press, New Brunswick, N.J., 1959, pp. 12–22.

rat. The quality as well as the quantity of the protein has been shown to be important. Stuart[10] has reviewed the evidence indicating that protein deficiency in human reproduction can cause inability to conceive, toxemia of pregnancy, and immature newborn.

Rations which are fully adequate in protein for maintenance, and for growth if this function is not completed, should be adequate also for conception and the initiation of fetal growth. The additional needs here are negligible. Since, however, the dry matter of the products of conception consist largely of protein, it is evident that there is an increased need as fetal growth proceeds. The data in Table 15.1 show that the quantitative need does not become of large importance until the last half of pregnancy, during which the daily storage increases rapidly. The average daily figure for the gestation period as computed from these data is approximately 14 g., but it is more than double this figure during the last two weeks. Calculations similar to those made for net energy (Sec. 15.6) indicate that the additional requirements for digestible protein for the products of reproduction, as a percentage of maintenance needs, are considerably higher than the energy increments called for. In other words, pregnancy in the sow increases the need for protein much more than for energy. Similar calculations, based on meager data, indicate that the same is true for the cow.

As in the case of energy, the protein intake during pregnancy should be set higher than the sum of the needs for maintenance and for the formation of the products of reproduction. For animals bred before they have reached their full growth, the further growth needs must be covered. The intake should also be sufficient to take advantage of the special ability of the pregnant animal to store protein in its own body as well as in the products of conception. This is important because early in lactation a negative-nitrogen balance frequently occurs despite very liberal protein nutrition at the time. Thus the dam's body protein is drawn upon to supply a part of the protein secreted in the milk. If advantage has been taken of her capacity to build reserves during gestation, this can occur without harm. These facts were first established in studies with women by Hunscher and associates.[11]

The N.R.C. requirements for bred gilts, mature dairy cows, beef heifers and mature cows, and ewes are given in Appendix Tables I, III, IV, and V, respectively. Further details are to be found in the reports from which these tables are taken.

15.8. Effects of Calcium and Phosphorus Deficiencies. The observations in the phosphorus-deficient areas (Sec. 7.2) throughout the world

[10] H. C. Stuart, Effect of protein deficiency on the pregnant woman and fetus and on the infant and child, *New England J. Med.*, **236**:507–513, 537–541, 1947.

[11] Helen A. Hunscher and associates, Metabolism of women during the reproductive cycle. V. Nitrogen utilization, *J. Biol. Chem.*, **99**:507–520, 1933.

are in agreement that reproductive troubles are very common and that they have caused very large losses in the animal industry. Conclusive proof for cows is furnished by the extensive studies of Theiler and associates[12] carried out in the phosphorus-deficient area in South Africa. The studies included observations on 200 animals over a period of two years. In groups in which the phosphorus-deficient pasture was supplemented by bone meal or other phosphorus sources, the calf crop was approximately 80 per cent in contrast to a figure of approximately 51 per cent in the control group. Similar evidence has been presented from various areas in the United States. The most frequently observed specific trouble is irregularity or cessation of estrus, corresponding to the commonly reported finding in rats. It has become apparent, however, that other deficiencies, such as lack of vitamin A or of protein, are also concerned in some of the reproduction troubles in phosphorus-deficient areas.

Calcium deficiency can upset the normal reproductive performance, particularly by decreasing the number of viable young in the case of multiple births. Severe deficiency results in intrauterine death of some of the fetuses in rats and pigs, possibly because of a lack of tone in the uterine muscle. Calcium deficiency is much less of an area problem than is the case for phosphorus.

Though of primary importance, regularity of breeding and normal pregnancy and parturition do not constitute complete proof that the calcium and phosphorus nutrition is adequate for reproduction. Despite a normal birth there may be pathological changes in the osseous system of the newborn as a result of mineral deficiency in the diet of the mother. Of equal importance, the mother's bones may be depleted to supply the minerals in the skeleton of the fetus. This has been shown to occur in various species of animals fed rations low in calcium and phosphorus. To the extent that it involves only the reserves of the minerals in the bones (Sec. 7.10), no structural injury is caused, but since, in the lactation to follow, the demand for these minerals is so large that losses from the bones cannot be prevented despite the most liberal nutrition (Sec. 16.29), it is clearly desirable to husband the reserve in the bones during gestation. It has been shown with sheep by Fraser and associates[13] and with swine by Evans[14] that losses from the bones which occur on a deficient ration can be prevented by increasing the intakes of the bone-forming minerals.

[12] A. Theiler, H. H. Green, and P. J. du Toit, Studies in mineral metabolism. III. Breeding of cattle on phosphorus deficient pasture, *J. Agr. Sci.*, **18**:369–371, 1928; Phosphorus in the live stock industry, *Union S. Africa J. Dept. Agr.*, **8**:460–504, 1924.

[13] A. H. H. Fraser, W. Godden, and W. Thomson, The effect of a calcium-deficient diet on pregnant ewes, *Vet. J.*, **89**:408–411, 1933.

[14] R. E. Evans, Protein and mineral metabolism in pregnant sows on a normal or high calcium diet, compared with a calcium-deficient diet, *J. Agr. Sci.*, **19**:752–798, 1929.

Similar findings have been reported from studies with women and with rats. Severe or continued depletion of the bones results in osteomalacia (Sec. 7.12).

The fact that the mother's bones can be sacrificed in the interests of the fetus provides a means of protecting the offspring of a first pregnancy from serious skeletal defects. X-ray studies have shown that calcification is best in infants from mothers showing the highest retentions of calcium and phosphorus during pregnancy. In a study with sows fed a ration deficient in calcium, Davidson[15] found that a calcium-deficient ration did not produce an immediate effect because of the store in the maternal body. In successive farrowings there was an increase in the number of pigs born weak or dead and a decrease in the number reared to weaning. There was a serious reduction and eventual failure of the milk supply. Several investigators have reported fetal rickets, gross hypoplasia of the enamel, and defective dentine in infants from mothers undernourished in bone-forming minerals during pregnancy.

15.9. Calcium and Phosphorus Requirements. In addition to providing for the growing fetus, the calcium and phosphorus intakes during gestation must be sufficient to meet the maintenance requirement of the mother and also to build up reserves in her bones in so far as this is possible. Data as to the amounts of these minerals present in the products of conception at birth are of limited value in arriving at the actual intake needs, for several reasons. For most species there is a lack of information as to the maintenance requirement, and there is no reliable figure as to the percentage retention which can be assumed where it is desired to ensure storage in the mother's bones to the fullest extent possible, as well as in the fetus. The efficiency of utilization is recognized to be low under these conditions. Further, the daily requirement for fetal growth cannot be based upon the average storage in products of conception, for almost all of this storage takes place in the last half of gestation and especially in the last fifth. This fact is clearly brought out in Table 15.1. The intake chosen for the period as a whole must be that which will be optimum for the last days of gestation, or provision must be made for increasing a lower initial intake in accordance with increasing storage.

While extensive data are available for rats, few studies have been made with farm animals providing information as to the minimum intakes of calcium and phosphorus which can be relied upon to be optimum over the gestation period alone. In a very extensive balance experiment with swine, Evans[16] compared intakes of approximately 0.6 and 0.04 per cent of calcium in a basal ration adequate in other nutrients including vitamin

[15] H. R. Davidson, Reproductive disturbances caused by feeding protein-deficient and calcium-deficient rations to breeding pigs, *J. Agr. Sci.*, **20**:233–264, 1930.

[16] Evans, *loc. cit.*

D. On the low level of intake only 15 g. of calcium was retained during gestation, although five times this amount was found in the products of conception at the close. A large depletion of the sow's skeleton therefore occurred. There was a lack of milk secretion following farrowing. The high level resulted in a storage in gestation greatly in excess of the demand for fetal growth, demonstrating the ability of the maternal organism to build up her reserves when the dietary supply is sufficiently large. The striking effect of an inadequate dietary supply of calcium on the bones of the gilt, as observed by Hogan, is shown in Fig. 15.2.

For pregnant sows the N.R.C. recommendation is 0.6 per cent of calcium and 0.4 per cent of phosphorus in the dry ration. These levels

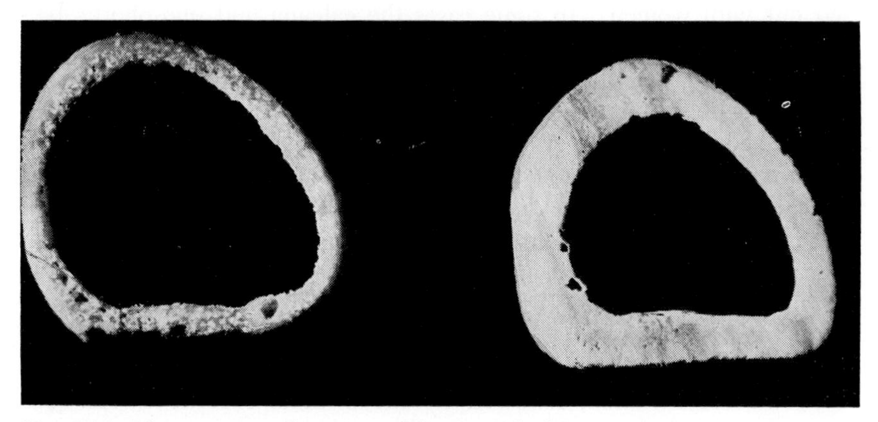

FIG. 15.2. Cross section of metacarpal bones. The bone on the left was taken from a gilt on a low-calcium ration. Note the thin-walled, spongy, porous condition compared to the bone on the right produced on an adequate ration. The poor bone contained only half as much calcium. (*Courtesy of A. G. Hogan, University of Missouri.*)

should be fully adequate for the last part of gestation when the needs are greatest. In terms of body size, pregnant cows have lower requirements for bone-forming minerals than do swine. Beef cows should have approximately 0.16 per cent of calcium and 0.15 per cent of phosphorus in their air-dry rations, according to the N.R.C. recommendations. A similar intake of phosphorus and a somewhat higher one of calcium are specified for sheep. For mature dairy cows these recommendations provide increments of 8 g. of calcium and 7 g. of phosphorus daily above maintenance needs (12 g. of each for a 1000- to 1200-lb. cow) during the last 2 to 3 months of gestation. Beyond the first gestation the needs overlap with the larger ones for lactation, as is discussed later.

For ewes, Riches and Godden[17] found that the average daily storage in

[17] Cited in R. C. Garry and D. Stiven, A review of recent work on dietary requirements in pregnancy and lactation, with an attempt to assess human requirements, *Nutrition Abstr. & Revs.*, **5**:855–887, 1936.

the lamb and its membranes was 0.6 g. of calcium. On an intake which supplied double this amount daily the calcium balance was negative. An intake of 6 g. daily was certainly adequate. The N.R.C. requirements for a 160-lb. bred ewe specify 3.5 g. during the first 15 weeks and 4.8 g. during the last 6 weeks of gestation.

15.10. Vitamin D. This vitamin is needed during fetal growth, as well as during body growth, to ensure adequate calcium and phosphorus assimilation. In the case of rats, most studies have reported an increased calcium and phosphorus retention during pregnancy and an increased content of the minerals and of the vitamin in the newborn where liberal intakes of the factor have been provided. Several studies have been carried out with women. In some cases the calcium and phosphorus balances have been improved by additions of the vitamin, in others not. It is generally agreed that the newborn infant from a mother who has received a liberal intake of the antirachitic factor is less susceptible to rickets, because of the storage of the vitamin in the fetus. In the case of the cow, however, Eaton and associates[18] did not find any significant placental transfer.

It is clear that the vitamin is needed for normal reproduction in farm animals, but rigid experimental conditions are required to demonstrate this need, as is illustrated by the studies of Wallis.[19] By keeping cows out of the light for a long period and by using a ration in which molasses beet pulp replaced hay, he was able to produce deficiency symptoms in the course of lactation, followed by the birth of rachitic calves. No recommendations are made in the N.R.C. reports as to vitamin D requirements for reproduction in cattle. In the case of swine an intake of 60 I.U. per pound of air-dried feed is proposed. Under conditions of practice, sunlight or the kind of ration that is statisfactory for growth will certainly take care of the vitamin D requirements of farm animals during reproduction.

15.11. Iron. The studies by Mitchell showed that the sow producing a litter of eight stored 580 mg. of iron in the products of conception. During the last week of pregnancy, the daily storage was 12.3 mg. (Table 15.1) and the average figure for the period as a whole was 5.5 mg. Even the latter figure is greatly in excess of the maintenance requirement. Studies with women have also indicated that the demands for fetal growth are much greater than those for maintenance. It is probable that, for all species, the maintenance requirement must be increased two or three times to cover the needs of gestation. This is readily understandable on

[18] H. D. Eaton and associates, The placental transfer and colostral storage of vitamin D in the bovine, *J. Dairy Sci.*, **30**:787–794, 1947.

[19] G. C. Wallis, Some effects of a vitamin D deficiency on mature dairy cows, *J. Dairy Sci.*, **21**:315–333, 1938.

the basis that the principal iron metabolism in maintenance results from the breakdown and resynthesis of hemoglobin, which involves no loss of iron from the body and thus no requirement for replacement (Sec. 7.26), whereas gestation calls for the building of new tissue as in growth.

If the intake during pregnancy is deficient, the needs of the fetus are supplied from the mother's reserves in her liver and spleen, but if the deficiency is extreme, the amount stored in the newborn will be less. This has been shown in rats by Lintzel and Radeff.[20] Pregnant rats, receiving a normal ration containing 11 mg. of iron per 100 g., produced litters in which the average iron content of the individuals was approximately 0.25 mg. This storage figure was reduced by one-quarter to one-half when the mother's diet was nearly iron-free. The mother's reserves were largely depleted, and hemoglobin iron was lowered. While the normal picture in the mother and young was restored by iron addition, the amount of iron stored in the young by the ration containing 11 mg. was not increased by doubling the dietary level. It has been explained (Sec. 7.27) that a large store in the newborn is needed to be drawn upon for blood formation during the suckling period, when milk, which is low in iron, is the principal food.

Despite the very large increase in the iron requirement which accompanies pregnancy, there is no evidence that a practical problem is here presented in the case of farm animals. In terms of the need, the commonly used feeds are rich (Sec. 7.29). It seems very unlikely that any deficiency exists, but the question may deserve critical study in swine in view of the common occurrence of anemia in the suckling young. Doubtless this trouble can occur even though the physiological capacity to store iron in the fetus is reached, but there may be dietary situations where the maximum storage does not take place.

15.12. Iodine. The occurrence of goiter in farm animals as a result of a deficiency in the diet of the mother during gestation has been discussed (Sec. 7.38). The increase in iodine metabolism during pregnancy is indicated by the fact that the blood level is doubled at this time. In areas where goiter troubles occur, the most practicable way of supplying the need for iodine is the use of iodized salt. It is common recommendation that cattle, sheep, and horses receive 1 per cent of stabilized iodized salt (containing 0.0076 per cent iodine) in the grain portion of their rations and that swine be fed this salt as 0.5 per cent of the grain ration. An actual requirement of approximately 0.2 mg. of iodine per 100 lb. body weight is mentioned in the N.R.C. report for swine. Where goiter troubles in mammals have been experienced, feeding iodized salt during

[20] W. Lintzel and T. Radeff, Über den Eisengehalt und Eisenansatz neugeborener Tiere (nach Versuchen an Kaninchen, Meerschweinchen, Ratte, Hund, Katze Schwein, Ziege, Rind), *Archiv. Tierernähr. Tierzucht.*, **6**:313–358, 1931.

the last three-quarters of the gestation period only has given protection. The need for supplementary iodine at other periods in the life of the animal and in areas where goiter troubles are not evident has been discussed (Sec. 7.40).

The information available for other minerals, such as manganese, which are known to play a significant role in reproduction has been discussed in Chap. 7.

15.13. Vitamin A. In all species, in so far as studied, the reproductive process is dependent upon an adequate supply of vitamin A. This is

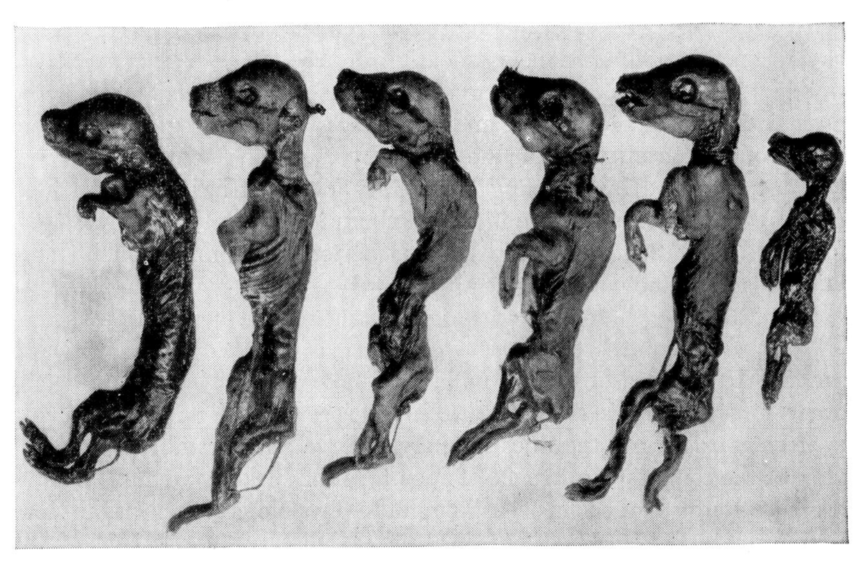

FIG. 15.3. Fetuses removed from sow in advanced vitamin A deficiency. These fetuses were obtained on a post-mortem examination 81 days after the sow was due to farrow. They reveal advanced stages of resorption. (*Kansas Agr. Expt. Sta. Tech. Bull.* 23, *courtesy of the authors.*)

true for both sexes. The generalized effect of this vitamin on the epithelial tissues explains its role in reproduction. In the male a deficiency causes a degeneration of the germinal epithelium of the testes, which results in a decrease in spermatogenesis and its eventual cessation if the deficiency is prolonged and severe. In the female the vaginal epithelium becomes cornified, which may result in irregularity of estrus and delayed breeding. The major reproductive disturbance in the female, however, occurs during the latter part of gestation, resulting in an abortion or the birth of weak or dead offspring. These results stem from a keratinization of the vaginal epithelium and degeneration of the placenta. In rats the injury to the epithelium has been reported to cause congenital malformations in the soft tissues.

The symptoms which occur in farm animals differ somewhat according to the severity of the deficiency, and some may be more prominent in one species than another. In cattle, Hart and Guilbert[21] have reported the birth of dead or weak calves with frequent retention of the placenta, a condition which simulates infectious abortion. Severe diarrhea resembling white scours was present in the weak, newborn calves. These results occurred in animals, negative to the blood test for abortion, which had been maintained for an extended period on dried-up range. Following a failure during gestation, the animals commonly did not come in heat again until they had access to green feed. The disastrous results which occur in dairy cows from the continuous feeding of low-grade timothy hay in contrast to the performance on high-quality alfalfa have been clearly shown by the work of Meigs and Converse.[22] Later studies by these workers found vitamin A to be the factor concerned.

In sows a disturbance of the estrus cycle and the farrowing of premature, weak, or dead pigs have been reported by Hughes and associates[23] (Fig. 15.3). In sheep the lambs die *in utero* or soon after birth. In a study by Miller and associates[24] with ewes depleted to night blindness, 65 per cent of them conceived, but every lamb was born dead or died within 48 hr.

15.14. Vitamin A Requirements. The N.R.C. requirements, expressed in milligrams of carotene per pound of feed, are given for swine, beef cattle, and sheep in Appendix Tables I, IV, and V, respectively. For dairy cattle the N.R.C. report expresses the requirement only on a per animal basis: 4 mg. carotene per 100 lb. live weight, to be increased by 30 mg. per head during the last 2 to 3 months of gestation.

There is no problem in meeting these needs in the case of cattle and sheep if reasonably good roughage is available, as is evident from a consideration of the data in Table 8.1. Similarly, the needs of sows can be met by the liberal inclusion of bright green alfalfa in the grain mixture when they are not on good pasture. Here yellow corn can make a substantial contribution unless its vitamin value has been depleted in storage.

Fortunately, the ability of animals to store vitamin A protects them from reproductive failure during short periods on feed deficient in this

[21] G. H. Hart and H. R. Guilbert, Vitamin-A deficiency as related to reproduction in range cattle, *California Agr. Expt. Sta. Bull.* 560, 1933.

[22] Edward B. Meigs and H. T. Converse, Some effects of different kinds of hay in the ration on the performance of dairy cows, *J. Dairy Sci.*, **16**:317–328, 1933; The vitamin requirements for reproduction and lactation under practical conditions, *ibid.*, **19**:438, 1936.

[23] J. S. Hughes, C. E. Aubel, and H. F. Leinhardt, The importance of vitamin A and vitamin C in the ration of swine, *Kansas Agr. Expt. Sta. Tech. Bull.* 23, 1928.

[24] R. F. Miller, G. H. Hart, and H. H. Cole, Fertility in sheep as affected by nutrition during the breeding season and pregnancy, *California Agr. Expt. Sta. Bull.* 672, 1942.

factor. The vitamin intake of the mother has little influence on the store in the newborn. Experiments have shown that massive intakes are required to increase the limited placental transfer that normally occurs. A liberal intake does result in a substantial liver store in the mother, which in turn provides the newborn with a colostrum and milk that are richer in the vitamin than otherwise. Thus the situation with respect to the placental and mammary transfer of A is the opposite of that for iron (Sec. 15.11).

15.15. Vitamin E. The effects of a deficiency of vitamin E in causing reproductive failure in rats, both male and female, have been described (Sec. 8.19). While there have been claims as to similar failures in farm animals which have been prevented or overcome by adding a source of the vitamin to the ration, carefully controlled experiments have failed to substantiate these claims. Gullickson and associates[25] have reported a study with cattle in which both males and females were fed a ration of rice, straw, and an E-low grain mixture. The observations included animals representing the fourth generation on the ration. No deleterious effects were noted on the estrus cycle or on spermatogenesis. Thirty services produced 25 conceptions, 19 normal parturitions, and no abortions. In studies with sheep and goats reproduction has been apparently unaffected on rations which result in failure in rats. Salisbury[26] has reported an extensive study with bulls used for artificial insemination, involving the collection of over 1250 semen samples and the insemination of over 8200 cows. Bulls fed wheat-germ oil, a vitamin E concentrate, showed no superiority in fertility over those receiving the same ration without the concentrate. Nor did studies of the semen volume and quantity or of other possible variables reveal any advantage for the vitamin. By contrast to these controlled experiments, in most of the field observations and studies in which vitamin E therapy has been reported to restore fertility and prevent abortion in cattle, the results have been complicated by other treatments and lack of parallel data on untreated animals.

Adamstone and associates[27] have reported a limited study with gilts in which an E-deficient diet resulted in a lowered reproductive performance apparently because of fetal death. Pigs from the sows reared on the deficient diet exhibited muscular incoordination caused by disintegration

[25] T. W. Gullickson and associates, Vitamin E in the nutrition of cattle. I. Effect of feeding vitamin E poor rations on reproduction, health, milk production and growth, *J. Dairy Sci.*, **32**:495–508, 1949.

[26] G. W. Salisbury, A controlled experiment in feeding wheat germ oil as a supplement to the normal ration of bulls used for artificial insemination, *J. Dairy Sci.*, **27**: 551–562, 1944.

[27] F. B. Adamstone, J. L. Krider, and M. F. James, Response of swine to vitamin E-deficient rations, *Ann. N.Y. Acad. Sci.*, **52**:260–268, 1949.

of the muscle fibers. It seems important that further studies be made with swine.

The question whether a low intake of vitamin E by the dam may be deleterious to the health of the newborn is an important one in view of the established beneficial role of vitamin E in the prevention or treatment of white muscle disease in lambs and calves (Sec. 8.19), the onset of which may occur shortly after birth. It has been established that placental transfer takes place and can be increased somewhat when a ration low in E is supplemented by a concentrated source of the vitamin. A higher level of E in the blood and liver of the newborn results. Thus, authorities recommend that the ration during pregnancy contain a liberal supply of the vitamin. This can readily be accomplished by the appropriate selection of natural feeds. This does not obviate, however, the need for an adequate supply of E in the lactation ration (Sec. 16.37).

15.16. B-factors. It is obvious that all of the B-factors required for growth are also required for reproduction because the production of a fetus is involved. On the basis of studies of several of them with rats it appears that the reproduction requirements for the B-vitamins do not increase appreciably above maintenance needs until the last quarter of the period. Here the rapidly increasing metabolism of the mother, including the deposition of vitamins in the fetus, calls for a greater dietary intake accordingly. Deficiency symptoms in the newborn resulting from inadequate intakes of specific B-factors by the mother during gestation have been noted in Chap. 8.

The N.R.C. requirements of thiamine, riboflavin, niacin, pantothenic acid, and vitamin B_{12} for reproduction in swine are listed in Appendix Table I. Adequate quantitative data are not available for the other B-factors. The general procedure for determining requirements is illustrated by the study of riboflavin by Miller and associates.[28]

There have been reports of unidentified factors needed specifically for reproduction, but the possibility remains that the deficiencies noted may have been due to inadequate intakes of one of the known factors for which quantitative requirements for reproduction have not been clearly established.

EGG PRODUCTION

Differing from mammals, which nourish the embryo inside their bodies, give birth to living young, and nurse them, birds produce eggs which contain sufficient nutrients for the embryo to develop outside the body and no special food is required after hatching. In the hen the egg-formation phase of reproduction has been extended into a continuous proc-

[28] Charles O. Miller and associates, The riboflavin requirement of swine for reproduction, *J. Nutrition,* **51**:163–170, 1953.

ess, aside from the molting period, whereby egg production has become a tremendous industry as a source of human food, as well as serving in the propagation of the species.

The egg of the hen is made up approximately as follows: yolk, 31 per cent; albumen or white, 59 per cent; and shell, 10 per cent. The development of the egg starts in the ovary where the yolk portion is formed. Here there are many ova, each enclosed in a follicle. The yolk is deposited in concentric layers, and when the process is completed, the follicle bursts and the yolk, surrounded by a membrane, passes into the oviduct. Here the albumen is put on and finally the shell, each process requiring several hours. During its passage through the oviduct, the developing egg is fertilized if sperm are present. After shell formation is completed, the egg passes out through the vent. Under proper temperature conditions, the fertilized egg develops into the chick in 21 days. The reproductive process in the cock is similar to that in mammals.

15.17. Nutritive Requirements for Egg Production. The hen ranks with the dairy cow in her productive performance. In a year she may produce up to four times as much dry matter as is contained in her body. Clearly an intensive metabolism and very large nutritive requirements are involved. The egg has the following approximate composition: water, 66 per cent; protein, 13 per cent; fat, 10.5 per cent; ash, 10.5 per cent. These figures reveal the fact that, in addition to the energy requirement, there are large demands for protein and especially for mineral matter. There are also important requirements for various vitamins. Besides the large nutritive demands for the formation of the egg as such, there are additional requirements for the production of an egg that will hatch and yield a strong chick. The magnitude and complexity of the demands for the intensive egg production which characterizes the modern commercial practice have made its nutrition a specialized field; which can be discussed only very briefly here.

The nutritional needs above maintenance depend upon the number and size of the eggs produced. These requirements are commonly expressed as percentages of the total feed intake. On this basis the protein requirement is similar to that during the latter part of growth. This protein must be of high quality, as indicated by the fact that egg protein stands at the top of all protein sources studied, in terms of biological value (Table 14.8). The average egg contains approximately 2 g. of calcium and 0.12 g. of phosphorus. Nearly all of the calcium is in the shell, which consists very largely of calcium carbonate, while the phosphorus is concentrated in the yolk, principally combined with protein. Owing to this need for shell formation, the calcium requirement of the laying hen is over twice that of the growing chick, per unit of feed, and an even greater excess of the need of any mammal for any purpose.

The intensity of the metabolism involved is reflected in a doubling of the level in the blood serum during the laying period. A 4-lb. hen which lays an egg daily requires for its eggs alone twice as much calcium as the child, many times the hen's size, needs for growth. A deficiency of the element results in thinner shells, a marked depletion of the bones of the hen, and a lowering of egg production. The same effect on the hen and upon her production occurs from a lack of phosphorus. Though this element is needed in much smaller amounts than is calcium, no mammal has as high a requirement, per unit weight, for any purpose.

Some mobilization of calcium and phosphorus from the bones during heavy egg production is a normal physiological process even as is the case for lactation (Sec. 16.29). This fact emphasizes the importance of building up the reserves in the growing chick and of continuing a high level of feeding at all times in the case of the hen, for the depleted bones must be restored during the period when production falls off or ceases.

The iron requirement of the laying hen is very large in proportion to her maintenance need, as is evident from the fact that the average egg contains 1.1 mg. of this element. Manganese is another mineral element of special importance from the standpoint of eggshell strength and hatchability.

All of the vitamins needed by chicks for growth are also required for laying and breeding hens. In the case of some of them the amounts needed for maximum egg production are not sufficient to produce eggs of high hatchability. This is true in the case of riboflavin, pantothenic acid, and folacin. Comparative data are not available in the case of all.

The N.R.C. nutritive requirements for breeding hens are set forth in Appendix Table II. It is noted that data are lacking for some of the vitamins. To ensure an adequate supply of all of these nutrients in a laying mash capable of high production, the supplementation of mixtures of common feeds with calcium, phosphorus, iodized salt, manganese, riboflavin, vitamin B_{12}, vitamin A, and vitamin D is generally recommended.

15.18. Effect of Ration on Nutritive Value of Eggs. While the mineral content of eggs, except for iodine and manganese, is not influenced by the nature of the diet, there are marked effects in the case of several of the vitamins. This is particularly true of vitamin A, vitamin D, and riboflavin. The kind of ration which will result in the best production and hatchability is also the kind that provides eggs of the highest nutritive value for human consumption.

SELECTED LITERATURE

Asdell, S. A.: Factors involved in the sterility of farm animals, *Iowa State Coll. J. Sci.*, **28**:127–132, 1953.

———: Cattle Fertility and Sterility, Little, Brown & Company, Boston, 1955.

Barrett, Margaret, and Gladys Everson: Deposition of B vitamins in normally developing fetuses as evidence for increased vitamin needs of the rat for reproduction. I. Thiamine and riboflavin, *J. Nutrition,* **45**:493–505, 1951.

French, C. E., and associates: The influence of dietary fat and carbohydrate on reproduction and lactation in rats, *J. Nutrition,* **48**:91–102, 1952.

Grainger, Robert B., Boyd L. O'Dell, and Albert G. Hogan: Congenital malformations as related to deficiencies of riboflavin and vitamin B_{12}, source of protein, calcium to phosphorus ratio and skeletal phosphorus metabolism, *J. Nutrition,* **54**:33–48, 1954.

Hafez, E. S. E.: Nutrition in relation to reproduction in sows, *J. Agr. Sci.,* **54**:170–178, 1960.

Kalter, Harold, and Joseph Warkany: Experimental production of congenital malformations in mammals by metabolic procedures, *Physiol. Revs.,* **39**:69–113, 1959.

Madsen, Louis L., and associates: Effectiveness of carotene and failure of ascorbic acid to increase sexual activity and semen quality of vitamin A deficient beef bulls, *J. Animal Sci.,* **7**:60–69, 1948.

Reid, J. T.: Effect of energy intake upon reproduction in farm animals, *J. Dairy Sci.,* **43**:103–132, 1960.

Ronning, Magnar, and coworkers: The carotene requirements for reproduction in Guernsey cattle, *J. Dairy Sci.,* **36**:52–56, 1953.

Taylor, T. G., and J. H. Moore: Skeletal depletion in hens laying on a low-calcium diet, *Brit. J. Nutrition,* **8**:112–124, 1954.

Wallace, L. R.: The growth of lambs, before and after birth, in relation to the level of nutrition, *J. Agr. Sci.,* **38**:93–153, 243–302, 367–401, 1948.

Chapter 16
Lactation

A 1200-lb. cow producing 10,000 lb. of milk in a year secretes in this milk approximately two and one-half times as much dry matter as is present in her entire body. There are records of cows which have produced in the year's milk over five times the organic matter of their own bodies and of cows which over a lifetime have secreted organic matter equivalent to thirty-five times that present in their own tissues. While less subject to direct measurement, it is apparent that milk secretion in the sow nursing a larger litter also represents a noteworthy physiological performance. The studies of Macy and coworkers[1] show that the human organism is capable of producing an astonishing output of milk. It is clear that the metabolism of lactation is tremendous. While this metabolism includes many processes such as the digestion, absorption, circulation, and mobilization of nutrients, it particularly involves the functioning of the mammary glands. As an introduction to a consideration of nutritional requirements for lactation an understanding of the physiological processes concerned is essential.

16.1. The Mammary Glands. The glands usually occur in pairs, the number of pairs varying with the species. They are modified cutaneous glands which make their appearance early in embryonic life but reach their full development only after a normal parturition. As far as is known they have no function other than milk secretion, for they can be removed at any stage of the life cycle without any observable harmful effect from their absence. A diagram showing the structure of the functioning udder is presented in Fig. 16.1.

The glands are present in a rudimentary form at birth and undergo little development until puberty, at which time a marked growth occurs. Thereafter there are periodic changes which are correlated with the

[1] Icie G. Macy and associates, Human milk flow, *Am. J. Diseases Children,* **39:** 1186–1204, 1930.

ovarian cycle. Histological studies show that at each estrus there is some duct growth in the gland, and an occasional secreting cell may be formed, which explains the fact that a watery secretion has been obtained before pregnancy. With the onset of gestation, there is a large increase in growth which involves the production of ducts, alveoli, and secreting cells. A secretory activity thus develops which results in an accumulation in the gland of products making up the colostrum. With the withdrawal of the secretion following parturition, its quantity gradually rises for a period which varies in different species and then gradually falls until lactation ceases. As cessation occurs, the gland shrinks

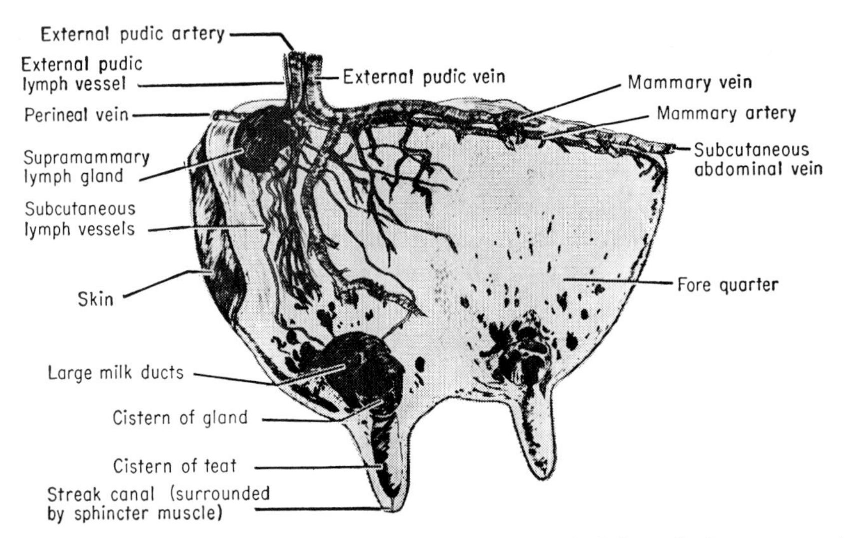

FIG. 16.1. Cross section of functioning udder. (*Furnished through the courtesy of C. W. Turner, University of Missouri.*)

enormously, owing to a decrease in size of the alveoli and ducts, and remains quiescent until another pregnancy starts a renewed growth and secretion.

16.2. Hormonal Control. The physiological mechanisms controlling these various events are still incompletely understood, but it is recognized that the activities of the ovary, uterus, and mammary glands are interrelated. It is now accepted that the essential stimulus for the growth and functioning of the gland is hormonal rather than nervous, and the present evidence indicates that at least a dozen hormones are concerned, directly or indirectly. Mention can be made here of only the principal ones as presently understood. The interaction of several results in mammary growth. In the main, estrogens are responsible for duct growth, and progesterone for alveolar growth, but neither of these hormones can produce its maximum effect unless somatotropin, the pituitary growth hormone, is present. Prolactin from the pituitary is also necessary for maximum growth. At full development of the gland, prolactin brings about the initiation of secretion. Maximum secretory activity is dependent on the presence of adrenocorticotropin (ACTH). The gradual decline in production, which follows the peak attained after parturition (Sec. 16.5), results from a gradual cessation of secretion by the cells built up during the previous pregnancy and the lack of new cellular growth.

For a detailed review of present knowledge and its experimental basis, the student is referred to the paper by Lyons.[2]

16.3. Influence of Iodinated Proteins on Milk Secretion. Reference was made in Sec. 14.7 to the role of thyroidal products in stimulating metabolism. Commercial sources of highly active iodinated proteins, notably iodinated casein, have been developed for studies of practical applications in animal production. These studies have been most active in the field of lactation, dating particularly from the initial work of Reinecke and Turner[3] who developed the method of producing an iodinated casein of high biological activity. In later studies the Missouri workers and several others have shown that the feeding of this or similar products results in significant and sustained increases in milk yield and even larger effects on fat yield, in cows in mid-lactation. Metabolism is speeded up, and so increased feed must be consumed to avoid loss of weight. An increased pulse rate, elevated body temperature, and hyperirritability are other undesirable effects that may result. The secretion tends to increase with the level of intake of the protein compound, but so also do the undesirable effects. For example, Blaxter, in England, has reported that an increased milk production of 35 per cent and of fat production of 54 per cent were accompanied by an increase of 30 per cent in the resting heart rate and of 34 per cent in the respiration rate, with a 9 per cent loss in body weight. The speeding up of the metabolism results in a higher heat production, the elimination of which is responsible for the rise in pulse rate in the nonsweating cow. High intakes of iodinated casein stimulate the metabolism of the cow beyond her ability to consume food; hence the weight loss.

The report of Thomas and associates[4] is an example of the type of re-

[2] W. R. Lyons, Hormonal synergism in mammary growth, *Proc. Roy. Soc. (London) B,* **149**:303–325, 1958.

[3] E. P. Reinecke and C. W. Turner, Formation in vitro of highly active thyroproteins, their biologic assay and practical use, *Missouri Agr. Expt. Sta. Research Bull.* 355, 1942.

[4] J. W. Thomas and associates, Effects on economy and efficiency of milk production when thyroprotein is fed for a short period to milking cows, *J. Dairy Sci.,* **37**: 877–888, 1954.

sults obtained. Feeding 15 g. of iodinated casein daily along with extra concentrates increased yields of milk by 20 per cent and also increased the fat test over short periods during the declining phase of lactation. The practice was shown to be advantageous under certain market conditions. When hormone feeding was discontinued, milk yields fell below expected levels, and this tended to eliminate the previous advantage. Swanson at Tennessee found that gradual withdrawal of iodinated casein over 18 to 25 days minimized the decline in milk yield apparently by permitting recovery of the animal's thyroid activity. In previous long-time studies Thomas and Moore at Beltsville found no advantage in milk yield or efficiency of feed use from iodinated casein fed during most of the lactation period. Feeding the hormone for several lactations seemed to depress total milk yield and breeding performance, but small numbers of animals were involved in the studies. Long-time feeding is not recommended.

16.4. Induction of Lactation by Synthetic Estrogens. Following an initial finding by DeFremery in Holland that udder growth could be induced in virgin goats by anointing the udder with a salve containing estradiol benzoate, Folley and associates in England found that use of diethylstilbestrol caused udder development and a secretion of milk as well.

Reports of other workers followed, describing the induction of lactation in cows by injection or inunction, or both, of the synthetic estrogens. Next, it was shown by Folley and associates and by Hammond and Day[5] that the subcutaneous implantation of tablets of stilbestrol or hexestrol was a simple and more effective procedure. Hammond and Day reported on the treatment of 140 cows and heifers that had failed to get in calf. While the treatment was not successful in every case and while sometimes the volume of secretion was low, most animals produced 2600 to 6600 lb. over periods of 40 to 64 weeks. A later report by Day and Hammond states that, of the cows thus treated with the estrogens because of failure to breed, 70 per cent of those anatomically normal got in calf following the induced lactation. A real disadvantage is the frequent occurrence of nymphomania following the treatment.

16.5. The Course of Milk Secretion. The normal lactation curve for the cow is shown in Fig. 16.2. The time involved in reaching the peak depends upon inherited factors and upon the condition of the cow prior to calving and how she is fed and managed thereafter. The rise in secretion following parturition does not run parallel with increased food intakes, and it extends over a much longer time than can be accounted for as the recovery period from the strain of calving. It may be caused

[5] J. Hammond, Jr., and F. T. Day, Oestrogen treatment of cattle: induced lactation and other effects, *J. Endocrinol.*, **4**:53–82, 1944.

by the gradual removal of the accumulated products, enabling the cells to reach their maximum rate. The impulse to secrete milk is so strong at the start of lactation that the animal readily draws on her own reserves for a short time to produce milk. However, unless current nutrition quickly balances milk output, the maximum yields cannot long be sustained on body reserves. Previous nutrition, which determines the status of the cow's reserves at calving, is thus concerned.

Following the peak, there is a regular decline in yield such that the curve is of the descending exponential type, each month's yield being a constant percentage of that of the preceding month. *Persistency* is the term used to denote the measure of this rate of decline, which varies

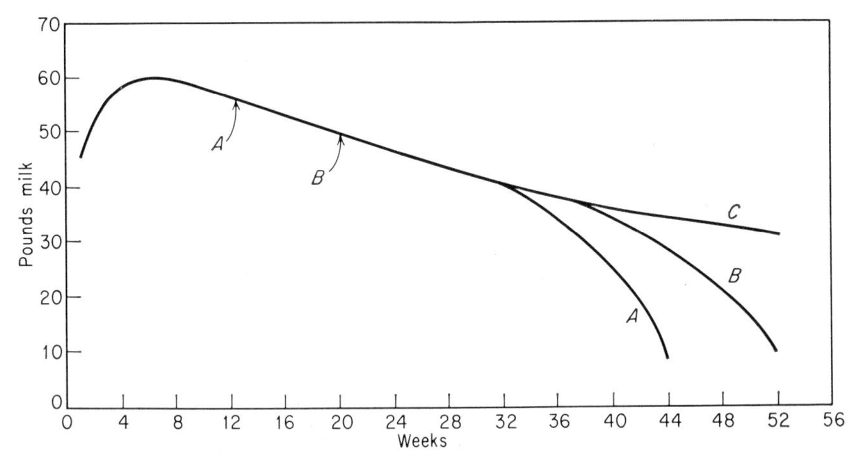

FIG. 16.2. Smoothed lactation curve of the cow. *A*, rebred to calve in 12 months. *B*, rebred to calve in 15 months. *C*, not pregnant.

with the individual and in different lactations and which is accelerated at the twenty-second week after a new conception. The onset of a new pregnancy is thus a determining factor in the length of the lactation of the cow, both because of this accelerated decline and because of the necessity of giving her a rest period before another lactation. The fact that many cows will continue to secrete some milk right up to parturition if milked regularly shows that there is no physiological mechanism for absolutely stopping the process before the event. Cows which remain unbred may continue to secrete milk at a decreasing rate for two or three years or even longer.

Failure to remove the milk regularly and completely from the gland lessens its activity and brings about cessation, a fact which finds practical application in the drying off of animals. The onset of a new pregnancy during lactation results, after a period, in a more rapid decline in the secretion than otherwise occurs. In animals nursing young, lactation is usually artificially terminated at weaning, since failure to remove the secretion stops the process. Underfeeding during the declining period of secretion has an immediate effect in lowering the output, in contrast to its lesser influence at the start of lactation, but no system of feeding will counteract in any way the normal decline.

The lactation curve of the goat is similar to that of the cow, and milk-secretion studies with sheep indicate a similar one for this species also. In the case of women, however, the peak is reached much later, or there is a plateau instead of a peak. The increase after parturition may continue to the twenty-eighth week, and the secretion may persist at or near its maximum level to the fortieth week.

With lactations of substantially equal length, the yield of the cow increases for the first four or five, on the average. The growth of the animal as a whole is a factor during the first three lactations, and there is markedly greater hypertrophy of the gland during the second pregnancy than during the first, with smaller increases in succeeding pregnancies. Persistency decreases in succeeding lactations. Since this is true, it is apparent that the higher yields which are obtained in succeeding lactations must be due to a greater secretion during the first part of the lactation. Expressed another way, it may be said that the level at which secretion begins increases to maturity but that the total yield for the lactation is not proportional to this rise because of a declining persistency factor.

The longer the dry period, the greater the persistency in the next lactation. Shortening the dry period before a second lactation lowers yield to a much greater extent than shortening it before a later lactation. This is readily explainable on the basis of the greater growth of body and gland that takes place before the second lactation than later. The importance of an adequate dry period to build up nutrient reserves is well understood.

16.6. Milk of Different Species. The chemical composition of the milk of various species is presented in Table 16.1. Data on other minerals and on the vitamins found in cow's milk are discussed later in the chapter. It should be emphasized that the figures for individual animals may vary widely from these average values. This is certainly true for cows of different breeds and for individuals within the breed as is discussed later (Sec. 16.19). Doubtless the variations have become greatly accentuated in this species as a result of breeding operations, but they must be expected to occur to a certain extent in all species. The data presented in the table are useful, nevertheless, to indicate the nutrients involved in milk secretion and to bring out certain differences which exist among the species. It is noted that the milk of the sow and ewe contains considerably more dry matter than the milk of any of the other species of farm animals and that this is reflected in a higher energy value and ash content. Particularly noteworthy is the much higher content of calcium and phosphorus. Clearly per unit of product, the nutritive requirements for milk secretion in the sow and ewe are markedly greater than in the cow, goat, or mare. It is also interesting to note that the least variable constituent for all species is lactose. The same is true among individuals and also for different samples from the same individual, as is brought out in later discussions for the cow.

A very comprehensive compilation of the comparative composition and properties of human, cow, and goat milk, prepared for the Food and Nutrition Board by Macy, Kelley, and Sloan,[6] has been published by the N.R.C. The tables include data for the various vitamins, trace minerals, amino acids, and other constituents.

TABLE 16.1. PERCENTAGE COMPOSITION OF MILK OF DIFFERENT SPECIES*

Species	Water	Protein	Fat	Lactose	Ash	Calcium	Phosphorus	Kcal.
Cow........	87.2	3.5	3.7	4.9	0.71	0.121	0.095	73
Sheep.......	80.1	5.8	8.2	4.8	0.92	0.250	0.166	127
Goat........	86.5	3.6	4.0	5.1	0.80	0.131	0.104	79
Mare.......	89.0	2.7	1.6	6.1	0.51	.....	.....	54
Sow.........	80.4	5.4	8.3	5.0	0.85	0.252	0.151	126
Woman.....	87.5	1.0	4.4	7.0	0.21	0.035	0.013	70
Bitch.......	75.4	11.2	9.6	3.1	0.73	.....	.....	164

* Data compiled from various sources in the literature. The data for human milk are expressed as grams per 100 ml. With the exception of this milk, the data for calorie content were calculated by the writers. The data are expressed as gross kilocalories, calculated by Atwater's specific values for milk, viz., protein, 5.65; fat, 9.25; lactose, 3.9. L. A. Maynard, *J. Nutrition,* **28**:443–452, 1944.

Studies have been made of milk production in the sow and ewe over the lactation period by weighing the young before and after suckling at short intervals. Such an experiment has been reported for sows by Barber and coworkers[7] and for ewes by Coombe and associates.[8]

THE SECRETION OF THE MILK CONSTITUENTS

16.7. The Composition of Blood and Milk. Most of the organic constituents of milk arise from specific synthetic processes of the mammary

[6] Icie G. Macy, Harriet J. Kelley, and Ralph E. Sloan, The composition of milks, *Natl. Acad. Sci. Natl. Research Council Publ.* 254, 1953.

[7] R. S. Barber, R. Braude, and K. G. Mitchell, Studies on milk production of large white pigs, *J. Agr. Sci.,* **46**:97–118, 1958.

[8] J. B. Coombe, I. D. Wardrop, and D. E. Tribe, A study of milk production of the grazing ewe, with emphasis on the experimental technique employed, *J. Agr. Sci.,* **54**:353–359, 1960.

gland, representing products which are not found elsewhere in nature. As an aid to a consideration of the physiology involved and the chemical changes which take place, data are presented in Table 16.2 on the composition of the milk and of the blood plasma of the cow. For convenience in later discussions, the different milk constituents are listed opposite the corresponding blood constituents. Several other constituents not shown in the table are present in both fluids, such as amino acids and other nonprotein nitrogen compounds, free and combined cholesterol, additional mineral elements, and the various vitamins. A study of the figures in the table makes it evident that milk has a quantitative composition very different from that of the blood plasma from

TABLE 16.2. COMPARATIVE COMPOSITION OF BLOOD PLASMA AND MILK OF THE COW

Blood plasma		*Milk*	
Constituent	*Per cent*	*Constituent*	*Per cent*
Water	91.0	Water	87.0
Glucose	0.05	Lactose	4.90
		Casein	2.90
Serum albumin	3.20	Lactalbumin	0.52
Serum globulin	4.40	Lactoglobulin	0.20
Neutral fat	0.06	Neutral fat	3.70
Phospholipids	0.24	Phospholipids	0.10
Calcium	0.009	Calcium	0.12
Phosphorus	0.011	Phosphorus	0.10
Sodium	0.34	Sodium	0.05
Potassium	0.03	Potassium	0.15
Chlorine	0.35	Chlorine	0.11
Citric acid	Trace	Citric acid	0.20

which it is made and that there are qualitative differences as well. The two fluids are isotonic.

Certain milk constituents, including lactose, casein, and some of the fatty acids, are clearly synthetic products of the gland, while others, such as the minerals and vitamins, pass in directly from the blood stream. There are various organic constituents for which there is a lack of information on whether they enter directly or arise as products of the gland's metabolism.

The milk of the individual cow tends to be of constant composition for most constituents, but there are periodic fluctuations, notably of fat, and there are characteristic changes over the course of the lactation. With the normal decline in yield, the percentage of fat rises, and so does the protein to a lesser degree. In contrast, the lactose declines slightly, and for the maintenance of osmotic relations, its decline is balanced by a rise in chlorides. These same changes tend to occur when the yield is subjected to an abnormal drop as the result of sickness, off-feed, or other disturbing factors.

In general, the nature of the ration has little influence on the percentage composition of milk. Special cases in which certain specific feeds have been found to affect the fat percentage are mentioned in Sec. 16.13. It has been shown that prolonged undernutrition, which results in a drop in milk yield and in body condition, can also result in a lowering of the percentage of *nonfat solids* (NFS.). The lowering occurs primarily in the protein fraction. The evidence indicates that the cause is a deficient intake of energy rather than of protein or any other specific nutrient. The concentration of certain vitamins in the milk are markedly influenced by the nature of the feed. By contrast, the percentages of the major mineral elements are not affected by commonly fed diets or other factors (Sec. 16.15).

16.8. Mechanism of Milk Secretion. A complex series of reactions are involved in the secretion process, viz., the passage of blood constituents into the cells, the synthesis of secretory granules and their later breakdown, the transfer of water to dissolve the granules, and the passage of the product into the ducts. Many explanations have been proposed for the physical changes concerned, but none of them are entirely satisfactory.

Milk secretion is a continuous process. As a result of the accumulation of milk in the udder, intermammary pressure builds up and gradually increases. This increasing pressure is considered to result eventually in a declining rate of secretion. Here lies the basis for the advocacy of frequent milking as a means of obtaining larger yields. Several studies, such as those by Schmidt,[9] have shown that the rate of milk secretion by high-producing cows does not decline significantly for 12 hr., but does decline thereafter. Intermammary pressure is the responsible agent for stopping the secretion when milk is left in the udder as a means of drying off the cow.

When the milking act is initiated, a small quantity of milk can be immediately removed, then there is a lag period followed by a large inflow of milk into the cistern of the udder. One says that the cow "has let down" her milk. This is believed to be a reflex action as a result of the stimulation of the teat in the act of milking or suckling. The explanation most widely accepted at present is that the stimulation of the sensory nerves in the skin and teats results in the secretion of the oxytocic principle of the posterior lobe of the pituitary, which, in turn, causes a contraction of the musculature of the gland whereby the milk is forced out of the alveoli and ducts.

[9] G. H. Schmidt, Effect of milking intervals on the rate of milk and fat secretion, *J. Dairy Sci.*, **43**:213–219, 1960.

16.9. Methods of Studying the Secretion of Milk Constituents. A useful method for the study of milk secretion is the analysis of the blood before and after passing the gland. Data obtained in this way have provided important information on the blood precursors of the milk constituents, but they cannot establish quantitative relations between blood changes and the constituents secreted unless the blood volume passing through the gland is measured also so as to arrive at the blood-milk ratio. In view of the many outgoing paths, including the lymphatics, such a measure appears impracticable. The blood-milk ratio can be obtained indirectly by measuring the uptake of an element, such as calcium, which is known to be absorbed, and analyzing the milk for the element as a means of arriving at the milk volume corresponding to the blood change. It is recognized that the disturbance of the cow incident to the drawing of blood samples and the possible slowing down of secretion accordingly limit the value of quantitative data. As a means of overcoming this difficulty, some workers have anesthetized the animal prior to drawing blood samples.

The perfusion method was early used to study the secretion of milk constituents but became subject to the criticism that the rapid deterioration of the gland tissues resulted in unreliable data. Later, Peterson and associates[10] described an apparatus which maintains the udder in good condition for several hours and which has been successfully used by several later workers. Mammary tissue slices and cell-free extracts of mammary tissues are also employed in in vitro studies.

During the past ten years radioactive traces have been widely used to study the blood source of various milk constituents. The radioactive atom is introduced into the source to be studied, which is, in turn, injected into the blood or used in a perfusion experiment. The perfusion technique has the advantage that the tagged compound in question enters the gland as such, whereas such a compound injected into the general circulation may be subject to metabolism in other tissues, such as the liver, with the result that the radioactive element may not enter the gland in the same combination as injected. In either case the identification of the element in a milk constituent shows that the compound into which it was introduced is a precursor, but it remains uncertain whether glandular action alone was involved.

Citations to the use of these various methods are made in the discussions which follow.

16.10. The Secretion of Lactose. It is generally accepted that glucose is the principal blood precursor of lactose. Kaufmann and Magne[11]

[10] W. E. Peterson, J. C. Shaw, and M. B. Vissher, A technique for perfusing excised bovine mammary glands, *J. Dairy Sci.*, **24**:139–146, 1941.

[11] M. Kaufmann and H. Magne, Sur le consommation du glucose du sang par le tissu de la glande mammaire, *Compt. rend. acad. sci.*, **143**:779–782, 1906.

took samples simultaneously from the jugular and mammary veins of a milking cow and found that the mammary blood contained 18 per cent less glucose, whereas similar samples from a dry cow showed no difference. Considering the jugular blood as representative of the supply of the gland, they suggested that the lactose of milk was made from the glucose of the blood. Somewhat later Foa obtained, by perfusion experiments, specific evidence that the gland can use glucose to make lactose. The finding of Kaufmann and Magne has been repeatedly confirmed by later studies.

There are many experiments using isotope-labeled glucose which have shown that it is the principal precursor of lactose. Such evidence has been presented by Dimant and associates[12] in a perfusion experiment. Similar evidence has also been obtained, without exception, in several studies in which the labeled glucose has been injected into the blood stream. Injections of labeled propionate, butyrate, and bicarbonate have also shown a definite, though small, incorporation of the labeled carbon into lactose. It is generally believed that these compounds first serve as precursors of glucose outside the gland. The various experiments dealing with the blood source of lactose and with the pathway by which glucose is changed into lactose in the gland are reviewed by Malpress.[13]

16.11. The Secretion of Fat. The fatty acids in milk occur almost entirely as triglycerides, in contrast to the situation in the plasma where they are present largely as phospholipids (Table 16.2). After studies had failed to confirm earlier evidence that milk fat arose from plasma phospholipids, the work of Lintzel[14] with goats and Maynard and associates[15] with cows showed that the triglycerides of the blood were precursors. This finding was confirmed by others. The data did not provide any quantitative information, however, on the extent to which milk fat was thus formed or on the origin of specific fatty acids, particularly the short-chain ones which do not occur in the blood plasma.

With the demonstration of Bloch and Rittenberg in 1945, using the isotope tracer technique, that fatty-acid chains could be built up from acetate, considerable amounts of which are continually being produced

[12] C. Dimant, Vearl R. Smith, and Henry A. Lardy, Lactose synthesis in the mammary gland perfused with 1-C^{14} glucose, *J. Biol. Chem.*, **201**:85–91, 1953.

[13] F. H. Malpress, The biosynthesis of lactose, *Proc. Roy. Soc. (London) B*, **149**: 362–380, 1958.

[14] Wolfgang Lintzel, Untersuchungen über den Chemismus der Milchfettbildung in Abhangigkeit von der Fütterung, *Z. Zucht. Riehe B, Z. Tierzucht. Zuchtungsbiol.*, **29**:219–242, 1934.

[15] L. A. Maynard and associates, Studies of the blood precursor of milk fat, *Cornell Agr. Expt. Sta. Mem.* 211, 1938; L. Voris, G. H. Ellis, and L. A. Maynard, The determination of neutral fat glycerol in blood with periodate: application to the determination of arteriovenous differences in blood fat, *J. Biol. Chem.*, **133**:491–498, 1940.

in body metabolism, attention was centered on this compound as a possible source of milk fat. In this connection the findings that the arterial blood of the cow and goat contain substantial amounts of acetic and propionic acids as absorbed products of rumen activity (Sec. 4.22) seemed particularly pertinent.

Direct evidence that the gland could make fatty acids from acetate commenced to appear around 1950 as a result of the studies of Folley, Popjak, and their associates at the National Institute for Research in Dairying in England. In vitro evidence was first obtained by the use of mammary gland slices. The most conclusive evidence was produced by the use of carbon-labeled acetate, in studies with lactating ruminants, by the above workers and by Kleiber and his associates at the University of California. From several years of investigation, it has been established that the principal source of the fatty acids from butyric to palmitic is acetate, the higher ones originating from triglycerides in the blood plasma, as previously discussed. The relative quantitative contribution of the two sources remains to be established. Glascock[16] has reviewed recent studies on the origin of milk fat.

According to Folley, the mammary tissue of the nonruminant cannot utilize acetate to make fat, but can use glucose for this purpose.

16.12. Variation in the Secretion of Fat. Fat is the most variable constituent of milk. In addition to its variation among breeds and individuals, its percentage in the milk of a given animal varies from milking to milking, from quarter to quarter, and increases progressively during the milking process. In a study with a Guernsey cow, Van Slyke found that the first fraction drawn, consisting of about 18 per cent of the whole, contained only 1 per cent of fat, whereas the final fraction of 30 per cent contained 10 per cent of fat. It is very difficult to find an explanation for these large variations. Hammond[17] has set forth important evidence that differences in fat percentage are caused by milk pressure, through the inhibition of the actual secretory process and through its effect on the ease with which the fat globules pass down the ducts to the cistern. He states that changes in the chemical composition of milk occur as the rate of secretion varies.

Periodic changes in fat percentage are inversely correlated with milk yield. A lowering of yield which results from an abrupt change in conditions, such as weather, surroundings, or even a change in the milker, is frequently accompanied by a rise in fat content. The sharply lowered yield which results during a period of off-feed is generally accompanied by a rise in fat percentage. This inverse relationship is also

[16] R. F. Glascock, Recent research on the origin of milk fat, *Proc. Roy Soc. (London) B*, **149**:402–413, 1958.

[17] John Hammond, The physiology of milk and butterfat secretion, *Vet. Record*, **16**: 519–537, 1936.

shown in the course of the lactation, for as the decline in yield progresses following the peak, the percentage of fat tends to rise.

There is a marked seasonal variation in the percentage of fat, the maximum occurring in winter and the minimum in summer. That environmental temperature is the primary cause of this variation is indicated by controlled studies in which it has been shown that within certain limits fat percentage increases regularly with drop in temperature. From one lactation to another there is no consistent change in fat percentage. While an increase in milk yield may be expected during the first four or five lactations, a cow which has a low-fat test as a heifer will not better it materially in succeeding years.

Maynard and coworkers[18] have made extensive studies of the possible relation between the level of blood lipids and the milk-fat percentage. Their comparative studies of the blood and milk from milking to milking, from day to day, and from week to week have revealed no changes in the blood which were correlated in any way with the large variation which frequently occurred in milk-fat percentage. A ration which resulted in a marked decrease in the concentration of the blood lipids did not produce any corresponding changes in the milk fat. Their studies show that, over the lactation cycle as a whole, the level of blood lipids tends to follow the course of milk and fat yield rather than the fat percentage.

16.13. Fat Percentage as Influenced by Feed. The previously described large variations in fat percentage early led investigators to study the possibility of increasing this percentage through feeding. The early literature is filled with contradictory data and conclusions. Most of these experiments were of short duration and failed to take account of the nondietary factors which cause large variations. Studies have produced some authentic cases of increased fat percentage through feeding. Such an effect has been caused by large intakes of soybeans (18 per cent fat). Purdue workers briefly reported persistent increases when the grain mixture contained 25 to 50 per cent of the beans. Byers and associates[19] reported such an increase from feeding 10 lb. of the beans daily as a supplement to alfalfa hay. Cornell workers found that the fat percentage increased from 3.5 to 4.5 and that the increase persisted for the 30-day test period when soybeans made up the entire concentrate portion of the ration. On the contrary, the feeding of soybeans at the lower

[18] Ch. Porcher and L. Maynard, La graisse du sang et la graisse du lait pendant la lactation, *Le lait,* **10**:601–613, 765–782, 1930; L. A. Maynard, E. S. Harrison, and C. M. McCay, The changes in the total fatty acids, phospholipid fatty acids, and cholesterol of the blood during the lactation cycle, *J. Biol. Chem.,* **92**:263–272, 1931; L. A. Maynard and C. M. McCay, The influence of a low-fat diet upon fat metabolism during lactation, *J. Nutrition,* **2**:67–81, 1929.

[19] J. H. Byers, I. R. Jones, and J. R. Haag, The comparative value of high and low fat concentrates with alfalfa hay, *J. Dairy Sci.,* **32**:596–603, 1949.

levels which would probably represent the maximum in practical rations have not resulted in significant increases in the fat percentage. There are European studies as reviewed by Breirem[20] and recent tests at Cornell University which have shown such an increase from feeding coconut meal and palm kernel meal, high in fat. All of these positive results are physiologically interesting and reveal an important field for further study. At present, however, it must be concluded that any modifications which seem practicable in the otherwise good rations fed in the United States cannot be expected to increase significantly and persistently the fat percentage. The special case of iodinated protein (Sec. 16.3) represents an exception. The claim that the feeding of vitamin E will increase fat percentage has been disproved.

A lowering of the fat percentage has also been demonstrated experimentally. Cod-liver oil exerts such an effect. This peculiar response was first observed by Golding and associates[21] in connection with studies of the influence of the oil on the vitamin content of the milk. It has since been confirmed in several laboratories. Feeding as small amounts as 2 oz. per day has caused a lowering, but larger and more consistent effects are observed with intakes of 4 to 6 oz. A 30 per cent decrease in the fat level has been noted. The specific factor in the oil which is responsible is found in the saponifiable fraction, but it has not been identified. The deleterious effect of the oil is eliminated by hydrogenation. This property of lowering the fat percentage is not shared by fish oils generally. Clearly, vegetable oils do not exert the effect. Reference has been made (Sec. 4.21) to studies showing that feeding the roughage in a finely divided condition and restricting its intake may lower the fat percentage as a result of a modification of rumen processes. Breirem[22] has reviewed European studies showing that severe underfeeding lowers this percentage. These various reports of decreases, as well as the previous discussed reports of increases, emphasize the need for further controlled studies of the feed factors influencing this percentage, though the present data appear to suggest no modifications in the currently recommended feeding practices.

16.14. The Secretion of Protein. In 1920 Cary of the U.S. Department of Agriculture showed that the free amino acid nitrogen of the blood plasma suffered a large drop in passing the gland, from which it was concluded that milk protein is formed from plasma amino acids.

[20] Knut Breirem, The influence of the feed on the composition of the milk and the quality of dairy products, *Roy. Agr. Coll. Norway Div. Animal Nutrition Reprint* 81, 1949.

[21] John Golding, Katharine Marjorie Soames, and Sylvester Solomon Zilva, The influence of the cow's diet on the fat-soluble vitamins of winter milk, *Biochem. J.*, **20**:1306–1319, 1926.

[22] Breirem, *loc. cit.*

Confirmatory evidence was later obtained by others using the same technique and also by perfusion experiments. Early work also suggested that plasma globulin was absorbed by the gland as a source of milk protein, but there has been no confirmatory evidence. Later studies have dealt with specific amino acids labeled with C^{14}. As regards the essential acids, which obviously must arise from the blood rather than from gland synthesis, it has been shown that the plasma amino acids are the principal precursors at least. The possibility that some of those in the milk may arise from plasma protein absorbed by the gland has not been ruled out, but there is no direct evidence in favor of this view. In so far as studied by isotopic methods, it is apparent that at least half of the nonessential amino acids in milk protein also arise from the same acids of the plasma, but the probability that some of them may be synthesized within the gland from other blood precursors is a reasonable one. Kleiber and his students at California have shown, by isotope studies, that glucose, acetic acid, and propionic acid are precursors of certain nonessential acids found in casein. The experiments with propionic acid are reported by Black and Kleiber[23] in a paper in which possible metabolic pathways are discussed. Barry[24] has reviewed many of the studies dealing with the blood precursors of milk proteins.

16.15. The Secretion of the Mineral Elements. Over thirty mineral elements have been found in milk, many of them present in traces. Thus, the list is more than double the number which have been found to be essential nutrients. They all enter from the blood plasma, but, as is illustrated in Table 16.2 for five of the major ones, the concentrations of many of them in the milk are very different from their concentrations in the blood. Milk contains approximately thirteen times as much calcium, ten times as much phosphorus, and five times as much potassium, but only one-seventh as much sodium and one-third as much chloride as does blood plasma. How the gland selectively secretes its minerals presents a physiochemical problem which is largely unexplained.

For a given animal, the principal mineral constituents normally show little variation, either periodically or over the lactation as a whole. This is brought out by the extensive mineral-balance studies of Forbes and coworkers.[25] Neither diet nor blood changes have any influence on the calcium, phosphorus, or iron content of milk. The small amount of

[23] Arthur L. Black and Max Kleiber, The transfer of carbon from propionate to amino acids in lactating cows, *J. Biol. Chem.*, **232**:203–209, 1958.

[24] J. M. Barry, The precursors in the blood stream of the proteins of milk, *Proc. Roy. Soc. (London) B*, **149**:380–391, 1958.

[25] Ernest B. Forbes and associates, The mineral requirements of milk production: the annual cycle of mineral and nitrogen metabolism of the milch cow as affected by alfalfa hay, timothy hay, bone flour and ground limestone, *Pennsylvania Agr. Expt. Sta. Tech. Bull.* 319, 1935.

iodine present in milk can be increased, however, by adding an iodine compound to the ration. There are several reports that the small amounts of manganese, zinc, copper, cobalt, and boron can also be influenced by their content in the ration. Citrates of the electropositive minerals make up 30 per cent of the milk ash. The role of citric acid in milk is only partially understood, and little is known regarding its secretion.

16.16. Pigments. Milk contains both fat-soluble and water-soluble pigments. Of the fat-soluble, carotenoid group of pigments, which are synthesized by plants but not by animals, *carotene* is the principal one found in the milk of the cow. Chlorophyll is destroyed in the digestive tract, and this is presumably true to a certain extent also for xanthophyll, only a small amount of which gets into the milk. The occurrence of carotene in milk is limited primarily to the bovine species. The milk of the sheep, goat, sow, and camel has little or none, and women's milk is nearly colorless. The reason for these breed and species differences is not known, but when there is no pigment in the blood plasma, the milk is also free. The principal water-soluble pigment of milk is *riboflavin.* Since carotene is the precursor of vitamin A, and since riboflavin is also a vitamin, the factors which govern their secretion in milk are best discussed later where the vitamin requirements for lactation are considered.

16.17. Colostrum. The first product from the mammary gland following parturition, the colostrum, is richer in total solids and total ash, much richer in protein, and lower in lactose than normal. Per unit of total solids, colostrum has approximately twice as much protein, the same amounts of fat and ash, but only one-third as much lactose. The proteins, which make up approximately 15 per cent of the product in the case of the cow, consist principally of globulin and albumin, in marked contrast to their very low content in normal milk. This lactoglobulin provides immune bodies transferred from the blood, which are in turn ingested by the newborn, and thus play an important role in disease resistance early in life. This is of special importance in ruminants because the placental transfer of antibodies does not occur in these species. As the product drawn from the gland assumes the composition of normal milk in the course of a few days following its first withdrawal, the immunizing properties disappear.

Colostrum has nutritive values that are of special importance for the newborn because of its richness in certain vitamins and iron compared with the later normal milk. For example, Sutton and associates[26] found that the first-milking colostrum of a group of pasture-fed cows of different breeds to be approximately ten times as potent in carotene, six

[26] T. S. Sutton, R. G. Warner, and H. E. Kaeser, The concentration and output of carotenoid pigments, vitamin A, and riboflavin in the colostrum and milk of dairy cows, *J. Dairy Sci.*, **30**:927–932, 1947.

times as potent in vitamin A, and three times as potent in riboflavin as the milk obtained at the twentieth milking. The vitamin A value of the colostrum of cows fed poor roughage during the gestation is much less than of those on pasture or dry roughage rich in carotene. Colostrum is several times richer in iron than is normal milk and also somewhat richer in thiamine and vitamin D. Both its special nutritive values and its immunizing properties indicate why it is so important for the new-born animal to receive the colostrum.

After the cow has been dried off in preparation for the next calving, the gland continues to secrete a fluid which is similar to colostrum, particularly rich in globulins. During the last two weeks there is a tremendous increase in the immune globulins. These globulins are immunologically similar to those in the maternal blood, and it is considered that they arise directly from the blood rather than as a synthetic product of the gland.

16.18. Abnormal Milk Constituents. It has been mentioned that some of the normal constituents of milk are apparently merely filtration products. Among these there are substances, such as urea, which represent useless products and which apparently pass into the milk in small amounts instead of being excreted entirely through the usual channels, because the membrane is not a perfect barrier. This fact raises the question as to the extent to which such substances as drugs and other nonnutritive or toxic substances may pass into the milk in health and in disease. This subject has been discussed very comprehensively by Kolda[27] with the general conclusion that the healthy gland is highly protective against the passage of foreign substances in harmful concentrations. Neither heavy metals, such as mercury and arsenic, nor volatile organic substances, such as alcohol, ether, and chloroform, pass into the milk in toxic amounts. The same was found true for salicylic acid, aspirin and related compounds, and various alkaloids such as morphine, atropine, and quinine. It is recognized, however, that certain essential oils may pass into milk to the extent of causing an odor and taste and that the poisonous principles of certain plants, such as white snake root and rayless goldenrod, may be secreted in sufficient amounts to render the milk harmful.

In diseases of the udder, particularly those characterized by inflammation, the membrane becomes much more permeable. The milk itself changes in the direction of the composition of blood with a resulting increase in protein and salts and a decrease in lactose. The protein fraction contains more albumin and less casein. With a more permeable gland, the danger from the entrance of harmful foreign substances is

[27] J. Kolda, Du passage des substances médicamenteuses dans le lait, *Le lait,* **6**: 12–24, 88–102, 180–194, 269–287, 1926.

greatly increased. In diseases not affecting the udder, the primary effect is on yield of milk rather than on its composition.

THE ENERGY REQUIREMENT

In addition to her maintenance requirement, the lactating animal must receive sufficient nutrients to supply those secreted in her milk and to cover the wastage involved in the process. It is obvious that a separate requirement can be stated for lactation only for those animals for which the current milk yield and its composition are known, i.e., for those used in commercial milk production. Thus we have specific knowledge of the

TABLE 16.3. COMPOSITION OF MILK AS RELATED TO FAT CONTENT*

Fat, per cent	Protein, per cent	Lactose, per cent	Ash, per cent	Energy, kcal. per 100 g.	Total solids, per cent
3.0	2.7	4.90	0.67	62	11.27
3.5	2.9	4.89	0.68	68	11.97
4.0	3.1	4.87	0.70	73	12.67
4.5	3.3	4.85	0.72	79	13.37
5.0	3.5	4.83	0.74	85	14.07
5.5	3.7	4.82	0.75	91	14.77
6.0	3.9	4.81	0.76	96	15.47

* The data for fat, protein, lactose, ash, and total solids in this table were compiled by A. C. Dahlberg, Cornell University, and are reproduced with his permission. The data for energy content were calculated by the writer using the appropriate Atwater coefficients. (See footnote, Table 16.1.)

nutritive needs for milk secretion only in the case of the dairy cow and goat. Nevertheless, the information gained in studies with these species has established principles which are useful in estimating the needs of others as well. The following discussions deal principally with the cow.

16.19. Variations in Milk Composition. While the milk of the individual cow tends to remain constant in composition, aside from fluctuations and cyclic changes in fat content, there are wide differences among individuals within a given breed as well as among the breeds themselves. Data are given in Table 16.3 on the average composition of milk of different fat contents. These data show that there is a regular increase in protein and ash with fat but that the lactose tends to decrease rather than otherwise. The large rise in energy value reflects the increasing fat level, primarily.

The data clearly show that the energy and protein requirements for milk production must be based on the composition of the milk. Since they increase with fat content, formulas can be devised for computing

much less readily accounted for, since this is dependent upon the quality of the protein in terms of its amino acid make-up.

16.24. The Biological Value of Protein for Lactation. The differences in the biological values of various proteins and combinations of them for growth, which modify the intakes required for this function according to the sources used, have been mentioned (Sec. 14.23). That similar differences exist as regards milk secretion is to be expected, since there is no evidence that the mammary gland has special powers for the synthesis of amino acids not possessed by other tissues of the body. In so far as farm animals are concerned, sows are the only ones for which differences in protein quality for lactation have been demonstrated. Here it appears that the kind or combinations of proteins that are efficient for growth are also efficient for milk production.

The evidence that protein quality is of much less importance for ruminants and the reasons therefore have been previously discussed. Carefully conducted feeding trials with milking cows have failed to reveal differences in efficiency among the protein combinations that show such differences in the case of nonruminants. They have shown, however, that urea and other simple nitrogen compounds can replace a part of the protein otherwise required for milk production. The nitrogen-balance procedure, which provides the most exact measure of the biological value of protein for growth, cannot be relied upon to produce significant data from lactation studies because there are variables that cannot be controlled. It seems probable that the nature of the protein fed is of some importance in the case of lactating ruminants, but it appears to be a minor consideration in selecting their rations. This is a field in which more critical studies are called for, guided by the information now obtainable by microbiological procedures as to the specific amino acid make-up of feeds and rations.

16.25. Protein Requirements as Measured by Feeding Trials. The protein requirements for milking cows recommended by current standards are based primarily on the results of feeding trials. Using combinations of feeds which are recognized to be satisfactory for milk production in other respects, the object has been to determine the protein intake which would certainly prove adequate for maximum production. Long-time feeding trials are essential for this purpose because an animal can keep up its production for an extended period, particularly in the first half of lactation, at the expense of its own tissues.

Haecker, whose long-time, pioneer studies have been referred to (Sec. 12.1), concluded that, allowing 0.7 lb. of digestible protein per 1000 lb. live weight for maintenance, an additional intake representing 138 per cent of that secreted in the milk was adequate for satisfactory production and condition. He rejected a lower figure, because he felt that it did not keep the animals in the best condition. In setting up a standard for practice, Haeker increased the figure of 138 per cent to 175 per cent to allow a "factor of safety."

Since the pioneer studies of Haecker, many other experiments have been conducted to determine the protein requirements for milk production. Harrison and Savage[35] made extensive studies in which concentrate mixtures containing 12, 16, 20, and 24 per cent of protein were fed with timothy–clover–mixed-hay and corn silage. In two studies extending over two complete lactation periods, the ration containing the 16 per cent protein grain mixture gave as satisfactory results as those containing more protein. It was concluded that, when 0.7 lb. per 1000 lb. live weight is allowed for maintenance, an additional intake corresponding to 128 per cent of that secreted in the milk, the level supplied by the 16 per cent combination, is adequate. In a later experiment by the alternation system, a ration containing a 12 per cent protein mixture proved definitely inadequate as compared with the higher levels. While no significant differences between the three higher levels were noticeable for any one year, considering the experiments as a whole, the investigators noted a distinct indication of a slightly larger production where the 20 per cent mixture was fed than was the case with the 16 per cent mixture. The ration containing the 20 per cent combination supplied 150 per cent of the protein in the milk, after deducting the allowance for maintenance.

16.26. Nitrogen-balance Data as Measures of Adequate Protein Nutrition. The fact that milk production can take place at the expense of body tissue has caused various workers to study the nitrogen balance as a further measure of the adequacy of intakes which were giving satisfactory production. When this has been done, it has generally been found that satisfactory production and nitrogen equilibrium can be maintained, at least over short periods, on intakes considerably below those recommended on the basis of feeding trials.

When the protein intake is reduced below the requirement, there may be a drop in production or its level may be maintained at the expense of the body and be reflected in a negative balance. Undoubtedly both take place over any long period on an inadequate protein intake. Such was found to be the case in a supplementary study of the ration containing the 12 per cent protein grain mixture used by Harrison and Savage. Clearly, nitrogen-balance data alone are not an adequate measure of a satisfactory protein intake for milk production, but they provide useful supplementary information in connection with feeding trials.

[35] E. S. Harrison and E. S. Savage, The effect of different planes of protein intake upon milk production, *Cornell Univ. Agr. Expt. Sta. Bull.* 504, 1932; E. S. Harrison, E. S. Savage, and S. H. Work, The effect of different planes of protein intake upon milk production. II. Further comparisons of 16-, 20-, and 24-per cent mixtures, *ibid.*, 578, 1933.

16.27. Protein Requirements for Practice. From a study of the various feeding trials reported, the N.R.C. committee decided that, in addition to the maintenance requirement of 0.6 lb. digestible protein per 1000 lb. body weight, the milking cow should receive, as digestible protein, approximately 135 per cent of the protein in the milk. The intakes which provide this amount for milks of different fat contents are set forth in the N.R.C. report. Despite the evidence that lower intakes have resulted in excellent production in several experiments, liberal allowances seem wise as general recommendations because of the indications that they may produce somewhat more milk under many conditions. From the standpoint of practice, however, the possible advantage of the higher level of intake may be overbalanced in many situations by the extra cost of high-protein feeds. The N.R.C. requirements for sows, ewes, and beef cows, covering both maintenance and lactation, are set forth in Appendix Tables I, IV, and V.

THE MINERAL REQUIREMENTS

Aside from the elements supplied by common salt, the minerals which most often require consideration in feeding rations to promote milk secretion are calcium and phosphorus. In some areas lack of copper and cobalt may limit performance. The other minerals which occur in milk are generally supplied adequately by the commonly used feeds.

16.28. Calcium and Phosphorus. Compounds of calcium and phosphorus make up approximately 50 per cent of the ash of milk, and thus its secretion requires a liberal supply of them in the ration. A cow producing 10,000 lb. of milk during her lactation secretes in it approximately 12 lb. of calcium and 10 lb. of phosphorus, and at the peak of her production the daily calcium output may exceed 30 g., with a somewhat smaller figure for phosphorus. These figures, however, do not represent the total requirements of the lactating animal because of the needs for maintenance, as well as for the pregnancy which normally occurs in the course of the lactation, and because of the fact that there is a large wastage of calcium and phosphorus in metabolism.

16.29. The Cycle of Calcium and Phosphorus Metabolism. Owing primarily to the pioneer and extensive work of Forbes and associates[36] begun in 1912 at the Ohio Experiment Station, it has come to be recognized that the natural and significant unit of time in the calcium and phosphorus metabolism of the dairy cow is the annual cycle of lactation and gestation. By means of balance experiments, Forbes found that the most liberal

[36] E. B. Forbes and F. M. Beegle, The mineral metabolism of the milch cow. I. *Ohio Agr. Expt. Sta. Bull.* 295, 1916; E. B. Forbes and associates, The mineral metabolism of the milch cow. II, *ibid.*, 308, 1917; E. B. Forbes, J. O. Halverson, and L. E. Morgan, The mineral metabolism of the milch cow. III, *ibid.*, 330, 1918.

feeding of calcium and phosphorus would commonly not meet the current needs of liberally producing cows during the first part of the lactation but that, toward the end of the lactation and particularly during the dry period, the earlier losses from the body ceased and were replaced by a storage of the elements. A similar cycle has been found to occur in lactating women, and there is evidence that the same is true for the rat and dog. Probably this depletion and restoration of the bone reserves are common occurrences in all mammals during the lactation cycle.

By continuous balance studies over the entire cycle of lactation and gestation both Ellenberger and coworkers[37] and Forbes and coworkers[38] have shown that liberally producing cows may be in negative calcium and phosphorus balance for extended periods early in lactation and still end the cycle with adequate body reserves of the minerals, as a result of storage later in the lactation and during the dry period. Data from one of the Vermont studies are presented in Fig. 16.4. This chart gives the record

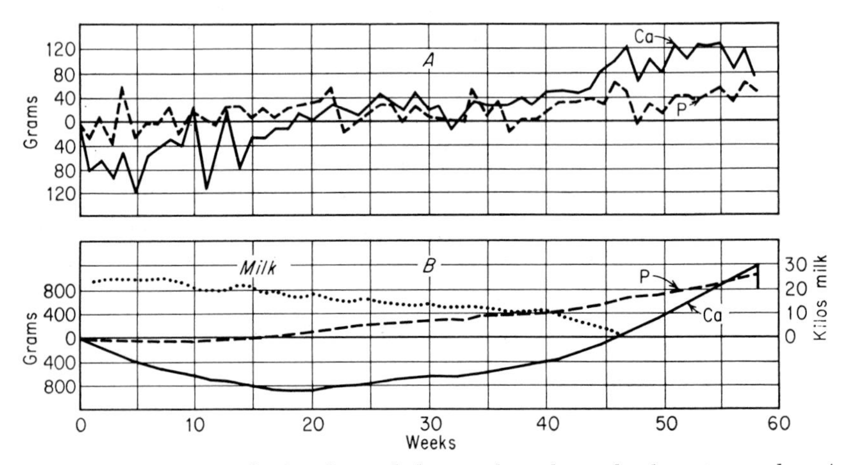

FIG. 16.4. Calcium and phosphorus balances throughout the lactation cycle. *A*, weekly balances of calcium and phosphorus. *B*, milk yield and cumulative balances of calcium and phosphorus. (*Ellenberger, Newlander, and Jones.*)

of a mature Ayrshire cow from the beginning of lactation over a period of 58 weeks until calving. She was in milk for 47 weeks and produced 11,254 lb. during this period. Her ration consisted of timothy hay, corn silage, and grain during the winter, but during the summer the silage was discontinued and fresh-cut grass was largely substituted for the hay. The

[37] H. B. Ellenberger, J. A. Newlander, and C. H. Jones, Calcium and phosphorus requirements of dairy cows. I. Weekly balances through lactation and gestation periods, *Vermont Agr. Expt. Sta. Bull.* 331, 1931; Calcium and phosphorous requirements of dairy cows. II. Weekly balances through lactation and gestation periods, *ibid.*, 342, 1932.

[38] Forbes and associates, *loc. cit.*

average daily intakes of calcium and phosphorus were approximately 45 and 60 g., respectively.

The weekly balances presented in the upper part of the chart, while showing considerable fluctuations, reveal losses of the elements, particularly of calcium, during the early weeks, in contrast to storages which regularly occurred during the last half of the period. The results over the period as a whole are better shown in the lower part of the chart, where the cumulative balances are presented. It is noted that the cow had lost calcium for 20 weeks and did not regain her losses completely until the forty-sixth week, a point which happened to coincide with the close of the lactation. During the following weeks, the calcium store accumulated rapidly. The curve for phosphorus shows a net loss through 12 weeks, followed by a storage which was accelerated as the decline in milk flow became more rapid. The dips in both curves at the end represent a subtraction of the minerals in the calf and placenta. Clearly, negative balances early in lactation do not necessarily mean that the ration is inadequate in calcium and phosphorus for the cycle as a whole, and it would appear that the utilization of reserves early in lactation is a normal process, not harmful to the animal provided the losses are not too great and provided they are fully made good later.

A similar cycle occurs in sheep, as is indicated by the extensive studies of Benzie and coworkers[39] of the skeletal changes in calcium and phosphorus during lactation. In the case of calcium, for example, with a daily intake of about 5 g. there was a loss of 6.5 per cent from the skeleton at mid-lactation, a loss that was fully replaced later. With an intake of 2 g., on the other hand, there was a loss of 18.2 per cent which was not replaced two months after the end of lactation. Replacement did occur, however, if the intake was raised to 5 g. at mid-lactation.

16.30. Effects of Calcium and Phosphorus Deficiencies. If, owing to an inadequate ration, the demands for calcium and phosphorus during lactation are in excess of the reserve supply, or if the losses are not made good, both the animal and her production eventually suffer. With rations which are extremely low in either of the minerals, the bones may become so impoverished in them as to break, destroying the usefulness of the animal. In less severe situations, the bones may become progressively weakened in succeeding lactations due to incomplete restoration of the losses, and thus it becomes increasingly difficult for the animal to keep up her milk flow. The production may fall off more rapidly than normal in a given lactation, or it may fail to reach previous levels in succeeding lacta-

[39] Benzie and coworkers, Studies of the skeleton of the sheep. II. The relationship between calcium intake and resorption and repair of the skeleton in pregnancy and lactation, *J. Agr. Sci.*, **48**:175–186, 1956. III. The relationship between phosphorus intake and resorption and repair of the skeleton in pregnancy and lactation, *ibid.*, **52**:1–12, 1959.

tions. The effect of small deficiencies of calcium and phosphorus may not become evident until after two or three or more years, the essential effect being to shorten the productive life of the animal.

Striking evidence of the effect on production of inadequate calcium and phosphorus nutrition has come from studies in the phosphorus-deficient areas. In South Africa[40] the feeding of bone meal to cows on deficient pasture increased the milk production by 40 per cent, while in Minnesota[41] the addition of phosphorus increased the yield by 50 to 146 per cent. It is estimated by the Minnesota authorities that the production losses in phosphorus-deficient areas cost the farmers over a million dollars in the five years prior to the discovery of the cause of the trouble. Undoubtedly the effect of phosphorus on appetite played a large role in these results. Severe calcium deficiency also causes serious effects, as reported from Florida by Becker and coworkers.[42] Owing to the very low content of this element in the roughages, broken hips and ribs were not an uncommon occurrence in the lactating animals. When the calcium intake was raised by the addition of bone meal, the yield, per lactation, increased by 50 per cent and the cows became more persistent producers. When they were slaughtered at the close of the experiment, tests of the bones revealed an excellent state of mineral storage. Depleted bones from an animal on the calcium-deficient ration are shown in Fig. 16.5.

To what extent a less severe and thus unnoticed bone depletion may limit milk production and productive life, by reason of rations inadequate in calcium and phosphorus, is unknown. In fact, it is possible that, even with the best mineral nutrition we know how to provide, productive life may be shortened by failure to meet the physiological demands of extremely high production. Evidence on the question would be very difficult to obtain.

The extent of the losses from the bones which can occur early in lactation without immediate detriment to production or the bones themselves, provided the losses are made good later, depends upon the state of the reserves at the start. It is clear that, in considering the entire cycle as a unit, we cannot ignore its various parts. The early losses of calcium and phosphorus can be kept at a minimum by liberal intakes at this time; in fact, some investigators have reported that cows producing from 60 to 80 lb. a day have been held in equilibrium either by the use of natural feeds rich in the minerals or by the addition of mineral supplements. While the majority of the experimental results show that such success is

[40] Arnold Theiler, H. H. Green, and P. J. du Toit, Phosphorus in the live stock industry, *Union S. Africa J. Dept. Agr.*, **8**:460–504, 1924.

[41] C. H. Eckles, T. W. Gullickson, and L. S. Palmer, Phosphorus deficiency in the rations of cattle, *Minnesota Agr. Expt. Sta. Tech. Bull.* 91, 1932.

[42] R. B. Becker, W. M. Neal, and A. L. Shealy, Effect of calcium-deficient roughages on the milk yield and bone strength of cattle, *J. Dairy Sci.*, **17**:1–10, 1934.

unusual, it is desirable to feed the minerals liberally so that excessive losses will certainly be avoided.

16.31. Calcium and Phosphorus Requirements. As a basis for estimating the requirements of the dairy cow, there are the annual balances previously discussed, data from slaughter experiments as to the state of

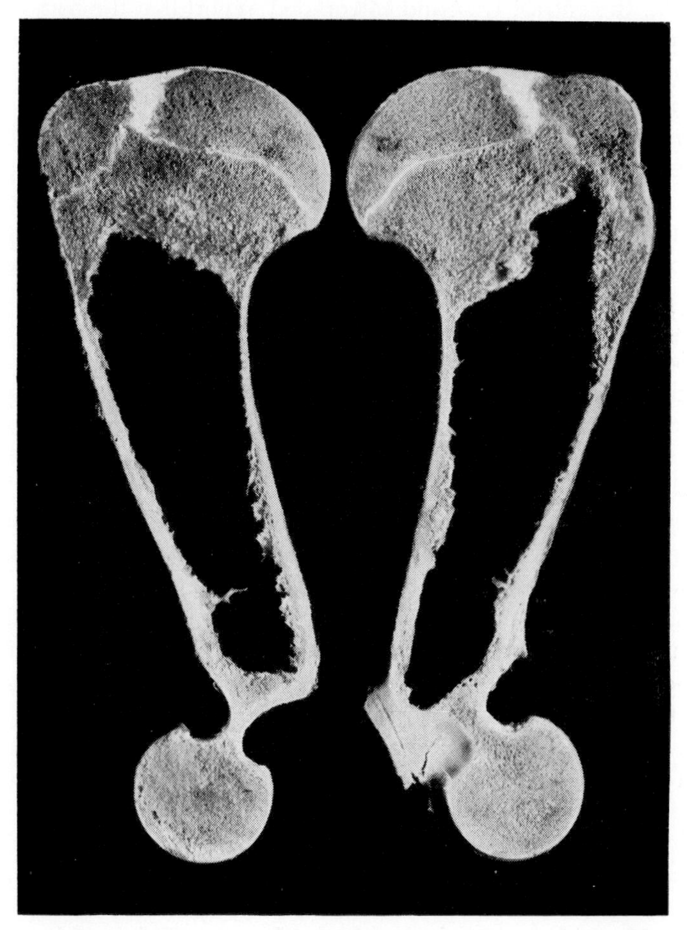

FIG. 16.5. Humeri depleted by a ration low in calcium. These bones were taken from a first-calf heifer. (*Courtesy of R. B. Becker, Florida Agricultural Experiment Station.*)

the bones after successive lactations and the results of long-time feeding trials. From the Vermont data, it is clear that 45 g. of calcium and 60 g. of phosphorus per day were certainly adequate for a cow producing around 11,000 lb. But they cannot be considered minimum values, especially in the case of phosphorus, in view of the net storages obtained. For a similar production, Forbes and associates, from their annual balances, express the view that a ration containing 39 g. of calcium and 33 g. of phosphorus is adequate. The phosphorus figure rests on the more certain basis. From slaughter experiments, Meigs and coworkers[43] reported that 25 g. of calcium was not quite adequate to maintain bones intact in successive lactations in cows producing around 6600 lb. of milk annually. In contrast Hart and coworkers[44] report that the bones of cows producing 10,000 to 12,000 lb. annually remained intact up to the fourth lactation on an average daily calcium intake of 25 to 28 g. and a phosphorus intake of 28 g. In this experiment timothy hay ranging from 0.35 to 0.5 per cent calcium was used. The lower value was employed in calculating the calcium figures reported. These calcium and phosphorus intakes could be supplied by rations which contain approximately 0.25 per cent of each of the elements in the dry matter. The figures suggested by Forbes and coworkers would require around 0.32 per cent of calcium and 0.3 per cent of phosphorus.

It is evident that expressing the requirements as averages for the cycle as a whole does not take account of the greatly varying demands according to the stage of lactation. While it is generally impossible to prevent losses from the bones during the height of secretion, it seems reasonable to provide intakes at this time in accordance with the amounts being secreted. Milk contains approximately 0.5 g. of calcium and 0.4 g. of phosphorus per pound. The intakes specified must allow for the wastage in assimilation, and the total allowances must also cover the needs of maintenance. The data for arriving at these figures are meager. Using 10 g. of phosphorus as the maintenance requirement for a 1000-lb. cow, Huffman and associates[45] concluded that there should be an additional allowance of 0.75 g. per pound of milk. The latter figure provides nearly double the amount secreted in the milk, and this provision seems wise in view of the losses in digestion and metabolism. On the same basis the calcium allowance per pound of milk should be 0.95 g., in addition to an estimated maintenance requirement of 8 g.

On the above basis a 1000-lb. cow producing 60 lb. of milk at the height of her lactation would require 65 g. of calcium and 55 g. of phosphorus. Huffman and associates concluded that the phosphorus intake should not go below 17 g. even when the cow is dry because of the needs for gestation as well as for maintenance. The same should be true for calcium.

[43] Edward B. Meigs and associates, The effects on calcium and phosphorus metabolism in dairy cows, of feeding low-calcium rations for long periods, *J. Agr. Research*, **51**:1–26, 1935.

[44] E. B. Hart, F. B. Hadley, and G. C. Humphrey, The relation of nutrition to contagious cattle abortion, *Wisconsin Agr. Expt. Sta. Research Bull.* 112, 1932.

[45] C. F. Huffman and associates, Phosphorous requirement of dairy cattle, when alfalfa furnishes the principal source of protein, *Michigan Agr. Expt. Sta. Tech. Bull.* 134, 1933.

Feeding in accordance with the allowances previously mentioned for maintenance and milk, with the 17 g. as the lower limit for either mineral would provide, in the case of the cow producing 10,000 lb., average intakes for the complete cycle close to those found adequate by Forbes and associates. This system of feeding would seem to be a satisfactory way of meeting the calcium and phosphorus requirements of the dairy cow. The N.R.C. recommendations of 1 g. of calcium and 0.7 g. of phosphorus per pound of milk are in accord with the above figures. When these requirements are expressed as percentages of the total ration, it is seen (Appendix Table III) that calcium should constitute 0.3 per cent and phosphorus 0.25 per cent of the ration for lactating cows.

There is no adequate basis for estimating the calcium and phosphorus needs of lactating ewes, sows, mares, or beef cows. Particular attention is needed in the case of the ewe and sow, since their milk is considerably richer in both calcium and phosphorus than is that of other species (Table 16.2). The N.R.C. requirements for these species and for beef cattle are set forth in Appendix Tables I, IV, and V.

In providing for the needs of lactating animals in practice, account must be taken of the composition of the feeds available, and in making up the ration, the same principles mentioned in connection with growth (Sec. 14.40) should apply.

16.32. Other Minerals. As is indicated in Table 16.2, milk contains considerable amounts of both sodium and chlorine. Studies have been cited in Sec. 7.25 showing that milk secretion is decreased by depriving lactating cows of salt and that the requirement for cows producing around 11,000 lb. per year is about 30 g. (1 oz.) per day in addition to that supplied in the feeds used. The addition of 1 per cent of salt to the grain mixture serves the double purpose of providing this needed mineral and increasing the palatability of the mixture. Giving cows free access to salt enables those who crave more to get it. This is obviously important when little or no grain is being fed.

While potassium is the mineral occurring in milk in the largest amount (Table 16.2), it is always abundantly supplied in the feeds of plant origin commonly consumed. As the lactating animal enters a new gestation, an iodine supplement is needed in iodine-deficient areas (Sec. 15.12). While the evidence of specific need is less clear, lactating animals, in areas where copper and cobalt have been found deficient in terms of growth and health, should receive supplements of those minerals.

THE ROLES OF VITAMINS IN LACTATION

Vitamins are important in lactation both as essential nutrients for the physiological process involved and as components of the secretion itself.

16.33. Vitamin A Value of Milk. The cow on its natural herbivorous ration receives vitamin A only in the form of carotene. A portion of the carotene ingested is secreted in milk as such, and a portion is transformed into vitamin A and so secreted. The more yellow the milk and butter, the larger the amount of carotene present, but this is not a true measure of vitamin A value for it gives no information as to the amount of the vitamin present as such. Jersey and Guernsey milk has much more color than Holstein milk because these cows convert a smaller proportion of their carotene intake into the vitamin. Most of the vitamin value of their milk is due to carotene, whereas Holstein milk contains less of the pigment and more of the colorless vitamin. As a result, when the cows are fed the same ration, Holstein butterfat has fully as high a vitamin A value as that from Jerseys or Guernseys despite the marked difference in color. The difference in degree of carotene conversion is also reflected in larger amounts of pigment in the adipose tissue and skin secretions. The extent of the conversion varies among individuals as well as among breeds. Those species which secrete a colorless milk (Sec. 16.16) make a complete conversion, and thus the vitamin value of their fat may be very high though no color is present.

Aside from the contribution which can temporarily be made by the reserves, the vitamin A value of milk is entirely dependent upon the amount present in the feed, and very large variations in the potency may accordingly occur. The amount found in the milk may be several times as great on feeds high in carotene as on feeds which contain very little. Of the natural feeds, pasture results in the richest milk, but nearly as large a potency can be obtained by feeding properly cured alfalfa, dried grass, or corn silage. Much higher potencies are also produced by feeding concentrated sources of the vitamin, notably shark-liver oil.

Despite the large differences in the vitamin A potency of milk according to the nature of the diet, the percentage of the intake that appears in the milk is very small. In the various experiments carried out, the percentage recovery has seldom exceeded 3 per cent.

It is evident that the vitamin value of milk can vary widely depending upon the nature of the feed, which commonly reflects the season in which the milk is produced. Dornbush and associates[46] have reported a study of carotene and vitamin A content of Wisconsin market milk by months throughout the year. The data reveal minima of 3.1 μg. of carotene and 7.2 μg. of preformed vitamin A per gram of butterfat in March and April, respectively. The maxima of 9.9 μg. of carotene and 12.8 μg. of vitamin A occurred in September. The total vitamin A potency per quart was 1060 I.U. in March and 2005 I.U. in September.

[46] A. C. Dornbush and associates, The carotene and vitamin A content of market milks, *J. Am. Med. Assoc.*, **114**:1748–1751, 1940.

A very comprehensive study of the vitamin A potency of the butter produced throughout the United States, in which the U.S. Department of Agriculture and the experiment stations of 20 states cooperated, has been carried out. A summary of the data has been issued by the U.S. Department of Agriculture.[47] This summary gives the weighted averages for winter and summer butter as 11,160 I.U. and 17,955 I.U. per pound, respectively. The weighted average of the annual production is 15,529 I.U. Winter milk had 1140 I.U. per quart (4 per cent fat basis), and summer milk, 1800 I.U. The average potency of the total annual production was found to be 1530 I.U. per quart. The report points to the fact that much of the summer milk has a potency from 2500 to 3000 I.U. as evidence that much can be accomplished in improving the average level of the annual output by appropriate feeding practices. Neither pasteurization nor irradiation decreases the vitamin A value of milk. Butter does not lose vitamin A or carotene in good commercial storage.

16.34. Vitamin A Requirements. It is clear that the animal nursing young should receive a liberal intake of vitamin A in order that its milk may contain an adequate amount for the nutrition of its offspring, at least until they are able to obtain this vitamin from supplementary foods. This is particularly true because the newborn generally has little reserve of the vitamin in its body even though the mother may have been fed liberally during pregnancy. The latter feeding does provide stores in the body of the mother which will be drawn upon for her milk and which lessen accordingly the necessity of large intakes during lactation. Unless the cow is fed for an extended period on very poor roughage, there should be no practical problem in meeting the needs of the suckling offspring, particularly when the calf is given access early to green, leafy roughage. The same should be true for lambs and colts. In the case of pigs, which are dependent on their mother's milk for a relatively longer period, the proper feeding of the mother may be of greater importance. Her needs should be met by selecting her ration in accordance with the same principles mentioned in the discussion of reproduction (Sec. 15.14). The needs of the dairy calf, which is early changed from whole milk to skim milk or a "calf starter," have been discussed (Sec. 14.43).

The mature animal requires vitamin A for various body functions, but whether this need increases for the specific function of lactation apart from the demand for secretion in the milk has not been definitely proved. Clearly, the first effect of a deficient diet is a lowering of the vitamin content of the milk. One would expect any eventual effect on production itself to be accompanied by signs of deficiency in the lactating animal. Several experiments have clearly shown that feeding massive doses of vitamin A as a supplement to rations containing adequate amounts for

[47] Anonymous, Vitamin A in butter, *U.S. Dept. Agr. Misc. Publ.* 571, 1945.

reproduction does not increase milk yield, though greatly increasing the level of the vitamin in the milk. For example, Blaxter and associates[48] fed 30 to 60 g. of shark-liver oil (80,000 I.U. per gram) daily with no effect on milk or fat yield, but the vitamin A content of the fat was increased by 1100 to 1850 per cent.

The N.R.C. requirements for lactation which, in the case of beef cows, ewes, and sows, are considered to provide an adequate level in the milk for the nutrition of the young are set forth in the Appendix Tables. For dairy cows the N.R.C. report states that the amount specified for reproduction (Sec. 15.14) should suffice for maximum milk production, though higher intakes would increase the level in milk.

16.35. Vitamin D. The early studies of Forbes (Sec. 16.29), showing that the negative calcium and phosphorus balances at the height of lactation could not be eliminated by increasing the content of these minerals in the ration, were made before vitamin D was known. With the discovery of its role in the improvement of calcium and phosphorus retention, investigations were undertaken with the expectation that the addition of this vitamin to the ration would do away with the negative balances previously noted. Some initial experiments with goats supported this viewpoint, but more extensive studies with cows gave only negative results. Sun-cured hay, cod-liver oil, irradiated yeast, or any other source of vitamin D, including direct irradiation, was found ineffective in preventing the losses of calcium and phosphorus which occurred in the liberally producing cow early in lactation, although the vitamin was absorbed and its level in the milk increased. Extensive studies of this question have been reported by Hart and associates.[49]

Wallis[50] has clearly demonstrated that dairy cows require vitamin D for lactation. Cows kept out of the sunlight and fed a ration in which molasses beet pulp replaced the hay and which was otherwise practically devoid of the vitamin eventually developed striking deficiency symptoms. These experiments cannot be considered to cast doubt, however, on the

[48] K. L. Blaxter, S. K. Kon, and S. Y. Thompson, The effect of feeding shark-liver oil to cows on the yield and composition and on the vitamin A and carotene content of the milk, *J. Dairy Research*, **14**:225–230, 1946.

[49] E. B. Hart, H. Steenbock, E. C. Teut, and G. C. Humphrey, Dietary factors influencing calcium assimilation. XI. The influence of cod-liver oil on calcium metabolism of milking cows, *J. Biol. Chem.*, **84**:359–365, 1929; XII. A study of the influence of hays cured with varying exposure to sunlight on the calcium metabolism of milking cows, *ibid.*, **84**:367–376, 1929. E. B. Hart, H. Steenbock, O. L. Kline, and G. C. Humphrey, Dietary factors influencing calcium assimilation. XIII. The influence of irradiated yeast on the calcium and phosphorus metabolism of milking cows, *ibid.*, **86**:145–155, 1930.

[50] G. C. Wallis, Some effects of vitamin D deficiency on mature dairy cows, *J. Dairy Sci.*, **21**:315–333, 1938; Vitamin-D deficiency in dairy cows, *South Dakota Agr. Expt. Sta. Bull.* 372, 1944.

earlier findings of Hart and associates that under normal conditions of feeding and management supplementary vitamin D will not materially benefit the calcium and phosphorus metabolism of the milking cow.

Hibbs and Pounden[51] have reported that feeding massive doses of vitamin D (30,000,000 I.U. per day) for 3 to 7 days prepartum and 1 day postpartum seemed to be effective in preventing milk fever in cows.

In the case of women, some investigators have reported a marked improvement in the calcium and phosphorus balances of lactation by feeding cod-liver oil, while others have noted little effect. Clearly, neither a uniform nor a complete response can be counted on. The N.R.C. recommendation for sows is 60 I.U. of vitamin D per pound of feed. There appears to be no basis for specific recommendations in the case of other farm animals. There is no reason for believing that the needs exceed those during growth and reproduction or that otherwise good rations require any supplementation, particularly in view of the role of sunlight.

No milk produced from natural feeds is a rich source of vitamin D in terms of the needs of the growing young. As a result of many studies, there is rather complete information as to the range of vitamin D content found in the milk of different breeds and under different conditions. For example, the following data were obtained by Bechtel and Hoppert[52] from a two-year study of the milk of the Guernseys and Holsteins in the Michigan College herd. In tests at monthly intervals, vitamin D values ranging from 4.8 to 43.8 U.S.P. units per quart were found in Guernsey milk, while for Holsteins the range was from 3.1 to 28 units. The highest value occurred in the summer and the lowest in winter, and there was a close correlation between the hours of sunshine and the vitamin level, indicating that sunlight was the principal factor involved in the variations. There was little difference in the potencies of the butterfats of the two breeds; thus the Guernsey milk was richer because of its higher fat content.

These variations in potency indicate that the vitamin D content of milk is under physiological control, but no system of feeding, other than massive intakes of the vitamin, has been found effective in increasing the potency above the normal summer level. Cod-liver-oil concentrates and irradiated ergosterol are more effective, but very large intakes are required to produce a relatively small change in the milk. Feeding cod-liver oil to the human mother will not cure rickets in the suckling infant. Experiments in which the cow has been irradiated have generally failed to increase the vitamin D content of the milk, but the studies of Campion

[51] J. W. Hibbs and W. D. Pounden, Studies on milk fever in dairy cows. IV. Prevention by short-time, prepartum feeding of massive doses of vitamin D, *J. Dairy Sci.*, **38**:65–72, 1955.

[52] H. Ernest Bechtel and C. A. Hoppert, A study of the seasonal variation of vitamin D in normal cow's milk, *J. Nutrition*, **11**:537–549, 1936.

and associates[53] have proved that the higher potency of milk produced by cows on pasture is due primarily to the action of sunshine.

16.36. Vitamin D Milk. The best milk that can be produced in summer or on any ration of natural feeds falls far short of meeting the requirements of children for protection against rickets.

The recognition of this fact and the discovery of methods of enriching milk to the effective level by direct irradiation or by feeding irradiated yeast to the cow have resulted in the production and use of vitamin D milk. This development has received the approval of medical authorities and nutritionists because, despite the knowledge of other effective methods of preventing rickets, the disease persisted unduly. It was felt that, if the vitamin were adequately supplied in a product which formed a considerable part of the daily diet of children, a more certain way of ensuring the needed intake would be provided.

The standard for vitamin D milk calls for a minimum level of 400 I.U. per quart. This level can be obtained either by irradiating the milk or by feeding irradiated yeast to the cow. Vitamin D milk can also be provided by the direct addition of a cod-liver-oil concentrate, activated ergosterol, or 7-dehydrocholesterol. This procedure is the one which has entirely displaced the others in practice because of the greater ease of control in providing the required level.

16.37. Vitamin E. Cow milk normally contains 20 to 35 mg. of vitamin E per gram of fat. The level can be increased by feeding tocopherols. It drops on rations very poor in the vitamin. Experimentally, muscular dystrophy has been produced in suckling rats by feeding a diet devoid of the vitamin. In the Cornell studies with suckling lambs previously described (Sec. 8.19) the blood serum, colostrum, and milk of mothers of the lambs which developed dystrophy were low in vitamin E. It has also been reported that pigs from sows on rations experimentally designed to be low in the vitamin exhibited muscular incoordination. Further studies in this general area, with particular reference to practical applications, are needed. Reference has been made in Sec. 8.21 to the wide distribution of total tocopherols in livestock feeds.

Krukovsky and associates[54] have shown that milk high in tocopherol content is more resistant to the development of oxidized flavors, and the levels of the vitamin in the milk were found to vary with the character of the ration. Thus tocopherols may be nutrients of importance from the standpoint of the stability and quality of market milk.

16.38. Thiamine. The physiological needs for thiamine increase in accordance with the amount of milk secreted because of its role in energy

[53] John Edward Campion et al., The source of vitamin D in summer milk, *Biochem. J.*, **31**:81–88, 1937.

[54] V. N. Krukovsky, J. K. Loosli, and F. Whiting, The effect of tocopherols and cod liver oil on the stability of milk, *J. Dairy Sci.*, **32**:196–201, 1949.

metabolism and because of its content in the milk. These needs present no dietary problem in cattle and sheep because of rumen synthesis. The N.R.C. requirement for sows is set at 0.5 mg. per pound of feed. In non-ruminants the thiamine content of the milk secreted drops when the ration is deficient in the vitamin. There is a low ceiling, however, above which the level cannot be raised no matter how much thiamine is added to the diet. The average level in cow milk is shown in Table 16.4 along with

TABLE 16.4. B-VITAMINS IN RAW WHOLE MILK*
(μg. per 100 ml.)

Thiamine	35 to 40	Vitamin B_6	50 to 60
Riboflavin	150 to 170	Biotin	2 to 5
Niacin	80 to 90	Choline	13,000 to 15,000
Pantothenic acid	300 to 400	Inositol	13,000 to 18,000
Vitamin B_{12}	0.3 to 0.4	Folic acid	0.1 to 0.4

* Data from S. K. Kon and K. M. Henry, Nutritive value of milk and milk products, *J. Dairy Research,* **16**:68–127, 1949; *ibid.,* **21**:245–298, 1954.

data for the other B-vitamins. These data are based largely on the extensive review by Kon and Henry on the nutritive value of milk and milk products. The nature of the feed has little influence on the thiamine content of the milk of ruminants. Commercial pasteurization commonly destroys 10 to 20 per cent of the level in cow milk, though this loss can be reduced below 5 per cent by careful control. Milk is not a rich source of thiamine in terms of human needs, a quart furnishing less than one-quarter of the recommended allowance for an active man.

16.39. Riboflavin. The story with respect to riboflavin is similar to that for thiamine. Ruminants need no dietary source, but sows do require a supply in their feed. The N.R.C. requirement for the sow is 1.5 mg. per pound of feed. For those species requiring it in the diet, the level in the milk varies markedly according to the feed supply. The nature of the feed does have some influence on the level in cow milk also. The average range found in this milk is shown in Table 16.4. In contrast to thiamine, cow milk is a rich source of riboflavin in terms of human needs, a quart as drawn containing enough to meet the full daily allowance of a physically active man. The milk which reaches the consumer, however, may have a markedly lower value because of exposure to sunlight. Bottled milk has been found to lose as much as three-fourths of its riboflavin in 2 hr. in bright sunlight.

16.40. Other B-vitamins. The contents of several other B-vitamins in cow milk are shown in Table 16.4. The levels in this milk are little influenced by the feed, but some of them are variable according to breed, stage of lactation, and season. Dietary intakes are of no importance in the case of ruminants. The N.R.C. has set forth requirements for the sow in the cases of niacin, B_{12}, and pantothenic acid. The quantitative needs for the others listed in Table 16.4 have not been established.

16.41. Ascorbic Acid. In those species requiring vitamin C in the diet, its level in the milk depends on the dietary supply. Its level in cow milk is affected somewhat by breed and seasonal influences but not by the ration. Only a small part of the total amount secreted is found in the market milk that reaches the consumer. As drawn from the udder the product contains 2.0 to 2.5 mg. per 100 ml., practically all in the reduced form. In contrast, Stewart and Sharp[55] have reported a survey showing that market milk in consumers' homes or retail stores contained 0.58 mg. per 100 ml. (0.34 mg. in the reduced form and 0.24 mg. as dehydroascorbic acid). Thus approximately three-fourths is lost in pasteurization and other marketing operations. Exposure to light is an even more destructive factor in the case of ascorbic acid than of riboflavin. Stewart and Sharp found that reconstituted powdered whole milk had twice as much vitamin C as the pasteurized fresh product. The losses from pasteurization and light exposure, which customarily occur in the processing and marketing of fresh milk, can be reduced to a minimum by appropriate procedures.

16.42. Unidentified Lactation Factors. There have been various reports in the literature during the past twenty-five years of factors required for lactation in addition to those definitely established as essential for growth. None of these "alleged factors" have been definitely identified, and thus their existence remains in doubt.

SELECTED LITERATURE

Barnhart, C. E., Damon Catron, and C. C. Culbertson: The effect of rations on selected vitamin content of sow's milk, *J. Animal Sci.*, **13**:375–382, 1954.

Evans, D. Elizabeth: Milk composition of mammals whose milk is not normally used for human consumption, *Dairy Sci. Abstr.*, **21**:277–288, 1959.

Folley, S. J.: The Physiology and Biochemistry of Lactation, Oliver and Boyd, Ltd., Edinburgh and London, 1955.

Hildith, T. P., and H. Jasperson: The component acids of milk fats of the goat, ewe and mare, *Biochem. J.*, **38**:443–447, 1944.

Jordan, W. H., and C. G. Jenter: The source of milk fat, *New York (Geneva) Agr. Expt. Sta. Bull.* 132, 1897.

———, ———, and F. D. Fuller: The food source of milk fat; with studies on the nutrition of milch cows, *New York (Geneva) Agr. Expt. Sta. Bull.* 197, 1901.

Keith, T. B., Henry Melendy, and R. F. Johnson: The performance of the pregnant and lactating ewe as affected by phosphorus sources and quantity, *Idaho Agr. Expt. Sta. Res. Bull.* 29, 1955.

Kleiber, Max, and associates: Propionate as a precursor of milk constituents in the intact dairy cow, *J. Biol. Chem.*, **203**:339–346, 1953.

[55] A. P. Stewart, Jr., and P. F. Sharp, Vitamin C content of market milk, evaporated milk, and powdered whole milk, *J. Nutrition*, **31**:161–174, 1946.

Kon, S. K., and E. H. Mawson: Human milk, *Med. Research Council (Brit.) Spec. Rept. Ser.*, No. 269, 1950.

Krukovsky, V. N., and associates: Influence of roughages on certain biochemical properties of milk, *J. Dairy Sci.*, **37**:1–9, 1954.

Linton, R. G.: The composition of mare's milk, *J. Agr. Sci.*, **21**:669–688, 1931.

Loosli, J. K., L. A. Maynard, and H. L. Lucas: Further studies of the influence of different levels of fat intake upon milk secretion. IV. *Cornell Univ. Agr. Expt. Sta. Mem.* 265, 1944.

Lucas, H. L., and J. K. Loosli: The effect of fat upon the digestion of nutrients by dairy cows, *J. Animal Sci.*, **3**:3–11, 1944.

———, ———, and L. A. Maynard: A study of the effect of dietary fat and fat-soluble vitamins upon milk and fat secretion, *Cornell Univ. Agr. Expt. Sta. Mem.* 251, 1943.

McGillivray, W. A., and J. W. G. Porter: Nutritional value of milk and milk products, *J. Dairy Research*, **25**:344–361, 1958.

Maynard, L. A., and E. Rasmussen: The influence of dietary fat on lactation performance in rats, *J. Nutrition*, **23**:385–398, 1942.

Putnam, P. A., and J. K. Loosli: Effect of feeding different ratios of roughage to concentrate upon milk production and digestibility of the ration, *J. Dairy Sci.*, **42**:1070–1078, 1959.

Smith, Vearl R.: Physiology of Lactation, 5th ed., Iowa State University Press, Ames, Iowa, 1959.

Trimberger, G. W., and coworkers: Forage intake and efficiency of feed utilization in dairy cattle, *J. Dairy Sci.*, **43**:1275–1281, 1960.

Visek, W. J., and associates: Calcium metabolism in dairy cows as studied with Ca^{45}, *J. Dairy Sci.*, **36**:373–384, 1953.

Chapter 17
Work Production

The previous discussions of nutritive requirements have dealt with the production and maintenance of body tissue and with the formation of products composed of nutrients such as milk and eggs. Body maintenance involves the performance of internal work in respiration, circulation, and other vital processes. It also includes a certain amount of external work represented by the voluntary activity of the animal and assessed as the activity factor (Sec. 13.8) when maintenance is estimated from basal metabolism. The work performed by the horse and also by the manual laborer is so greatly in excess of that which properly belongs to maintenance as to call for a special consideration of its physiology and nutritive requirements. The daily energy requirement of the horse or man at hard work is approximately double the maintenance need, while the maximum work which can be performed during a short period may involve a metabolism ten times as great as at rest. While the use of the horse for work production has greatly declined, the nutritional factors involved in muscular activity remain an important field for study. An extreme example has been cited in Sec. 13.11, namely, grazing dairy cows were found to expend 40 per cent more energy than when housed in the barn.

17.1. Nutrients Involved in Muscle Activity. The muscles are the agencies by which mechanical work is performed. In their contraction, nutrients are catabolized. The early physiologists considered that the muscle was broken down in the process, and since the muscle was known to consist mostly of protein, the assumption arose that protein yielded the energy for the work done. Such was Liebig's view. For many years he taught that work production involved an increased excretion of nitrogenous end products and, therefore, required an increased intake of protein in accordance with the amount of work performed. Because of his eminence Liebig's views continued to be accepted, though apparently not based upon experimental results, even after Voit showed in 1860 that work could be performed by a dog without increasing the protein catabolism.

In 1866 Fick and Wislicenus ascended a Swiss mountain 6418 ft. high after having abstained from nitrogenous food for 17 hr. and measured their urea output before and during the ascent. They found no considerable increase in the output while the work was being performed, and their calculations revealed that the total nitrogen excretion could account for only a fraction of the catabolism which must have occurred to furnish the energy needed for the work done. In 1879 Kellner showed that, as long as the total amount of feed of the work horse was ample, the protein catabolism was not increased by work. If, however, the feed was restricted and the work was increased to the point where the animal lost flesh, then a larger nitrogen excretion occurred. Thus it gradually came to be accepted that the muscle is not broken down in work and that its energy is normally supplied by nonnitrogenous food but that, if the food supply is insufficient, body protein as well as fat may be drawn on.

17.2. The Chemistry of Muscle Action. The conversion of glycogen to lactic acid has long been recognized as the outstanding chemical reaction occurring in muscle contracting anaerobically (in the absence of oxygen). The primary source of muscle energy, however, is derived from adenosine triphosphate (ATP) (Sec. 3.7). The contraction of the muscle fibers appears to be brought about by the direct reaction between ATP and the muscle proteins.

$$\text{(1)} \quad \text{ATP} + \text{muscle proteins} \longrightarrow \text{contraction of muscle} + \text{ADP}$$

Muscle contains only small quantities of ATP, but normally its level is maintained through the intervention of creatine phosphate (phosphocreatine, or "phosphagen"), another compound containing a high-energy phosphate bond and present in muscle tissue in relatively large amounts.

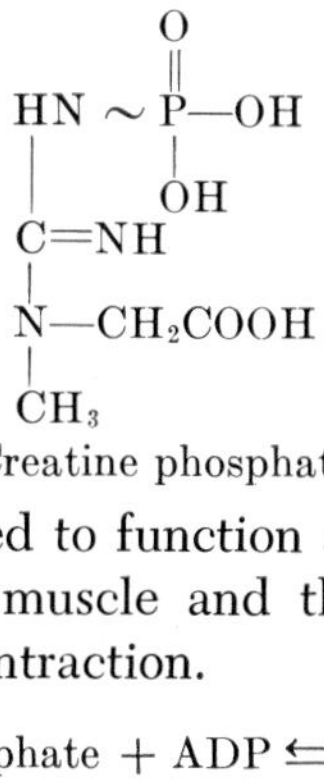

```
        O
        ‖
HN ~ P—OH
|       |
|       OH
C=NH
|
N—CH2COOH
|
CH3
```

Creatine phosphate

Creatine phosphate is believed to function as a reserve or depot of high-energy phosphate bonds in muscle and thus to maintain the level of ATP for continued muscle contraction.

$$\text{(2)} \quad \text{Creatine phosphate} + \text{ADP} \rightleftarrows \text{ATP} + \text{creatine}$$

Although the primary energy of muscle contraction is derived from ATP, the ultimate source of energy is carbohydrate (muscle glycogen). Glycogen in the presence of phosphoric acid and the enzyme phosphorylase undergoes phosphorolysis and breakdown, stepwise, through a series of controlled chemical reactions, involving hexose and triose phosphates, to pyruvic acid (anaerobic cycle). In the absence of oxygen, pyruvic acid goes to lactic acid. Normally, however, in mammalian muscle with an intact blood circulation and thus well supplied with oxygen, very little lactic acid appears to be formed. The pyruvic acid is completely oxidized to CO_2 and H_2O (aerobic or tricarboxylic acid cycle). Any lactic acid or excess pyruvic acid formed diffuses into the circulation and is transported to the liver where it is converted to liver glycogen.

The energy resulting from the breakdown of glycogen to pyruvic acid has been demonstrated to be liberated and trapped in the high-energy phosphate bonds of ATP. It is believed that, likewise, the large amount of energy released by the oxidation of pyruvic acid to CO_2 and H_2O is captured in the form of ATP. The excess, over and above the immediate cellular needs, is used for synthetic purposes, e.g., conversion of blood sugar to muscle glycogen, and for storage as readily available energy in the form of creatine phosphate. The latter process has been indicated by the reversible reaction previously shown (2).

Thus, the sequence of chemical events in muscle contraction are as follows: (1) ATP breaks down to ADP to supply the immediate energy. (2) Creatine phosphate splits, furnishing energy for the resynthesis and maintenance of ATP. Subsequently muscle glycogen decomposes, the energy becoming available as ATP. In the absence of oxygen, lactic acid is formed and eventually converted to liver glycogen. Normally, in the presence of oxygen, pyruvic acid resulting from glycogen breakdown is oxidized to CO_2 and H_2O, by a series of enzyme actions. One of the most important requires thiamine pyrophosphate as its coenzyme. The energy of the process appears as heat and in a form (ATP) which can be used for work by living cells. In the muscle the excess, over and above the immediate requirements for the contraction, is used to phosphorylate creatine to make creatine phosphate.

Thus the process is not the same as occurs in the heat engine where the fuel burns before the work is done. Rather, it is analogous to the operation of a storage battery. Contraction takes place as a result of a discharge of energy stored in the muscle. "Charging" occurs during the recovery period with energy obtained by oxidation. The muscle differs from the heat engine in another fundamental respect. The heat produced by the engine provides the energy for the work accomplished, while in the muscle the energy which appears as heat is entirely a waste.

Although it is convenient to evaluate foods and body products in terms of heat units, it should be remembered that the body is in no sense a heat engine.

The fact that an anaerobic reaction furnishes the immediate energy for muscle contraction and that recovery can occur anaerobically by means of the energy supplied by lactic acid formation makes it possible for muscle action to take place temporarily without oxygen. The process is stopped by the accumulation of lactic acid. Then oxidation is required to remove the acid and to furnish energy for building up the system so it can start again. The anaerobic mechanism also means that the muscle can temporarily do much more work than represented by the amount of oxygen currently required to accomplish it. When this occurs, the deficit of oxygen is spoken of as the *oxygen debt.* This provision of nature enables a man or an animal to exert itself eight or ten times as strenuously as would be possible if all of the oxygen had to be supplied currently. A well-trained athlete cannot take in more than about 4 liters of oxygen per minute, yet he can temporarily perform work which would require oxygen at the rate of 30 liters per minute since it is possible for him to go into oxygen debt. The same is true for the horse.

17.3. Units of Work and Power. Work done may be measured in *foot-pounds,* and power, the rate of doing work, may be measured in *foot-pounds per second.* The development of 1 *horsepower* (hp.), also a unit of power, necessitates the performance of work at the rate of 33,000 ft.-lb. per minute. The work done in moving a body is measured by the product of the force required and the distance the body moves along the line of action of the force. Suppose that a horse must exert a force of 200 lb. to pull a load at a speed of 3 miles per hour (264 ft. per minute). In pulling the load a distance of 264 ft. the horse does 52,800 ft.-lb. of work. Since the work is done in 1 min., the power developed is simply 52,800 ft.-lb. per minute, and if this is divided by 33,000, the result is approximately 1.6 hp. One horsepower-hour, also a unit of work, is the energy expended when work is done at the rate of 1 hp. for 1 hr. It is thus $33{,}000 \times 60$, or 1,980,000 ft.-lb. In studying the energy efficiency of work production, it is convenient to translate foot-pounds into kilocalories, using the factor 1 ft.-lb. = 0.000324 kcal.

17.4. Efficiency of Muscle Work. The mechanical efficiency of the animal machine can be computed even as is true for the heat engine. It represents the percentage of the chemical energy used which can be transformed into useful work. The *gross,* or *over-all,* efficiency is defined by the following equation:

$$\text{Gross efficiency} = \frac{\text{mechanical work accomplished}}{\text{total energy expended while working}}$$

It is obvious that only a part of the total energy consumed is actually used for the production of useful work. A portion must serve for the usual processes of maintenance; another portion is dissipated by the increased internal activities, such as circulation and respiration, which are demanded by muscle action; and a further portion is used up in waste movements. Not more than 40 per cent of the energy consumed by the muscle is actually transformed into work. The rest appears as heat in connection with the exothermic chemical processes previously mentioned. The gross efficiency which is shown by the man or horse, while working is approximately 25 per cent. This is a high figure, however, compared with the steam or gas engine but low compared with the diesel engine according to the following figures from Hill:

Steam engine without condenser	7.5 per cent
Steam engine with condenser	9 to 19 per cent
Gas engine	14 to 18 per cent
Diesel engine	29 to 35 per cent

SOURCE: A. V. Hill, Muscular Movements in Man, Cornell University Press, Ithaca, N.Y., 1927.

It is a high figure also compared with the ignition-type tractor, which has an efficiency for draft of approximately 13 per cent in experiments by Brackett and associates.[1] The diesel-type tractor has an efficiency of 22 per cent at the drawbar.

In comparing the horse and tractor, however, it must be borne in mind that the horse can work only part of the time. Its true efficiency for farm labor is what it can accomplish regularly in a 24-hr. day. Brody and Cunningham[2] found the *all-day* efficiency, as measured by metabolism data, of a horse working 8 hr. a day to be 14 per cent. Morrison[3] has arrived at the lower figure of 8.9 per cent, by calculating the amount of work which a 1500-lb. horse could be expected to accomplish daily and the amount of feed which should represent a satisfactory allowance. The N.R.C. report for horses gives a calculated figure of 12.6 per cent but concludes that in practice most horses work at an all-day gross efficiency below this figure. Because of its capacity for incurring oxygen debt the horse can work for short periods at a much higher efficiency than represented by the 25 per cent figure.

Another measure which is used in studies of work production is the *net efficiency*. Here the work accomplished is calculated as a percent-

[1] E. Brackett, C. W. Smith, E. B. Lewis, Carlton L. Zink, and C. F. Adams, Nebraska tractor tests, 1930–1934, *Nebraska Agr. Expt. Sta. Bull.* 292, 1935.

[2] Samuel Brody and Richard Cunningham, Growth and development. XL. Comparison between efficiency of horse, man, and motor, with special reference to size and monetary economy, *Missouri Agr. Expt. Sta. Research Bull.* 244, 1936.

[3] Frank B. Morrison, Feeds and Feeding, 22nd ed., Morrison Publishing Company, Ithaca, N.Y., 1956, p. 823.

age of the total energy intake minus that used for maintenance. Such a figure is a truer measure of the muscular efficiency, since it eliminates the overhead expenditure of maintaining the body as a whole. Certain questions arise as to just what should be deducted from the gross expenditure. Should the deduction represent merely the metabolism of the resting animal, or should certain movements which are normally made by the idle animal and which do not result in useful work be included in the deduction? Such questions are of minor importance if the same basis is used where efficiencies are compared. Brody defines net efficiency by the following equation:

$$\text{Net efficiency} = \frac{\text{work done}}{\text{total energy used} - \text{energy of standing animal}}$$

As a comparative measure, net efficiency has the advantage over gross efficiency in being less affected by variations in the intensity and amount of work done over a given period. Net efficiency thus becomes of the order of 35 per cent, compared with the 25 per cent gross figure. Brody defines the *absolute efficiency* as follows:

$$\text{Absolute efficiency} = \frac{\text{work accomplished}}{\text{energy expended above that of walking without load}}$$

The figure thus arrived at approaches the maximum of 40 per cent.

17.5. Measurement of Energy Expended in Work. Zuntz was a pioneer in measuring the energy expended by horses in different kinds of work. Using the respiration apparatus which he devised, he was able to arrive at the energy output by indirect calorimetry. He used a tread power which could be set at various inclinations for measuring the work required for different degrees of ascent. Provision was made for driving the power by a steam engine so that locomotion only could be studied. The energy requirements for carrying various loads were measured. By determining the energy output during rest as well as during work, the amount needed in excess of maintenance and the net efficiency were computed. Many of these experiments are reported by Zuntz and Lehmann.[4]

Brody and associates have conducted somewhat similar studies. Some data taken from one of their experiments are presented in Table 17.1 to illustrate the nature of the results produced. These data were obtained with a Percheron gelding walking at the rate of 2.2 miles per hour. The draft and the distance traveled in the tread power having been measured, the data as to kilocalories of work accomplished and the horsepower were readily computed using the relationships previously

[4] N. Zuntz and C. Lehmann, Untersuchungen über den Stoffwechsel des Pferdes bei Ruhe und Arbeit, *Landw. Jahrb.*, **18**:1–156, 1889.

defined (Sec. 17.3). The energy expense was estimated from the oxygen consumed as measured with a closed-circuit respiration apparatus. The total energy consumption was recorded as the over-all energy. The net-energy expenditure is calculated by subtracting the output during standing from the total measured during walking or working. By adding to the energy of standing, the further amount expended in walking, and subtracting this from the over-all consumption, the *absolute energy* used in the work of draft is obtained.

TABLE 17.1. ENERGY CONSUMPTION AND OUTPUT BY A WORK HORSE*

Experiment	Draft, lb.	Energy output, kcal. per hr.		Energy expense, kcal. per hr.			Efficiency of work, %		
		Work done	Hp.	Over-all	Net	Absolute	Over-all	Net	Absolute
Standing......	0	....	....	670					
Walking......	0	....	....	1607	937				
Working......	125	470	0.73	2908	2238	1301	16.2	21.0	36.1
	150	564	0.88	3113	2443	1506	18.1	23.1	37.5
	175	658	1.03	3350	2680	1743	19.6	24.6	37.8
	200	752	1.17	3651	2981	2044	20.6	25.2	36.8
	225	846	1.32	4031	3361	2424	21.0	25.2	34.9
	250	941	1.47	4232	3562	2625	22.2	26.4	35.8
	275	1035	1.61	4650	3980	3043	22.3	26.0	34.0
	300	1129	1.76	5008	4338	3401	22.5	26.0	33.2
	325	1223	1.91	5400	4730	3793	22.6	25.9	32.2
	350	1317	2.05	5651	4981	4044	23.3	26.4	32.6
	375	1411	2.20	5752	5082	4145	24.5	27.8	34.0
	400	1505	2.35	6337	5667	4730	23.7	26.6	31.8

* Data from Robert C. Procter, Samuel Brody, Mack M. Jones, and D. W. Chittenden, Growth and development. XXXIII. Efficiency of work in horses of different ages and body weights, *Missouri Agr. Expt. Sta. Research Bull.* 209, 1934; Samuel Brody and Richard Cunningham, Growth and development. XL. Comparison between efficiency of horse, man, and motor, with special reference to size and monetary economy, *Missouri Agr. Expt. Sta. Research Bull.* 244, 1936.

These three different energy expenditures provide the bases for computing the three different measures of efficiency with which the work recorded is accomplished. The over-all efficiency increases with load because the fixed overhead expenditure of maintenance is thus distributed over an increasing output of useful work. In contrast, the absolute efficiency tends to decrease, reflecting the larger wastage as heat which tends to result from increasing the load on the muscle. The net efficiency represents a balance between the trend to an increased efficiency with load, which results from eliminating the overhead of walking, and the opposite trend in absolute efficiency with increasing load.

Thus the figures for net efficiency reveal an increase for the lighter loads only.

17.6. Factors Affecting Work Efficiency. The previous discussion indicates that various factors influence the efficiency with which work is done and that they affect the various measures of efficiency in different ways. The practical measure is the over-all efficiency because the horse must be maintained whether it is working or not. The net or absolute measure, however, is the more useful for comparing the relative efficiencies with which different kinds of work are accomplished. Increasing the speed beyond a certain point decreases the net efficiency with which work is done. It is evident that a man uses up much more energy in running 100 yd. at top speed than in running it at a trot. Zuntz and associates found that approximately 15 per cent more energy was required by the horse for locomotion at 3.66 miles per hour than at a rate of 2.91 miles. At a trot nearly twice as much energy was expended as at a walk. The horse is most efficient when working at a speed between 2.5 and 3 miles per hour. Though gross efficiency increases with load and speed, a heavy load at low speed is more efficient than a light load at high speed.

Of all the forms of work investigated by Zuntz and associates, the ascent of a moderate grade appeared to be the most efficient on the net basis, but the efficiency decreased as the grade became steeper. Draft up a grade was performed less efficiently than draft alone, and as the grade increased from 1.5 per cent to 8.5 per cent, the net efficiency decreased from 31.3 to 22.7 per cent.

It is a familiar fact that training increases working efficiency. When the horse or man attempts an unaccustomed task, many unnecessary muscles are brought into play which are not used when skill in performing the work has been acquired. One the other hand, efficiency decreases as the animal becomes fatigued.

According to the studies of Brody and associates, if large and small horses perform work in proportion to their weights, there is no difference in the gross efficiency with which the work is accomplished. From observations that the maximum over-all efficiency of the 1500-lb. horse, the 600-lb. horse, and the 150-lb. man is approximately 25 per cent in each case, Brody concludes that this efficiency is independent of body weight. He also believes that the work-rate capacity is proportional not to body weight but to the basal metabolism, i.e., body weight raised to the 0.7 power (Sec. 13.2).

17.7. Energy Requirements. The previous discussion of the physiology of muscular work makes it evident that the major requirement is for energy-producing food. This need is most easily visualized as net energy, representing the chemical energy which the body must expend to produce the work in question. This net-energy requirement can be directly measured by respiration experiments such as the one reported in Table 17.1. As an alternative procedure, the net-energy requirement can be calculated from the energy represented by the work done and by the percentage efficiency represented by the work in question. This procedure is illustrated by Armsby[5] as follows. He cites data showing that a horse, hauling a load having a draft of 100 lb. for 20 miles on a level road, would perform mechanical work equivalent to 3421 kcal. Taking the net efficiency of the horse for draft as 31.3 per cent, the calculation thus becomes:

$$3421 \div 0.313 = 10{,}929 \text{ kcal. of net energy}$$

This calculation accounts only for the energy needed for the work of draft itself. The horse expended energy for walking and for maintenance which must be added to that of the draft accomplished in arriving at the total net-energy requirement.

A little thought makes it evident that calculations of this kind have a very limited application to the estimation of the net-energy requirements of horses in practice because of the difficulty of arriving at the amount of work done and the efficiency with which it is performed. Armsby recognized this fact, and in stating the requirements for work production, he limited them to the basis of "full work," "half work," and "one-fourth work." For example, his recommendation to cover both the maintenance and production of a horse at full work was 18.2 Therms of net energy per day per 1000 lb. live weight. Armsby recognized that there were no directly determined net-energy values of feeds for work production by the horse. This fact, coupled with the more recent recognition of the variability of such values according to the level of production and the nature of the ration (Sec. 12.8), has prevented the adoption of the net-energy system in computing rations for horses.

Brody and Cunningham[6] have derived the following equation for expressing the over-all requirements of the horse in terms of pounds of total digestible nutrients:

$$\text{TDN} = 0.053M^{0.73} + 1.27 \text{ (hp.-hr.)}$$

The first term to the right of the equality sign represents the maintenance requirement in TDN when M is live weight in pounds. The work requirement is obtained by multiplying horsepower-hours by the factor 1.27, to give the TDN which would be needed for the work done. Brody and Cunningham present an alignment chart, or nomograph, from which the requirements for animals of different weights performing vary-

[5] Henry Prentiss Armsby, The Nutrition of Farm Animals, The Macmillan Company, New York, 1917, p. 564.

[6] Brody and Cunningham, *loc. cit.*

ing amounts of work can be obtained at a glance. Their computed values for different body weights are also set forth in tables in terms both of the horsepower-hours of work done and also of the number of hours worked per day. As an example, the requirement for a 1000-lb. horse working an 8-hr. day is stated as 14.1 lb. of TDN. Their values are based on an assumed tractive pull of a load equivalent to 10 per cent of the body weight and upon a speed of 2.2 miles per hour.

The energy requirements for the horse can be determined in feeding trials by ascertaining the amount of feed which is needed to maintain the animal in weight and in good working condition while doing a definite amount of work. The feed intake can be expressed as TDN either by running a digestion trial or by using coefficients of digestibility which have been previously determined for the feeds in question. In translating the results into a feeding standard, a difficult problem arises in estimating the amount of work actually performed on a basis which will apply to other conditions. In addition to the factors previously mentioned (Sec. 17.6) as influencing work efficiency, there are differences in working conditions from day to day which markedly affect the amount of feed required to do a given amount of work. The nature of the roadbed, whether hard, soggy, or icy, is an important example in this connection.

The N.R.C. allowances for horses of different weights are expressed as combined figures for maintenance and light, medium, or hard work. It is assumed that the energy needs for both maintenance and work are proportional to metabolic size. Thus the allowance for light work (2 to 3 hr. daily) is three times the BMR (basal metabolic rate, Sec. 13.1); for medium work (4 to 5 hr.), 3.5 times the BMR; and for hard work (8 hr.), 4.3 times the BMR. For example, the allowances for a 1200-lb. animal at light, medium, and hard work are 11.6, 13.5, and 16.7 lb. of TDN, respectively. The figures recommended do not differ markedly from the averages of the ranges set forth in the Morrison standards. Feeding standards are useful to indicate how the feed requirements vary in accordance with amount of work performed, but in practice, they can serve only as general guides. Having selected a suitable ration, it should be fed in accordance with the amounts needed to keep the horse in good working condition rather than as arbitrarily specified allowances.

17.8. Protein Requirements. While it is now accepted, as discussed at the beginning of the chapter, the protein is not the normal fuel of muscular work, some still adhere to the view that protein catabolism is increased during the work even though there is an ample supply of non-nitrogenous nutrients. To many, it is inconceivable that the muscle cells are entirely resistant to wear, and they believe that destruction and renewal must occur. It is stated that such a destruction may occur and yet not be reflected in an increased excretion because of a reutilization of the catabolic products. Such a viewpoint is very difficult to prove or disprove. There are experiments in which an increased output of urinary nitrogen has been recorded during work and others in which no such increase has been found. At least some of the positive experiments are inconclusive because of the uncertainty as to whether the intake of nonnitrogenous nutrients was adequate to meet the needs for energy.

Any increase in protein catabolism during work is certainly small. Harvey and associates[7] have reported that 1800-lb. Percheron horses fed protein at a maintenance level remained in positive nitrogen balance when working at rates as high as 1.27 hp. per hour for over 4 hr. daily. Forbes[8] states that recent experiments with man confirm earlier ones in showing that the protein needs are not measurably increased above maintenance by muscular activity, despite the popular ideas of athletes and hard workers. In studies with three miners over a 32-week period Kraut and Lehmann[9] found that the minimum nitrogen intake to keep the men in positive nitrogen balance was the same with and without work, viz., 7 to 8 g. daily. They noted, however, that at hard work there was a decrease in working capacity as well as psychic depression when the intake fell below 9 to 10 g. daily. This intake is below the N.R.C. allowance for a sedentary man. Other German studies, growing out of the Second World War, have shown that, as the customary intakes of hard workers are markedly reduced in quantity and quality, though not down to the maintenance level, working capacity suffered. Experience in this country has shown that intakes of protein, particularly of animal origin, have important psychic effects on work capacity at levels far higher than any demonstrated physiological need. It is frequently stated that a protein intake above the maintenance need gives the working horse "more life and spirit."

From the standpoint of an efficient ration for work production by horses, other considerations appear more important than the question as to whether the protein requirement is actually increased during work. A satisfactory maintenance ration for an idle horse has a nutritive ratio of approximately 1:10. During hard work the need for energy is approximately doubled, and the nutritive ratio becomes 1:20 accordingly if the protein intake is not increased. Working horses have been kept in satisfactory condition on even wider ratios than would here result, but that such rations are equally efficient in terms of energy utilization

[7] A. L. Harvey and associates, The effects of limited feeding of oats and timothy hay during work on the nitrogen balance of draft geldings, *Proc. Am. Soc. Animal Production,* 1939, pp. 94–103.

[8] W. H. Forbes, The effects of hard physical work upon nutritional requirements, *Milbank Mem. Fund Quart.,* **23**:89–96, 1945.

[9] Heinrich Kraut and Gunther Lehmann, Der Eiweissbedarf des Schwerarbeiters. I. Physiologisches und funktionelles Eiweissminimum, *Biochem. Z.,.* **319**:228–246, 1949.

has not been shown. Reference has been made to the fact that digestibility is depressed by wide ratios and that, at least in so far as rats and chicks are concerned, such a ration increases the heat losses (Sec. 11.16). While these questions have not been specifically studied with the horse, indirect evidence suggests that its protein intake should be increased during work although the increase is not specifically needed for muscular activity. This viewpoint is recognized in the N.R.C. allowances which provide an increase in digestible protein, over the maintenance figures of approximately 25 per cent in the case of light work, 45 per cent for medium work, and 65 per cent for hard work. These allowances are generally exceeded in the customary rations fed in the amounts required to supply the TDN intakes called for. They are lower than those set forth in the Morrison standard.

17.9. Mineral Requirements during Work. The large increase in the output of sodium and chlorine in the perspiration incident to hard work, particularly during warm weather, has been mentioned (Sec. 7.25). Thus there is an increased need for salt by the working horse. This need can be taken care of by ad libitum feeding and requires no special attention.

The active phosphorus metabolism which occurs during muscular activity (Sec. 17.2) has directed attention to the question of an increased requirement for this mineral. During the First World War Emden conducted experiments on German soldiers with acid phosphate drinks, with apparently beneficial results. Their use became popular, accordingly, particularly with athletes. Later studies, however, have increased the skepticism regarding any effect of high-phosphate intake on muscular performance. Harvey and associates[10] have reported that hard work has no effect on the calcium and phosphorus balance in horses. The N.R.C. report provides no increased intakes of these minerals for work over those specified for maintenance.

Some increase in hemoglobin destruction and resynthesis during hard work is to be expected in view of the greatly increased activity in oxygen transport, but this does not necessarily involve a higher iron requirement, because the catabolized iron can be used again. There is some loss of iron, calcium, and phosphorus in the sweat. Studies by Caine[11] revealed no benefit, either in condition or in feed economy, from adding supplements of calcium, phosphorus, and iron to a ration of timothy hay, corn, oats, and salt.

The added feed which must be given to supply the energy for work production inevitably means a mineral addition also. If the mainte-

[10] A. L. Harvey and associates, Effect of work on the calcium and phosphorus retention of Percheron geldings, *J. Animal Sci.*, **2**:103–111, 1943.

[11] A. B. Caine, Feeding and management of horses, *Iowa Agr. Expt. Sta. Circ.* 130, 1931.

nance ration is adequate in minerals for that purpose, the supplementary feed required for work will certainly supply any additional minerals that may be called for.

17.10. Vitamin Requirements. There appears to be no physiological reason why muscular activity should call for additional intakes of the fat-soluble vitamins. Forbes[12] states work does not appreciably increase the needs for vitamin A, D, or K. The need for thiamine obviously increases with the increased energy metabolism, but this presents no practical problem in the case of the horse because of the nature of its ration. There is clear evidence from experiments with rats that activity does not increase the riboflavin requirement. There are no adequate data regarding niacin or the other B-vitamins. It seems improbable that there need be concern about possible deficiencies of any of the B-vitamins in the commonly fed rations of working horses. The N.R.C. Committee has not recommended any specific allowances in the case of any of the vitamins. A review[13] cites data indicating a lack of benefit from supplementing a diet of natural foods with B-vitamins and ascorbic acid in the case of men undergoing hard physical work.

A review of the nutrient requirements of the horse for maintenance, work, reproduction, and lactation is presented by Olsson and Rudvere.[14] Of the approximately 150 articles cited, nearly 90 per cent were published prior to 1940, reflecting the limited recent studies on the horse, due, presumably, to its declining use as a farm animal.

SELECTED LITERATURE

Barborka, C. J., E. E. Foltz, and A. C. Ivy: Relationship between vitamin B complex intake and work output in trained subjects, *J. Am. Med. Assoc.*, **122**:717–720, 1943.

Darling, R. C., and associates: Effects of variations in dietary protein on the physical well being of men doing manual work, *J. Nutrition*, **28**:273–281, 1944.

Kraut, Heinrich, Gunther Lehmann, and Alexander Szakall: Der Eiweissbedarf des Schwerarbeiters. III. Der Einfluss von reinem Eiweiss und von Extraktivstoffen auf die Leistungsfähigkeit, *Biochem. Z.*, **320**:99–111, 1949.

Lehmann, Gunther, and Hans Ferdinand Michaelis: Der Eiweissbedarf des Schwerarbeiters. II. Messungen der Leistungsfähigkeit an Arbeitergruppen, *Biochem. Z.*, **319**:247–256, 1948.

Nitsche, H.: Der Bedarf an Eiweiss bei Arbeitspferden in Ruhe und bei allmählich gesteigerter Arbeit *Biedermanns zentr. B. Tierernähr.*, **11**:214–244, 1939.

Swift, Raymond W., and Cyrus E. French: Energy Metabolism and Nutrition, The Scarecrow Press, Washington, D.C., 1954.

[12] Forbes, *loc. cit.*

[13] Anonymous, Vitamin supplementation and human performance, *Nutrition Revs.*, **13**:102–104, 1955.

[14] N. Olsson and A. Rudvere, The nutrition of the horse, *Nutrition Abstr. & Revs.*, **25**:1–16, 1955 (trans. by I. Leitch).

Appendix

TABLE I. NUTRIENT REQUIREMENTS OF SWINE*
(In percentage or amount per pound of feed)

	Growing pigs		Finishing pigs, meat type			Bred gilts	Lactating gilts
Live weight, lb.	25.0	50.0	100.0	150.0	200.0	300.0	350.0
Expected daily gain, lb.	0.8	1.2	1.6	1.7	1.9	1.0	?†
Crude protein, per cent	17.0	15.0	13.0	12.0	12.0	15.0	15.0
TDN, per cent	80.0	75.0	75.0	75.0	75.0	70.0	75.0
Digestible energy, kcal	1600.0	1500.0	1500.0	1500.0	1500.0	1400.0	1500.0
Inorganic nutrients:							
Calcium, per cent	0.65	0.65	0.50	0.50	0.50	0.6	0.6
Phosphorus, per cent	0.50	0.50	0.40	0.40	0.40	0.4	0.4
Salt (NaCl), per cent	0.50	0.50	0.50	0.50	0.50	0.5	0.5
Vitamins:							
Carotene, mg.‡	1.12	0.75	0.75	0.75	0.75	2.5	2.5
Vitamin A, I.U.‡	600.0	400.0	400.0	400.0	400.0	1200.0	1200.0
Vitamin D, I.U	90.0	90.0	60.0	60.0	60.0	60.0	60.0
Thiamine, mg	0.5	0.5	0.5	0.5	0.5	0.5	0.5
Riboflavin, mg	1.4	1.2	1.0	1.0	1.0	1.5	1.5
Niacin, mg	8.0	6.0	5.0	5.0	5.0	5.0	5.0
Pantothenic acid, mg	5.0	5.0	4.5	4.5	4.5	6.0	6.0
Pyridoxine, mg	0.5	0.5	?	?	?	?	?
Choline, mg	400.0	?	?	?	?	?	?
Vitamin B_{12}, mcg	7.0	5.0	5.0	5.0	5.0	5.0	5.0

* Condensed from Tables 2 and 4, N.R.C. Report on Nutrient Requirements of Swine, 1959.

† ? Indicates requirement not established.

‡ Carotene and vitamin A values based on 1 mg. carotene equals 533 I.U. vitamin A for the pig. Vitamin A requirements can be met by either carotene or vitamin A; both are not needed.

TABLE II. NUTRIENT REQUIREMENTS OF POULTRY*
(In percentage or amount per pound of feed)

	Starting chicks, 0 to 8 wk.	Growing chicks, 8 to 18 wk.	Laying hens	Breeding hens	Starting poults, 0 to 8 wk.	Growing turkeys, 8 to 16 wk.
Protein	20.0	16.0	15.0	15.0	28.0	20.0
Minerals:						
Calcium, per cent	1.0	1.0	2.25[1]	2.25[1]	2.0	1.7[2]
Phosphorus,[3] per cent	0.6	0.6	0.6	0.6	1.0	0.85[2]
Sodium,[4] per cent	0.15	0.15	0.15	0.15	0.15	0.15
Potassium, per cent	0.2	0.16	?	?	?	?
Manganese, mg	25.0	?	?	15.0	25.0	?
Zinc, mg	20.0	?	?	?	25.0[2]	?
Iodine, mg	0.5	0.2	0.2	0.5	?	?
Vitamins:						
Vitamin A activity,[5] U.S.P.	1200.0	1200.0	2000.0	2000.0	2400.0	2400.0
Vitamin D, I.C.U	90.0	90.0	225.0	225.0	400.0	400.0
Thiamine, mg	0.8	?	?	?	?	?
Riboflavin, mg	1.3	0.8	1.0	1.7	1.7	?
Pantothenic acid, mg	4.2	4.2	2.1	4.2	5.0	?
Niacin, mg	12.0	5.0[2]	?	?	32.0[2]	?
Pyridoxine, mg	1.3	?	1.3	1.3	?	?
Biotin, mg	0.04	?	?	?	?	?
Choline, mg	600.0	?	?	?	850.0	?
Folacin, mg	0.25	?	0.11	0.16	0.4	?
Vitamin B_{12},[2] mg	0.004	?	?	0.002	?	?

* Condensed table from N.R.C. Report on Nutrient Requirements of Poultry, 1961. These figures are estimates of requirements and include no margins of safety.

[1] This amount of calcium need not be incorporated in the mixed feed, inasmuch as calcium supplements fed free choice are considered as part of the ration.

[2] Tentative figure.

[3] At least 0.45 per cent of the total feed of starting chickens should be inorganic phosphorus. All of the phosphorus of nonplant feed ingredients is considered to be inorganic. Approximately 30 per cent of the phosphorus of plant products is non-phytin phosphorus and may be considered as part of the inorganic phosphorus required. A portion of the phosphorus requirement of growing chickens and laying and breeding hens must also be supplied in inorganic form. For birds in these categories the requirement for inorganic phosphorus is lower and not as well defined as for starting chickens.

[4] Equivalent to 0.37 per cent of sodium chloride.

[5] May be vitamin A or provitamin A.

TABLE III. NUTRIENT REQUIREMENTS OF DAIRY CATTLE*
(In percentage or amount per pound of air-dry ration)

Body weight, lb.	Total daily feed, lb.	Feed per cent of weight	Digestible protein, per cent	TDN, per cent	DE,† Therms/ lb.	Ca, per cent	P, per cent	Carotene, mg./lb.	Vitamin D, I.U./lb.
				Normal growth of dairy heifers					
50	0.9	1.6	22.0	110	2.22	0.98	0.73	?	170
100	2.0	2.0	20.0	100	2.02	0.77	0.66	2.0	150
150	4.0	2.7	12.5	75	1.52	0.66	0.44	1.5	110
200	6.0	3.0	10.0	67	1.35	0.48	0.40	1.3	100
400	11.0	2.8	7.3	59	1.19	0.26	0.30	1.5	?
600	15.0	2.7	5.7	57	1.15	0.19	0.22	1.6	?
800	19.0	2.5	4.7	53	1.07	0.15	0.15	1.7	?
1000	22.0	2.2	4.3	50	1.01	0.13	0.13	1.8	?
1200	24.0	2.0	4.2	50	1.01	0.12	0.12	2.0	?
				Maintenance of mature cows					
800	12	1.8	3.6	50	1.01	0.12	0.12	2.3	?
1000	14	1.6	3.7	50	1.01	0.12	0.12	2.5	?
1200	16	1.5	3.9	50	1.01	0.12	0.12	2.7	?
1400	19	1.4	3.8	50	1.01	0.12	0.12	2.7	?
1600	21	1.3	3.8	50	1.01	0.12	0.12	2.8	?
				Lactating cows‡					
?	?	?	6.5	60	1.21	0.30	0.25	1.2	?
				Maintenance of breeding bulls					
1200	18	1.5	5.6	58	1.17	0.12	0.12	2.7	?
1600	22	1.4	5.5	58	1.17	0.13	0.13	2.9	?
2000	27	1.3	5.4	58	1.17	0.13	0.13	3.0	?
2400	31	1.3	5.2	58	1.17	0.14	0.14	3.1	?

* Condensed from N.R.C. Report on Nutrient Requirements of Dairy Cattle, 1958.

† DE (digestible energy) may be converted to metabolizable energy by multiplying by 82 per cent.

‡ The reader is referred to the original N.R.C. report for details on amounts of nutrients required per pound of milk.

TABLE IV. NUTRIENT REQUIREMENTS OF BEEF CATTLE*
(In percentage or amount per pound of air-dry feed)

Body weight, lb.	Av. daily gain,[1] lb.	Daily feed per animal, lb.	Percentage of ration or amount, per pound of feed					
			Digestible protein, per cent	TDN, per cent	DE, Therms/lb.	Ca, per cent	P, per cent	Carotene, mg./lb.
Fattening calves finished as short yearlings								
400	2.3	12	8.2	67	1.33	0.37	0.28	0.6
600	2.4	16	8.2	68	1.36	0.28	0.23	0.6
800	2.2	20	7.5	68	1.36	0.22	0.20	0.7
1000	2.2	22	7.5	68	1.36	0.20	0.20	0.8
Fattening yearling cattle								
600	2.4	18	7.5	65	1.30	0.25	0.21	0.6
800	2.8	22	7.5	65	1.30	0.20	0.20	0.6
1000	2.5	26	7.5	65	1.30	0.17	0.20	0.7
1100	2.3	27	7.5	65	1.30	0.16	0.20	0.7
Wintering weanling calves								
400	1.0	11	6.2	55	1.10	0.26	0.20	0.6
500	1.0	13	6.2	54	1.08	0.22	0.17	0.7
600	1.0	15	5.5	53	1.05	0.19	0.15	0.7
Wintering yearling cattle								
600	1.0	16	5.0	50	1.00	0.18	0.15	0.6
800	0.7	18	4.5	50	1.00	0.16	0.15	0.8
900	0.5	18	4.5	50	1.00	0.16	0.15	0.8
Wintering mature pregnant cows								
800	1.5	22	4.5	50	1.00	0.16	0.15	1.5
1000	0.4	18	4.5	50	1.00	0.16	0.15	2.2
1200	0.0	18	4.5	50	1.00	0.16	0.15	2.6
Cows nursing calves, first 3–4 months postpartum								
900–1100	0.0	28	5.0	60	1.20	0.24	0.18	3.6
Normal growth heifers and steers								
400	1.6	12	7.0	58	1.16	0.29	0.21	0.6
600	1.4	16	5.6	53	1.06	0.20	0.16	0.6
800	1.2	19	4.7	50	1.00	0.17	0.15	0.7
1000	1.0	21	4.7	50	1.00	0.14	0.15	0.8
Bulls, growth and maintenance (moderate activity)								
600	2.3	16	7.5	63	1.26	0.29	0.21	2.2
1000	1.6	20	7.2	60	1.20	0.21	0.17	3.0
1400	1.0	24	6.0	59	1.18	0.16	0.15	3.5
1800	0.0	26	5.6	54	1.08	0.13	0.15	4.2

* Condensed from N.R.C. Report on Nutrient Requirements for Beef Cattle, 1958.

[1] Average daily gain for fattening cattle is based upon cattle receiving stilbestrol. Fattening cattle not receiving stilbestrol gain from 10 to 20 per cent slower than the indicated values.

TABLE V. NUTRIENT REQUIREMENTS OF SHEEP*
(In percentage or amount per pound of air-dry ration)

Body weight, lb.	Total feed, lb.	Percentage of ration or amount per pound of feed						
		Digestible protein, per cent	TDN, per cent	DE, Therms	Ca, per cent	P, per cent	Carotene, mg./lb.	Vitamin D, I.U./lb.
Ewes, nonlactating and first 15 weeks of gestation								
100	2.6	4.2	50	1.0	0.27	0.21	0.7	96
120	3.0	4.2	50	1.0	0.24	0.19	0.7	100
140	3.4	4.2	50	1.0	0.22	0.17	0.7	103
160	3.8	4.2	50	1.0	0.20	0.16	0.7	105
Ewes, last 6 weeks of gestation								
100	3.8	4.5	53	1.1	0.24	0.18	1.5	66
120	4.2	4.3	52	1.1	0.23	0.17	1.6	71
140	4.6	4.3	52	1.1	0.22	0.16	1.7	76
160	4.8	4.2	52	1.1	0.22	0.16	1.8	83
Ewes, first 8–10 weeks of lactation								
100	4.6	4.8	59	1.2	0.30	0.22	1.3	54
120	5.0	4.6	58	1.2	0.28	0.21	1.4	60
140	5.4	4.6	57	1.2	0.28	0.20	1.5	65
160	5.6	4.6	57	1.2	0.28	0.20	1.6	71
Ewes, last 12–14 weeks of lactation								
100	3.8	4.5	53	1.1	0.26	0.20	1.5	66
120	4.2	4.3	52	1.1	0.25	0.19	1.6	71
140	4.6	4.3	52	1.1	0.24	0.18	1.7	76
160	4.8	4.2	52	1.1	0.24	0.18	1.9	83
Lambs, fattening								
60	2.7	6.3	60	1.2	0.23	0.21	0.4	56
70	3.1	5.8	61	1.2	0.20	0.18	0.4	56
80	3.4	5.6	62	1.2	0.19	0.17	0.4	59
90	3.8	5.3	63	1.3	0.17	0.15	0.4	59
100	4.0	5.0	65	1.3	0.17	0.15	0.4	62

* Condensed from N.R.C. Requirements of Sheep, 1957.

Visual-aids Bibliography

The films listed below and on the following pages can be used as visual aids to the study of this book. The films have been grouped under two broad headings—principles of digestion and nutrition and feeding practices in animal production—but it is recommended that they be reviewed before using, in order to determine their suitability for particular groups of students or units of work.

The abbreviations "MP" and "FS" indicate motion pictures and filmstrips. Immediately following this identification is the name of the primary distributor. Abbreviations of the names of the distributors are identified in the list of sources at the end of the bibliography. In most instances, the films can be borrowed or rented from local or state 16 mm film libraries. (A nationwide list of these local sources is given in *A Directory of 3660 16 mm Film Libraries*, available for $1 from the Superintendent of Documents, Washington 25, D.C.) Unless otherwise indicated, the motion pictures are 16 mm sound black-and-white films, and the filmstrips are 35 mm black-and-white and silent. The length of motion pictures is given in minutes (min), that of filmstrips in frames (fr).

This bibliography is a selective one, and film users should examine the latest edition and supplements of Educational Film Guide and Filmstrip Guide, published by The H. W. Wilson Company, New York. These standard reference books are available in most school, college, and public libraries. Film users should also refer to the film reviews in professional medical and veterinary journals, film bibliographies and catalogs of the U.S. Department of Agriculture, and the reference lists on animal health, feeding, and management issued annually by the Food and Agriculture Organization of the United Nations.

PRINCIPLES OF DIGESTION AND NUTRITION

Alimentary Tract (MP, EBF, 1938, 11 min). Shows different types of movements in the stomach and intestines, motility of intestinal villi, colon motility in the dog and cat, and the processes of antiperistalsis.

The Cobalt Cure for Pining Sheep (MP, FAO, 1950, 15 min color). Explains methods of using cobalt for the prevention and cure of pining disease of sheep. With the aid of animated graphs of weights, shows series of experiments done in Scotland. Sponsored by the Mond Nickel Company, Ltd., United Kingdom.

The Cure for Pining Disease in Sheep (MP, FAO, 1952, 12 min color). Experiments on Bodmin Moor, Cornwall, demonstrate value of cobalt additions to sheep's diet in a severely deficient area. Illustrates methods of using cobalt. Sponsored by the Mond Nickel Company, Ltd., United Kingdom.

Digestion of Foods (MP, EBF, 1938, 11 min). Explains the digestive process, including the work performed in the mouth, stomach, and small intestines; secretions, enzymes, and systems affected; and the relationship of the circulatory and nervous systems to the digestive process. (Supplementary filmstrip, same title, 65 fr, also available.)

Digestion. Part 1: Mechanical (MP, UWF, 1950, 15 min color or b&w). Explains the muscular and mechanical processes involved in the digestion of food; structure and functions of the alimentary canal; peristalsis in the esophagus, small intestine, and colon; muscular movements of the stomach wall; and absorption of food, water, and salts into the blood.

Digestion. Part 2: Chemical (MP, UWF, 1950, 18 min color or b&w). Explains chemical changes involved in the digestion of carbohydrates, proteins, and fats; describes secretion and action of saliva, gastric, pancreatic, and intestinal juices and bile on each type of food; and shows diagrams of the digestive process.

Digestive System (FS, SVE, 1947, 35 fr). Explains the role of various digestive organs of the body in the digestion of food.

Energy Release from Foods (MP, Upjohn, 1946, 26 min color). Through animated diagrams, schematizes the roles of nicotinic acid, thiamine, and riboflavin in the energy exchanges of carbohydrate metabolism as assisted by enzymes and illustrates certain clinical deficiencies of the B vitamin complex. Reviewed in *J. Am. Med. Assoc.*, **133**:717, 1947.

Foods and Nutrition (MP, EBF, 1940, 11 min). Explains the metabolic processes of the distribution of carbohydrates, fats, proteins, minerals, vitamins, etc., through the body. (Supplementary filmstrip, same title, 86 fr, also available.)

Fundamentals of Diet (MP, EBF, 1943, 10 min). Gives a functional classification of foods and depicts experiments with animals illustrating the results of food deficiencies.

Mineral Deficiencies, Copper and Cobalt (MP, FAO, 1949, 22 min color). Pictures harmful effects of deficiency of copper and cobalt in soil of southeastern coastal areas of Australia, sheep pastured on such areas affected by wasting diseases, and recent scientific research to overcome disease and increase the amount of wool per head. Sponsored by Australian Wool Bureau.

Nicotinic Acid Deficiency (MP, Lilly, 1947, 40 min silent color). Relates the incidence of vitamin deficiency and factors which may contribute to the development of vitamin deficiency; compares normal and nicotinic-acid deficient dogs; pictures a pellagrin following vitamin therapy and pellagrins with severe and moderately severe macrocytic anemia. Discusses the prevalence of borderline cases of vitamin deficiences and aspects of prevention.

Riboflavin Deficiency (MP, Lilly, 1942, 42 min silent color). Discusses incidence and etiological factors of vitamin deficiency. Covers chemistry of riboflavin, riboflavin deficiency in rats, and ariboflavinosis in humans. Demonstrates clinical manifestations of cheilitis, corneal vascularization, and ocular lesions and recommends therapeutic diets.

A Study of Cobalt Deficiency in Ireland (MP, FAO, 1954, 28 min color). Reviews three investigations of pining diseases: First, confirms value of cobalt applications where sheep have access only to minimal amounts of natural minerals in pastures. Second, demonstrates value of "hospital" plots on large tracts of hill grazings. Third, shows lambs successfully reared by cobalt treatment on strongly calcareous soils containing no cobalt. Sponsored by the Mond Nickel Company, Ltd., United Kingdom, in cooperation with the Department of Agriculture of Ireland.

Thiamine Chloride Deficiency (MP, Lilly, 1942, 30 min silent color). Discusses incidence and etiology of thiamine deficiency and the chemistry of thiamine chloride; contrasts normal and B_1 deficient rats and pigeons and shows effects of therapy; demonstrates clinical manifestations and X-ray therapy of wet beriberi in humans; discusses dietary management of thiamine deficiency.

Understanding Vitamins (MP, EBF, 1952, 14 min color or b&w). Describes the scientific research which has been conducted in determining the role of vitamins; explains what vitamins are, how they work, and why they are necessary for good health; describes the natural sources of vitamins; explains how vitamin deficiencies in the diet can be supplemented by the use of synthetic vitamins.

Vitamins and Some Deficiency Diseases (MP, Lederle, 1955, 30 min color). Discusses vitamins and their relationship to deficiency diseases.

Through laboratory scenes, illustrates deficiencies in experimental animals. Clinical deficiencies include cheilosis, scurvy, rickets, pellagra, and vitamin K deficiency. Shows early ocular changes of vitamin A and riboflavin deficiencies as seen through the slit lamp and motor disturbances in pigs suffering from pyridoxine and pantothenic acid deficiencies.

FEEDING PRACTICES IN ANIMAL PRODUCTION

Antibiotics for Animals (MP, Fla Ag, n.d., 14 min). Reports on the uses of the "wonder drugs" in animal production. Kinescope of television program.

Better Farming: More Milk (MP, UWF, 1947, 10 min color). Explains that more milk can be obtained from a cow that is clean, healthy, and well fed; gives practical suggestions to farmers.

Challenge to New York Dairymen (MP, NY Ag, n.d., 47 min color). Explains feeding practices on dairy farms; lists crops to grow—hay, pasture, corn, and small grains—and their use in feeding.

Extra Feeding Pays (MP, UWF, 1947, 8 min color). Explains the need for storing cattle feed and suggests the use of a trench silo and haystack; emphasizes the value of good pasture land and recommends the planting of several kinds of grasses.

Feeding Dairy Cattle (MP, Fla Ag, n.d., 14 min). Shows and discusses the feeds needed to provide a balanced diet for dairy cows. Kinescope of television program.

Feeding Farm Animals (MP, USDA, 1946, 19 min). Shows the basic principles of feeding farm animals, the six classes of nutrients—carbohydrates, fats, proteins, vitamins, minerals, and water—and the results of correct feeding.

Green Dollars (MP, Ill, n.d., 35 min color). Explains the need for a legume grass program in Illinois and shows the use of legume grass mixtures in livestock and dairy feeding.

Hay Is What You Make It (MP, USDA, 1946, 18 min color). Shows how to improve the quality of hay by cutting at the right stage of growth, curing the right length of time, and storing properly.

Hogs for Profit (MP, Minn Ag, n.d., 25 min color). Describes practices in swine production, including feeding.

Protein for Cattle (MP, Fla Ag, n.d., 12 min). Explains the needs of cattle for protein, discusses protein supplements, and shows ways of feeding such supplements to calves, breeding cows, and fattening cattle.

Radioisotopes in Animal Nutrition (MP, Fla Ag, n.d., 14 min color). Shows ways in which radioisotopes are being used in Florida research studies of nutrition of laboratory animals, large animals, and poultry.

Twelve Months Green (MP, Miss Ag, n.d., 22 min color). Story of a Mississippi farmer who doubled his milk production through year-round grazing.

MAIN SOURCES OF FILMS

EBF—Encyclopaedia Britannica Films, Inc., Wilmette, Ill.
FAO—Food and Agriculture Organization, United Nations, Viale delle Terme di Caracalla, Rome, Italy. Requests from the United States should be directed to FAO, c/o U.S. Department of Agriculture, Washington 25, D.C.
Fla Ag—Florida Agricultural Extension Service, Gainesville, Fla.
Ill—Illinois Film Library, Capital Building, Springfield, Ill.
Lederle—Lederle Laboratories Division, American Cyanamid Co., Pearl River, N.Y.
Lilly—Eli Lilly and Co., Indianapolis, Ind.
Minn Ag—Minnesota Agriculture Extension Service, University of Minnesota Farm, St. Paul, Minn.
Miss Ag—Mississippi Agricultural Service, State College, Miss.
NY Ag—New York Agricultural Service, College of Agriculture, Ithaca, N.Y.
SVE—Society for Visual Education, Inc., 1345 W. Diversey Pkwy., Chicago 14, Ill.
Upjohn—The Upjohn Co., 301 Henrietta St., Kalamazoo 99, Mich.
USDA—U.S. Department of Agriculture, Washington 25, D.C.
UWF—United World Films, Inc., 1445 Park Ave., New York 29, N.Y.

Name Index

Subject Index